D1233535

THE WORKS OF
THOMAS DELONEY

THE WORKS OF THOMAS DELONEY

EDITED FROM THE

EARLIEST EXTANT EDITIONS & BROADSIDES

WITH AN INTRODUCTION AND NOTES

BY

FRANCIS OSCAR MANN

OXFORD

AT THE CLARENDON PRESS

Oxford University Press, Ely House, London W. 1

GLASGOW NEW YORK TORONTO MELBOURNE WELLINGTON
CAPE TOWN SALISBURY IBADAN NAIROBI LUSAKA ADDIS ABABA
BOMBAY CALCUTTA MADRAS KARACHI LAHORE DACCA
KUALA LUMPUR HONG KONG TOKYO

FIRST PUBLISHED 1912
REPRINTED LITHOGRAPHICALLY IN GREAT BRITAIN
AT THE UNIVERSITY PRESS, OXFORD
BY VIVIAN RIDLER
PRINTER TO THE UNIVERSITY
1967

NOTE

My grateful acknowledgements are due to those noblemen and gentlemen who have accorded such generous access to their private libraries; to the Earl of Ellesmere for the loan of the 1626 *Iacke of Newberie* and the 1623 *Thomas of Reading*, which are here reprinted for the first time, to the Earl of Crawford for the opportunity of collating four Deloney broadsides, and to Mr. Christie-Miller, of Britwell, Bucks, for the ready facility with which he placed his unique 1602 edition of *Strange Histories* at my disposal. The ballad on the Babington Conspiracy (p. 460) is reprinted by kind permission of the Society of Antiquaries, and *A most sweet Song of an English-Merchant* (p. 485) by courtesy of the Governors of Magdalene College, Cambridge. My further thanks are due to Professor Sir Walter Raleigh, at whose suggestion this edition was undertaken, and who has given valuable help in its preparation.

F. O. MANN.

TABLE OF CONTENTS

NOTE ON THE TEXT

THE plan adopted in preparing the text has been to reprint from the earliest extant editions. Where, however, the text seems doubtful, or later editions show any important variation, footnotes are appended. The comparative value of the texts of the various editions is sometimes indicated by the order of the letters used.

INTRODUCTION

I. THOMAS DELONEY.

THE recorded facts of Deloney's life are very scanty. His earliest venture appears to have been *A Declaration made by the Archbishop of Cullen vpon the Deede of his Mariage* (1583), and Kempe in April, 1600, refers to him as having just died. Thus his working literary life lasted about seventeen years, but it is impossible to give even a rough guess at the date of his birth, although Ebbsworth suggests (apparently capriciously) 1543.[1] He appears to have drifted into literature from the more substantial occupation of silk-weaving, and his novels show the most intimate acquaintance with London life, but Nash's epithet 'the Balletting Silke Weauer of Norwich'[2] seems to point to that town as the place of his birth, and it is significant that one of his earliest ballads— *The Lamentation of Beckles* (1586)—was printed 'for Nicholas Coleman of Norwich'. His name may indicate French ancestry, and this, combined with his strong Anti-Catholicism, perhaps points to descent from a Protestant silk-weaving family, one of those which took refuge in East Anglia from Continental religious persecution. From the earliest times Norwich had been colonized by Flemish and Walloon refugees, and in 1571 there were 3,925 aliens dwelling within the city.[3] The number of silk workers (Deloney's own craft) seems to have increased considerably during the latter half of the sixteenth century. 'Among the trading Strangers', writes Strype, 'that came over into England from Flanders and those Parts for their Religion, in the said Queen Elizabeths Reign, there were divers of this Sort that dealt in dressing and preparing Silk for the other trades';[4] and it may be remembered that alien artisans figure very prominently in Deloney's novels.

Of his earlier life and education nothing is known, but his translation of the proclamation and letters in the Cologne tract

---

[1] *Dict. of Nat. Biography*, art. Thomas Deloney.

[2] *Haue with You to Saffron Walden* (1596), *Works* (McKerrow), vol. iii, p. 84.

[3] *Beauties of England and Wales* (*Norfolk*), p. 132; Bloomfield's *History of Norfolk*, vol. iii, p. 282.

[4] *Survey of London* (Stow, edited Strype, 1720), bk. v, p. 233.

(p. 274) show him to have had a good working knowledge of Latin. There is some probability that he knew French, for in *Iacke of Newberie* he apparently refers to a passage[1] in Montaigne's Essays, which were not Englished by Florio until 1603. Similarly the 'Spirit of Mogunce'[2] may have been remembered from Belleforest's *Histoires Prodigieuses*; the story of the *Kings daughter of France*[3] seems definitely drawn from the *Histoires Tragiques*; while even the French-English of John in *The Gentle Craft* (*I*) is of some importance in this connexion. He was at any rate a man of some culture, and had probably received such education as an Elizabethan Grammar-school allowed, adding to it a know-ledge of the Continental languages, acquired either from the foreign artisans with whom he rubbed shoulders, or perhaps from his own family.

Elderton of the 'ale-crammed nose', so famous in contemporary pamphlets, was the king of the London Ballad-makers until his death in 1592, and him Deloney seems to have followed and finally succeeded as the popular ballad-journalist of the day, at first combining the weaving of good silk with the production of popular poetry. His earliest extant performances in this direction are of a rather lugubrious description, such as *The Lamentation of Beckles* and *The Death and Execution of Fourteen Most Wicked Traitors* (1586). About this time he appears as a married man, living in the parish of St. Giles, Cripplegate, for the baptismal entry in the church registers can scarcely apply to any but him :

> *Richard the son of Thomas Deloney. Weaver. bap. Octr 16th 1586.*

Although little of the work of his next eight years is extant, there can be no doubt that during this time he was writing prolifically, and had become one of the most notorious authors of the Eliza-bethan Grub Street that catered for the 'groundlings'.

Greene, in apologizing for the matter of his *Defence of Conny Catching* (1592), singles him out as a typical ballad-writer :

'Such triviall trinkets and threedbare trash, had better seemed T.D. whose braines beaten to the yarking up of Ballades, might more lawfully have glaunst at the quaint conceites of conny-catching and crosse-biting'.[4]

---

[1] p. 7, l. 25, and note. [2] p. 24, l. 40, and note.
[3] pp. 333–8, and note.
[4] *The Works of Robert Greene* (Grosart), vol. xi, p. 49.

Gabriel Harvey, in *Pierce's Supererogation* (1593),[1] classes him with 'Philip Stubs, Robert Armin, and the common Pamfleteers of London', advising Nash 'to boast lesse with Thomas Delone, or to atchieve more with Thomas More'.

Strype, in his edition of Stow's *Survey*, notes that 'abusive Ballads and Libels were too common in the City in Queen Elizabeth's Time, therein reflecting too boldly and seditiously upon the Government, particularly in case of Dearth'. His relation of an incident of 1596 throws light both upon the activities of Thomas Deloney and the difficulties of sixteenth-century popular journalism.[2]

'In the next Year [1596] Sir Stephen Slany, Maior, in the Month of July was brought to his Hands a certain Ballad, containing a Complaint of great Want and Scarcity of Corn within the Realm. And forasmuch as it contained in it certain vain and presumptuous matters, bringing in the Queen, speaking with her People Dialogue wise in very fond and undecent sort (as the said Maior in his letter, wrote also to the Lord Treasurer shewed) and prescribing Order for the remedying of this Dearth of Corn ; which was extracted, as it seemed, out of a Book, published by the Lords the last Year, but done in that Vain and indiscreet manner, as that thereby the Poor might aggravate their Grief, and take occasion of some Discontentment : therefore he thought fit to acquaint the said Lord, that he called before him both Printer and the Party by whom it was put to print; who pretended a License for it. But that finding it to be untrue, he committed him to one of the Counters, and took Sureties of the printer himself for his appearance.

.   .   .   .

The Maker of this scurrilous Ballad was one Delonie, an idle Fellow, and one noted with the like Spirit, in printing a Book for the Silk Weavers : Wherein was found some such like foolish and disorderly matter. Him the Maior also was in Search for, but could not yet find him ; as he signified also the said Lord, and sent him a Copy of the foresaid Ballad.'

The *Ballad on the Want of Corn* has entirely disappeared, together with the 'Book for the Silk Weavers'. But it seems fairly certain that Deloney was now installed as the poet of the people, and his voicing of popular cries was beginning to bring him into trouble. Slany's letter to Lord Burghley is still extant and is the original source of Strype's information. It is dated the

---

[1] *The Works of Gabriel Harvey* (Grosart), vol. ii, pp. 280–1.
[2] *Survey of London* (Stow, edited Strype, 1720), bk. v, p. 333.

Introduction.

25th of July, 1596, and may be read in Wright's *Elizabeth and her Times* (vol. ii, p. 462).

'I loathe to speake it', says the author of the *Epistle to Martin Mar-Sixtus* (1592), 'euery red-nosed rimester is an author, euery drunken man's dreame is a booke, and he whose talent of little wit is hardly worth a farthing, yet layeth about him so outragiously, as if all Helicon had run through his pen, in a word, scarce a cat can look out of a gutter, but out starts a halfpenny chronicler, and presently A propper new ballet of a strange sight is entited '.[1] The ballad-singer was a common enough figure of popular Eliza-bethan life, and Tudor legislation had found it necessary to include him in a sweeping scheme of social reform. By the 14th of Elizabeth, Cap. V,

'All fencers, bearwards, common players in interludes and minstrels, not belonging to any baron of this realm or towards any other honourable personage of greater degree; ... which ... shall wander abroad and have not license of two justices of the peace ... shall be deemed rogues, vagabonds and sturdy beggars '.[2]

Chettle, in *Kind-Hartes Dreame* (1592), describes the ballad-singer's peculiar garb.

' His head was couered with a round cap, his body with a side skirted tawny coate, his legs and feete trust vppe in leather bus-kins, ... his treble violl in his hande, assured me of his profession. On which (by his continual sawing, hauing left but one string) after his best manner, hee gaue me a huntsup.'[3]

With this we may compare Deloney's own account of Antony Now-now in *The Gentle Craft* (*II*). But Chettle goes on to describe the ballad-singers further:

' A company of idle youths, loathing honest labour and dis-pising lawful trades, betake themselues to a vagrant and vicious life, in euery corner of Cities and market Townes of the Realme, singing and selling of ballads and pamplets full of ribaudrie, and all scurrilous vanity, to the prophanation of God's name, and with-drawing people from christian exercises, especially at faires, mar-kets, and such publike meetings.'[4]

Northbrooke and Stubbes attacked them with the proper dignity of Puritan morality, and Stubbes denounces their indifference to

[1] Quoted in Chappell's *Popular Music of the Olden Time*, vol. i, p. 106.
[2] Prothero's *Statutes and other Constitutional Documents*, p. 69.
[3] *Kind-hartes Dreame* (N.S.S. · *Shakspere Allusion Bks.*), pt. i, p. 43.
[4] Ibid., p. 47.

Thomas Deloney. xi

moral issues with rhetorical fervour : ' Who be more bawdie than
they ? who vncleaner than they ? who more licentious and loose-
minded ? '[1]

To this honourable fraternity Thomas Deloney, the fervent
Puritan-Protestant, joined himself, rising to more prominence in
proportion as he left silk-weaving behind him. His novels show
the closest acquaintance with the life of travelling craftsmen, with
the legends, customs, and topography of certain districts, and
especially those round which the Elizabethan textile industries
were centred,[2] an acquaintance which could scarcely have been
gained except by personal experience. He writes of Petworth
and the high road thence to London,[3] of Gloucester,[4] Canterbury,[5] and Colnbrook,[6] with the casual accuracy which betokens
familiarity, and his skilful imitation of the Northern dialect[7]
indicates a very real knowledge of its peculiarities. There cannot
be the slightest doubt that he must have lived at Newbury long
enough to have become well acquainted with its traditions and
customs,[8] with the surrounding countryside and the names and
reputations of local gentlefolk. Probably Berkshire as a whole
was well known to him, for both *Iacke of Newberie* and *Thomas of
Reading* seem largely derived from traditional sources. His
knowledge of Newbury streets and suburbs is remarkably detailed
and correct.[9] Parry,[10] Englefield,[11] and Hungerford[12] in *Iacke of
Newberie*, and Nevel, Abridges, and Rainsford[13] in *The Gentle
Craft (II)*, are the names of Berkshire county families adopted
boldly into fiction. ' It was her lucke vpon a Bartholomew day
(hauing a Fayre in the toun) to spy her man Iohn giue a paire of
Gloues to a proper maide for a Fayring,' he writes in *Iacke of
Newberie*;[14] and Ashmole, in the *Antiquities of Berkshire* (sub
Newbury), mentions five yearly fairs, one upon August 24th,

[1] *Anatomy of Abuses* (N. S. S.), p. 171.
[2] Note on Sources of *Thomas of Reading, infra*, pp. 547-8.
[3] p. 176, l. 1 ; p. 178, l. 31 ; p. 185, l. 39, and notes.
[4] p. 222, ll. 5-10, and notes.   [5] p. 97, ll. 31, 45, and notes.
[6] Note on Sources of *Thomas of Reading, infra*, p. 549.
[7] e. g. p. 227, ll. 34-8 ; p. 244, ll. 20-7.
[8] p. 27, l. 6 ; p. 32, l. 33 ; p. 33, l. 12, and notes.
[9] e. g. p. 5, l. 21 ; p. 6, l. 8 ; p. 15, l. 36, and notes.
[10] p. 22, l. 10, and note.   [11] p. 24, l. 5, and note.
[12] p. 22, l. 11, and note.
[13] Note on Sources of *Gentle Craft (II), infra*, pp. 532-3.
[14] p. 10, ll. 5-7.

Bartholomew day. Hence Deloney is here referring to an actual fact of local topography, the casual nature of the reference making it all the more certain that he speaks of a custom familiar to him by continued experience. He may have frequented Newbury with his ballads on fair days, an Autolycus among the villages of Bohemia, but more probably he worked there at his trade of silk-weaving. The silk industry reached considerable importance in Berkshire in Elizabeth's time, especially at Reading, and at Newbury itself it survived until the early nineteenth century.[1] Deloney's knowledge of Newbury customs and people appears too detailed to have been acquired in any other way than by actual residence in the town, and *Canaans Calamitie*[2] is actually dedicated to Richard Kingsmill of Highclere, near by.

Nash's *Haue With You to Saffron-Walden* (1596) gives a list of Deloney's pamphlets, some of which have entirely perished or cannot be identified with certainty.

'—as Thomas Deloney, the Balletting Silke-Weauer, of Norwich, hath rime inough for all myracles, and wit to make a Garland of Good will, more than the premisses, with an epistle of Momus and Zoylus; whereas his Muse, from the first peeping foorth, hath stood at Liuery at an Alehouse wispe, neuer exceeding a penny a quart, day or night, and this deare yeare, together with the silencing of his looms, scarce that; he being constrained to betake him to carded Ale: whence it proceedeth that, since Candlemas or his Iigge of John for the King, not one merrie Dittie will come from him, but the Thunder-bolt against Swearers, Repent, England, repent, and the strange iudgments of God.'[3]

Deloney's muse, from the first, was probably nourished on very small beer, and by 1596 the dear year and the slackness of trade seem to have driven him from his loom to rely entirely for sustenance on his ballads and romances. If this be the case, the issue was happy enough, for Deloney's chief claims for remembrance rest upon his novels, *Iacke of Newberie*, registered March 7, 1596–7; *The Gentle Craft* (*I*), October 19, 1597; and *The Gentle Craft* (*II*) and *Thomas of Reading*, written between 1597 and 1600, all of which seem to be the product of enforced idleness from his loom.

The author of *Skialetheia or the Shadow of Truth* (1598) found

---

[1] *Victoria County History of Berks*, vol. i, p. 395.

[2] See note on p. 33, l. 12; also Note on Authorship of *Canaans Calamitie*, *infra*, p. 593.

[3] *The Works of Thomas Nash* (McKerrow), vol. iii, p. 84.

Deloney a poet of sufficient importance to satirize, noting at once the great popularity of his ballads and his choice of dolorous subjects.

To Deloney [8]

Like to the fatal ominous Rauen which tolls
The sicke mans dirge within his hollow beake,
So euery paper-clothed post in Poules,
To thee (Deloney) mourningly doth speake,
And tells thee of thy hempen tragedy,
The wracks of hungry Tyburne nought to thine.
Such massacre's made of thy balladry,
And thou in griefe, for woe thereof maist pine.

To Kemp's *Nine Daies Wonder* (April, 1600) is appended 'Kempes humble request to the impudent generation of Ballad-makers and their coherents, that it would please their Rascalities, to pity his pains in the great journey he pretends; and not fill the country with lies of his never-done-acts, as they did in his late Morrice to Norwich. To the tune of *Thomas Deloney's* Epitaph.' [1] A further reference follows which fixes the date of Deloney's death as about March, 1600, and clearly shows that if he kept his position as 'general' of the ballad-mongers up to the last, it at least did little to fill his needy pockets.

'I have made a privy search, what private Jigmonger of your jolly number hath been the Author of these abominable Ballets written of me.

'I was told it was the great Ballad-maker, T. D., alias Thomas Deloney, Chronicler of the memorable lives of the Six Yeomen of the West, Jack of Newbury, the Gentle Craft, &c., and such like honest men, omitted by Stow, Hollinshed, Grafton, Halle, Froissart, and all the rest of those well deserving writers.

'But I was given since to understand, your late general, Thomas, died poorly (as ye all must do) and was honestly buried, which is much to be doubted of some you.' [2]

It is difficult to say much of a writer of whom so meagre details have been preserved, but Deloney's work to a certain extent betrays his character. He was doubtless an eager reader of such printed matter as came in his way, from the jest-book of *Long Meg of Westminster* to the *Chronicles* of Grafton and Holinshed, the *Acts and Monuments* of Fox, and *The Golden Legend* of Caxton. There are reasons to think he had dipped into some classical and

---

[1] *Social England Illustrated* (*An English Garner* , pp. 159, 160.
[2] Ibid., vol. vii, p. 36.

foreign literature, nor did he neglect the contemporary stage, founding one of his ballads on the play of *Edward III* and often remembering Shakespeare in the plot and dialogue of his novels. Besides this, he had stored his memory with fragments of folk-songs and quaint local customs and sayings, picked up on his wanderings about the country ; and out of this vivid information he spun much of the stuff of his prose and rhyme. None of the contemporary references to him are hostile or ill-tempered, and if the littérateurs of the day treated him with little respect, at least it was with good humour. Nash, although writing satirically in what he considered the vein of the ' Diuine Aretino ', is pleasantly enough disposed to the ale-house muse ; Harvey recognizes the unpretentious merit which is really present in Deloney's poetry, while Kemp's reference is a testimony to a respectability almost pathetic. He ' died poorly . . . and was honestly buried '.

From his surviving work we can gather his acquaintance and sympathy with trade and handicraftsmen of all sorts, his admiration and satisfied acceptance of blue blood and the established order of things, which particularly marks the bourgeois class to which he belonged. Simon Eyer and John Winchcombe, the successful merchants endowed with all the popular virtues of generosity and good spirits, were his heroes of real life, but his sentimental conviction was the pre-eminent virtue of an aristocracy, so that all his kings are truly ' royal ' and their ladies ' gracious '. He had all the democratic value for the commonplace virtues, and the democratic enjoyment of sheer life, pathetic, ridiculous, or merely coarse. A strong patriot and Protestant, he hated Spain and the Catholic Church with an honourable virulence, while his pride in substantial aldermen and civic corporations bespeaks him a typical Elizabethan Londoner, by adoption if not by birth.

He is the chief representative of a host of writers (mostly nameless) who catered for that Elizabethan vulgar, eager for entertainment either in prose or verse.

II. DELONEY AND THE ELIZABETHAN NOVEL.

In the work of Thomas Deloney we may justly find the highest achievement of the Elizabethan novel ; and yet to the modern reader fresh from the art of the great novelists of the eighteenth and nineteenth centuries there must appear even in his work a lack of construction and seriousness which contrasts vividly with the great achievements of the same age in drama and poetry.

Before 1400 Chaucer had written *Troilus and Criseyde*, in method an almost perfect example of the novel, in spite of its poetic form. Yet in the late sixteenth century novelists are working out in the dark the very rudiments of their art and, almost incapable of construction, can scarcely fill in more than the simplest outlines of characterization. The subtlety of handling and the mastery of material by which Chaucer vivified a common mediaeval story into a drama of quick and human interest is exchanged for the crudity and barbaric emphasis of a *Jack Wilton* or *Don Simonides*, and while *Troilus and Criseyde* shows us the art of the novelist in its most subtle form, the novels of the Elizabethans seem little more than elementary experiments in an unknown medium.

Nevertheless, in the sixteenth century one step had been taken of the greatest importance in the development of the English novel. Fielding defines the novel as the 'prose epic', and in scope it certainly embraces aspects of human life hostile to poetic treatment. The death of Barkis in *David Copperfield* may touch the realms of poetry, but Mr. Micawber can only move in the atmosphere of prose; Esmond is 'himself a true poem', but Tom Tusher would be strangely out of place in the poetic conventions. Hence it was imperative for the just development of the novel that the medium adopted should be prose and not poetry, and by the time of the Elizabethans this change of medium had already taken place, so that if contemporary novelists produced nothing approximating to *Troilus and Criseyde*, at least they were subduing the hand to that it worked in, and experimenting in prose as a medium of creative literature.

But the character of the sixteenth century was hardly favourable to the development of the novel in its higher forms. The tendencies of an ambitious Renaissance were towards poetic form and method, and the popularity of the drama and poetry led writers of the day to throw the most prosaic matter into the more popular shape. Drayton endeavoured to sublimate the details of topography into the Songs of *Polyolbion*, and Sir John Davies discussed metaphysics in the four-lined stanzas of *Nosce Teipsum*. While poetic energy was potent enough to hammer out such unmalleable subjects as these, there can be little wonder that other prosaic but more vivid matter, which seems to a modern reader best fitted for the treatment of the novelist, should have found its expression in verse, and more especially in the drama. While the latest murder found artistic elaboration in *The Yorkshire Tragedy* or *Arden of Feversham,* and Ben Jonson illustrated the humours of Elizabethan life in *Bartholomew Fair* or *The Alchemist,* the use of the novel as a medium of literature was apt to be overlooked by the more important writers and despised by the more cultured readers. Renaissance ideals pointed to the great epic and the great tragedy as the two pinnacles of literary achievement, and it needed a prophetic soul to appreciate the ultimate possibilities of the rough contemporary work in prose fiction.

But while poetry claimed the first attention of the educated, there was a large Elizabethan audience clamouring for literature of any kind, provided only that it should be sufficiently amusing. Eager publishers were not slow to reckon up the tastes of the vulgar, and not only were the old romances set forth again in a new and attractive rhetoric, but a host of writers who depended for sheer livelihood on popular approval set to work to ' yark up ' new pamphlets of pothouse jests, of London rogueries, of out-rageous knight-errantry, of anything and everything which might satisfy the thirst for novelty and amusement. Greene poured forth the tragic reminiscences of his own life in *The Repentance of Robert Greene, M.A.,* and his series of ' cony-catching ' pamphlets ; Nash lashed himself into the vein of ' lusty Juvenal ' to attack the vices of London and the age in *Christs Teares* and the *Anatomie of Absurditie* ; Dekker fancifully set forth the humours of men and things in *The Bachelors Banquet, The Guls Horn Book*, and a dozen more such pamphlets ; while Painter, Whetstone, Fenton and their brother translators introduced to the contemporary public the popular stories of Italy, France, and Spain.

Amidst this torrent of miscellaneous literature the Elizabethan novel took its shape and developed its characteristics, and it is to the prose audience for whom these authors wrote that we owe the Elizabethan novel.

There was no lack of good stories in the Middle Ages. The epic legends which the Teutons brought with them in their descent upon the south were softened down by Christianity and a more elaborate civilization into the romance of Chrétien de Troyes and Godfrey of Strasbourg. The sentiment of chivalry, with its half mystic refinements upon love and honour, replaced the old glorification of magnificent slaughter, and while nice points of honour were debated in the lord's court or lady's bower, the growth of a powerful burgher class in the twelfth and thirteenth centuries led to the rise of the fabliau, or town literature, which dealt preferably with the crude realities of life rather than with courtly theories of conduct or etherealized adventures.

'Why were taverns invented but to ripen men's wits? and why were tales devised but to make men pleasant?' asks the anonymous author of the *Cobler of Canterburie* (1608), and doubtless much of the realistic literature of the Middle Ages took rise from the tavern talk of those who, like Langland's *Gula*, missed mass for the alehouse. Here, travellers beguiled the time by the mutual relation of good stories, which passed down from mouth to mouth and from generation to generation until the tradition was lost or received a final literary shape at the hand of a Boccaccio or a Bandello. Chaucer shows us the Canterbury Pilgrims whiling away their journey with tales, and Chaucer's own work shows us how various were the sources, classical, romantic, and popular, upon which the mediaeval artist could draw for his material.

Besides the stories—naked and undisguised—told in the taverns, clerical zeal made collections of tales for moral edification, these being fragments from the floating mass of mediaeval oral and written literature, quaintly moralized. The *Gesta Romanorum* contains all sorts of stories from all sorts of sources, and its publication in 1517 by Wynkyn de Worde may be taken as a sign of its continued popularity in the sixteenth century.

While the mediaeval minstrel read or sang his romances to gentle or simple, and the mediaeval bourgeoisie scattered their satirical and realistic fabliaux broadcast, the more tragic episodes of life that touched the heart and imagination of the people found their expression in the ballad, a traditional literature that stayed with us longest of all, and has not yet finally disappeared. Thus in the Middle Ages, the story or 'novel' was an especially popular form of literature, in whatever guise it appeared, and whether it dealt with the matter of romance, the matter of town life, or the matter of tragedy.

The continuity of the mediaeval and Tudor ages has been strangely overlooked, and this continuity is plainly marked in the early history of the English novel. For while the Renaissance set before Englishmen new ideals in literature and flooded England with new and strange material for fiction, yet it did not, as elsewhere, choke the springs of native genius, and the foreign matter was rather absorbed by the English literary tradition than triumphed over it. In spite of Ascham and Lyly English prose developed on its own lines, and in spite of the 'enchantments of Circes' brought from Italy our novel of the sixteenth century is characteristically English. The two main streams of mediaeval literature, the realistic and the romantic, as they express themselves in the novel, may be seen in continuous development in popular Tudor prose, in the *Hundred Merry Tales* and *Long Meg of Westminster* on the one hand, and in the *Morte Arthur* and *Montelion* on the other.

For the popularity of simple prose romances in Elizabethan times there is ample evidence. 'As the Lord de la Noue in the Sixth Discourse of his Politic and Military Discourses, censureth the books of Amadis de Gaul, which, he saith, are no less hurtful to youth than the works of Machiavelli; so these books are accordingly to be censured of, whose names follow,' writes Meres in *Palladis Tamia* (1598), and adds a list of romances, including *Huon of Bordeaux, Guy of Warwick, Four Sons of Aymon, Arthur of the Round Table, The Seven Champions of Christendom,* and other well-known mediaeval stories. The early English printing-press had in the first place busied itself with the dissemination of the culture and literature of an age which was passing away. In Caxton's *Golden Legend,* Capgrave's *Nova Legenda Angliae* was passed on to the Elizabethans, and Copland's translations from the French handed down the spirit of knight-errantry in romances such as *Guy of Warwick* and *The Knight of the Swan.* Ascham's censure witnesses the popularity of *Morte Arthur,* and Shakespeare's Oberon reminds us of the vogue of Berners's *Huon of Bordeaux.* But these versions of French romance, popular though they were, really belong to another civilization than the Tudor. For the Elizabethan children of the Renaissance looked out upon a world of garbled glories, and the haunting pathos of a dying age that broods upon the pages of Malory and Berners could find no real echo in the hearts of men who saw the New World unrolled before them like a scroll and took all human learning and experience to be their province. More violent emotions shook society and the individual, and the excitement of the age coloured even its language and its novels. Thus while the old stories in their old settings never ceased to be read, later writers who re-edited them for the press, or wrote similar romances of their own, decorated them with a more florid style and seasoned them with a more Renaissance sentiment.

With this change in romantic method and the rise of the professional author, the old tales were degraded from their earlier dignity and addressed to a more popular audience. The end of this process is to be seen in the chap-books of the eighteenth century, when the stories originally invented for the delight of courtly lords and ladies end in the penny tracts of *Guy of Warwick, Bevis of Hampton* and *The Seven Wise Masters.* More cultured Elizabethan readers preferred the brand-new phrases and sentimentalities of the Euphuistic romances to the old simple stories of endless adventures; and even writers who, like Richard Johnson, wrote more distinctly for the vulgar, made their old-fashioned stories bright with a new and often astonishing rhetoric. Johnson's *Tom a Lincolne, the Red Rose Knight* is a tangled romance of the usual mediaeval kind, but it is evidently pitched for a bourgeois audience, and the characters constantly break out into violent apostrophes.

' Despaire, where art thou? I'll saddle winged Pegasus, and scale the mansion place of Jove, I will ransack all the corners of the sky, I will throw doun the sun, the moon and stars.'

A comparison of Johnson's romance with Copland's *Knight of the Swan* shows clearly how the knightly romance had changed its literary method with its audience. Dignity and restraint have been replaced by over-emphasis and mere extravagance, and the subdued colourings of late mediaeval romance are transformed into the garish bravadoes of a bastard poetic prose. Of this school the chief writer was Emanuel Ford, and *Ornatus and Artesia, Parismus,* and the rest of his novels add to the mediaeval confusion of incident and sequence the Renaissance confusion of rhetoric and affectation. Antony Munday's numerous translations from the Spanish brought to native invention the tangles of foreign growth, and the romance of knight-errantry flourished with un-diminished popularity into the seventeenth century, until it was swallowed up into the heroic novel and the heroic drama.

But when the University wits, educated in the school of Lyly, took up the novel of romance, a more ambitious method, addressed to a more cultured audience, makes a definite appearance. The readers of *Tom a Lincolne* were content with 'ginger, hot i' the mouth', a torrent of rhetoric and adventure, but the interest of Greene's *Philomela* or Lodge's *Margarite of America* obviously lay in a different direction. George Petty's *Petite Palace of Petty his Pleasure, containing many pretty stories by him set forth in comely colours* (1576) was dedicated, like Lyly's *Euphues*, to the ' Gentle women of England', and with Petty, and not with Lyly as M. Jusserand would persuade us, we enter upon the prose literature of the drawing-room. Petty, like Lyly, Greene, and Lodge, has all the tricks of euphuism at his fingers' ends, the 'pickt words and choise phrases' that would recommend him to readers interested in the nice use of language, and his real business is not the depicting of character or action, but the discussion of emotions and delicate points of conduct. Here we have all the dignified morality, the sententiousness and interminable monologues and conversations of *Euphues*, two years before *Euphues* was published. So distinctly does Petty's interest lie in the sentiment and in the moralizations which seem more properly to belong to the essay than the novel, that he passes over the finest possibilities of a story to indulge his euphuistic vein. In the story of Horatia, when the heroine's husband is slain by her brother, we have a theme as keenly tragic as any in the old ballads. The born novelist or tragedian would have known how to use such a situation, but Petty slurs over the tragic crisis in a shower of mere words.

'But seeing afar off about her brother's shoulders the coat armour of her Curiatus, which she herself with needlework curiously had made, being thereby fully assured of his death, she was drawn into these doleful plaints.

'Oh heauens, what hellish sight do I see ; far more dolorous and dangerous than Medusa's head. And is my Curiatus slain ? then care come cut in sunder my corps, then dole deliuer me to the dreadful darts of death.'

'*Euphues* I read when I was a little Ape at Cambridge,' wrote Nash, 'and I then thought it was ipse ille,' and *Euphues*, published in 1578, the final elaboration of Petty's style and sentiment, was the guiding influence that permeated the romantic novels of Lodge and Greene. So essential indeed had euphuism become to romance that Greene, like Deloney, while using the plainer English for ordinary occasions, relapses into the euphuistic method immediately he takes in hand a romantic subject. Like Lyly, Greene aims at morality, 'how young gentlemen that aim at honour should level the end of their affections'; the construction of his novels is as loose as his master's, and his characters equally indefinite. Heroes and heroines retire to private closets or cool arbours 'to powder forth their complaints' at remorseless length, and are really nothing more than mouths through which the author pours sententious platitudes and pleasing rhetoric. But Greene, aiming at the elegant discussion of sentimental emotion, really achieves something in the management of courtly conversation, and *Pandosto* and *Menaphon* show an agreeable variety of colour and movement. Lodge's work, while sharing the general characteristics of Greene's, rises to more reality in *A Margarite of America*, and in *Rosalynde* achieves a vivacity which explains the close relation of the novel and *As You Like It*.

But while mediaeval romance had thus changed under the moulding influences of the Renaissance, the mediaeval fabliau had also been developed to a more elaborate form. In the *Gesta Romanorum* the Universal Church had held good wit prisoner for the sake of righteousness, but with the progress of the sixteenth century men began to print good stories without the excuse of allegory. The Tudor jest-books, carried in the pocket or passed from hand to hand, were the successors of the *Exempla Predicatorum*, and they bear traces in their 'significations' of their honourable lineage. The *Hundred Merry Tales* (1528) is the earliest example extant of a literature which was popular all through the Tudor period, and which survives in a debased form even in the age of free education and public libraries. Many of the tales are those excellent jokes of all time that reappear with unfailing regularity, though in slightly altered guise, in the columns of modern publications. Some are attached to actual localities, as the story of the 'archdekyn of Essex' and that of the curate of Botley. There are few or none that seem to have a definitely literary source, and yet in many cases they are told with an art that has perhaps never been excelled in the history of the written joke. The story of the Welshmen in heaven is related with a satirical reserve and malice that shows how completely the art of simple jest was understood by the writers of earliest Tudor English.

'I find written among old gestes, how God made St Peter
porter of heauen, and that God of his goodness, soon after his
passion, suffered many men to come to the kingdom of heauen
with small deseruing; at which time there was in Heauen a great
company of Welshmen, which with their cracking and babbling
troubled all the other. Wherefore God said to St Peter, that he
was weary of them, and that he would fain haue them out of
Heauen. To whom St Peter said : Good Lord, I warrant you,
that shal be done. Wherefore St Peter went out of heauen gates
and cried with a loud voice Cause bobe, that is as much to say as
roasted cheese, which thing the Welshmen hearing ran out of
heauen a great pace. And when St Peter saw them all out he
suddenly wente into Heauen, and locked the door, and so sparred
all those Welshmen out.'

The *Sackful of News* (1557) is full of stories nearly as good,
but *Merry Tales, Witty Questions and Quick Answers* (1567)
draws distinctly from literary sources, from Diogenes Laertius,
Aesop, and Plutarch, and there is a corresponding decrease in
vigour and effect. As a matter of fact, the temper of the age was
becoming more literary, and the isolated joke belonging more
distinctly to the oral literature of an age when books were rare,
lacked the continuity and size demanded by the readers of Lyly
and Greene. The essence of the joke is its brevity and point ;
for a collection of jokes to become a humorous book some sort
of constructional framework is necessary. The unsatisfactoriness
of a torrent of unconnected 'japes' had been felt in the Middle
Ages, and had resulted in the creation of Reynard the Fox, the
gigantic burlesque hero to whom could be attached all the
rogueries and cunning tricks known to the mediaeval story-teller.
But Caxton's prose epic of Reynard was the finished product of
a civilization different from and more elaborated than that of
the Tudors, and the earlier sixteenth-century attempts at unifying
the jest-book seem childish in comparison with the broad outlines
of the Reynard cycle. Tudor printers, however, found it profitable
to ascribe collections of jokes to well-known jesters, such as
Scogin (1565) and Dr. Skelton (1567), and these, like Tarlton at
a later date, tended to become the central figures of buffoonery,
and thus to give a biographical unity to an otherwise disconnected
series of fragments. This unity had already been exemplified in
the *Oule Glasse* version of the Eulenspiegel stories printed by
Copland in 1530, where Owleglasse is a grotesque lubberly hero,
a practical joker of magnified dimensions. The jest-books

by their very nature were realistic and often crude; hence their development is towards the realistic novel, a development which is clearly illustrated by the relation of the jest-book called *Long Meg of Westminster* to the story of Richard Casteler in Deloney's *Gentle Craft*[1] (*Part II*). *Long Meg* is extant in an edition of 1582, and as it stands is a collection of rough practical jokes, ascribed to an Amazonian maiden in service at a Westminster inn. But it was impossible to ascribe such doings to Long Meg without investing her with a personality of her own, coarse and crude, but distinct and vigorous enough. To describe 'the pranks of Long Meg' was to describe her character and life; and Deloney easily transferred this roughly-sketched character to his own pages, endowing it with new life and more human personality.

The Famous Historie of Fryer Bacon (before 1594?) is little more than an elaborated jest-book, where full advantage is taken of Bacon's magical powers to work practical jokes on a larger scale than is ordinary, 'How Fryer Bacon deceiued an old Vsurer,' 'How Miles, Fryer Bacons man did coniure for meat, and got meate for himselfe and his hoast,' &c.; and *The History of Doctor Faustus* (1587-9?), in spite of the magnificence of the plot upon which the rather stupid incidents are hung, may be adequately described in the same way. Nevertheless the titles of both plainly indicate that the jest-book was rapidly becoming the Life and Adventures of a picaresque hero.

While these books of printed jokes thus brought the stuff of realism to the making of the Elizabethan novel, miscellaneous popular prose literature exerted a similar influence by its frank treatment of contemporary life. The Elizabethan age had an insatiable appetite for information about life of all kinds, for then human nature seemed to be discovering itself anew, and hence side by side with the literature of Arcadia runs the literature of Southwark and the bordello. Mediaeval satire in Langland had sat at the alehouse door and painted misery and vice with a masterful veracity that made *Piers Plowman* a favourite Elizabethan poem, and Skelton in his *Eleanor Rumnyge* had carried on the tradition of unrelenting realism into the literature of the sixteenth century—into the poetry of Spenser and into the prose of the pamphleteers.

[1] See Note on Sources of *The Gentle Craft* (*II*), *infra*, pp. 531-2.

Awdeley's *Fraternity of Vacabonds* (1560) shows the author writing with 'his eye upon the object', and Harman in his *Caveat to Common Cursitors* describes from first-hand experience life among the Tudor vagrants, with a vividness and pathos that anticipates the work of Defoe. Harman reached the rock bottom of the realistic literary method when he gave a faithful transcript of a phase of human life he knew thoroughly well, and the truth and value of his work may be judged from the unscrupulous use that Greene and Dekker made of it in their own pamphlets on London low life. But while Dekker added little to his stolen material but the ornamentation of exuberant fancy, Greene worked into his 'cony-catching' pamphlets much of his own seamy experience, so that his *Notable Discouerie of Cosenage* (1591) and the *Defence of Cony Catching* (1592) have a distinct value of their own, full as they are of vigorous character-drawing and conversation.

In *Never Too Late* and *The Repentance of Robert Greene, M.A.* he gave his own pathetic biography to the world, and in the 'cony-catching' pamphlets his accounts of London rogues, wrought from the matter of his own experience, constantly tend to the biographical form. To the *Disputation betweene a Hee Conny catcher and a shee Conny catcher* (1592) he added an account of the conversion of an English courtesan, which equals *Moll Flanders* in realistic power as it surpasses it in all true and fine feeling. Harman's description of the English rogues had been by no means lacking in sympathy, and Greene, forced too often to rub shoulders with crossbiters and cutpurses, was not without a fellow-feeling for the criminals he describes. The biography of the rogue told with sympathy and admiration becomes the picaresque novel, and in the *Black Book's Messenger, Laying open the Life and Death of Ned Browne*, Greene definitely takes for his hero 'one of the most notable Cutpurses, Crosbiters, and Conny catchers that euer liued in England', attempting that kind of novel of which *Gil Blas* is the final type. While Reynard the Fox and Owleglass may be in some sense regarded as picaresque rogues, yet David Rowland's translation of *Lazarillo de Tormes* in 1567 really provided a new model for the imitation of English writers. For *Lazarillo* has much of that humorous subtlety which, attaining its full richness in the pages of *Don Quixote*, appears distinctive of the realistic Spanish novel, and is written with a sureness of touch and unity of design unknown to contemporary

English fiction. But in spite of these merits, it is doubtful whether it had much influence on the development of the Elizabethan novel of roguery. Chettle's *Pierce Plainness* appears to be the only direct imitation of its method, and the realistic novels of Greene, Nash, and Deloney belong distinctly to the English tradition of the jest-book, alike in their vigour and directness as in their faults of construction. *The Life and Death of Ned Browne* is little more than a collection of conny-catching stories, told with zest and enjoyment, and put into the mouth of a highwayman before he is turned off at Tyburn, just as *The Gentle Craft* is a collection of jests and stories elaborated and fitted into a framework.

Nash's *Jack Wilton* is the most complete example of the Elizabethan picaresque novel, and in writing it Nash owed little or nothing to *Lazarillo*, but much to contemporary realistic prose and his own experience. For the material, his own travels and adventures sufficed ; for the arrangement, it evolves itself from the autobiographical character of the novel, and is only the arrangement of a number of stories and incidents that, like the Theseids mentioned by Aristotle, owe their only unity to the fact that they happened within the experience of a single person. The 'life' of Jack Wilton is a string of breathless experiences huddled together with little or no regard to importance or grouping, and the real strength of Nash's method lies in its characterizations, its movement and melodramatic power. Nash has infused his own vigour into the narrative, and by the heat of his own fury welded an unpromising material into something like unity. In language *Jack Wilton* is the complete antithesis of *Lazarillo* ; English in its vigorous crudity, where the Spaniard is good-humouredly ironic. The malicious reserve of Lazarillo's 'My father (whom God pardon)' was beyond the art of Nash, who plays the 'Lusty Juvenal' amidst his gallery of grotesques, lashing and trouncing the puppets of his own creation with an unsparing hand, and while the full merit of his 'biting portraits' must be allowed, it may be doubted whether the method of the satirist was that best adapted to the legitimate development of the novel. Thackeray calls himself the 'showman', and his characters the 'puppets', artistic creations that seem, however, to work freely of themselves. Nash, however, has none of this aloofness ; he cannot stand aside and let his characters unfold themselves, but openly introduces them with abuse, as that unfortunate 'bursten belly inkhorn orator called Vanderhulke . . . one that had a sulphurous big swollen large face, like a Saracen, eyes like two Kentish oysters, a mouth that opened as wide every time he spake, as one of those old knit trap doors, a beard as though it had been made of a birds nest pluckt in pieces, which consisteth of straw, hair and dust mixed together'. But while Nash lacked the sympathetic outlook that was needed for the development of the novel as the 'prose epic', he by no means omitted that vein of extravagant sentiment which formed the staple of the romantic novel, and the introduction of the Earl of Surrey and Lady Geraldine into *Jack Wilton* served at once to flavour realism with the 'Arabian spiceries of sweet passions' and to give a certain solidity to the novel by reason of the historical matter.

Two main methods have been traced in the Elizabethan novel— the realistic, derived from the jest-book and popular satire, and the romantic, derived from mediaeval romance, both being reinforced to some extent by foreign influence as it filtered through in the numerous translations and imitations of that age. But these two streams of Elizabethan development cannot be strictly shut off, the one from the other, and realism and romanticism are seen running side by side in such novels as Greene's *Never Too Late*, Nash's *Jack Wilton*, and Deloney's *Thomas of Reading*. While, however, the two methods are not mutually exclusive in the same novel, nevertheless the romantic episodes usually break clearly away from the realistic, and the alternation of the one with the other tends to faulty construction and incongruity in style. As a rule the Elizabethan novelist preferred the abnormal and dealt with the sublimations of sentiment or the very crudities of fact. Nash is equally violent in his description of a 'greasy ale-knight', as in the alliterative raptures of the Earl of Surrey, and Greene only deserts the racy slang of the 'conny-catcher' to pour out the full flowers of euphuism in a love scene.

The exaggeration of Elizabethan romance has little charm for the modern reader, and Fenton's *Tragical Discourses of Bandello* prove how unreal the exaggeration of realism may become. What sixteenth-century fiction required was its direction toward the more normal phases of human life, and its riddance on the one hand of merely abstract sentiment and on the other of meaning-less discordant detail. The romantic novel had sought its heroes and heroines in Arcadia, and found shadows and rhetoric ; the realistic jest-book and novel had sought the stuff of life in taverns, and found hearty animals and some dirt. Romance required incident and reality, realism a saner ideal and sense of order. Both were defective inasmuch as they avoided the faithful delineation of normal life, but it was realism on the whole which was more fruitful for English literature. Lyly's *Euphues* and Greene's *Mamillia* have an interest for the literary historian, but *The Caveat to Common Cursitors* and the *Hundred Merry Tales* have a present and human value in themselves, and while romance was satisfied with the constant repetition of the same platitudes and situations, if only in a sufficiently pleasing manner, the progress of realism, in the jest-book and satirical essay alike, was towards characterization and construction, that is to say, towards the English novel as we know it to-day.

Riche, in his *Farewell to the Militarie Profession* (1581), had left on one side the exaggerations of romance and realism, and striven to a certain extent to represent in literature the more ordinary life of the times. But it is in the novels of Thomas Deloney that we find the first consistent attempt at drawing material for fiction from the everyday life of everyday people. Familiar with local gossip and tradition, and with a mind eagerly absorbent of such printed literature as came within his reach, he found the sources of his stories anywhere, but their characterization and colour are the accurate reflection of Elizabethan life in Cheapside and Westminster, among the cobblers of Whitehall and the drapers of Candleweek Street. The difference in the subjects and method of his work from those of contemporary novelists is perhaps to be chiefly explained by the circumstances of his life and by the audience he addressed. Unlike Lodge or Nash or Greene, he belonged to no circle of University wits ; Renaissance ambition had touched him but little, and he aimed not at fine writing but profitable story-telling. The English writers Italianate would scarcely sink to the life of 'base mechanicals', their proclivities and culture led them much rather to the unsubstantialities of Arcadia and the brothels of Southwark.

While Greene wrote for the young gallants, 'how young gentlemen that aim at honour should leuel the end of their affections ',[1] and Petty for 'Gentle Readers, whom by my will I would haue

---

[1] *Tullies Love*, title-page.

only Gentlewomen ',[1] Deloney dedicated his novels to the ' famous Cloth Workers in England '[2] or ' To the Master and Wardens of the worshipfull company of Cordwaynors ',[3] and wrote as an artisan for the jolly companions of his craft, with whom he had worked at his loom in Norwich or tramped the high roads of East Anglia. But he by no means breaks away altogether from the traditional separation of realism and romanticism. In *Thomas of Reading* the bourgeois history of the clothiers is interwoven with, although not blended with, the romantic life and love of the Duke of Normandy and the Fair Margaret, and the story of St. Hugh in the First Part of the *Gentle Craft* is a knight-errant romance of the most ordinary kind, preceding the hearty domestic story of Sir Simon Eyer. But these are his least successful work ; his hand is out when he deals in such bloodless abstractions as St. Hugh and St. Winifred, and Margaret is only real as the servant of Gray of Gloucester. The story of Crispine and Crispianus (*Gentle Craft, I*) owes its merits to the vein of healthy realism which breaks through the plot of a sentimental story, and Deloney's artistic mastery only finds full scope in the handling of such realistic themes of bourgeois life as the *Historie of Iacke of Newberie* and the love affairs of Florence with her foreign suitors (*Gentle Craft, I*). It is here that the influence of the jest-book on the shaping of his novels is most apparent, betraying itself in the matter used, and the happy unrestraint of attitude. His use of the material of the jest-books can be amply illustrated, not only in the signal reconstruction of *Long Meg of Westminster* but also in the many comic episodes which he slenderly links together upon the thread of a personality, incidents such as the adventure of Dr. Burcot (*Gentle Craft, II*), the disappointment of Benedict (*Iacke of Newberie*), and the deception of Sir William Ferris (*Thomas of Reading*). Elizabethan novels, usually discursive and unformed, are apt to become even more shapeless when based upon materials such as these, but Deloney, while never aiming at the size and structure of the modern novel, none the less attains a clearness of construction and homogeneity of atmosphere which is missing in most contemporary fiction, for he writes straightforwardly from a simple point of view, fitting his stories into an appropriate framework, and informing them with the same vivid life, so that the whole novel is

---

[1] *Pettys Palace,* ' To the Gentle Gentlewomen Readers.'
[2] *Iacke of Newberie,* p. 2.   [3] *Gentle Craft (II),* p. 139.

one in atmosphere, if not in connected incident—a book like *Iacke of Newberie*, for 'all famous Cloth-Workers in England ',[1] or like *The Gentle Craft*, 'for the worshipfull company of Cordwaynors '.[2] Further, the single biographical aim 'to set to sight the long hidden History ' of the bourgeois heroes of the loom and the cobbling last removes much of the temptation to irrelevancy ; nor were Deloney's readers likely to be of that class which Lyly and Greene edified with endless digressions on nice points of morals and manners, while the introduction of historical matter gave a background and solidity to his narrative as a whole. Lodge had drawn on history in his feeble *William Longbeard* (1593), and Nash had introduced historical events and characters into the *Life of Iacke Wilton* ; but Deloney, endowed with a democratic facility for the fabulizing of history, could more successfully blend the matters of fact and of fiction. His life as a travelling artisan had led him from town to town and county to county, and, chatting with fellow artisans and chance travellers picked up on the way, he had gathered local tradition and history first hand from incidental gossip, and thus history was to him, even more than to other Elizabethans, a garner-house of stories, and the printed pages of Holinshed and Grafton only further material for weaving into pleasant romances. To folk tradition belongs a vivacity and colour unmatchable even 'in the great Chroniclers ', and the vigorous personality of Iacke of Newberie is the vivid figure of countryside gossip preserved to us by Deloney's literary skill, while *Thomas of Reading* is probably a blending of the history of Holinshed with a now lost Berkshire tradition. In the tales of Simon Eyer, Richard Casteler, and Master Peachey it is impossible to decide how much is taken from the printed page, how much from tradition, and how much is Deloney's own invention. Certainly he commonly took familiar phrases and customs, the origins of which had been forgotten, and wove around them his own stories of explanation, 'Tom Drum's entertainment'[3] suggesting the rough courting of Mistress Farmer, and the quaint usages at *Bosoms Inn*[4] Cuthbert of Kendal's intrigue with the host's wife. The jest-book of itself tended towards characterization and biography, but in dealing with the heroes of weaving and cobbling,

---

[1] p. 2, l. 2.   [2] p. 139, l. 2.
[3] Note on Sources of *Gentle Craft* (*II*), *infra*, p. 535.
[4] Note on Sources of *Thomas of Reading, infra*, p. 549.

and elaborating the more or less commonly known circumstances
of their lives, Deloney was bound to develop this tendency further,
and the happy mingling of traditional history and the matter of
the jest-book resulted in the creation of such characters of flesh
and blood as Richard Casteler, Simon Eyer, and John Winchcombe,
who, unlike the heroes of the early jest-books, really dominate the
situation and occupy the real interest.

Deloney's excellence lies in his faithful and sympathetic render-
ing of commonplace human life. Where he attempts the
romanticism of subject and language fashionable in his time, he
is as successful as his contemporaries in wearying the modern
reader, but the straightforward pleasures of a healthy middle class
he presents with a gusto and vivacity which is an ample apology
for an occasional coarseness. He understood thoroughly the
artisan class of whom he wrote ; his pity was for the ' poore people '
'who laboured to get their owne bread', 'whom,' as he quaintly says,
' God lightly blesseth with most children'[1] ; and he gave a willing
admiration to the master-workmen and successful merchants who
paid a fair day's wages for a fair day's work, to Iacke of Newberie
who would not have his people ' pincht of their victualls ', and to
Simon Eyer who remembered from prentice days his debt of
' pudding-pies ' and ' feasted all the Prentices on Shrove Tuesday '.
He describes with faithful enjoyment the life and love of the
Elizabethan workshop, how the widow woos her man, or how the
sparing Richard Casteler marries a Dutch maiden who ' could doe
diuers pretty feates to get her owne liuing '. He tells us of that
warm-blooded bourgeois life of Elizabethan times with a spirit
and wealth of detail to be found in no other author, describing
a phase of society which most contemporary literature chose to
overlook contemptuously. His delight in telling his stories is
that of a man who describes what he has enjoyed ; his railing
conversations between Long Meg and Gillian of the George, or
Tom Drum and the cobblers of Petworth, have all the point and
good-humour of the dialogue of the market-place, while the
description of how Iacke of Newberie's servants were revenged on
Mistress Franks glorifies the content of the jest-book into excellent
prose comedy. Nor is he less successful in dealing with more
tragic material. It would be hard to overrate the art of that
chapter[2] where Old Cole is murdered at his inn, and where

[1] p. 213, ll. 18-9. [2] *Thomas of Reading*, chap. 11.

circumstance is made to follow on circumstance and so to culminate in inevitable catastrophe, but with a restraint and sureness unsurpassed by any work of more ambitious contemporary novelists. A masterpiece of bourgeois pathos, it may well be suggested [1] that Shakespeare was indebted to it in those scenes of *Macbeth* where a host and hostess similarly plot together to murder a guest, or where Lady Macbeth sees the visionary blood on her hand as Old Cole saw it on the hands of his hostess at the Crane.

Deloney has no problems of life or conduct to discuss as his modern successors in fiction are apt to have, but simply holds 'the mirror up to nature' without the interposition of himself or his views. Hence, however slightly his characters be sketched they are shown to us in a clear and transparent medium, and his worthies move freely and vividly in the pleasant atmosphere of their own occupations, honest craftsmen of the Elizabethan workshop or good housewives of the Elizabethan home. How popular his novels were may be judged from the long period in which they held the public estimation, often reprinted through the seventeenth century and surviving plentifully in chapbook form into the eighteenth.[2] 'The Book of the Gentle Craft hath had a general acceptance of the Cordwainers, and the History of the Six Worthy Yeomen of the West, and Jack of Newbery the like from the weavers', wrote Winstanley in 1668 in the preface to *The Honor of the Merchant Taylors* ; and Winstanley's own book, servilely founded on the novels he mentions, is only one specimen of a whole class of popular literature that sprang up in the tradition that Deloney created. But the spontaneity and vigour of the original were not to be repeated by meaner hands ; the novels of his imitators may be allowed to rest on the library shelves for the curious, but his own have a permanent literary value and deserved a recognition less belated.

III. THE POETRY OF DELONEY.

Deloney's novels seem to have been, more or less, experiments, entered upon in the last three years of his life. With the ex-

---

[1] By Professor Sir Walter Raleigh.

[2] e. g. The British Museum and the Bodleian together contain seven eighteenth-century chapbook versions of the *Gentle Craft* (*I*).

C

ception of the tracts relating to the Archbishop of Cologne, his earlier extant work is entirely in verse, and in contemporary opinion he stands forth, not so much as a novelist but as the 'great Ballad-maker T.D.' Deloney was an artisan, seeking originally no doubt to increase a scanty wage by literary work, and to such a one the medium of the ballad was the easiest for reaching a wide and popular audience. Thus, with the exception of *Canaans Calamitie* (a more ambitious piece of work), his poetic faculty exercised itself entirely in the ballad style and metre, and his work is completely representative of the ballad activity of the later sixteenth century.

The term 'ballad' in modern literature seems to be used loosely for nearly every kind of lyric, but more scientifically for those traditional poems which retain in part the conventions and spirit of an earlier poetic age, when literary composition was more communal than individual, and the emotional atmosphere more simple and epic. The true ballad, whether taken down from a twentieth-century tradition or found in a fifteenth-century manuscript, has distinguishing features of its own which mark it off from the poetry of more complex and sophisticated ages, and these peculiar features are fully explained by the circumstances of primitive composition. The poet of modern civilization is a lonely Heine or prophetic Blake pouring forth bitterness or celestial intoxication from the height of his own egoism. Primitive poetry was the voice of the people, more the rhythm of an elemental civilization than the expression of individual desires and convictions. The source of modern poetry is the individual soul brooding on 'things past, present, and to come', the source of ancient poetry was the gathering of the people for work or play, who lightened communal labour at the oar or reinforced communal pleasure in the dance by rhythmic music and rhymes. Now a Byron or Shelley sings to a merely receptive audience; then the people were audience and performer too and bore the burden

> *Binnorie, O Binnorie,*

or took up the alternate lines:

> She sat down below a thorn,
> *Fine flowers in the valley;*
> And there she has her sweet babe born,
> *And the green leaues they grow rarely.*

With the metres of Provence, the French *ballata* or round

dance conquered Teutonic Europe, and the 'glad animal move-
ments' of the 'carols' demanded a tune to dance to, and a kind
of poetry in which all could take part. Hence doubtless the form
of both ballads and nursery rhymes. The formal peculiarities of
the genuine folk-ballad can be catalogued with some preciseness,
and among these may be noted the almost verbatim repetition of
speeches and messages, the tendency to accentuate the last and
weak syllable of a metrical line, the use of assonance, the spirited
openings *in medias res*, the delight in bright elemental colours, and
the use of magic numbers such as seven and three.

But while the folk-ballad flourished in mediaeval England and
owed so much of its dramatic intensity and lyrical spontaneity to
the circumstances of its communal composition, the individual
minstrel whose songs were his own property and who only sang
them in return for some gratuity to an audience entirely passive
must have existed from the earliest times.

> Men speke of romances of prys,
> Of Horn child and of Ypotys,
> Of Bevis and sir Gy,

wrote Chaucer in his *Sir Thopas*, his own delicate parody of the
popular poesy of his age, and the minstrel, leaving aside the tragic
themes of contemporary life which made the very stuff of the
communal ballad, hawked round the country from alehouse to
alehouse decrepit versions of sentimental French romance, striking
up in the usual medicant key,

> Lythe and listen, gentlemen,
> A story I yow bitelle,

and demanding perhaps a gratuity in pence or ale. Less
often his wares would consist of love-lyrics such as *Bytuene
Mershe and Aueril*, or of political songs such as those of Laurence
Minot (c. 1350). Wherever men and women came together, for
work or play, at the fairs and markets, or travelling the great
roads on business or on pilgrimage, the professional minstrel was
sure to make one of the company to help while away the leisure
hour or tedious journey. Chaucer's pilgrims amused themselves
with their own stories, but the ordinary devotees of St. Thomas of
Canterbury or Our Lady of Walsingham were not so self-sufficing.
'When divers men and women will go thus,' William Thorpe told
his examiners, 'they will ordain before to have with them both

men and women that can well sing wanton songs.'[1] Laurence Minot stands out as the first definite figure of the professional minstrel in mediaeval England, one who strikes a clear individual note, and, half poet, half journalist, clothes political feeling and contemporary events in the garb of populár metres.

> How Edward þe King came to Braband
> And tok homage of all þe land

> How Edward at Hogges vnto land wan,
> And rade thurgh France or euer he blan.

Intinerant minstrelsy was no less popular in Tudor than in mediaeval times, and with the invention of printing the oral ballad, whether of traditional or individual composition, began to be thrown into type and circulated in broadsides. But the sixteenth-century broadside versions of the older and true ballads are unfortunately by no means mere transcripts from tradition, but have usually passed through the hands of an editor with a literary method of his own, appealing to a different kind of audience. The folk-ballad, governed by the conditions of its composition, told the story in lyrical glimpses and tense dialogue, originally no doubt eked out by action and dancing, but the Elizabethan editor, with his eye on passive and not too intelligent listeners, aimed at a remorseless recounting of the whole story from beginning to end. Hence, instead of the opening *in medias res* of

> Hie upon Hielands,
> And low upon Tay,
> Bonnie George Campbell
> Rode out on a day,

the Elizabethan ballad type begins with a long explanatory introduction.

> Both gentlemen, or yeomen bould,
> Or whatsoeuer you are,
> To haue a stately story tould
> Attention now prepare.

> It is a tale of Robin Hood,
> Which I to you will tell,
> Which being rightly vnderstood,
> I know will please you well.

---

[1] *The Examination of William Thorpe* (1407), in Arber's *Garner.*

> This Robbin (so much talked on)
> Was once a man of fame,
> Instiled earle of Huntingdon,
> Lord Robert Hood by name.

Similarly the old lyric narrative, such as,

> O ye've had a cruel mither, Willie,
> And I have had anither,
> But we shall sleep in Clyde's water
> Like sister and like brither,

is replaced by prosaic explanation :

> And to his little daughter Iane
> Fiue hundred pounds in gold,
> To be paid down on marriage-day,
> Which might not be controlled.
> But if the children chance to die
> Ere they to age should come,
> Their vncle should possess their wealth ;
> For so the will did run.

Yet in spite of this change from an intense method of poetry to another, dangerously prosaic, a fair amount of genuine folk-poetry was often enclosed in the shapeless padding of the later editor. The *Robin Hood Ballads* as they appear in the broadsides of the sixteenth and seventeenth centuries are excellent examples of the way in which the ancient habits of traditional poetry cling on in an age of professional balladists. Endless dilutions and accretions have reduced this popular epic to an average level of pedestrianism, but here and there the old literary methods strike out the old vigour from a page of dull narrative.

> Come thou hither to mee, thou lovely page,
> Come thou hither to mee ;
> For thou must post to Nottingham,
> As fast as thou can dree.

In many cases, no doubt, the traditional ballad was only lightly touched and modernized, and where the editor was a versifier of some skill it is difficult to distinguish between the original and the later additions. While the history of the *Robin Hood Ballads* can be fairly well made out, from Langland's reference to them in the fourteenth century until their appearance in the various *Garlands* of the seventeenth, the question of the originals of *Come over the Borne, Bessie,* of *Walsingham,* and of many another popular Elizabethan poem remains entirely obscure. We can only surmise that the printed ballads of the sixteenth century represent a small and edited portion of a large oral tradition, most of which has now perished unrecorded.

The broad question of the relation of traditional poetry to the work of the individual ballad-writer suggests itself at once in connexion with the poems of Deloney. There can be no doubt that in many of his poems, and especially in those which seem most successful to the modern reader, he has either merely written down or closely imitated folk tradition. In *Iacke of Newberie* he plainly indicates the communal origin of the song of Flodden Field : 'Wherefore in disgrace of the Scots, and in remembrance of the famous atchieued victory, the Commons of *England* made this Song : which to this day is not forgotten of many'[1]; and the two other traditional versions of the same song given in Child's *Ballads* conclusively prove that in this case at least Deloney was merely printing a traditional ballad. Similarly *The Faire Flower of Northumberland* (*Iacke of Newberie*, p. 33) in *motif* and treatment alike might be purely traditional, and *Walsingham*[2] (p. 365) is almost certainly built up on a traditional foundation. But lacking further evidence we can only draw strong inferences from style and matter, without reaching any absolutely definite conclusion.

The great bulk of sixteenth-century ballad literature, however, is the lineal descendant, not of the communal ballad, but rather of the minstrel's songs of the Middle Ages, and plainly the individual work of the professional entertainer, catering for the amusement of the general public with matter drawn from all sources. While the communal ballad was the folk expression of large simple emotions, the ordinary Elizabethan ballad is journalism pure and simple, and Autolycus the ballad-hawker, eternally alive in the *Winter's Tale*, hawks round, not the *Douglas Tragedy* or the *Death of the Earl of Murray*, but *How a usurer's wife was brought to bed of twenty money-bags at a burden*, and 'another ballad *Of a fish that appeared vpon the coast on Wednesday the fourscore of April, forty thousand fathom aboue water, and sung this ballad against the hard hearts of maids*'. A glance at the *Roxburghe Ballads*, the *Shirburn Collection*, or the *Registers of the Stationers' Company*, will show that Shakespeare has scarcely done more than 'hold the mirror up to nature'. The following

[1] p. 25, ll. 34-6, and note.   [2] See note thereon, *infra*, pp. 579-80.

are representative titles of ballads registered with the Stationers' Company :

A true relacon of the birth of Three Monsters in the Citty of Namen in Flaunders.

The wofull complaynt of Ffraunce for the deathe of the late kinge Henry *the Ffourth.*

A lamentacon of a Yonge man for the deathe of his Mother.

How Maydes shulde penne the Dore &c.

A ballet intituled taken out of Ye XIII Chapter of Saynt Luke.

Tydinges of a Huge and Ougly childe borne at Arneheim in Gelderland.

A ballet against Swerynge.

Thus it may be gathered the Elizabethan ballad was the vehicle for popular edification, instruction, and amusement, and supplied the vulgar with sermons, history, politics, sentiment, and the latest news. Of this multifarious activity Deloney is almost completely representative, combining in his work all the different functions of the sixteenth-century ballad-maker. As a modern newspaper reporter hurries his exclusive news into print, so Deloney registered *A ioyfull songe of the Roiall Receauing of the queenes maiestie into her camp at Tilbery : the 8 and 9 of August 1588*, the very day after the event ; and as modern newspapers send broadcast over the land accounts of criminals, trials, inquests, and accidents, so Deloney circulated the *Lamentation of Pages Wife of Plymouth*, the *Death and Execution of Fourteen most wicked Traitors*, the *Lamentation of Beccles*, and probably many another news sheet of which no trace remains. The Elizabethan appetite for history he satisfied with paraphrases from the Chronicles of Holinshed and Grafton ; he touched on social questions of the day in his ballad on the *Scarcity of Corn* ; dealt with the religious and political question in *Truth and Ignorance* and *Judith and Holofernes*, and served up moral exhortations and advice in *Repent, England, Repent* and *Salomons good houswife.* Nor did he forget the business of mere amusement, but in the *Kings daughter of France, Patient Grissel*, and *King Edward the third, and the faire Countesse of Salisbury*, set forth the pretty sentimental stories as dear to the Elizabethan heart as to the mediaeval.

While Deloney is so completely representative of the sixteenth-century ballad-writers, from the very conditions which called forth his work, it was impossible for him to maintain any constant level of excellence. The public was his master, and to please it he ransacked all the sources at his command—the chroniclers, the stage, tradition, and contemporary history, but he could not handle all these topics with the same degree of facility. Such lyrics as the *Weauers Song* in *Iacke of Newberie*, or Cutbert's *Countrey Iigge* in *Thomas of Reading*, flowed easily and delightfully from his pen, but in his narrative ballads he seems often to have flagged, and perhaps more especially in the *Strange Histories*, which may have been a volume hastily 'yarked up' for the printer, to supply immediate necessity. The great fault of the average Elizabethan ballad is lack of imagination, and in the ballads 'taken from the chronicles' Deloney has seldom assimilated the story completely enough to reproduce it in an artistic or dramatic form. Hence his poems are too often little more than a metrical paraphrase of the prose, and refractory rhymes deliver him over to all sorts of temptations. Thus where Holinshed writes: 'Thomas Gurney . . . flieng vnto Marcels, three years after being knowne, taken and brought toward England was beheaded on the sea', Deloney renders the passage:

> Commandement was sent by one called Lea
> he should be beheaded forth with on the sea, [1]

inventing a fictitious name to solve the difficulty of rhyming, and where he describes the imprisonment of Edward II by his Queen, an epithet contradictory to the sense is his only escape from the same *impasse*:

> Our comely King, her husband *deere*,
> Subdued by strength as did appeare,
> By her was sent to prison stronge. [2]

Ballad-making to him was often merely a mechanical process; he used words and metre not to body forth a dramatic story, hot and incandescent in his mind, but to worry a narrative into the compass of a catch, and thus he does not escape at times a woful pedestrianism of style.

> The Saylers and the shipmen all,
> through foule excesse of wine,
> Were so disguisde that at the sea,
> they shewd themselues like swine. [3]

. . . .

[1] p. 410, ll. 77–8.   [2] p. 402, ll. 3–5.   [3] p. 387, ll. 46–9.

Three score and ten were dround in all,
    and none escaped death,
But one poore Butcher which had swome
    himself quite out of breath.[1]
Nor is this pedestrianism entirely limited to the narrative ballads.
In *The Widdowes Solace* a beautiful verse :—

'Twas neither *Cressus* treasure,
    nor Alexanders fame,
Nor Solomon by wisdome,
    that could deaths fury tame.
No Physicke might preserue them
    when Nature did decay :
What man can hold for ever,
    the thing that will away ?

is followed by this bathetic advice :—

If he were true and faithfull,
    and louing unto thee,
Doubt not but ther's in *England*,
    enough as good as he.
But if that such affection,
    within his heart was none :
Then giue God praise and glory,
    that he is dead and gone.[2]

Such alternations seem to show a certain unsureness of taste and feeling that was shared by other and much greater writers of the Elizabethan age, but there is an individual strain of bourgeois materialism in Deloney's work which recalls the same weakness in the powerful Hogarth. ' O faulce and foule disloyall men !' cries Deloney of the Babington conspirators :

what person would suppose,
That clothes of veluet and of silke
    should hide such mortall foes ?[3]

and Hogarth brings the Industrious Apprentice safely to the arms of his master's daughter and the Mayoral seat in the Guildhall.

But Deloney must not be judged by his worst poems. His ballads on the stirring events of his time are comparable with those of Laurence Minot for a vigour and force that marks them for contemporary documents. As Minot wrote from the exultation of a fierce English heart :

Whare er ȝe, Skottes of Saint Johnes toun ?
þe boste of ȝowre baner es betin all doune,

[1] p. 389, ll. 117-20.   [2] p. 331.
[3] p. 467, ll. 102-5.

so Deloney in a truer, greater cause could write even while the wrack of the great Armada was still strewing the northern seas :

> O Noble *England*,
>   fall doune vpon thy knee :
> And praise thy God with thankfull hart
>   which still maintaineth thee
> The forraine forces,
>   that seekes thy vtter spoil :
> Shall then through his especiall grace
>   be brought to shamefull foile.
> With mightie power
>   they come vnto our coast :
> To ouer runne our country quite,
>   they make their brags and boast.
> In strength of men
>   they set their only stay :
> But we, vpon the Lord our God,
>   will put our trust alway.[1]

The patriotism that saved Elizabeth's England lends a boldness and vigour to the *Winning of Cales* and his three *Armada Ballads*, and where he touches religion sincerity infuses his verse with the energy of poetry, as in *Truth and Ignorance* :

> But many Kings and Prophets
>   as I may say to thee :
> Haue wisht the light that you haue,
>   and neuer could it see,

or in *Holofernes* :

> Lo here behold how God prouides
>   for them that in him trust :
> When earthly hope is all in vain,
>   he takes vs from the dust.

He writes with real sympathy of the emotions and troubles of domestic life, so that his paraphrase of *Salomons good houswife, in the* 31 *of his Prouerbes* is completely delivered from the monotony of mere hack-work, and the *Lamentation of Mr. Pages Wife* becomes informed with a touching indignation. Where he deals with the topics of common artisan life, in the poems scattered through his novels, he writes with a singular freshness in that happily careless vein that is lacking in modern poetry. His more slender lyrics, such as *Walsingham, The Spanish Ladies Love,* and *Age and Youth,* are distinguished by a delicacy of diction and a

---

[1] p. 468.

rare simplicity of feeling that has made them remembered in later times when their author's name was forgotten or ignored.

Perhaps the chief literary influence moulding the ballad of the sixteenth century was exercised by the *Mirrour for Magistrates*. The tragic encyclopaedia of the *Fall of Princes* had eternal attractions for mediaeval readers, and the literary tradition merely took new form with the same popularity in the Elizabethan collection of doleful tragedies, related in the first person and clothed in long-drawn leisurely verse. Its influence is seen chiefly in the ' Lamentation' type of ballad, exemplified in Deloney's work by the *Lamentation of Shores Wife* and the *Lamentation of Beccles*, and in the lugubrious choice of historical topics illustrated by ballads such as *The lamentable death of King Iohn* ; *Of Edward the second, being poysoned* ; and the *Imprisonment of Queene Elenor*. The *Mirrour for Magistrates* (1587) had previously treated many of the subjects of Deloney's ballads,[1] and *Strange Histories* may perhaps be regarded as a bourgeois imitation of the more aristocratic prototype, even in its inclusion of the prose passage amongst the verse.[2] But while the balladist of necessity squeezed 'strange and lamentable' histories into the compass of a common rhythm and bore in mind always that his audience wanted rhymes 'to the tune of *Fortune*' or '*Prince Arthur died at Ludlow*', authors like Daniel and Drayton could treat the same subject in much the same spirit in the larger and statelier stanzas of ten-syllabled verse. While Deloney scribbled his verses to the thin quavering of a street tune running through his head, Drayton and Daniel unfolded their tragic themes in the long march and rich cadences of the literary metres that had developed with the school of Spenser. *Canaans Calamitie* is the evidence that Deloney, writing up history into ballads for the market-place and tavern-door, did not nevertheless escape altogether the literary ambitions of his age, and, not merely content with the metrical paraphrasing of dolorous passages from the chronicles, really aimed, once at least, at a poem of some size and construction, where the treatment of tragic history and the metrical arrangement should be definitely nobler in tradition. The stanza he chose was that of Shakespeare's popular *Venus and Adonis*, and the subject, epic ; in the choice of the one he reflects the Renaissance desire for dignified form, in the choice of the

[1] e. g. King John's Death, Locrine, Albanact and Humber, Edward II.
[2] p. 415.

other its desire for dignified matter. The 'little epic' was
a favourite variety of Elizabethan poetry, which lent scope for the
skilful handling of metre, for description, action, and narrative,
giving many of the opportunities of the epic without its difficulties
of construction,—a variety which is exemplified in Shakespeare's
Venus and Adonis and *The Rape of Lucrece*, in Marlowe's *Hero
and Leander*, and profusely in the works of Drayton and Daniel.

In *Canaans Calamitie* Deloney leaves the simpler opportunities
of the ballad metre and manages to attain in some degree to the
dignity which marks the smaller epic, his first stanza recalling in
the determination of its melancholy the opening verse of Milton's
immature and mannered poem on *The Passion* :

> Like to a Mourner clad in dolefull black,
>   That sadly sits to heare a heauie tale :
> So must my pen proceed to shew the wrack,
>   That did with terror *Syon* hill assaile.
> What time *Ierusalem* that Cittie faire,
> Was sieg'd and sackt by great *Vespatians* heire.
>
> > *Canaans Calamitie.*

> For now to sorrow must I tune my song,
> And set my harp to notes of saddest woe,
> Which on our dearest Lord did seize ere long,
> Dangers, and snares and wrongs, and worse than so,
> Which he for us did freely undergo :
> Most perfect Hero, tried in heaviest plight
> Of labours huge and hard, too hard for human wight.
>
> > *The Passion.*

But Deloney's muse, though not only of the ale-house to which
Nash relegated it, was not capable of filling a canvas with such
a large historical piece as the destruction of Jerusalem. His
stanzas are never entirely secure from the pedestrianism that
marks his inferior ballads, and his diction lacks the strength to
support an epic story. Hence he endeavours to escape from the
larger tragic issues of his subject by sliding into the 'Lamentation'
point of view—

> God grant we may our hatefull sins forsake,
> And by the Jewes a Christian warning take

—by dropping easily into the narrative method of the poetical
chronicler, and weakening the tragedy of a catastrophe by over-
emphasis of the pathetic elements. In common with many of the
Elizabethan dramatists Deloney had the power of creating pathetic

situations from the simplest and barest elements of life, and probably the episode of Miriam and her son, in spite of its extravagant subject and grotesque exaggeration of circumstance and feeling, is the best part of his ambitious poem.   In its fantastic setting of discordant and unpleasing detail there is a simple directness of feeling in the entreaty of Miriam's son for food, which recalls the vivid dialogue of the murderous father and his son in *The Yorkshire Tragedy*—'O what will you do, father? I am your white boie.'—'Thou shalt be my red boie.'[1]   Deloney from much the same situation creates the same kind of pathos :

> I am (deere Mother) hungry at the heart,
> And scalding thirst, makes me I cannot speake,
> I feele my strength decay in euery part,
> One bit of bread, for me good Mother breake,
>   My lesson I haue learnd, where you did lay it,
>   Then giue me some-what : you shall heere me say it.[2]

But this measure of success is an indication of his limitations. A story dealing with the more simple and elemental emotions he could throw into verse with success, and embody a fancy in a pleasant lyric.   But probably the complex and graver emotions never came home to his heart nor hence the adequate means of their expression home to his mind, and he remains, when all is said and done, not so much the author of *Canaans Calamitie* as ' the great Ballad-maker T.D.'

[1] sc. iv.   [2] p. 434, ll. 505-10.

The pleasant Historie

OF

I O H N W I N C H C O M B,

In his yonguer yeares called

l A C K of N E W B E R Y,

The famous and worthy Clothier of
England; declaring his life and loue,
together with his charitable deeds
and great Hospitalitie.

And how hee set continually fiue hundred poore
people at worke, to the great benefite of
the Common-wealth.

Now the tenth time Imprinted, corrected and enlarged
by *T. D.*

Haud curo invidiam.

L O N D O N,
Printed by H Lownes, and are to be sold by *Cuthbert*
Wright in S. *Bartholomews*, neer the enttance
into the Hospitall, 1 6 2 6.

To all famous Cloth-

Workers in England, I wish all

happinesse of life, prosperity and

brotherly affection.

A Mong all manuall Arts vsed in this Land, none is more famous for desert, or more beneficiall to the Commonwealth, than is the most necessary Art of Clothing. And therefore as the benefite there of is great, so are the professors of the same to be both loued and maintained. Many wise men therefore, hauing deepely
10 considered the same, most bountifully haue bestowed their gifts for vpholding of so excellent a commoditie, which hath been, and yet is, the nourishing of many thousands of poor people. Where-fore to you, most worthy Clothiers, do I dedicate this my rude worke, which hath raised out of the dust of forgetfulnesse a most famous and worthy man, whose name was *Iohn Winchcombe*, alias *Iack* of *Newberie*, of whose life and loue I haue briefely written, and in a plaine and humble manner, that it may be the better vnderstood of those for whose sake I took pains to compile it, that is, for the well minded Clothiers ; that heerein they may behold the
20 great worship and credit which men of this trade haue in former time come vnto. If therefore it bee of you kindly accepted, I haue the end of my desire, and think my paines well recompenced : and finding your gentlenesse answering my hope, it shall moue mee shortly to set to your sight the long hidden History of *Thomas* of *Redding, George* of *Glocester, Richard* of *Worcester*, and *William* of *Salisbury*, with diuers others ; who were all most notable members in the Commonwealth of this Land, and men of great fame and dignity. In the meane space, I commend you all to the most high God, who euer increase, in all perfection and prosperous
30 estate, the long honoured trade of English-Clothiers.

Yours in all humble seruice,

T. D.

THE MOST PLEA-
sant and delectable Historie of Iohn
Winchcombe, *otherwise* called *Iacke* of
Newberie: and first of his loue and
pleasant life.

CHAP. I.

IN the daies of King *Henrie* the eight, that most noble and
victorious Prince, in the beginning of his reigne, *Iohn Winchcomb*, a broad cloth Weauer, dwelt in *Newberie*, a towne in
Barkshire: who for that he was a man of a merry disposition, & 10
honest conuersation, was wondrous wel-beloued of Rich and Poore,
specially, because in euery place where hee came, hee would
spend his money with the best, and was not at any time found
a churle of his purse. Wherefore being so good a companion,
hee was called of old and yongue *Iacke* of *Newberie*: a man
so generally well knowne in all his countrey for his good fellowship,
that hee could goe in no place but he found acquaintance; by
meanes whereof, *Iacke* could no sooner get a Crowne, but straight
hee found meanes to spend it : yet had hee euer this care, that hee
would alwaies keepe himselfe in comely and decent apparell : 20
neyther at any time would hee bee ouercome in drinke, but so
discreetly behaue himselfe with honest mirth, and pleasant conceits,
that he was euery Gentlemans companion.

After that *Iack* had long led this pleasant life, beeing (though
he were but poore) in good estimation: it was his Masters chance
to dye, and his Dame to be a widow, who was a very comely
ancient woman, and of reasonable wealth. Wherefore she, hauing
a good opinion of her man *Iohn*, committed vnto his gouernement
the guiding of all her worke-folkes for the space of three yeares
together : In which time shee found him so carefull and diligent, 30
that all things came forward and prospered woundrous well. No
man could entice him from his businesse all the weeke, by all the
intreaty they could vse : Insomuch that in the end some of the
wild youths of the town began to deride and scoffe at him.

Doubtlesse (quoth one) I thinke some female spirit hath
inchaunted *Iacke* to his treadles, and coniured him within the
compasse of his Loome, that he can stirre no further.

You say true (quoth *Iacke*) and if you haue the leasure to stay till
the Charme be done, the space of six dayes and fiue nights, you
shall finde me ready to put on my holy-day-apparell, and on Sunday 40

morning for your paines I will giue you a pot of Ale ouer against the Maypole.

Nay (quoth another) Ile lay my life, that as the Salamander cannot liue without the fire, so *Iack* cannot liue without the smel of his Dames smock.

And I maruell (quoth *Iacke*) that you being of the nature of a Herring (which so soon as he is taken out of the Sea, presently dyes) can liue so long with your nose out of the pot.

Nay *Iacke*, leaue thy iesting (quoth another) and goe along with
10 vs, thou shalt not stay a iot.

And because I will not stay; nor make you a lyer (quoth *Iacke*) Ile keepe me here still : and so farewell.

Thus then they departed : and after they had for halfe a score times tryed him to this intent, and saw he would not bee ledde by their lure, they left him to his owne will. Neuerthelesse, euery Sunday in the afternoone, and euery Holy-day, *Iacke* would keep them company, and be as merry as a Pye, and hauing still good store of money in his purse, one or other would euer be borrowing of him, but neuer could he get pennie of it againe : which when
20 *Iacke* perceiued, he would neuer after carry aboue twelue pence at once in his purse : and that being spent, he would straight returne home merrily, taking his leaue of the company in this sort.

> *My masters, I thanke you, its time to packe home,*
> *For he that wants money is counted a mome :*
> *And twelue pence a Sunday being spent in good cheare,*
> *To fifty two shillings amounts in the yeare ;*
> *Enough for a Crafts-man that liues by his hands :*
> *And he that exceeds it, shall purchase no lands.*
> *For that I spend this day, Ile work hard to morrow.*
30 *For woe is that partie that seeketh to borrow.*
> *My money doth make me full merry to be ;*
> *And without my money none careth for me :*
> *Therefore wanting money, what should I doe heere ?*
> *But hast home, and thanke you for all my good cheere ?*

Thus was *Iackes* good gouernement and discretion noted of the best and substantiallest men of the Towne : so that it wrought his great commendations, and his Dame thought her selfe not a little blest to haue such a seruant, that was so obedient vnto her, and so carefull for her profite : for shee had neuer a Prentise that
40 yeelded her more obedience than he did, or was more dutifull : so that by his good example, hee did as much good as by his diligent labour and painfull trauel : which his singular vertue being noted by the widow, shee beganne to cast a very good countenance to her man *Iohn*, and to vse very much talk with him in priuate : and first by way of communication, she would tell vnto him what suters she had, as also the great offers they made her, what gifts they sent her, and the great affection they bare her, crauing his opinion in the matter.

When *Iacke* found the fauour to be his Dames Secretarie, he thought it an extraordinary kindnesse : and ghessing by the yarne it would proue a good web, beganne to question with his dame in this sort.   Although it becommeth not mee your seruant to pry into your secrets, nor to bee busie about matters of your loue : yet for so much as it hath pleased you to vse conference with me in those causes, I pray you let me intreat you to know their names that be your sutors, and of what profession they be.

Marry *Iohn* (sayth she) that you shall, and I pray thee take a cushion and sit downe by me.   10

Dame (quoth he) I thanke you : but there is no reason I should sit on a cushion till I haue deserued it.

If thou hast not thou mightest haue done (said she): but some Souldiers neuer finde fauour.

Iohn replied, that maketh me indeed to want fauour : for I neuer durst try maydens because they seeme coy, nor wiues for feare of their husbands, nor widowes doubting their disdainfulnes.

Tush *Iohn* (quoth she) he that feares and doubts womankinde, cannot be counted mankinde : and take this for a principle, All things are not as they seeme.   But let us leaue this, and proceed 20 to our former matter.   My first sutor dwels at *Wallingford*, by trade a Tanner, a man of good wealth, and his name is *Crafts*, of comely personage and very good behauiour, a widower, wel thought of among his neighbours : he hath proper land, a faire house well furnished, and neuer a childe in the world, and hee loues me passing well.

Why then Dame (quoth *Iohn*) you were best to haue him.

Is that your opinion (quoth shee) ? now trust mee, so it is not mine : for I finde two speciall reasons to the contrary : the one is, that he being ouerworne in yeares, makes me ouerloth to loue 30 him : and the other, that I know one neerer hand.

Beleeue me dame (quoth *Iack*) I perceiue store is no sore, & proffered ware is worse by ten in the hundred than that which is sought : but I pray who is your second sutor ?

Iohn (quoth she) it may seeme immodesty in me to bewray my louers secrets : yet seeing thy discretion, and being perswaded of thy secrecy, I will shew thee : the other is a man of middle yeares, but yet a Batchellor, by occupation a Taylor, and dwelling at *Hungerford* : by report a very good husband, such a one as hath crownes good store, and to mee he professes much good will : for 40 his person, he may please any woman.

I dame (quoth *Iohn*) because he pleaseth you.

Not so (said she) for my eyes are vnpartiall Iudges in that case : and albeit my opinion may be contrary to others, if his Art deceiue not my eye-sight, hee is worthy of a good wife, both for his person and conditions.

Then trust mee Dame (quoth *Iohn*) for so much as you are without doubt of your selfe that you will proue a good wife, and

so well perswaded of him, I should thinke you could make no
better a choice.

Truly *Iohn* (quoth shee) there be also two reasons that moue
mee not to like of him : the one, that being so large a ranger, he
would at home be a stranger : and the other, that I like better of
one neerer hand.

Who is that (quoth *Iacke*) ?

(Saith she) the third Suter is the Parson of *Spinhom-land*, who
hath a proper liuing, he is of holy conuersation and good estima-
10 tion, whose affection to me is great.

No doubt Dame (quoth *Iohn*) you may doe wondrous well with
him, where you shall haue no care but to serue GOD, and to make
ready his meate.

O *Iohn* (quoth she) the flesh and the spirit agrees not : for he
will bee so bent to his booke, that he will haue little minde of his
bed : for one moneths studying for a Sermon, will make him forget
his wife a whole yeare.

Truly Dame (quoth *Iohn*) I must needs speak in his behalfe
and the rather, for that he is a man of the Church, and your
20 neere neighbour,to whom (as I guesse) you beare yᵉ best affection :
I doe not thinke that he will bee so much bound to his booke, or
subiect to the spirit, but that he will remember a woman at home
or abroad.

Well *Iohn* (quoth she) I wis my minde is not that way : for I
like better of one neerer hand.

No maruell (quoth *Iacke*) you are so peremptory, seeing you
haue so much choice : but I pray ye Dame (quoth he) let me know
this fortunate man that is so highly placed in your fauour?

Iohn (quoth shee) they are worthy to know nothing, that
30 cannot keepe something : that man (I tell thee) must goe namelesse : for he is Lord of my loue, and King of my desires : there
is neyther Tanner, Taylor, nor Parson may compare with him, his
presence is a preseruatiue to my health, his sweete smiles my
hearts solace, and his words heauenly musicke to my eares.

Why then Dame (quoth *Iohn*) for your bodies health, your hearts
ioy, and your eares delight, delay not the time, but entertaine him
with a kisse, make his bed next yours, and chop vp the match in
the morning.

Well (quoth shee) I perceiue thy consent is quickly got to any,
40 hauing no care how I am matcht so I be matcht : I wis, I wis I
could not let thee goe so lightly, being loth that any one should
haue thee, except I could loue her as well as my selfe.

I thanke you for your kindnesse and good will, good Dame
(quoth hee) but it is not wisedome for a yongue man that can
scantly keepe himselfe, to take a wife : therefore I hold it the best
way to leade a single life : for I haue heard say, that many sorrowes follow marriage, especially where want remains : and beside,
it is a hard matter to finde a constant woman : for as yongue

maides are fickle, so are old women iealous: the one a griefe too
common, the other a torment intolerable.

What *Iohn* (quoth she) consider that maidens ficklenesse
proceedes of vaine fancies, but old womens iealousie of super-
abounding loue: and therefore the more to bee borne withall.

But Dame (quoth hee) many are iealous without cause: for is it
sufficient for their mistrusting natures to take exceptions at a
shadow, at a word, at a looke, at a smile, nay at the twinkle of an
eye, which neither man nor woman is able to expell? I knew
a woman that was ready to hang her selfe, for seeing but her hus- 10
bands shirt hang on a hedge with her maides smocke.

I grant that this fury may haunt some (quoth shee) yet there bee
many other that complaine not without great cause.

Why, is there any cause that should moue iealousie (quoth *Iohn*)?

I by *S. Mary* is there (quoth she): for would it not grieue a woman
(being one euery way able to delight her husband) to see him forsake her, despise and contemne her, being neuer so merry as when
he is in other company, sporting abroad from morning till noone,
from noone till night, and when he comes to bed, if hee turnes to
his wife, it is in such solemnesse, and wearisome drowsie lamenesse, 20
that it brings rather lothsomnesse than any delight? can you then
blame a woman in this case to be angry and displeased? Ile tell
you what, among brute beasts it is a griefe intolerable: for I heard
my Grandame tell, that the Bel-weather of her flocke fancying one
of the Eawes aboue the rest, and seeing *Gratis* the Sheepheard
abusing her in abominable sort (subuerting the law of Nature)
could by no meanes beare that abuse; but watching opportunity
for reuenge, on a time found the said Shepheard sleeping in the
field, and suddenly ranne against him in such violent sort, that by
the force of his wreathen hornes, he beat the braines out of the 30
Shepheards head and slew him. If then a Sheepe could not endure that injury, thinke not that women are so sheepish to suffer it.

Beleeue mee (quoth *Iohn*) if euery horne-maker should be so
plagued by a horned beast, there should bee lesse hornes made in
Newbery by many in a yeare. But Dame (quoth hee) to make an
end of this prattle, because it is an argument too deepe to be discussed between you and I, you shall heare me sing an old song,
and so we will depart to supper.

> *A maiden faire I dare not wed,*
> *For feare to haue* Acteons *head.*   40
> *A maiden blacke is often proude:*
> *A maiden little will be loud.*
> *A maiden that is high of growth,*
> *They say is subiect vnto sloath.*
> *Thus faire or foule, little or tall,*
> *Some faults remaine among them all:*
> *But of all the faults that be,*
> *None is so bad as iealousie.*

For iealousie is fierce and fell,
And burnes as hot as fire in hell:
It breedes suspicion without cause,
And breaks the bonds of reasons lawes.
To none it is a greater foe,
Than vnto those where it doth grow.
And God keepe me both day and night,
From that fell, fond and ougly spright:
For why? of all the plagues that be,
10   *The secret plague is iealousie.*
Therefore I wish all women kinde,
Neuer to beare a iealous minde.

Well said *Iohn* (quoth she) thy song is not so sure, but thy voice
is as sweete: but seeing the time agrees with our stomackes,
though loth, yet will we giue ouer for this time, and betake our
selues to our suppers.   Then calling the rest of her seruants, they
fell to their meate merrily, and after supper, the Goodwife went
abroad for her recreation, to walke a while with one of her
neighbours.   And in the meane space *Iohn* got him vp into his
20 chamber, and there began to meditate on this matter, bethinking
with himselfe what hee were best to doe: for well hee perceiued
that his Dames affection was great towards him: knowing therefore the womans disposition, and withall, that her estate was
reasonable good, and considering beside, that he should finde a
house ready furnished, seruants ready taught, and all other things
for his trade necessary, hee thought it best not to let slip that good
occasion, lest he should neuer come to the like.   But againe,
when hee considered her yeares to be vnfitting to his youth, and
that she that sometime had been his Dame, would (perhaps)
30 disdaine to bee gouerned by him that had been her poore seruant,
and that it would prooue but a bad bargaine, doubting many
inconueniencies that might grow thereby, hee therefore resolued
to be silent, rather than to proceed further: wherefore he got him
straight to bed, and the next morning settled himselfe close to his
businesse.
His Dame comming home, and hearing that her man was gone to
bed, tooke that night but small rest, and early in the morning
hearing him vp at his worke, merrily singing, shee by and by arose,
and in seemely sort attyring her selfe, shee came into the workeshop,
40 and sate her downe to make quills.
(Quoth *Iohn*) Good morrow Dame, how doe you to day?
God a mercy *Iohn* (quoth shee) euen as well as I may: for I
was sore troubled in my Dreames.   Mee thought two Doues
walked together in a corne field, the one (as it were) in communication with the other, without regard of picking vp any thing to
sustaine themselues: and after they had with many nods spent
some time to their content, they both fell hard with their pretty bills

to pecke vp the scattered corne, left by the weary Reapers hand.
At length (finding themselues satisfied) it chanced another Pigion
to light in that place, with whom one of the first Pigions at length
kept company : and after, returning to the place where she left her
first companion, perceiued hee was not there : shee kindely
searching vp and downe the high stubble to finde him, lights at
length on a Hogge fast asleepe, wherewith mee thought, the poore
Doue was so dismaid, that presently shee fell downe in a trance.
I seeing her legges faile, and her wings quiuer, yeelding her selfe
to death, moued with pity ranne vnto her, and thinking to take
vp the Pigion, mee thought, I had in my hands my owne heart,
wherein mee thought an arrow stucke so deep, that the bloud
trickled downe the shaft, and lay vpon the feathers like the siluer
pearled deaw on the greene grasse, which made me to weepe
most bitterly.   But presently, mee thought there came one to
mee crowned like a Queene, who told me my heart would dye
in time, except I got some of that sleeping Hogs grease to heale
the wounds thereof.   Whereupon I ranne in all haste to the Hog
with my heart bleeding in my hand, who (mee thought) grunted
at mee in most churlish sort, and vanisht out of my sight.
Whereupon comming straite home, mee thought, I found this Hog
rustling among the Loomes, wherewith I presently awaked,
sodainely after midnight, being all in a sweate and very ill : and I
am sure you could not choose but heare mee groane.

Trust mee Dame, I heard you not (quoth *Iohn*) I was so sound
asleepe.

And thus (quoth shee) a woman may dye in the night before
you will haue the care to see what she ailes, or aske what she
lackes.   But truly *Iohn* (quoth she) all is one : for if thou
shouldest haue come, thou couldest not haue got in, because my
chamber door was lockt : but while I liue this shall teach mee wit :
for henceforth I will haue no other locke but a latch, till I am
marryed.

Then Dame (quoth he) I perceiue though you be curious in
your choice, yet at length you will marry.

I truely (quoth shee) so thou wilt not hinder me.

Who I (quoth *Iohn*)? on my faith Dame, not for a hundred
pounds, but rather will further you to the vttermost of my power.

Indeede (quoth shee) thou hast no reason to shew any
discourtesie to me in that matter, although some of our neighbours
do not stick to say, that I am sure to thee already.

If it were so (quoth *Iohn*) there is no cause to deny it, or to bee
ashamed thereof, knowing my selfe farre vnworthy of so high a
fauour.

Well, let this talk rest (quoth shee) and take there thy quils, for
it is time for mee to goe to market.

Thus the matter rested for two or three dayes, in which space
shee daily deuised which way shee might obtaine her desire, which

was to marry her man. Many things came in her head, and
sundry sleights in her minde, but none of them did fit her fancy,
so that she became wondrous sad, and as ciuill as the nine *Sibbels*;
and in this melancholy humour continued three weekes or a
moneth, till at last it was her lucke vpon a *Bartholomew* day
(hauing a Fayre in the towne) to spie her man *Iohn* giue a paire
of Gloues to a proper maide for a Fayring, which the maiden with
a bashfull modesty kindly accepted, and requited it with a kisse:
which kindled in her an inward iealousie: but notwithstanding
10 very discreetly shee couered it, and closely past along vnspied of
her man or the maid.

Shee had not gone farre, but she met with one of her sutors,
namely the Taylor, who was very fine and briske in his apparell,
and needes hee would bestow the wine vpon the Widow: and after
some faint deniall, meeting with a Gossip of hers, to the Tauerne
they went, which was more courtesie than the Taylor could euer
get of her before, shewing her selfe very pleasant and merry; and
finding her in such a pleasing humour, the Taylor after a new
quart of wine, renewed his old sute: the Widow with patience
20 heard him, and gently answered, that in respect of his great good
will long time borne vnto her, as also in regard of his gentlenesse,
cost, and curtesie at that present bestowed, she would not flatly
deny him. Therefore (quoth shee) seeing this is not a place to
conclude of such matters, if I may intreate you to come to my
poore house on thursday next, you shall be heartily welcome, and
be further satisfied of my minde: and thus preferred to a touch of
her lips, hee payed the shot and departed.

The Taylor was scant out of sight, when she met with the
Tanner: who albeit he was aged, yet lustily hee saluted her, and
30 to the wine she must, there was no nay. The Widow seeing his
importunacy, calls her gossip, and along they walked together.
The old man called for wine plenty, and the best cheere in the
house: and in an hearty manner hee bids the Widow welcome.
They had not sitten long, but in comes a noise of Musitians in
tawny coates, who (putting off their caps) asked if they would
haue any musicke. The Widow answered no, they were merry
enough.

Tut (quoth the old man) let vs heare good fellowes what you
can doe, and play mee *The beginning of the World*.
40   Alas (quoth the widow) you had more need to hearken to yee
ending of the world.

Why Widow (quoth hee) I tell thee the beginning of the world
was the begetting of Children: and if you finde mee faulty in that
occupation, turne mee out of thy bed for a bungler, and then send
for the Sexton.

Hee had no sooner spoken the word, but the Parson of *Speen*
with his corner cap, popt in at the doore, who seeing the Widow
sitting at the table, craued pardon, and came in.

(Quoth shee) for want of the Sexton, heere is the Priest if you
need him.

Marry (quoth the Tanner) in good time, for by this meanes wee
neede not goe farre to be married.

Sir (quoth the Parson) I shall doe my best in conuenient place.

Wherein (quoth the Tanner)?

To wed her my selfe (quoth the Parson).

Nay soft (said the Widow) one Swallow makes not a Summer,
nor one meeting a marriage : as I lighted on you vnlookt for, so
came I hither vnprouided for the purpose.   10

I trust (quoth the Tanner) you came not without your eyes to
see, your tongue to speake, your eares to heare, your hands to
feele, nor your legs to goe.

I brought my eyes (quoth she) to discerne colours, my tongue
to say No to questions I like not, my hands to thrust from mee
the things that I loue not, my eares to iudge twixt flattery and
friendship, & my feet to run from such as would wrong mee.

Why then (quoth the Parson) by your gentle abiding in this
place, it is euident that here are none but those you like & loue.

God forbid I should hate my friends (quoth the widow) whom   20
I take all these in this place to bee.

But there bee diuers sorts of loues (quoth the Parson).

You say truth (quoth the Widow) : I loue your selfe for your
profession, and my friend the Tanner, for his curtesie and kindnesse, and the rest for their good company.

Yet (quoth the Parson) for the explaining of your loue, I pray
you drinke to them you loue best in the company.

Why (quoth the Tanner) haue you any hope in her loue ?

Beleeue me (saith the Parson), as much as another.

Why then Parson sit downe (said the Tanner) : for you that   30
are equall with mee in desire, shall surely be halfe with mee
in the shotte : and so Widow, on Gods name fulfill the Parsons
request.

Seeing (quoth the Widow) you are so pleasantly bent, if my
courtesie might not breede contention between you, and that
I may haue your fauour to shew my fancy, I will fulfill your
request.

(Quoth the Parson) I am pleased howsoeuer it bee.

And I (quoth the Tanner).

Why then (quoth shee) with this cup of Claret wine and Sugar, 40
I heartily drinke to the Minstrels boy.

Why, is it he you loue best (quoth the Parson)?

I haue reason (said shee) to like and loue them best, that will
bee least offended with my doings.

Nay, Widow (quoth they) wee meant you should drinke to him
whom you loued best in the way of marriage.

(Quoth the Widow) you should haue said so at first : but to tell
you my opinion, it is small discretion for a woman to disclose her

secret affection in an open assembly : therefore, if to that purpose you spake, let mee intreat you both to come home to my house on Thursday next, where you shall bee heartily welcome, and there be fully resolued of my minde : and so, with thankes at this time, Ile take my leaue.

The shot being paid, and the Musitians pleased, they all departed, the Tanner to *Wallingford*, the Parson to *Speen*, and the widow to her own house : where in her wonted solemnes shee settled her selfe to her businesse.

10   Against Thursday shee drest her house fine and braue, and set her selfe in her best apparell : the Taylor nothing forgetting his promise, sent to the Widow a good fat Pigge, and a Goose. The Parson being as mindfull as hee, sent to her house a couple of fat Rabbets and a Capon : and the Tanner came himselfe, and brought a good shoulder of Mutton, and halfe a dozen Chickens, beside hee brought a good gallon of Sacke, and halfe a pound of the best Sugar. The Widow receiuing this good meate, set her maide to dresse it incontinent, and when dinner time drew neere, the Table was couered, and euery other thing prouided in con-
20 uenient and comely sort.

At length the guests being come, the Widow bade them all heartily welcome. The Priest and the Tanner seeing the Taylor, mused what hee made there : the Taylor on the other side, maruelled as much at their presence. Thus looking strangely one at another, at length the Widow came out of the Kitchen, in a faire traine gowne stucke full of siluer pinnes, a fine white Cap on her head, with cuts of curious needle worke vnder the same, and an Apron before her as white as the driuen snow : then very modestly making curtsie to them all, she requested them to sit
30 downe. But they straining courtesie the one with the other, the Widow with a smiling countenance tooke the Parson by the hand, saying, Sir, as you stand highest in the Church, so it is meete you should sit highest at the Table : and therefore I pray you sit downe there on the bench side. And Sir (said shee to the Tanner) as age is to bee honoured before youth for their experience, so are they to sit aboue Bachelers for their grauity : and so shee set him downe on this side the Table, ouer against the Parson. Then comming to the Taylor, she said, Batcheler, though your lot bee the last, your welcome is equall with the first,
40 and seeing your place points out it selfe, I pray you take a cushion and sit downe. And now (quoth she) to make the bord equall, and because it hath been an old saying, that three things are to small purpose, if the fourth be away : if so it may stand with your fauour, I will call in a Gossip of mine to supply this voide place.

With a good will (quoth they).

With that shee brought in an old woman with scant euer a good tooth in her head, and placed her right against the Batcheler. Then was the meate brought to the boord in due order by the

Widowes seruants, her man *Iohn* being chiefest seruitor. The
Widow sate downe at the Tables end, betweene the Parson and
the Tanner, who in very good sort carued meate for them all, her
man *Iohn* waiting on the Table.

After they had sitten awhile, and well refreshed themselues, the
Widow, taking a Chrystal glasse fild with Claret Wine, drunke
vnto the whole company, and bade them welcome. The Parson
pledged her, and so did all the rest in due order: but still in their
drinking, the cup past ouer the poore old womans Nose; insomuch
that at length the old woman (in a merry vaine) spake thus vnto 10
the company: I haue had much good meate among you, but as
for the drinke I can nothing commend it.

Alas, good Gossip (quoth the Widow) I perceiue no man hath
drunke to thee yet.

No truly (quoth the old woman): for Churchmen haue so much
minde of yongue Rabbets, old men such ioy in young Chickens,
and Batchelers in Pigs flesh take such delight, that an old Sow,
a tough Henne, or a gray Cony are not accepted: and so it
is seen by mee, else I should haue beene better remembred.

Well old woman (quoth the Parson) take here the legge of 20
a Capon to stop thy mouth.

Now by *S. Anne*, I dare not (quoth she).

No, wherefore (said the Parson)?

Marry, for feare lest you should goe home with a crutch (quoth
shee).

The Taylor said, then taste here a peece of a Goose.

Now God forbid (said the old woman) let Goose goe to his
kinde: you haue a yongue stomacke, eate it your selfe, and much
good may it doe your heart, sweet yongue man.

The old woman lackes most of her teeth (quoth the Tanner): 30
and therefore a peece of a tender Chicke is fittest for her.

If I did lacke as many of my teeth (quoth the old woman) as
you lacke points of good husbandry, I doubt I should starue before
it were long.

At this the Widow laught heartily, and the men were striken
into such a dumpe, that they had not a word to say.

Dinner being ended, the Widow with the rest rose from the
Table, and after they had sitten a prety while merrily talking, the
Widow called her man *Iohn* to bring her a bowle of fresh Ale,
which he did. Then said the Widow: My masters, now for your 40
courtesie and cost I heartily thanke you all, and in requitall of all
your fauour, loue and good will, I drinke to you, giuing you free
liberty when you please to depart.

At these words her sutors looked so sowerly one vpon another,
as if they had beene newly champing of Crabs. Which when the
Taylor heard, shaking vp himselfe in his new russet Ierkin, and
setting his Hat on one side, hee began to speake thus. I trust
sweet Widow (quoth hee) you remember to what end my comming

was hither to day : I haue long time beene a sutor vnto you, and this day you promised to giue mee a direct answer.

'Tis true (quoth shee) and so I haue : for your loue I giue you thankes, and when you please you may depart.

Shall I not haue you (said the Taylor)?

Alas (quoth the Widow), you come too late.

Good friend (quoth the Tanner) it is manners for yongue men to let their elders bee serued before them : to what end should I be here if the Widow should haue thee ? a flat deniall is meete
10 for a sawcy sutor : but what saiest thou to me, faire Widow (quoth the Tanner ?)

Sir (said shee) because you are so sharpe set, I would wish you as soon as you can to wed.

Appoint the time your selfe (quoth the Tanner).

Euen as soone (quoth shee) as you can get a wife, and hope not after mee, for I am already promised.

Now Tanner, you may take your place with the Taylor (quoth the Parson): for indeede the Widow is for no man but my selfe.

Master Parson (quoth shee) many haue runne neer the goale,
20 and yet haue lost the game, and I cannot helpe it though your hope be in vaine: besides, Parsons are but newly suffered to haue wiues, and for my part I will haue none of the first head.

What (quoth the Taylor) is your merriment growne to this reckoning ? I neuer spent a Pig and a Goose to so bad a purpose before: I promise you, when I came in, I verily thought, that you were inuited by the Widow to make her and I sure together, and that this iolly Tanner was brought to be a witnesse to the contract, and the old woman fetcht in for the same purpose, else I would neuer haue put vp so many dry bobs at her hands.

30 And surely (quoth the Tanner) I knowing thee to bee a Taylor, did assuredly thinke, that thou wast appointed to come and take measure for our wedding apparell.

But now wee are all deceiued (quoth the Parson) : and therefore as we came fooles, so we may depart hence like asses.

That is as you interpret the matter (said the Widow) : for I euer doubting that a concluding answer would breede a iarre in the end among you euery one, I thought it better to be done at one instant, and in mine owne house, than at sundry times, and in common Tauernes: and as for the meate you sent, as it was vn-
40 requested of mee, so had you your part thereof, and if you thinke good to take home the remainder, prepare your wallets and you shall haue it.

Nay Widow (quoth they) although wee haue lost our labours, we haue not altogether lost our manners : that which you haue, keepe ; and GOD send to vs better lucke, and to you your hearts desire. And with that they departed.

The Widow being glad shee was thus rid of her guests, when her man *Iohn* with all the rest sate at supper, she sitting in a Chaire by, spake thus vnto them. Well my masters, you saw, that this day your poore Dame had her choice of husbands, if shee had listed to marry, and such as would haue loued and maintained her like a woman.

'Tis true (quoth *Iohn*) and I pray God you haue not withstood your best fortune.

Trust mee (quoth she) I know not, but if I haue, I may thank mine owne foolish fancy.

Thus it past on from *Bartholmewtide*, till it was neere Christmas, at what time the weather was so wonderfull cold, that all the run- 10 ning Riuers round about the Towne were frozen very thicke. The Widow being very loth any longer to lye without company, in a cold winters night made a great fire, and sent for her man *Iohn*, hauing also prepared a Chaire and a cushion, shee made him sit downe therein, and sending for a pinte of good Sacke, they both went to supper.

In the end, bed time comming on, she caused her maid in a merriment to plucke off his hose and shooes, and caused him to be laid in his masters best bed, standing in the best Chamber, hung round about with very faire curtaines. *Iohn* being thus pre- 20 ferred, thought himselfe a Gentleman, and lying soft, after his hard labour and a good supper, quickly fell asleepe.

About midnight, the Widow being cold on her feet, crept into her mans bed to warme them. *Iohn* feeling one lift vp the cloathes, asked who was there? O good *Iohn* it is I (quoth the Widow); the night is so extreme cold, and my Chamber walles so thin, that I am like to bee starued in my bed, wherefore rather than I would any way hazzard my health, I thought it much better to come hither and try your courtesie, to haue a little roome beside you.

Iohn being a kind yongue man, would not say her nay, and so 30 they spent the rest of the night both together in one bed. In the morning betime she arose vp and made her selfe readie, and wild her man *Iohn* to run and fetch her a linke with all speede : for (quoth shee) I haue earnest businesse to doe this morning. Her man did so. Which done, shee made him to carry the Linke before her, vntill she came to Saint *Bartholmewes* Chappell, where Sir *Iohn* the Priest with the Clark and Sexton, stood waiting for her.

Iohn (quoth she) turne into the Chappell : for before I goe fur- ther, I will make my prayers to S. *Bartholmew*, so shall I speed 40 the better in my businesse.

When they were come in, the Priest according to his order, came to her, and asked where the Bridegroome was ?

(Quoth she) I thought he had been here before me. Sir (quoth she) I will sit downe and say ouer my Beades, and by that time hee will come.

Iohn mused at this matter, to see that his Dame should so sud- denly be married, and he hearing nothing thereof before. The

Widow rising from her prayers, the Priest told her that the Bride-groome was not yet come.

Is it true (quoth the Widow)? I promise you I will stay no longer for him, if hee were as good as *George a Green* : and therefore dispatch (quoth she) and marry mee to my man *Iohn*.

Why Dame (quoth he) you do but iest.

I trow, *Iohn* (quoth shee) I iest not: for so I meane it shall bee, and stand not strangely, but remember that you did promise mee on your faith, not to hinder mee when I came to the Church
10 to be married, but rather to set it forward : therfore set your link aside, and giue mee your hand : for none but you shall be my husband.

Iohn seeing no remedy, consented, because hee saw the matter could not otherwise bee amended; and married they were presently.

When they were come home, *Iohn* entertained his Dame with a kisse, which the other seruants seeing, thought him somewhat sawcy. The Widow caused the best cheare in the house to bee set on the Table, and to breakfast they went, causing her new
20 husband to be set in a chaire at the tables end, with a faire napkin laid on his trencher : then shee called out the rest of her seruants, willing them to sit downe and take part of their good cheare. They wondring to see their fellow *Iohn* sit at the tables end in their old masters chaire, began heartily to smile, and openly to laugh at the matter, especially because their Dame so kindly sate by his side : which shee perceiuing, asked if that were all the manners they could shew before their master? I tell you (quoth shee) he is my husband : for this morning we were married, and therefore hence forward looke you acknowledge your duety
30 towards him.

The folkes looked one vpon another, maruelling at this strange newes. Which when *Iohn* perceiued, he said : My masters, muse not at all : for although by Gods prouidence, and your Dames fauour, I am preferred from being your fellow to be your master, I am not thereby so much puft vp in pride, that any way I will forget my former estate : Notwithstanding, seeing I am now to hold the place of a master, it shall be wisedome in you to forget what I was, and to take mee as I am, and in doing your diligence, you shall haue no cause to repent that God made me your
40 master.

The seruants hearing this, as also knowing his good gouern-ment before time, past their yeares with him in dutifull manner.

The next day, the report was ouer all the Towne, that *Iacke* of *Newberie* had married his Dame : so that when the woman walked abroad, euery one bade God giue her ioy : some said that she was matcht to her sorrow, saying, that so lusty a yongue man as hee, would neuer loue her being so ancient. Whereupon the woman made answer, that shee would take him downe in his wedding

shooes, and would try his patience in the prime of his lustinesse :
whereunto, many of her Gossips did likewise encourage her.
Euery day therefore for the space of a moneth after shee was
married, it was her ordinary custome, to goe forth in the morning
among her Gossips and acquaintance to make merry, and not to
returne home till night, without any regard of her houshold.
Of which, at her comming home her husband did very oftentimes
admonish her in very gentle sort, shewing what great incon-
uenience would grow thereby : the which sometime shee would
take in gentle part, and sometime in disdaine, saying.   10

I am now in very good case, that hee that was my seruant but
the other day, will now bee my master : this it is for a woman to
make her foote her head. The day hath beene, when I might
haue gone forth when I would, and come in againe when it had
pleased mee without controulement, and now I must be subiect
to euery *Iackes* checke. I am sure (quoth she) that by my
gadding abroad, and carelesse spending, I waste no goods of
thine. I, pittying thy pouerty, made thee a man, and master of
the house, but not to the end I would become thy slaue.
I scorne, I tell thee true, that such a yongueling as thy selfe, 20
should correct my conceit, and giue mee instructions, as if I were
not able to guide my selfe : but yfaith, yfaith, you shall not vse
me like a babe nor bridle me like an Asse : and seeing my
going abroad grieues thee, where I haue gone forth one day,
I will goe abroad three ; and for one houre, I will stay fiue.

Well (quoth her husband) I trust you will be better aduised :
and with that hee went from her about his businesse, leauing her
sweating in her fustian furies.

Thus the time past on, till on a certaine day she had been
abroad in her wonted manner, and staying forth very late, hee 30
shut the doores and went to bed. About midnight shee comes
to the doore, and knockes to come in : to whom hee looking out
of the window, answered in this sort :

What ? is it you that keepes such a knocking ? I pray you get
hence, and request the Constable to prouide you a bed, for this
night you shall haue no lodging here.

I hope (quoth shee) you will not shut mee out of doores like
a dogge, or let me lye in the streetes like a Strumpet.

Whether like a dogge or drab (quoth hee) all is one to mee,
knowing no reason, but that as you haue staied out all day for 40
your delight, so you may lye forth all night for my pleasure.
Both birds and beastes at the nights approach repaire to their
rest, and obserue a conuenient time to returne to their habitation.
Looke but vpon the poore Spider, the Frog, the Flye, and euery
other silly Worme, and you shall see all these obserue time to returne to their home : and if you, being a woman, will not doe the
like, content your selfe to beare the brunt of your owne folly : and
so farewell.

The woman hearing this, made pittious mone, and in very
humble sort intreated him to let her in, and to pardon this offence,
and while shee liued vowde neuer to doe the like.   Her husband
at length being moued with pitty towards her, slipt on his shooes,
and came downe in his shirt: the doore being opened, in she
went quaking, and as he was about to locke it againe, in very
sorrowfull manner she said, Alacke husband, what hap haue I? my
wedding Ring was euen now in my hand, and I haue let it fall
about the doore: good sweet *Iohn* come forth with the candle,
10 and helpe me to seeke it.

The man incontinent did so, and while hee sought for that
which was not there to bee found, shee whipt into the house, and
quickly clapping to the doore, she lockt her husband out.   He
stood calling with the candle in his hand to come in, but she
made as if shee heard not.   Anon shee went vp into her chamber,
and carried the key with her: but when he saw she would not
answer, hee presently began to knocke as lowd as hee could at
the doore.   At last she thrust her head out at the window, saying:
Who is there?
20   Tis I (quoth *Iohn*) what meane you by this? I pray you come
downe and open the doore that I may come in.

What sir (quoth shee) is it you? haue you nothing to doe but
dance about the streetes at this time of night, and like a Spright
of the Buttery hunt after Crickets, are you so hote that the house
cannot hold you?

Nay, I pray thee sweet heart (quoth he) doe not gybe no
longer, but let mee in.

O sir, remember (quoth shee) how you stood euen now at the
window, like a Iudge on the Bench, and in taunting sort kept mee
30 out of mine owne house.   How now *Iacke*, am I euen with you?
What, *Iohn* my man, were you so lusty to locke your Dame out of
doores? Sirra, remember you bade mee go to the Constable to
get lodging, now you haue leisure to try if his wife will preferre
you to a bed.   You sir sawce, that made me stand in the cold,
till my feet did freeze, and my teeth chatter, while you stood
preaching of birds and beasts, telling me a tale of Spiders, Flies,
and Frogs: goe trye now if any of them will bee so friendly to let
thee haue lodging.   Why go you not man? feare not to speake
with them ; for I am sure you shall finde them at home : thinke not
40 they are such ill husbands as you, to be abroad at this time of night.

With this *Iohns* patience was greatly mooued, insomuch, that
hee deepely swore, that if shee would not let him in, hee would
breake downe the doore.

Why *Iohn* (quoth shee) you neede not be so hote, your cloathing
is not so warme, and because I thinke this will be a warning for
you against another time, how you shut mee out of my house,
catch, there is the key, come in at thy pleasure, and looke thou goe
to bed to thy fellowes, for with mee thou shalt not lye to night.

With that shee clapt to the casement, and got her to bedde, lock-
ing the chamber doore fast. Her husband that knew it was in
vaine to seeke to come into her chamber, and being no longer able
to indure the cold, got him a place among his prentises, and
there slept soundly. In the morning his wife rose betime, and
merrily made him a Cawdle, and bringing it vp to his bed side,
asked him how he did?

(Quoth *Iohn*) troubled with a shrew, who the longer shee liues,
the worse shee is : and as the people of *Illyris* kill men with their
lookes, so she kills her husbands heart with vntoward conditions. 10
But trust mee wife (quoth hee) seeing I finde you of such crooked
qualities, that (like the Spider) ye turne the sweete flowers of good
counsell into venemous poyson, from henceforth I will leaue you
to your owne wilfulnesse, and neither vexe my mind, nor trouble
my selfe to restraine you : the which if I had wisely done last
night, I had kept the house in quiet, and my selfe from cold.

Husband (quoth shee) thinke that women are like starlings, that
will burst their gall before they will yeeld to the Fowler : or like
the Fish *Scolopendra*, that cannot be toucht without danger.
Notwithstanding, as the hard steele doth yeeld to the hammers 20
stroke, being vsed to his kinde, so will women to their husbands,
where they are not too much crost. And seeing ye haue sworne
to giue me my will, I vow likewise that my wilfulnesse shall not
offend you. I tell you husband, the noble nature of a woman is
such, that for their louing friends they will not sticke (like the
Pellican) to pierce their owne hearts to doe them good. And
therefore forgiuing each other all iniuries past, hauing also tride
one anothers patience, let vs quench these burning coales of
contention, with the sweete iuyce of a faithfull kisse, and shaking
hands, bequeath all our anger to the eating vp of this Cawdle. 30

Her husband courteously consented : and after this time, they
liued long together, in most godly, louing and kind sort, till in the
end she dyed, leauing her husband wondrous wealthy.

Chap. II.

Of *Iacke* of *Newberie* his great wealth, and number of
seruants : and also how hee brought the Queene
Katharine two hundred and fifty men prepared for
the warre at his owne cost against the king of Scots
at *Floden field.*

Now *Iack* of *Newberie* being a widower, had the choice of 40
many wiues, mens daughters of good credit, & widowes of
great wealth. Notwithstanding he bent his only like to one of his

owne seruants, whom he had tried in the guiding of his house a
year or two: and knowing her carefulnesse in her businesse,
faithfull in her dealing, an excellent good huswife, thought it better
to haue her with nothing, than some other with much treasure.
And beside as her qualities were good, so was she of very comely
personage, of a sweet fauour, and faire complexion. In the end,
hee opened his minde vnto her, and craued her good will. The
maid (though shee took this motion kindly) said, shee would do
nothing without consent of her parents. Whereupon a Letter was
10 writ to her father, being a poore man dwelling at *Alesburie* in
Buckingamshire: who being ioyfull of his daughters good fortune,
speedily came to *Newberie*, where of her master he was friendly
entertained: who after he had made him good cheare, shewed
him all his seruants at worke, and euery office in his house.

Within one roome being large and long,
There stood two hundred Loomes full strong:
Two hundred men the truth is so,
Wrought in these Loomes all in a row.
By euery one a pretty boy,
20 *Sate making quils with mickle ioy;*
And in another place hard by,
An hundred women merily,
Were carding hard with ioyfull cheere,
Who singing sate with voices cleere.
And in a chamber close beside,
Two hundred maidens did abide,
In petticoates of Stammell red,
And milke-white kerchers on their head:
Their smocke-sleeues like to winter snow,
30 *That on the Westerne mountaines flow,*
And each sleeue with a silken band,
Was featly tied at the hand.
These pretty maids did neuer lin,
But in that place all day did spin:
And spinning so with voices meet,
Like Nightingals they sung full sweet.
Then to another roome came they,
Where children were in poore aray:
And euery one sate picking wool,
40 *The finest from the course to cull:*
The number was seuen score and ten,
The children of poore silly men:
And these their labours to requite,
Had euery one a penny at night,
Beside their meat and drinke all day,
Which was to them a wondrous stay.
Within another place likewise,
Full fifty proper men he spies,

And these were Shearemen euery one,
Whose skill and cunning there was showne :
And hard by them there did remaine,
Full fourscore Rowers taking paine.
A Dye-house likewise had he then,
Wherein he kept full forty men :
And likewise in his fulling Mill,
Full twenty persons kept he still.
Each weeke ten good fat oxen he
Spent in his house for certaintie :   10
Beside good butter, cheese, and fish,
And many another wholesome dish.
He kept a Butcher all the yeere,
A Brewer eke for Ale and Beere :
A Baker for to bake his Bread,
Which stood his hushold in good stead.
Fiue Cookes within his kitchin great,
Were all the yeare to dresse his meat.
Sixe scullian boyes vnto their hands,
To make cleane dishes, pots, and pans,   20
Beside poore children that did stay,
To turne the broaches euery day.
The old man that did see this sight,
Was much amaz'd, as well he might :
This was a gallant Cloathier sure,
Whose fame for euer shall endure.

When the old man had seene this great houshold and family,
then was he brought into the Ware-houses, some being fild with
wool, some with flockes, some with woad and madder, and some
with broadcloathes and kersies ready dyed and drest, beside a 30
great number of others, some strecht on the Tenters, some hanging on poles, and a great many more lying wet in other places.
Sir (quoth the old man) I wis che zee you bee bominable rich, and
cham content you shall haue my daughter, and Gods blessing and
mine light on you both.

But Father (quoth *Iacke* of *Newberie*) what will you bestow with
her ?

Marry heare you (quoth the old man) I vaith cham but a poore
man, but I thong God, cham of good exclamation among my
neighbours, and they will as zoone take my vice for any thing as a 40
richer mans : thicke I will bestow, you shall haue with a good will,
because che heare very good condemnation of you in euery place,
therefore chil giue you twenty Nobles and a weaning Calfe, and
when I dye and my wife, you shall haue the reuelation of all my
goods.

When *Iacke* heard his offer, he was straight content, making
more reckoning of the womans modesty, than her Fathers money.

So the marriage day being appointed, all things was prepared
meete for the wedding, and royall cheere ordained, most of the
Lords, Knights, and Gentlemen thereabout, were inuited thereunto : the Bride being attyred in a gowne of sheepes russet, and
a kertle of fine woosted, her head attyred with a billiment of gold,
and her haire as yeallow as gold, hanging downe behinde her,
which was curiously combed and pleated, according to the manner
in those dayes : shee was led to Church betweene two sweete
boyes, with Bride-laces & Rosemary tied about their silken sleeues :
10 the one of them was sonne to Sir *Thomas Parry*, the other to
Sir *Francis Hungerford*. Then was there a fair Bride-cup of
siluer and gilt carried before her, wherein was a goodly branch of
Rosemary gilded very faire, hung about with silken Ribands of all
colours : next was there a noyse of Musicians that played all the
way before her : after her came all the chiefest maydens of the
Country, some bearing great Bride Cakes, and some Garlands of
wheate finely gilded, and so she past vnto the Church.

It is needlesse for mee to make any mention here of the Bride-
groome, who being a man so well beloued, wanted no company,
20 and those of the best sort, beside diuers Marchant strangers of the
Stillyard, that came from *London* to the Wedding. The marriage
being solemnized, home they came in order as before, and to
dinner they went, where was no want of good cheare, no lacke of
melody : Rennish Wine at this wedding was as plentifull as Beere
or Ale : for the Marchants had sent thither ten Tunnes of the
best in the Stillyard.

This wedding endured ten dayes, to the great reliefe of the
poore that dwelt all about : and in the end, the Brides Father and
Mother came to pay their Daughters portion : which when the
30 Bridegroome had receiued, hee gaue them great thankes : Notwithstanding he would not suffer them yet to depart, and against
they should goe home, their sonne in law came vnto them, saying ;
Father and Mother, all the thankes that my poore heart can yeeld,
I giue you for your good will, cost, and courtesie, and while I liue
make bold to vse mee in any thing that I am able, and in requitall of
the gift you gaue me with your daughter, I giue you here twenty
pound to bestow as you finde occasion, and for your losse of time,
and charges riding vp and downe, I giue you here as much broadcloath as shall make you a cloake, and my mother a holiday
40 gowne, and when this is worne out, come to me and fetch
more.

O my good zonne (quoth the old woman) Christs benizon bee
with thee euermore : for to tell thee true, we had zold all our
kine to make money for my daughters marriage, and this zeauen
yeare we should not haue been able to buy more : Notwithstanding
we should haue zold all that euer wee had, before my poore wench
should haue lost her marriage.

I (quoth the old man) chud haue zold my coate from my backe, and my bed from vnder mee, before my gyrle should haue gone without you.

I thanke you good father and mother (said the Bride) and I pray God long to keepe you in health : then the Bride kneeled downe and did her duty to her parents, who weeping for very ioy, departed.

Not long after this, it chanced while our noble king was making warre in France, that *Iames* king of *Scotland,* falsly breaking his oath, inuaded *England* with a great Army, and did much hurt vpon the Borders : whereupon on the sudden, euery man was appointed according to his ability, to bee ready with his men and furniture, at 10 an houres warning, on paine of death. *Iacke* of *Newberie* was commanded by the Iustices to set out sixe men, foure armed with Pikes, and two Caliuers, and to meete the Queen in *Buckingham-shire,* who was there raising a great power to goe against the faithlesse king of Scots.

When *Iacke* had receiued this charge, hee came home in all hast, & cut out a whole broadcloath for horsemens coates, and so much more as would make vp coates for the number of a hundred men : in short time hee had made ready fifty tall men well mounted in white coates, and red caps with yellow Feathers, Demilances in 20 their hands, and fifty armed men on foote with Pikes, and fifty shotte in white coates also, euery man so expert in the handling of his weapon, as few better were found in the field.   Himselfe like-wise in complet armour on a goodly Barbed Horse, rode foremost of the company, with a Lance in his hand, and a faire plume of yellow Feathers in his.crest, and in this sort he came before the Iustices : who at the first approach did not a little wonder what he should be.

At length when thee had discouered what hee was, the Iustices and most of the Gentlemen gaue him great commendations for 30 this his good and forward minde shewed in this action : but some other enuying hereat, gaue out words that hee shewed himselfe more prodigall than prudent, and more vaine-glorious than well aduised, seeing that the best Nobleman in the Country would scarce haue done so much : and no maruell (quoth they) for such a one would call to his remembrance, that the King had often occasions to vrge his subiects to such charges ; and therefore would doe at one time as they might be able to doe at another : but *Iack* of *Newberie* like the Stork in the Spring-time, thinks the highest Cedar too lowe for him to build his nest in, and ere the 40 yeare be halfe done may be glad to haue his bed in a bush.

These disdainfull speeches being at last brought to *Iacke* of *Newberies* eare, though it grieued him much, yet patiently put them vp till time conuenient.   Within a while after, all the souldiers of *Barkshire, Hampshire,* and *Wiltshire,* were commanded to shew themselues before the Queene at *Stonny Stratford,* where her Grace, with many Lords, Knights, and Gentlemen were assembled, with tenne thousand men.   Against *Iacke* should goe to the Queene, he caused his face to bee smeared with bloud, and his white coate in like manner.

When they were come before her Highnesse, she demanded (aboue all the rest) what those white coats were ? Whereupon, Sir *Henry Englefield* (who had the leading of the *Barkshire* men) made answer.

May it please your Maiesty to vnderstand, that hee which rideth formost there, is called *Iacke* of *Newbery*, and all those gallant men in white, are his owne seruants, who are maintained all the
10 yeare by him : whom hee at his owne cost hath set out in this time of extremity, to serue the King against his vaunting Foe : and I assure your Maiesty, there is not, for the number, better souldiers in the field.

Good sir *Henry* (quoth the Queene) bring the man to mee, that I may see him : which was done accordingly. Then *Iacke* with all his men allighted, and humbly on their knees fell before the Queen.

Her Grace said, Gentleman arise ; and putting forth her lilly white hand, gaue it him to kisse.
20 Most gracious Queene (quoth hee) Gentleman I am none, nor the sonne of a Gentleman, but a poore Clothier, whose lands are his Loomes, hauing no other Rents but what I get from the backes of little sheepe: nor can I claime any cognisance but a wodden shuttle. Neuerthelesse, most gratious Queene, these my poore seruants and my selfe, with life and goods, are ready at your Maiesties command, not onely to spend our blouds, but also to lose our liues in defence of our King and Country.

Welcome to mee *Iack* of *Newberie* (said the Queene) though a Clothier by trade, yet a Gentleman by condition, and a faithfull
30 subiect in heart : and if thou chance to haue any sute in Court, make account the Queene will bee thy friend, and would to God the King had many such Clothiers. But tell mee, how came thy white coate besmeared with bloud, and thy face so bescratcht ?

May it please your Grace (quoth hee) to vnderstand, that it was my chance to meete with a monster, who like the people *Cynomolgy*, had the proportion of a man, but headed like a dogge, the biting of whose teeth was like the poisoned teeth of a Crocodile, his breath like the Basilisks, killing afarre off. I vnderstand, his name was Enuie, who assailed mee inuisibly, like the wicked
40 spirit of *Mogunce*, who flung stones at men, & could not bee seene : and so I come by my scratcht face, not knowing when it was done.

What was the cause this monster should afflict thee aboue the rest of thy company, or other men in the field ?

Although, most Souereigne Queen (quoth hee) this poysoned curre snarleth at many, and that few can escape the hurt of his wounding breath, yet at this time he bent his force against mee, not for any hurt I did him, but because I surpast him in hearty affection to my Souereigne Lord, and with the poore Widow, offered all I had to serue my Prince and Country.

It were happy for *England* (said the Queene) if in euerie
market Towne there were a Iybbet to hang vp curres of that kinde,
who like *Æsops* dogge lying in the Manger, will doe no good himselfe, nor suffer such as would to doe any.

This speech being ended, the Queene caused her Army to be
set in order, and in warlike manner to march toward *Flodden*,
where King *Iames* had pitcht his field. But as they passed
along with Drum and Trumpet, there came a Post from the
valiant Earle of *Surrey*, with tydings to her Grace, that now she
might dismisse her Army, for that it had pleased God to grant the 10
noble Earle victory ouer the Scotts : whom he had by his wisedome
and valiancy vanquished in fight, and slaine their King in battell.
Upon which newes, her Maiesty discharged her forces, and ioyfully
tooke her iourney to *London*, with a pleasant countenance, praysing
God for her famous victory, and yeelding thankes to all the noble
Gentlemen and Souldiers for their readinesse in the action, giuing
many gifts to the Nobilitie, and great rewards to the Souldiers :
among whom, she nothing forgot *Iacke* of *Newbery*, about whose
necke she put a rich chaine of gold : at what time he with all the
rest gaue a great shout, saying, God saue *Katherine* the noble 20
Queen of *England*.

Many Noble men of *Scotland* were taken prisoners at this battell,
and many more slaine : so that there neuer came a greater foile to
Scotland than this : for you shall vnderstand, that the Scottish
King made full account to bee Lord of this Land, watching opportunity to bring to passe his faithlesse and trayterous practise :
which was when our King was in *France*, at *Turney*, and *Turwin* :
in regard of which warres the Scots vaunted there was none left in
England, but shepheards and ploughmen who were not able to
lead an Army, hauing no skill in martiall affaires. In consideration 30
of which aduantage, hee inuaded the Countrey, boasting of victory
before he had wonne : which was no small griefe to Queene
Margaret, his wife, who was eldest sister to our noble King.
Wherefore in disgrace of the Scots, and in remembrance of the
famous atchieued victory, the Commons of *England* made this
Song : which to this day is not forgotten of many.

THE SONG.

King Iamie *had made a vowe,*
keepe it well if he may :
That he will be at louely London,
vpon Saint Iames *his day.*   40

Vpon Saint Iames *his day at noon,*
at faire London *will I be ;*
And all the Lords in merry Scotland,
they shall dine there with me.

Then bespake good Queene Margaret,
  the teares fell from her eies :
Leaue off these wars most noble King,
  keepe your fidelity.

The water runs swift and wondrous deep,
  from bottome vnto the brimme :
My brother Henry *hath men good enough,*
  England *is hard to winne.*

Away (quoth he) with this silly foole,
  in prison fast let her lie :
For she is come of the English bloud,
  and for these words she shall dye.

With that bespake Lord Thomas Howard,
  the Queenes Chamberlaine that day :
If that you put Queen Margaret *to death,*
  Scotland *shall rue it alway.*

Then in a rage King Iamie *did say,*
  Away with this foolish Mome :
He shall be hanged, and the other be burned,
  so soone as I come home.

At Flodden Field *the Scots came in,*
  which made our Englishmen faine,
At Bramstone-greene *this battell was seene :*
  there was King Iamie *slaine.*

Then presently the Scots did flie,
  their Cannons they left behinde,
Their ensignes gay were won all away,
  our Souldiers did beate them blinde.

To tell you plaine, twelue thousand were slaine,
  that to the fight did stand ;
And many prisoners tooke that day,
  the best in all Scotland.

That day made many a fatherlesse childe,
  and many a widow poore ;
And many a Scottish gay Lady
  sate weeping in her bowre.

Iacke *with a feather was lapt all in leather,*
  his boastings were all in vaine :
He had such a chance with a new morrice dance,
  he neuer went home againe.

27. won *1633* : worne *1626*

Chap. III.

How *Iacke* of *Newberie* went to receiue the King, as he went in progresse into *Barkshire* : and how he made him a banquet in his owne house.

About the tenth year of the kings reigne, his Grace made his progresse into *Barkshire*, against which time *Iack* of *Newbery* cloathed 30. tall fellowes, being his houshold seruants, in blew coates, faced with Sarcenet, euery one hauing a good sword & buckler on his shoulder, himselfe in a plaine russet coate, a paire of white kersie breeches without welt or guard, and stockens of the same peece sowed to his slops, which had a great codpeece, whereon he stucke his pinnes : who knowing the King would come ouer a certain meadow, neere adioining to the Towne, got himselfe thither with all his men ; and repairing to a certaine Ant-hill, which was in the field, tooke vp his seat there, causing his men to stand round about the same with their swords drawne.

The King comming neer the place with the rest of his Nobility, and seeing them stand with their drawne weapons, sent to know the cause. *Garret* King at Armes was the Messenger, who spake in this sort. Good fellowes, the Kings Maiesty would know to what end you stand here with your swords and bucklers prepared to fight.

With that, *Iacke* of *Newbery* started vp, and made this answer. Harrold (quoth he) returne to his Highnesse, it is poore *Iacke* of *Newbery*, who being scant Marquesse of a Mole-hill, is chosen Prince of Ants : and here I stand with my weapons and Guard about mee, to defend and keep these my poore and painefull subiects, from the force of the idle Butterflies, their sworne enemies, lest they should disturbe this quiet Common-wealth, who this Summer season are making their Winters prouision.

The messenger returning, told his Grace that it was one *Iacke* of *Newbery*, that stood there with his men about him, to guard (as they say) a company of Ants, from the furious wrath of the Prince of Butterflies. With this newes the King heartily laught, saying : Indeed it is no maruell he stands so well prepared, considering what a terrible tyrant he hath to deale withall. Certainly my Lords (quoth hee) this seemes to be a pleasant fellow : and therefore we will send to talke with him.

The messenger being sent, told *Iacke* he must come speak with the King. (Quoth he) his Grace hath a horse and I am on foote ; therefore will him to come to mee : beside that, while I am away, our enemies might come and put my people in hazzard, as the Scots did *England*, while our King was in *France*.

How dares the Lambe be so bold with the Lyon (quoth the Herald) ?

Why (quoth hee) if there be a Lyon in the field, here is neuer a cocke to feare him : and tell his Maiesty, he might thinke me a very bad Gouernour, that would walke aside vpon pleasure, and leaue my people in perill.   Herald (quoth hee) it is written, He that hath a charge must looke to it, and so tell thy Lord my King.

The Message being done, the King said : My Lords, seeing it will bee no other, wee will ride vp to the Emperour of Ants, that is so carefull in his gouernment.

At the Kings approach, *Iack* of *Newbery* and his seruants put
10 vp all their weapons, and with a ioyfull cry flung vp their caps in token of victory.   Why how now my masters (quoth the King) is your wars ended : Let mee see, where is the Lord Generall of this great Campe ?

With that, *Iacke* of *Newbery* with all his seruants fell on their knees, saying : God saue the King of *England*, whose sight hath put our foes to flight, and brought great peace to the poore labouring people.

Trust mee (quoth our King) here bee pretty fellowes to fight against Butterflies : I must commend your courage, that dares
20 withstand such mighty gyants.

Most dread Soueraigne (quoth *Iacke*) not long agoe, in my conceit, I saw the most prouident Nation of the Ants, summoned their chiefe Peeres to a Parliament, which was held in the famous city *Dry Dusty*, the one and twentith day of September : whereas, by their wisedomes, I was chosen their King, at what time also many bills of complaint were brought in against diuers il members in the common-wealth : among whom, the Moule was attainted of high treason to their State : and therefore was banished for euer from their quiet Kingdome : so was the Grashopper and the
30 Catterpiller, because they were not onely idle, but also liued vpon the labours of other men, amongst the rest, the Butterflie was very much misliked, but few durst say any thing to him, because of his golden apparell : who through sufferance grew so ambitious and malapert, that the poore Ant could no sooner get an egge into her nest, but he would haue it away, and especially against Easter, which at length was misliked.   This painted asse tooke snuffe in the nose, and assembled a great many other of his owne coate, by windie warres to roote this painefull people out of the land, that hee himselfe might bee seated aboue them all.   (These were
40 proud Butterflies, quoth the King.)   Whereupon I with my men (quoth *Iack*) prepared our selues to withstand them, till such time as your Maiesties royall presence put them to flight.

Tush (said the King) thou must think that the force of flies is not great.

Notwithstanding (quoth *Iacke*) their gay gownes make poore men affraid.

I perceiue (quoth Cardinall *Wolsie*) that you being a King of Ants doe carry a great grudge to the Butterflies.

I (quoth *Iacke*) wee bee as great foes, as the Foxe and the Snake are friends : for the one of them being subtle, loues the other for his craft : but now I intend to be no longer a Prince, because the maiesty of a King hath eclipst my glory : so that looking like the Peacocke on my blacke feet makes me abase my vaine-glorious feathers, and humbly yeeld vnto his Maiesty all my Souereigne rule and dignity, both of life and goods, casting my weapons at his feete, to doe any seruice wherein his Grace shall command me.

God a mercy good *Iack* (quoth the King) I haue often heard of 10 thee, and this morning, I mean to visite thy house.

Thus the King with great delight rode along vntill hee came to the Townes end, where a great multitude of people attended to see his Maiesty : where also Queen *Katharine* with all her traine met him. Thus with great reioycing of the Commons, the King and Queen passed along to this iolly Clothiers house, where the good wife of the house with threescore maidens attending on her, presented the King with a Bee-hiue, most richly gilt with gold, & all the Bees therein were also made of gold curiously by Art, and out of the top of the same Hiue, sprung 20 a flourishing greene tree, which bore golden Apples, and at the roote thereof lay diuers Serpents, seeking to destroy it, whom Prudence and Fortitude trode vnder their feete, holding this inscription in their hands :

> *Loe here presented to your Roiall sight,*
> *The figure of a flourishing Common-wealth :*
> *Where vertuous subiects labour with delight,*
> *And beate the drones to death which liue by stealth :*
>   *Ambition, Enuie, Treason, loathsome serpents be,*
>   *Which seeke the downefall of this fruitfull tree.*   30

> *But Lady Prudence with deep searching eye,*
> *Their ill intended purpose doth preuent,*
> *And noble Fortitude standing alwaies nye,*
> *Disperst their power prepar'd with bad intent.*
>   *Thus are they foild that mount with meanes vnmeet,*
>   *And so like slaues are troden vnder feet.*

The King fauourably accepted this Embleme, and receiuing it at the womens hands, willed Cardinal *Wolsie* to look thereon, commanding it should be sent to *Windsor* Castle. This Cardinall was at that time Lord Chancellor of *England*, and a 40 wonderfull proud Prelate, by whose meanes great variance was set betwixt the King of *England* and the French King, the Emperour of *Almaine*, and diuers other Princes of Christendome, whereby the trafficke of those Merchants was vtterly forbidden, which bred a generall woe through *England*, especially among Clothiers : insomuch, that hauing no sale for their cloath, they were faine to put away many of their people which wrought for them, as hereafter more at large shall be declared.

Then was his Maiesty brought into a great Hall, where foure long tables stood ready couered: and passing through that place, the King and Queene came into a faire and large Parlour, hung about with goodly Tapistry, where was a Table prepared for his Highnesse and the Queenes Grace. All the floore where the King sate was couered with broad cloathes in stead of greene rushes: these were choice peeces of the finest wooll, of an Azure 10 colour, valued at an hundred pound a cloath, which afterward was giuen to his Maiesty. The King being set with the chiefest of the Councell about him, after a delicate dinner, a sumptous banquet was brought in, serued all in glasse: the description wherof were too long for mee to write, and you to read. The great Hall was also filled with Lords, Knights, and Gentlemen, who were attended by no other but the seruants of the house. The Ladies of Honour and Gentlewomen of the Court were all seated in another Parlour by themselues: at whose table the maidens of the house did waite in decent sort. The Seruing-men by them-20 selues, and the Pages & footmen by themselues, vpon whom the prentices did attend most diligently. During the Kings abiding in this place, there was no want of delicates: Rhenish wine, Claret wine & Sacke, was as plentifull as small Ale. Thus from the highest to the lowest, they were serued in such sort, as no discontent was found any way, so that great commendations re-downded vnto the goodman of the house.

The Lord Cardinall that of late found himselfe galde by the Allegory of the Ants, spake in this wise to the King. If it should please your Highnesse (quoth he) but to note the vain-glory of 30 these Artificers, you should finde no small cause of dislike in many of their actions. For an instance, the fellow of this house, hee hath not stucke this day to vndoe himselfe, onely to become famous by receiuing of your Maiesty: like *Herostratus* the Shoo-maker that burned the Temple of *Diana,* onely to get himself a name, more than for any affection he beares to your Grace, as may well be proued by this: Let there be but a simple Subsidie leuied vpon them for the assistance of your Highnesse Warres, or any other waightie affaires of the Common-wealth and state of the Realme, though it bee not the twentieth part of their substance, 40 they will so grudge and repine, that it is wonderfull: and like people desperate cry out, they bee quite vndone.

My Lord Cardinall (quoth the Queen) (vnder correction of my Lord the King) I durst lay an hundred pound *Iack* of *Newbery* was neuer of that minde, nor is not at this instant: if yee aske him, I warrant he will say so. My selfe also had a proofe thereof at the Scottish inuasion, at what time this man being seased but at sixe men, brought (at his owne cost) an hundred and fiftie into the field.

1 would I had moe such subiects (said the King) and many of
so good a minde.

Ho, ho, *Harry* (quoth *Will Sommers*) then had not *Empson* and
Dudley been chronicled for knaues, nor sent to the Tower for
treason.

But then they had not knowne the paine of imprisonment (quoth
our King) who with their subtilty grieued many others.

But their subtilty was such that it broke their neckes (quoth
Will Sommers).

Whereat the King and Queene laughing heartily, rose from the 10
Table. By which time *Iacke* of *Newbery* had caused all his folkes
to goe to their worke, that his Grace and all the Nobility might
see it : so indeed the Queen had requested. Then came his
Highnesse where hee saw an hundred Loomes, standing in one
roome, and two men working in euery one, who pleasantly sung
on this sort.

The Weauers Song.

When Hercules *did vse to spin,*
  and Pallas *wrought vpon the Loome,*
Our trade to flourish did begin,
  while Conscience went not selling Broome. 20
    Then loue and friendship did agree,
    To keep the band of amitie.

When Princes sons kept sheepe in field,
  and Queenes made cakes of wheaten flowre,
Then men to lucre did not yeeld,
  which brought good cheere in euery bower.
    Then loue and friendship did agree,
    To hold the bands of amitie.

But when that Giants huge and hie, 30
  did fight with speares like Weauers beames,
Then they in iron beds did lie,
  and brought poore men to hard extreames.
    Yet loue and friendship did agree,
    To hold the bands of amitie.

Then Dauid *tooke his sling and stone,*
  not fearing great Goliahs *strength,*
He pierst his braine, and broke the bone,
  though he were fifty foote of length.
    For loue and friendship, &c. 40

But while the Greekes besieged Troy,
  Penelope *apace did spin,*
And Weauers wrought with mickle ioy,
  though little gaines were comming in.
    For loue and friendship, &c.

21. Broomes. *1626*

Had Helen *then sate carding wooll,*
 (whose beauteous face did breed such strife)
She had not beene sir Paris *trull,*
 nor caus'd so many lose their life.
  Yet we by loue did still agree, &c.

Or had King Priams *wanton sonne*
 beene making quills with sweet content.
He had not then his friends vndone,
 when he to Greece *a gadding went.*
10 *For loue and friendship did agree, &c.*

The Cedar tree indures more stormes,
 than little shrubs that sprout not hie :
The Weauer liues more void of harmes,
 than Princes of great dignitie.
  While loue and friendship doth agree, &c.

The Shepheard sitting in the field,
 doth tune his pipe with hearts delight :
When Princes march with speare and shield,
 the poore man soundly sleepes all night.
20 *While loue and friendship doth agree, &c.*

Yet this by proofe is daily tride,
 For Gods good gifts we are ingrate :
And no man through the world so wide,
 liues well contented with his state.
  No loue nor friendship we can see,
   to hold the bands of amitie.

Well sung good fellowes (said our King) : Light hearts and
merry mindes liue long without gray haires.

But (quoth *Will Sommers*) seldome without red noses.

30 Well (said the King) there is a hundred angells to make cheere
withall : and looke that euery yeare once you make a feast among
your selues, and frankely (euery yeare) I giue you leaue to fetch
foure Buckes out of *Dunington* Parke, without any mans let or
controulement.

O I beseech your Grace (quoth *Will Sommers*) let it be with
a condition.

What is that (said our King)?

My Liege (quoth hee) that although the Keeper will haue the
skins, that they may giue their wiues the hornes.

40 Goe to (said the Queene) thy head is fuller of knauery, than thy
purse is of crownes.

The poore workemen humbly thanked his Maiesty for his
bountifull liberality : and euer since, it hath beene a custome
among the Weauers, euery yeare presently after *Bartholmewtide,*
in a remembrance of the Kings fauour, to meet together, and
make a merry feast.

His Maiesty came next among the spinsters and carders, who were merrily a working : whereat *Will Sommers* fell into a great laughter.

What ailes the foole to laugh (said the King)?

Marry (quoth *Will Sommers*) to see these maidens get their liuing as Buls doe eate their meate.

How is that (said the Queene)?

By going still backward (quoth *Will Sommers*) : and I will lay a wager, that they that practise so well being maides to goe backward, will quickly learne ere long to fall backward. 10

But sirra (said the Cardinall) thou didst fall forward when thou brokest thy face in master *Kingsmills* seller.

But you my Lord sate forward (quoth *Will Sommers*) when you sate in the stockes at Sir *Amie Paulets*. Whereat there was greater laughing than before.

The King and Queene, and all the Nobility heedfully beheld these women, who for the most part were very faire and comely creatures, and were all attired alike from top to toe. Then (after due reuerence) the maidens in dulcet manner chaunted out this Song, two of them singing the Ditty, and all the rest bearing the 20 burden.

The Maidens Song.

It was a Knight in Scotland *borne,*
follow my loue, leap ouer the strand :
Was taken prisoner and left forlorne,
euen by the good Earle of Northumberland.

Then was he cast in prison strong,
follow my loue, leap ouer the strand :
Where he could not walke nor lye along,
euen by the good Earle of Northumberland. 30

And as in sorrow thus he lay,
follow my loue, come ouer the strand :
The Earles sweet Daughter walkt that way,
and she the faire flower of Northumberland.

And passing by, like an Angell bright,
follow my loue, come ouer the strand :
This prisoner had of her a sight,
and she the faire flower of Northumberland.

And lowd to her this knight did cry,
follow my loue, come ouer the strand : 40
The salt teares standing in his eie,
and she the faire flower of Northumberland.

Faire Lady (*he said*) *take pitty on me,*
  follow my loue, come ouer the strand :
And let me not in prison dye,
  and you the faire flower of Northumberland.

Faire Sir, how should I take pitty on thee,
  follow my loue, come ouer the strand :
Thou being a foe to our Country,
  and I the faire flower of Northumberland.

Faire Lady, I am no foe (*he said*)
10 *follow my loue, come ouer the strand :*
Through thy sweete loue here was I staid,
  for thee the faire flower of Northumberland.

Why shouldst thou come here for loue of me,
  follow my loue, come ouer the strand :
Hauing wife and children in thy Countrie,
  and I the faire flower of Northumberland.

I sweare by the blessed Trinitie,
  follow my loue, come ouer the strand :
I haue no wife nor children I,
20 *nor dwelling at home in merry* Scotland.

If courteously you will set me free,
  follow my loue, come ouer the strand :
I vow that I will marry thee,
  so soone as I come in merry Scotland.

Thou shalt be Lady of Castles and Towres,
  follow my loue, come ouer the strand :
And sit like a Queen in princely bowers,
  when I am at home in faire Scotland,

Then parted hence this Lady gay,
30 *follow my loue, come ouer the strand :*
And got her fathers ring away,
  to help this sad knight into faire Scotland.

Likewise much gold she got by sleight,
  follow my loue, come ouer the strand :
And all to help this forlorne knight,
  to wend from her father to faire Scotland.

Two gallant steeds both good and able,
  follow my loue, come ouer the strand :
She likewise tooke out of the stable,
40 *to ride with this knight into fair* Scotland.

And to the Iaylor she sent this ring,
  follow my loue, come ouer the strand :
The knight from prison forth to bring,
  to wend with her into faire Scotland.

This token set this prisoner free,
    follow my loue, come ouer the strand:
Who straight went to this faire Lady,
    to wend with her into faire Scotland.

A gallant steed he did bestride,
    follow my loue, come ouer the strand:
And with the Lady away did ride,
    and she the faire flower of Northumberland.

They rode till they came to a water cleere,
    follow my loue, come ouer the strand: 10
Good sir how should I follow you here,
    and I the faire flower of Northumberland.

The water is rough and wonderfull deep,
    follow my loue, come ouer the strand:
And on my saddle I shall not keep,
    and I the faire flower of Northumberland.

Feare not the foord, faire Lady (quoth he)
    follow my loue, come ouer the strand:
For long I cannot stay for thee,
    and thou the faire flower of Northumberland.   20

The Lady prickt her wanton steed,
    follow my loue, come ouer the strand:
And ouer the riuer swom with speed,
    and she the faire flower of Northumberland.

From top to toe all wet was she,
    follow my loue, come ouer the strand:
This haue I done for loue of thee,
    and I the faire flower of Northumberland.

Thus rode she all one winters night,
    follow my loue, come ouer the strand: 30
Till Edenborow *they saw in sight,*
    the chiefest towne in all Scotland.

Now chuse (quoth he) thou wanton flower,
    follow my loue, come ouer the strand:
Whether thou wilt be my Paramour,
    or get thee home to Northumberland.

For I haue wife and children fiue,
    follow my loue, come ouer the strand:
In Edenborow *they be aliue,*
    then get thee home to faire England.   40

This fauour shalt thou haue to boote,
    follow my loue, come ouer the strand:
Ile haue thy horse, goe thou a foote,
    goe get thee home to Northumberland.

O false and faithlesse knight (quoth she)
  follow my loue, come ouer the strand:
And canst thou deale so bad with me,
  and I the faire flower of Northumberland?

Dishonour not a Ladies name,
  follow my loue, come ouer the strand:
But draw thy sword, and end my shame,
  and I the faire flower of Northumberland.

He tooke her from her stately Steed,
10 *follow my loue, come ouer the strand:*
And left her there in extreme need,
  and she the faire flower of Northumberland.

Then sate she downe full heauily,
  follow my loue, come ouer the strand:
At length two knights came riding by,
  two gallant knights of faire England.

She fell downe humbly on her knee,
  follow my loue, come ouer the strand:
Saying, courteous Knights take pitty on me,
20 *and I the faire flower of* Northumberland.

I haue offended my father deere,
  follow my loue, come ouer the strand:
And by a false knight that brought me here,
  from the good Earle of Northumberland.

They tooke her vp behinde him then,
  follow my loue, come ouer the strand:
And brought her to her fathers againe,
  and he the good Earle of Northumberland.

All you faire maidens be warned by me,
30 *follow my loue, come ouer the strand:*
Scots were neuer true, nor neuer will be,
  to Lord, nor Lady, nor faire England.

FINIS.

After the Kings Maiesty and the Queene had heard this song
sweetely sung by them, hee cast them a great reward: and so
departing thence, went to the Fulling-mils, and Dye-house, where
a great many were also hard at worke: and his Maiesty perceiuing
what a great number of people were by this one man set on worke,
both admired, and commended him, saying further, that no Trade
40 in all the Land was so much to bee cherished and maintained as
this, which (quoth hee) may well be called, The life of the poore.
And as the King returned from this place with intent to take horse
and depart, there met him a great many of children in garments

of white silke, frienged with gold, their heads crowned with golden Bayes, and about their armes each one had a scarfe of green sarcenet fast tied, in their hands they bore siluer bowes, and vnder their girdles golden arrowes.

The foremost of them represented *Diana*, Goddesse of Chastity, who was attended on by a traine of beautifull Nymphes, and they presented to the King foure prisoners :

The first was a sterne and grisly woman, carrying a frowning countenance, and her forehead full of wrinkles, her hayre as black as pitch, and her garments all bloudy, a great sword shee had in 10 her hand all stained with purple gore : they called her name *Bellona*, Goddesse of warres, who had three daughters : the first of them was a tall woman, so leane and ill-fauoured, that her cheeke bones were ready to start out of the skinne, of a pale and deadly colour : her eyes sunke into her head : her legges so feeble, that they could scantly carry the body ; all along her armes & hands through the skinne you might tell the sinewes, ioints and bones : her teeth were very strong and sharpe withall : she was so greedy, that shee was ready with her teeth to teare the skinne from her owne armes : her attyre was blacke, and all torne and ragged, she went 20 barefooted, and her name was *Famine*.

The second was a strong and lusty woman, with a looke pittilesse, and vnmercifull countenance : her garments were all made of Iron and Steele, and she carried in her hand a naked weapon, and she was called the *Sword*.

The third was also a cruell creature, her eyes did sparkle like burning coales : her hayre was like a flame, and her garments like burning brasse : she was so hote, that none could stand neere her, and they called her name *Fire*.

After this they retyred againe, and brought vnto his Highnesse 30 two other Personages, their countenance was Princely and amiable, their attyre most rich and sumptuous : the one carried in his hand a golden Trumpet, and the other a Palme tree : and these were called *Fame* & *Victorie*, whom the Goddesse of Chastity charged to waite vpon this famous Prince for euer. This done, each childe after other with due reuerence, gaue vnto his Maiesty a sweete smelling Gilliflower, after the manner of the Persians, offering something in token of loyalty and obedience.

The King and Queene beholding the sweete fauour and countenance of these children, demanded of *Iacke* of *Newberie* 40 whose children they were ?

Who answered : It shall please your Highnesse to vnderstand, that these are the children of poore people, that doe get their liuing by picking of wooll, hauing scant a good meale once in a weeke.

With that the King began to tell his Gilliflowers, whereby he found that there was 96. children.

Certainely (said the Queene) I perceiue God giues as faire

children to the poore as to the rich, and fairer many times : and
though their dyet and keeping bee but simple, the blessing of God
doth cherish them.   Therefore (said the Queene) I will request to
haue two of them to waite in my Chamber.

Faire *Katharine* (said the King) thou and I haue iumpt in one
opinion, in thinking these children fitter for the Court than the
Countrey : whereupon he made choise of a dozen more, foure he
ordained to be Pages to his royall Person, and the rest he sent to
the Uniuersities, allotting to euery one a Gentlemans liuing.
10 Diuers of the Noble-men did in like sort entertaine some of those
children into their seruices, so that (in the end) not one was left
to picke wooll, but were all so prouided for, that their Parents
neuer needed to care for them : and God so blessed them, that
each of them came to bee men of great account and authority in
the Land, whose posterities remaine to this day worshipfull and
famous.

The King, Queene, and Nobles, being ready to depart, after
great thankes and gifts giuen to *Iacke* of *Newbery* his Maiesty
would haue made him Knight, but he meekely refused it, saying,
20 I beseech your Grace let mee liue a poore Clothier among my
people, in whose maintenance I take more felicity, than in all the
vaine titles of Gentility : for these are the labouring Ants whom
I seeke to defend, and these be the Bees which I keepe : who
labour in this life, nor for our selues, but for the glory of GOD, and
to do seruice to our dread Souereigne.

Thy Knighthood need be no hinderance of thy Faculty (quoth
the King).

O my dread Soueraigne (said *Iacke*) honour and worship may
bee compared to the Lake of *Lœthe*, which makes men forget
30 themselues that taste thereof : and to the end I may still keepe in
minde from whence I came, and what I am, I beseech your Grace
let mee rest in my russet coate, a poore Clothier to my dying day.

Seeing then (said the King) that a mans minde is a Kingdome
to himselfe, I will leaue thee to the riches of thy owne content, and
so farewell.

The Queenes Maiesty taking her leaue of the good wife with
a Princely kisse, gaue her in token of remembrance a most precious
and rich Diamond set in gold, about the which was also curiously
set sixe Rubies and sixe Emeralds in one peece, valued at nine
40 hundred Markes : and so her Grace departed.

But in this meane space, *Will Sommers* kept company among
the maides, and betooke himselfe to spinning as they did, which
among them was held as a forfeit of a gallon of wine, but *William*
by no meanes would pay it, except they would take it out in kisses,
rating euery kisse at a farthing.

This paiment wee refuse for two causes (quoth the maides) : the
one for that we esteeme not kisses at so base a rate ; and the
other, because in so doing we should giue as much as you.

Chap. IIII.

How the maidens serued *Will Sommers* for his sawcinesse.

The madens consented together, seeing *Will Sommers* was so
busie both with their worke and in his words, and would not pay his
forfeiture, to serue him as he deserued : first therefore they bound
him hands and feet, and set him vpright against a post, tying
him there to : which hee tooke in ill part, notwithstanding he
could not resist them. And because he let his tongue run at
randome, they set a fair gagge in his mouth, such a one as he 10
could not for his life put away : so that hee stood as one gaping for
winde. Then one of them got a couple of dogs droppings, and
putting them in a bagge, laid them in soke in a bason of water,
while the rest turned downe the coller of his Ierkin, and put an
house-cloath about his necke in stead of a fine towell : then came
the other maide with a bason and water in the same, and with the
perfume in the pudding-bagge, flapt him about the face and lips,
till he looked like a tawnie Moore, and with her hand washt him
very orderly : the smell being somewhat strong, Will could by no
meanes abide it, and for want of other language, cryed, *Ah ha ha* 20
ha. Faine hee would haue spet, and could not, so that hee was
faine to swallow downe such licour as hee neuer tasted the like.
When hee had a pretty while been washed in this sort, at the
length he croucht downe vpon his knees, yeelding himselfe to their
fauour : which the maidens perceiuing, pulled the gag out of his
mouth.

Hee had no sooner the liberty of his tongue, but that he curst
and swore like a diuell : the maids that could scant stand for
laughing, at last askt how hee liked his washing ?

Gods ounds (quoth hee) I was neuer thus washt, nor euer met 30
with such Barbers since I was borne : let mee goe (quoth he) and
I will giue you whatsoeuer you will demand, wherewith hee cast
them an English Crowne.

Nay (quoth one of the Maides) you are yet but washt, but wee
will shaue you ere yee goe.

Sweete Maides (quoth hee) pardon my shauing, let it suffice that
you haue washt mee : if I haue done a trespasse to your Trade,
forgiue it mee, and I will neuer hereafter offend you.

Tush (said the Maides) you haue made our wheeles cast their
bands, and bruised the teeth of our cardes in such sort, as the 40
offence may not bee remitted without great pennance. As for your
gold, wee regard it not : therefore as you are perfumed fit for the
dogs, so wee enioine you this night to serue all our hogs, which
pennance, if you will sweare with all speede to performe, wee will
let you loose.

O (quoth *Will*) the huge Elephant was neuer more fearefull of the silly sheep, than I am of your displeasures : therefore let mee loose, and I will doe it with all diligence.

Then they vnbound him, and brought him among a great company of Swine, which when *Will* had wel viewed ouer, he draue out of the yard all the Sowes :

Why how now (quoth the Maides) what meane you by this?

Mary (quoth *Will*) these be all sowes, and my pennance is but to serue the hogs.

10 Is it true (quoth they) haue you ouertaken vs in this sort? Well, looke there be not one hog vnserued wee would aduise you.

William Sommers stript vp his sleeues very orderly, and clapt an apron about his motly hosen, and taking a paile serued the hogs handsomely. When he had giuen them all meat, he said thus :

> *My taske is duely done,*
> *My liberty is wonne,*
> *The hogs haue eate their crabs,*
> *Therefore farewell you drabs.*

Nay soft friend (quoth they) the veriest hog of all hath yet had
20 nothing.

Where the diuell is he (said *Will*) that I see him not?

Wrapt in a motley Ierken (quoth they) take thy selfe by the nose, and thou shalt catch him by the snout.

I was neuer so very a hog (quoth he) but I would alway spare from my own belly to giue a woman.

If thou doe not (say they) eate (like the prodigall Childe) with thy fellow hogs, we will so shaue thee, as thou shalt deerly repent thy disobedience.

Hee seeing no remedy, committed himselfe to their mercy : and
30 so they let him goe. When he came to the Court, he shewed to the King all his aduenture among the weauers maidens, wherat the King and Queene laughed heartily.

Chap. V.

Of the pictures which *Iacke* of *Newbery* had in his house, whereby he encouraged his seruants to seeke for fame and dignitie.

IN a faire large Parlour which was wainscotted round about, *Iacke* of *Newbery* had fifteene faire Pictures hanging, which were couered with Curtaines of greene silke, fringed with gold,
40 which he would often shew to his friends and seruants.

In the first was the Picture of a shepheard, before whom kneeled a great King named *Viriat*, who sometime gouerned the people of *Portugall*.

See here (quoth *Iacke*) the father a shepheard, the sonne a Soueraigne. This man ruled in *Portugall,* and made great warres
against the Romanes, and after that inuaded *Spaine,* yet in the end
was traiterously slaine.

The next was the Portraiture of *Agathocles,* which for his surpass-
ing wisedome and manhood, was created King of *Sicilia,* and maintained battell against the people of *Carthage.* His father was
a poore Potter, before whom he also kneeled. And it was the vse
of this King, that whensoeuer he made a banquet, he would haue
as well vessels of earth as of gold set vpon the Table, to the intent 10
he might alwayes beare in minde the place of his beginning, his
Fathers house and family.

The third was the picture of *Iphicrates* an *Athenian* born, who
vanquished the Lacedemonians in plaine and open battaile. This
man was Captaine Generall to *Artaxerxes,* King of *Persia,* whose
father was notwithstanding a Cobler, and there likewise pictured.
Eumenes was also a famous Captaine to *Alexander* the great, whose
father was no other than a Carter.

The fourth was the similitude of *Aelius Pertinax,* sometime
Emperour of *Rome,* yet was his father but a Weauer : and after- 20
ward, to giue example to others of low condition to beare mindes
of worthy men, he caused the shop to be beautified with Marble
curiously cut, wherein his father before him was wont to get his
liuing.

The fift was the picture of *Dioclesian,* that so much adorned *Rome*
with his magnificall and triumphant victories. This was a famous
Emperour, although no other than the sonne of a Booke-binder.

Valentinian stood the next, painted most artificially, who was
also crowned Emperour, and was but the sonne of a poore Rope-
maker : as in the same picture was expressed ; where his father was 30
painted by him, vsing his trade.

The seuenth was the Emperour *Probus,* whose father being
a Gardener, was pictured by him holding a spade.

The eighth picture was of *Marcus Aurelius,* whom euery age
honoureth, he was so wise and prudent an Emperour ; yet was he
but a Cloth-weauers son.

The ninth was the Portraiture of the valiant Emperour *Maximinus,* the son of a Blacksmith, who was there painted as he was
wont to worke at the Anuill.

In the tenth table was painted the Emperour *Gabianus,* who at 40
the first was but a poore shepheard.

Next to this picture, was placed the pictures of two Popes of
Rome, whose wisedome and learning aduanced them to that
dignitie. The first was the liuely Counterfeit of Pope *Iohn* the
22 whose father was a Shoomaker : hee being elected Pope,
encreased their rents and patrimonie greatly.

The other was the Picture of Pope *Sixtus* the fourth of that
name, being a poore Marriners son.

The thirteenth Picture was of *Lamusius* King of *Lombardie*, who was no better than the son of a common Strumpet : being painted like a naked childe walking in the water, and taking hold of the poynt of a Launce, by the which hee held fast, and saued himselfe. The reason whereof, was this : After his lewde mother was deliuered of him, shee vnnaturally threw him into a deepe stinking Ditch, wherein was some water. By hap king *Agilmond* passed that way, and found this childe almost drowned ; who mouing him softly with the point of his Launce, the better to perceiue what hee
10 was, the childe (though then newely borne) tooke hold thereof with one of his pretty hands, not suffering it to slide or slip away againe : which thing the King considering, being amazed at the strange force of this yongue little Infant, caused it to be taken vp, and carefully to be fostered. And because the place where hee found him was called *Lama*, hee named the childe *Lamusius* : who afterward grew to be so braue a man, and so much fauoured of Fortune, that in the end hee was crowned King of the *Lombards*, who liued there in honour, and in his succession after him, euen vntill the time of the vnfortunate King *Albouina*, when all came to
20 ruine, subuersion and destruction.

In the fourteenth picture *Primislas* King of *Bohemia* was most artificially drawne ; before whom there stood an Horse without Bridle or Saddle, in a field where Husband-men were at plough. The cause why this King was thus painted (quoth *Iacke*) was this. At that time the King of the *Bohemians* died without issue, and great strife being amongst the Nobility for a new king, at length they all consented that a horse should bee let into the field, without bridle or saddle, hauing all determined with most assured purpose to make him their king, before whom this horse rested :
30 At what time it came to passe, that the horse first stayed himselfe before this *Primislas*, being a simple creature, who was then busie driuing the plough, they presently made him their Souereigne, who ordered himselfe and his kingdome very wisely. Hee ordained many good lawes, hee compassed the Citie of *Prague* with strong walles, besides many other things, meriting perpetuall laud and commendations.

The fifteenth was the Picture of *Theophrastus*, a Philosopher, a counsellor of Kings, and companion of Nobles, who was but sonne of a Taylor.
40 Seeing then my good seruants, that these men haue been aduanced to high estate and Princely dignities, by wisedome, learning and diligence, I would wish you to imitate the like vertues, that you might attaine the like honours : for which of you doth know what good fortune God hath in store for you ? there is none of you so poorely borne, but that men of baser birth haue come to great honours. The idle hand shall euer goe in a ragged garment, and the sloathfull liue in reproach : but such as doe lead a vertuous life, and gouerne themselues dis-

creetly, shall of the best be esteemed, and spend their daies in
credit.

C H A P. V I.

How all the Clothiers in *England* ioined together, &
with one consent complained to the King of their
great hindrance sustained for want of Traffique into
other Countries, whereupon they could get no sale
for their Cloath.

BY meanes of the warres which our King had with other
countries, many Merchant strangers were prohibited for 10
comming to *England*, as also our owne Merchants (in like sort)
were forbidden to haue dealings with *France* or the Low-countries :
by meanes whereof the Clothiers had most of their cloath lying
on their hands, and that which they sold was at so low a rate,
that the money scantly paid for the wooll and workemanship.
Whereupon they sought to ease themselues by abating the poore
workemens wages.   And when that did not preuaile, they turnd
away many of their people, Weauers, Shearmen, Spinsters and
Carders, so that where there was a hundred Looms kept in one
towne, there was scant fifty : and hee that kept twenty put downe 20
tenne.   Many a poore man (for want of worke) was hereby vndone, with his wife and children, and it made many a poore
widow to sit with a hungry belly.   This bred great woe in most
places in *England*.   In the end *Iack* of *Newberie* intended (in
the behalfe of the poore) to make a Supplication to the King :
and to the end hee might do it the more effectually, hee sent
Letters to all the chiefe cloathing townes in *England* to this
effect.

The Letter.

WElbeloued friends and brethren, hauing a taste of the 30
generall griefe, and feeling (in some measure) the extremitie of these times, I fell into consideration by what meanes
we might best expell these sorrowes, and recouer our former
commodity.
   When I had well thought hereon, I found that nothing was
more needefull herein, than a faithfull vnity among our selues.
This sore of necessity can no way be cured but by concord : for
like as the flame consumes the candle, so men through discord
waste themselues.   The poore hate the rich, because they will
not set them on worke ; and the rich hate the poore, because they 40
seeme burdenous : so both are offended for want of gaine.   When
Belinus and *Brennus* were at strife, the Queen their mother in

their greatest fury perswaded them to peace, by vrging her
conception of them in one wombe, and mutuall cherishing of
them from their tender yeares: so let our Art of Cloathing, which
like a kinde mother hath cherished vs with the excellency of her
secrets, perswade vs to an vnity.   Though our Occupation be decaied, let vs not deale with it as men doe by their old shooes,
which after they haue long borne them out of the myre, doe in
the end fling them on the dunghill: or as the Husband-man
doth by his Bees, who for their Honey burnes them.   Deare
10 friends, consider that our Trade will maintaine vs, if wee will
vphold it: and there is nothing base, but that which is basely
vsed.

Assemble therefore your selues together, and in euery towne
tell the number of those that haue their liuing by meanes of this
Trade, note it in a Bill, and send it to mee.   And because sutes
in Courts are like Winter nights, long and wearisome, let there
be in each place a weekely collection made to defray charges:
for I tell you, Noble mens Secretaries and cunning Lawyers haue
slow tongues and deafe eares, which must bee daily noynted with
20 the sweete oyle of Angells.   Then let two honest discreet men
bee chosen and sent out of euery towne to meete mee at *Blackwell Hall* in *London* on *All Saints Eeue*, and then we will present
our humble petition to the King.   Thus I bid you heartily
farewell.

Copies of this Letter being sealed, they were sent to all the
cloathing Townes of *England*, and the Weauers both of linnen
and woollen gladly receiued them: so that when all the Bills were
brought together, there were found of the Clothiers, and those they
maintained, threescore thousand and sixe hundred persons.
30 Moreouer, euery cloathing Towne sending vp two men to *London*,
they were found to bee an hundred and twelue persons, who in
very humble sort fell downe before his Maiesty walking in
S. *James* his Parke, and deliuered to him their Petition.

The King presently perusing it, asked if they were all
Clothiers?

Who answered (as it were one man) in this sort: Wee are
(most gracious king) all poore Clothiers, and your Maiesties faithfull subiects.

My Lords (quoth the King) let these mens complaint bee
40 thoroughly lookt into, and their griefs redressed: for I account
them in the number of my best Common-wealths men.   As the
Clergy for the soule, the Souldier for defence of his countrey, the
Lawyer to execute iustice, the Husband-man to feede the belly:
so is the skilfull Clothier no lesse necessary for the cloathing of
the backe, whom we may reckon among the chiefe Yeomen of
our Land: and as the christall sight of the eye is tenderly to be
kept from harmes because it giues the whole body light: so is the
Clothiers whose cunning hand prouides garments to defend our

naked parts from the Winters nipping frost. Many more reasons there are, which may moue vs to redresse their griefes : but let it suffice that I command to haue it done.

With that, his Grace deliuered the Petition to the Lord Chauncellor, and all the Clothiers cryed, God saue the King.

But as the King was ready to depart, hee suddenly turned about, saying : I remember there is one *Iacke* of *Newberie*, I muse hee had not his hand in this businesse, who profest himselfe to bee a defender of true Labourers.

Then said the Duke of *Sommerset* : It may bee his purse is 10 answerable for his person.

Nay (quoth the Lord Cardinall) all his treasure is little enough to maintaine warres against the butterflies.

With that *Iack* shewed himselfe vnto the King, and priuately told his Grace of their griefe anew.

To whom his Maiesty said : Giue thy attendance at the Councell Chamber, where thou shalt receiue an answer to thy content. And so his Highnes departed.

Finally, it was agreed that the Marchants should freely traffique one with another, and that Proclamation therof should bee made 20 as well on the other side the Sea, as in our Land : but it was long before this was effected, by reason the Cardinall being Lord Chancellor, put off the matter from time to time.

And because the Clothiers thought it not best to depart before it was ended, they gaue their daily attendance at the Cardinalls house : but spent many dayes to no purpose : sometime they were answered, My Lord was busie, and could not be spoke with-all ; or else he was asleepe, & they durst not wake him : or at his study, and they would not disturbe him : or at his prayers, and they durst not displease him : and still one thing or other stood in the 30 way to hinder them. At last, *Patch* the Cardinalls foole, being (by their often repaire thither) well acquainted with the Clothiers, came vnto them and said: What, haue you not spoken with my Lord yet ?

No truly (quoth they) we heare say he is busie, and we stay till his grace bee at leasure.

Is it true (said *Patch*) ? and with that in all haste he went out of the hall, and at last came in againe with a great bundle of straw on his backe.

Why how now *Patch* (quoth the Gentlemen) what wilt thou doe with that straw ? 40

Mary (quoth he) I will put it vnder these honest mens feete, lest they should freeze ere they finde my Lord at leasure.

This made them all to laugh, and caused *Patch* to beare away his straw againe. Well, well, (quoth hee) if it cost you a groates worth of faggets at night, blame not me.

Trust me (said *Iacke* of *Newbery*) if my Lord Cardinalls father had beene no hastier in killing of Calues, than hee is in dispatch-ing of poor mens sutes, I doubt he had neuer worne a Myter.

This he spake betwixt themselues softly, but yet not so softly, but that he was ouer-heard by a flattering Fellow that stood by, who made it knowne to some of the Gentlemen, and they straight certified the Cardinall therof.

The Cardinall (who was of a very high spirit, and a loftie aspiring minde) was maruellously displeased at *Iacke* of *Newbery* : wherefore in his rage hee commanded and sent the Clothiers all to prison, because the one of them should not sue for the others releasement. Foure dayes lay these men in the *Marshalsey*, till
10 at last they made their humble Petition to the King for their release : but some of the Cardinals friends kept it from the kings sight. Notwithstanding, the Duke of *Sommerset*, knowing thereof, spake with the Lord Cardinall about the matter, wishing hee would speedily release them, lest it breed him some displeasure : for you may perceiue (quoth the Duke) how highly the King esteemes men of that Faculty.

Sir (quoth the Cardinall) I doubt not but to answer their imprisonment well enough, being perswaded that none would haue giuen me such a quip but an Heretike : and I dare warrant you
20 were this *Iacke* of *Newbery* well examined, hee would bee found to bee infected with *Luthers* spirit, against whom our King hath of late written a most learned Booke, in respect whereof, the Popes holinesse hath intitled his Maiesty *Defender of the Faith* : therefore I tell you such fellowes are fitter to be faggots for fire, than Fathers of Families : notwithstanding (at your Graces request) I will release them.

Accordingly the Cardinall sent for the Clothiers afore him to *White hall*, his new built house by *Westminster*, and there bestowing his blessing vpon them, said : Though you haue offended mee
30 I pardon you ; for as *Steuen* forgaue his enemies that stoned him, and our Sauiour those sinfull men that crucified him, so do I forgiue you that high trespasse committed in disgrace of my birth : for herein doe men come neerest vnto God, in shewing mercy and compassion. But see hereafter you offend no more. Touching your sute it is granted, and to morrow shall be published through *London*.

This being said they departed : and according to the Cardinalls words, their businesse was ended. The Stillyard Marchants ioyfull hereof, made the Clothiers a great banquet. After which, each
40 man departed home, carrying tydings of their good successe ; so that within short space, Clothing was againe very good, and poore men as well set on worke as before.

C H A P. V I I.

How a yongue Italian Marchant comming to *Iack* of *Newberies* house, was greatly inamoured of one of his maidens, and how he was serued.

AMong other seruants which *Iacke* of *Newbery* kept, there was in his house threescore maidens, which euery Sunday waited on his wife to Church and home againe, who had diuers offices. Among other, two were appointed to keepe the beames and waights, to waigh out wooll to the Carders and Spinsters, and to receiue it in againe by waight. One of them was a comely maiden, 10 faire and louely, borne of wealthy Parents, and brought vp in good qualities, her name was *Ione* : so it was, that a yongue wealthy Italian Marchant, comming oft from *London* thither to bargaine for cloath (for at that time Clothiers most commonly had their cloath bespoken, and halfe paid for afore hand). This Master *Benedicke* fell greatly inamoured of this maiden : and therefore offered much courtesie to her, bestowing many gifts on her, which she receiued thankefully : and albeit his outward countenance shewed his inward affection, yet *Ione* would take no knowledge thereof. Halfe the day sometime would hee sit by her, as shee was waighing 20 wooll, often sighing and sobbing to himselfe, yet saying nothing, as if he had been tonguelesse, like the men of *Coromandæ* ; and the loather to speake, for that hee could speak but bad English. *Ione* on the other side that well perceiued his passions, did as it were triumph ouer him, as one that were bondslaue to her beauty, and although shee knew well enough before that shee was faire, yet did shee neuer so highly esteeme of her selfe as at this present : so that when she heard him either sigh, or sob, or groane, shee would turne her face in a carelesse sort, as if she had been borne (like the woman of *Taprobana*) without eares. 30

When Master *Bennedicke* saw shee made no reckoning of his sorrowes, at length hee blabored out this broken English, and spake to her in this sort. Metressa *Ione*, be me tra and fa, mee loue you wod all mine hart, and if you no shall loue me again, me know mee shall die, sweet Mistresse loue a me, & be me fa and tra you sal lack noting. First ; me wil giue you de silke for make you a Frog : Second, de fin fin Camree for make you ruffes ; and the turd shal be for make fin handkercher, for wipe your nose.

Shee mistaking his speech, began to be collericke, wishing him to keepe that bodkin to picke his teeth. 40

Ho ho Metresse *Ione* (quoth hee) be Got, you be angry. Oh Metresse *Ione*, bee no chafe with you friene for noting.

Good sir (quoth she) keepe your friendship for them that cares for it, and fixe your loue on those that can like you, as for mee I tell you plain, I am not minded to marry.

Oh tis no matter for marrye, if you will come in my chamber, beshit my bed, and let mee kisse you.

The Maide though she were very much displeased, yet at these words, shee could not forbeare laughing for her life.

Ah ah Metresse *Ione* : mee is very glad to see you merrie, holde your hand I say, and there is foure Crowne because you laugh on mee.

I pray you Sir keepe your Crownes, for I need them not.

Yes be Got you shal haue them Metresse *Ione*, to keepe in
10 a pox for you.

Shee that could not well vnderstand his broken language, mistooke his meaning in many things : & therfore wild him not to trouble her any more.   Notwithstanding such was his loue toward her, that he could not forbeare her company, but made many iournies thither for her sake.   And as a certaine spring in *Arcadia* makes men to starue that drinke of it : so did poore *Bennedicke*, feeding his fancy on her beauty : for when he was in *London*, he did nothing but sorrow, wishing he had wings like the monsters of *Tartaria*, that he might fly to and fro at his pleasure.   When any
20 of his friends did tell her of his ardent affection toward her, shee wisht them to rub him with the sweat of a Mule, to asswage his amorous passion, or to fetch him some of the water in *Boetia*, to coole & extinguish the heate of his affection : for (quoth she) let him neuer hope to be helpt by me.

Well (quoth they) before he saw thy alluring face, he was a man reasonable and wise, but is now a starke foole, being by thy beauty bereft of wit, as if hee had drunk of the riuer *Cea*, & like bewitching *Circes* thou hast certainely transformed him from a man to an Asse.   There are stones in *Pontus* (quoth they) that the deeper
30 they be laid in the water, the fiercer they burn : vnto the which fond Louers may fitly be compared, who the more they are denyed, the hotter is their desire : but seeing it is so, that he can find no fauour at your hand, wee will shew him what you haue said, and eyther draw him from his dumpes, or leaue him to his owne will.

Then spake one of the Weauers that dwelt in the Towne, and was a kinsman to this maide, I muse (quoth he) that master *Bennedicke* will not bee perswaded, but like the Moath, will play with the flame that will scortch his wings.   Mee thinkes, hee should for-
40 beare to loue, or learne to speake, or else woo such as can answer him in his language : for I tell you, that *Ione* my kinswoman, is no taste for an Italian.

These speeches were told to *Bennedicke* with no small addition. When our yongue marchant heard the matter so plaine, he vowed to be reuenged of the Weauer, and to see if hee could finde any more friendship of his wife : therefore dissembling his sorrow and couering his griefe, with speede hee tooke his iourney to *Newberie*, and pleasantly saluted Mistresse *Ione* : and hauing his purse full

of crownes, he was very liberall to the workefolkes, especially to
Iones kinsman, insomuch that hee got his fauour many times to
goe forth with him, promising him very largely to doe great matters,
and to lend him a hundred pound, wishing him to bee a seruant no
longer, beside he liberally bestowed on his wife many gifts, and if
she washt him but a band, he would giue her an Angell : if hee
did but send her childe for a quart of Wine, hee would giue him
a shilling for his paines. The which his courtesie changed the
Weauers minde, saying he was a very honest Gentleman, and
worthy to haue one farre better than his kinswoman.   10

This pleased master *Bennedick* well to heare him say so, notwithstanding he made light of the matter, and many times when
the Weauer was at his Masters at worke, the Merchant would be
at home with his wife, drinking and making merry. At length
time bringing acquaintance, and often conference breeding familiarity, master *Bennedick* began somewhat boldly to iest with *Gillian*,
saying that her sight and sweet countenance, had quite reclaymed
his loue from *Ione*, and that she onely was the mistresse of his
heart : and if she would lend him her loue, he would giue her
golde from *Arabia*, orient pearles from *India*, and make her 20
bracelets of most precious Diamonds. Thy garments shall be of
the finest silke that is made in *Venice*, and thy purse shall still be
stuft with Angels. Tell me thy minde my loue, and kill mee not
with vnkindnesse, as did thy scornefull kinswoman, whose disdaine
had almost cost me my life.

O master *Bennedicke*, thinke not the wiues of *England* can be
won by rewards, or enticed with fayre words, as children are with
Plums : it may be that you being merrily disposed, do speak this
to try my constancy. Know then, that I esteeme more the honour
of my good name, than the slyding wealth of the world.   30

Master *Bennedick* hearing her say so, desired her, that considering it was loue that forced his tongue to bewray his hearts
ardent affection, that yet she would be secret : and so for that time
tooke his leaue.

When hee was gone, the woman began to call her wits together,
and to consider of her poore estate, and withall the better to note
the comelinesse of her person, and the sweet fauour of her face :
which when shee had well thought vpon, shee began to harbour
new thoughts, and to entertaine contrary affections, saying, Shall
I content myselfe to be wrapt in sheepes russet that may swim in 40
silks, & sit all day carding for a groat, that can haue crownes at my
command ? No (quoth she) I will no more beare so base a minde,
but take Fortunes fauours while they are to be had. The sweet
Rose doth flourish but one moneth, nor Womens beauties but in
yongue yeares. As the Winters frost consumes the Summer
flowers, so doth old age banish pleasant delight. O glorious gold
(quoth shee) how sweet is thy smell ? how pleasing is thy sight ?
Thou subduest Princes, and ouerthrowest kingdomes, then how

should a silly woman withstand thy strength? Thus she rested meditating on preferment, purposing to hazzard her honesty to maintaine her selfe in brauerie : euen as occupiers corrupt their consciences to gather riches.

Within a day or two master *Bennedicke* came to her againe, on whom she cast a smiling countenance: which hee perceiuing (according to his old custome) sent for Wine, and very merry they were. At last, in the middest of their cups, he cast out his former question : and after farther conference, she yeelded, and appointed 10 a time when he should come to her : for which fauour, he gaue her halfe a dozen portigues.

Within an houre or two after, entring into her owne conscience, bethinking how sinnefully she had sold her selfe to folly, began thus to expostulate. Good Lord (quoth shee) shall I breake that holy vowe which I made in marriage, and pollute this body of mine which the Lord hath sanctified ? Can I breake the commandement of my God, and not rest accursed ? or be a traytor to my husband, & suffer no shame ? I heard once my brother read in a book, that *Bucephalus*, *Alexanders* Steed, being a beast, 20 would not be backt by any but the Emperour, and shall I consent to any but my husband ? *Artemisa* being a Heathen Lady, loued her husband so well, that shee drunke vp his ashes, and buried him in her owne bowels, and should I, being a Christian, cast my Husband out of my heart ? The Women of *Rome* were wont to crowne their Husbands heads with Bayes, in token of victorie, and shall I giue my husband hornes in token of infamie ? An Harlot is hated of all vertuous minded people, and shall I make my selfe a Whore ? O my God forgiue my sin (quoth shee) and cleanse my heart from these wicked imaginations.

30 And as she was thus lamenting, her husband came home : at whose sight her teares were doubled, like vnto a riuer whose streame is encreased by showers of raine. Her husband seeing this, would needes know the cause of her sorrow : but a great while she would not shew him, casting manie a piteous looke vpon him, and shaking her head, at last she said, O my deare husband, I haue offended against God and thee, and made such a trespasse by my tongue, as hath cut a deepe scarre in my conscience, and wounded my heart with griefe like a Sword : like *Penelope* so haue I been wooed, but like *Penelope* I haue not answered.

40 Why woman (quoth he) what is the matter ? If it be but the bare offence of thy tongue, why shouldest thou so grieue ? considering that womens tongues are like Lambs tayles, which seldome stand still : And the Wise man saith, Where much talke is, must needes be some offence. Womens beauties are fayre markes for wandring eyes to shoote at : but as euery Archer hits not the white, so euery Wooer winnes not his mistresse fauour. All Cities that are besiged are not sackt, nor all women to be mislikt that are loued. Why wife, I am perswaded thy faith is more firme, and thy constancie

greater to withstand Louers alarums, than that any other but my selfe should obtaine the fortresse of thy heart.

O sweet husband (quoth she) we see the strongest Tower, at length falleth downe by the Canons force, though the Bullets be but Iron : then how can the weake Bulwarke of a Womans breast make resistance, when the hot Canons of deepe perswading wordes are shotte off with golden Bullets, and euery one as big as a Portigue?

If it be so wife, I may think my selfe in a good case, and you to be a very honest woman. As *Mars* and *Venus* danc't naked together in a Net, so I doubt, you and some knaue haue played naked together in a bed : but in faith thou queane, I will send thee to salute thy friends without a Nose : and as thou hast sold thy honesty, so will I sell thy company.

Sweete Husband, though I haue promised, I haue performed nothing : euery bargain is not effected, and therefore as *Iudas* brought again the thirty siluer plates, for the which he betrayed his Master : so repenting my folly, Ile cast him againe his gold, for which I should haue wronged my Husband.

Tell me (quoth her husband) what he is.

It is master *Bennedicke* (quoth shee) which for my loue haue left the loue of our kinswoman, and hath vowed himselfe for euer to liue my seruant.

O dissembling Italian (quoth hee) I will be reuenged on him for this wrong. I know that any fauour from *Ione* our kinswoman, will make him runne like vnto a man bitten with a mad dogge : therefore be ruled by mee, and thou shalt see me dresse him in his kinde.

The woman was very well pleased, saying, hee would be there that night.

All this works well with me (quoth her husband) and to supper will I inuite *Ione* my kinswoman, and in the mean space make vp the bed in the Parlour very decently.

So the goodman went forth, and got a sleepy drench from the Poticaries, the which he gaue to a yongue Sow, which hee had in his yard, and in the euening layde her downe in the bed in the Parlour, drawing the Curtaines round about.

Supper time beeing come, master *Bennedicke* gaue his attendance, looking for no other company but the good wife : Notwithstanding at the last mistresse *Ione* came in with her kinsman, and sate downe to supper with him.

Master *Bennedicke* musing at their sudden approach, yet neuerthelesse glad of mistresse *Iones* company, past the supper time with many pleasant conceits, *Ione* shewing her selfe that night more pleasant in his company than at any time before : wherefore he gaue the good man great thankes.

Good master *Bennedicke*, little doe you think how I haue trauelled in your behalfe to my kinswoman, and very much adoe I had to bring the peeuish Wench into any good liking of your loue : notwithstanding by my very great diligence and per-

swasions, I haue at length won her good will to come hither, little
thinking to finde you here, or any such good cheere to entertain
her : all which I see is fallen out for your profite.   But trust me,
all the world cannot now alter her minde, nor turne her loue from
you : In regard whereof, shee hath promised me to lye this night
in my house, for the great desire she hath of your good company :
and in requitall of all your great courtesies shewed to me, I am
very well content to bring you to her bed.   Marry this you must
consider, and so she bad me tell you, that you should come to
10 bed with as little noyse as you could, and tumble nothing that
you find, for feare of her best gowne and her hat, which she will
lay hard by the bed side, next her best partlet, and in so doing,
you may haue company with her all night, but say nothing in any
case till you be a bed :

O (quoth he) Mater *Ian*, be Got Mater *Ian*, me wil not spoile
her clothes for a towsand pound, ah me loue metres *Ione* more
than my wife.

Well, supper being done, they rose from the table.   Master
Bennedick imbracing mistresse *Ione*, thankt her for her great
20 curtesie and company, and then the good man and he walkt
into the Towne, and *Ione* hyed her home to her masters, knowing
nothing of the intended iest.   Master *Bennedicke* thought euery
houre twaine, till the Sun was downe, and that he were a bed
with his beloued.   At last he had his wish, and home hee came
to his friends house.

Then said *Iohn*, master *Bennedick* you must not in any case
haue a candle when you go into the chamber, for then my kinswoman will be angry, and darke places fits best Louers desires.

O Mater *Ian* (quoth he) its no such matter for light, mee
30 shall find Metres *Ione* well enough in the darke.

And entring in the parlour, groping about, hee felt a gowne and
hat.   O Metres *Ione* (quoth hee) heere is your gowne and hat,
me shal no hurt for a tousand poun.

Then kneeling downe by the bed side, insteade of mistresse
Ione, he saluted the sow in this sort.   O my loue and my delight,
it is thy faire face that hath wounded my heart, thy gray sparkling
eyes, and thy Lilly white hands, with the comely proportion of thy
pretty body, that made mee in seeking thee to forget my selfe, &
to find thy fauour, lose my owne freedom : but now is the time
40 come wherein I shall reape the fruits of a plentifull haruest.   Now
my deare, from thy sweet mouth let mee sucke the hony balme of
thy breath, and with my hand stroke those Rosie cheekes of
thine, wherein I haue tooke such pleasure, Com with thy
pretty lips and entertaine me into thy bed with one gentle kisse :
Why speakest thou not my sweete heart, and stretch out thy
Alabaster armes to infold thy faithfull friend ?   Why should ill
pleasing sleepe close vp the chrystall windowes of thy body so
fast, and bereaue thee of thy fiue Lordly attendants wherewith

thou wast wont to salute thy friends? let it not offend thy gentle eares that I thus talk to thee. If thou hast vowed not to speake, I will not break it: and if thou wilt command me to bee silent, I will be dumbe: but thou needest not feare to speak thy minde, seeing the cloudy night concealeth euery thing.

By this time master *Bennedicke* was vnready, and slipt into bed, where the Sowe lay swathed in a sheete, and her head bound in a great linnen cloth: As soone as he was laid, he began to embrace his new bedfellow, and laying his lips somewhat neer her snout, hee felt her draw her breath very short. 10

Why how now loue (quoth he) be you sick, be Got mistris *Ione* your breat be very strong: haue you no cacke a bed?

The Sow feeling her selfe disturbed, began to grunt and keep a great stirre: whereat master *Benedick* (like a mad man) ran out of the bed, crying, de deuil de deuil. The good man of the house (being purposely prouided) came rushing in with halfe a dozen of his neighbours, asking what was the matter.

Got ound (quoth *Benedicke*) here be de great deuil cry hoh, hoh, hoh, bee Gossen I tinke you play the knave wid me, and me wil be reuenge be Got. 20

Sir (quoth hee) I knowing you loued mutton, thought porke nothing vnfit: & therefore prouided you a whole Sow, and as you like this entertainment, spend Portegues. Walke, walk, *Barkeshire* maides will be no Italians strumpets, nor the wiues of *Newbery* their bauds.

Barkeshire dog (quoth *Benedick*) owle face shack hang dou and dy veife, haue it not be for me loue to sweete Metresse *Ione*, I will no come in your houz: but farewell tell I cash you, be Goz bode, I make your hog nose bud.

The good man and his neighbours laught aloud, away went 30 master *Benedick*, and for very shame departed from *Newbery* before day.

Chap. VIII.

How *Iacke* of *Newberie* keeping a very good house, both for his seruants and reliefe of the poore, won great credite thereby: and how one of his wiues gossips found fault therewith.

GOod morrow good Gossip: now by my truly I am glad to see you in health. I pray you how doth master *Winchcombe*? What neuer a great belly yet? now fie: by my fa your 40 husband is waxt idle.

Trust mee Gossip (saith mistresse *Winchcombe*) a great belly comes sooner than a new coate: but you must consider we haue not beene long married: But truely gossip you are welcome:

I pray you to sit downe, and we will haue a morsell of something by and by.

Nay truely gossip, I cannot stay (quoth shee) in troth I must be gone : for I did but euen step in to see how you did.

You shall not chuse but stay a while (quoth mistresse *Winchcomb*) : and with that a faire napkin was laide vpon the little table in the Parlour, hard by the fire side, whereon was set a good cold Capon, with a great deale of other good cheere, with ale and wine plentie.

10   I pray you good Gossip eate, and I beshrew you if you spare (quoth the one).

I thanke you hartily good Gossip (saith the other). But good gossip I pray you tell me : doth your husband loue you well, and make much of you ?

Yes truly, I thanke God (quoth shee).

Now by my troth (said the other) it were a shame for him if he should not : for though I say it before your face, though he had little with you, you were worthy to be as good a mans wife as his.

20   Trust me, I would not change my *Iohn* for my lord Marquesse (quoth shee) a woman can be but well, for I liue at hearts ease, & haue all things at will, & truly he will not see me lack any thing.

Mary Gods blessing on his hart (quoth her Gossip) it is a good hearing : but I pray you tell me, I heard say, your husband is chosen for our Burgesse in the Parliament house, is it true ?

Yes verily (quoth his wife) : I wis it is against his will : for it will be no small charges vnto him.

Tush woman, what talke you of that ? thankes be to God, there is neuer a Gentleman in all *Barkshire* that is better able to beare it. But heare you, gossip, shall I bee so bold to aske you one question more ?

30   Yes, with all my heart (quoth she).

I heard say that your husband would now put you in your hood and silke gowne, I pray you is it true ?

Yes in truth (quoth mistresse *Winchcombe*) but far against my minde Gossip : my french-hood is bought already, and my silke gowne is a making : likewise the Goldsmith hath brought home my chaine and bracelets : but I assure you gossip, if you will beleeue me, I had rather goe an hundred miles, than weare them : for I shall bee so ashamed that I shall not looke vpon any of my neighbours for blushing.

40   And why, I pray you ? (quoth her Gossip) I tell you deare woman, you neede not bee any thing abashed or blush at the matter, especially seeing your husbands estate is able to maintaine it : now trust mee truly, I am of opinion you will become it singular well.

Alas (quoth mistresse *Winchcombe)* hauing neuer beene vsed to such attyre, I shall not know where I am, nor how to behaue my selfe in it : and beside, my complexion is so blacke, that I shall carry but an ill fauoured countenance vnder a hood.

Now, without doubt (quoth her Gossip) you are to blame to say so : beshrew my heart if I speak it to flatter, you are a very faire and well fauoured yongue woman, as any is in *Newberie.* And neuer feare your behauiour in your hood : for I tell you true, as old and withred as I am my selfe, I could become a hood well enough, and behaue my selfe as well in such attyre, as any other whatsoeuer, and I would not learne of neuer a one of them all : what woman, I haue been a pretty wench in my dayes, and seene some fashions. Therefore you neede not to feare, seeing both your beauty and comely personage deserues no lesse than a french- 10 hood : and be of good comfort. At the first (possible) folkes will gaze something at you : but bee not you abashed for that, it is better they should wonder at your good fortune, than lament at your misery : but when they haue seene you two or three times in that attyre, they will afterward little respect it : for euery new thing at the first seemes rare, but being once a little vsed, it growes common.

Surely Gossip you say true, (quoth shee) and I am but a foole to bee so bashfull : it is no shame to vse Gods gifts for our credits, and well might my husband thinke me vnworthy to haue them, if I would not weare them : and though I say it, my hoode is a faire 20 one, as any woman weares in this Country, and my gold chaine and bracelets are none of the worst sort, and I will shew them you, because you shall giue your opinion vpon them : and therewithall shee stept into her chamber and fetcht them forth.

When her Gossip saw them, shee said, now beshrew my fingers but these are faire ones ʻindeede. And when doe you meane to weare them Gossip ?

At Whitsontide (quoth shee) if God spare mee life.

I wish that well you may weare them (said her Gossip) and I would I were worthy to bee with you when you dresse your selfe, 30 it should bee neuer the worse for you. I would order the matter so, that you should set euery thing about you in such sort, as neuer a Gentlewoman of them all should staine you.

Mistris *Winchcombe* gaue her great thanks for her fauour, saying, that if she needed her helpe, she would be bold to send for her.

Then began her Gossip to turne her tongue to another tune, and now to blame her for her great house keeping. And thus shee began : Gossip, you are but a yongue woman, and one that hath had no great experience of the World, in my opinion you are something too lauish in expences : pardon mee good Gossip, I 40 speake but for good will ; and because I loue you, I am the more bold to admonish you : I tell you plaine, were I the mistresse of such a house, hauing such large allowance as you haue, I would saue 20. pound a yeare that you spend to no purpose.

Which way might that bee (quoth Mistris *Winchcombe* ?) indeed I confesse I am but a greene huswife, and one that hath had but small triall in the World, therefore I would bee very glad to learne any thing that were for my husbands profit and my commoditie.

Then listen to mee (quoth shee) : You feede your folkes with the best of the beefe, and the finest of the wheate, which in my opinion is a great ouersight : neither doe I heare of any Knight in this countrie that doth it.   And to say the truth, how were they able to beare that port which they doe, if they saued it not by some meanes ?   Come thither, and I warrant you that you shall see but browne bread on the boord : if it bee wheate and rye mingled together, it is a great matter, and the bread highly commended : but most commonly they eate eyther barly bread, or rye mingled with pease, and such like course graine : which is doubtlesse but of small price, and there is no other bread allowed, except at their owne boord.   And in like manner for their meate : it is well knowne, that neckes and points of beefe is their ordinarie fare : which because it is commonly leane, they seeth therewith now and then a peece of bacon or porke, whereby they make their pottage fat, and therewith driues out the rest with more content.   And thus must you learne to doe.   And beside that, the midriffes of the Oxen, and the cheekes, the sheepes heads, and the gathers, which you giue away at your gate, might serue them wel enough : which would bee a great sparing to your other meate, and by this meanes you would saue in the yeare much mony, whereby you might the better maintaine your hoode and silke gowne.   Againe, you serue your folkes with such superfluities, that they spoile in a manner as much as they eate : beleeue mee were I their Dame, they should haue things more sparingly, and then they would thinke it more dainty.

Trust mee Gossip (quoth Mistresse *Winchcombe*) I know your wordes in many things to bee true : for my folkes are so corne fed, that wee haue much adoo to please them in their dyet : one doth say this is too salt, and another saith this is too grosse, this is too fresh, and that too fat, and twenty faults they will finde at their meales : I warrant you they make such parings of their cheese, and keepe such chipping of their bread, that their very ortes would serue two or three honest folkes to their dinner.

And from whence I pray you proceedes that (quoth her Gossip) but of too much plentie ? but yfaith were they my seruants, I would make them glad of the worst crummes they cast away, and thereupon I drink to you, and I thank you for my good cheere with all my heart.

Much good may it do you good gossip (said mistresse *Winchcomb*) : and I pray you when you come this way, let vs see you.

That you shall verily (quoth she) and so away she went.

After this, mistresse *Winchcombe* tooke occasion to giue her folks shorter commons, and courser meate than they were wont to haue : which at length being come to the good mans eare, hee was very much offended therewith, saying : I will not haue my people thus pincht of their victualls.   Empty platters makes greedy stomackes, and where scarcity is kept, hunger is nourished : and therefore wife as you loue mee, let mee haue no more of this doings.

Husband (quoth shee) I would they should haue enough : but it is sinne to suffer, and a shame to see the spoile they make : I could bee very well content to giue them their bellies full, and that which is sufficient, but it grieues mee, to tell you true, to see how coy they are, and the small care they haue in wasting of things : and I assure you, the whole Towne cries shame of it, and it hath bred mee no small discredit for looking no better to it. Trust mee no more, if I was not chekt in my owne house about this·matter, when my eares did burne to heare what was spoken.

Who was it that chekt thee, I pray thee tell mee ? was it not your old gossip, dame dainty, mistresse trip and goe ? I beleeue it was.

Why man if it were she, you know shee hath beene an old house-keeper, and one that hath known the World, and that shee told mee was for good will.

Wife (quoth hee) I would not haue thee to meddle with such light braind huswiues, and so I haue told thee a good many times, and yet I cannot get you to leaue her company.

Leaue her company ? why husband, so long as she is an honest woman, why should I leaue her company ? She neuer gaue me hurtfull counsell in all her life, but hath alwaies been ready to tell mee things for my profit, though you take it not so. Leaue her company ? I am no gyrle I would you should well know, to bee taught what company I should keepe : I keepe none but honest company, I warrant you. Leaue her company ketha ? Alas poore soule, this reward shee hath for her good will. I wis, I wis, she is more your friend, than you are your owne.

Well, let her bee what shee will (said her husband) : but if shee come any more in my house, she were as good no. And therefore take this for a warning I would aduise you : and so away he went.

Снар. IХ.

How a Draper in *London*, who owed *Iacke* of *Newbery* much mony, became bankrout, whom *Iack* of *Newbery* found carrying a porters basket on his neck, and how he set him vp againe at his owne cost, which Draper afterward became an Alderman of *London*.

THere was one *Randoll Pert* a Draper, dwelling in *Watling-streete*, that owed *Iacke* of *Newbery* fiue hundred pounds at one time, who in the end fell greatly to decay, in so much that hee was cast in prison, and his wife with her poore children turned out of doores. All his creditors except *Winchcombe* had a share of his goods, neuer releasing him out of prison, so long as he had one peny to satisfie them.   But when this tidings was brought to *Iack* of *Newberies* eare, his friends counselled him to lay his action against him.

Nay (quoth he) if hee be not able to pay me when he is at liberty, he will neuer be able to pay mee in prison : and therefore it were as good for me to forbear my mony without troubling him, as to adde more sorrow to his grieued heart, and be neuer the neerer.   Misery is troden down by many, and once brought low,
10 they are seldome or neuer relieued : therefore he shall rest for me vntoucht, and I would to God he were cleare of all other mens debts, so that I gaue him mine to begin the world againe.

Thus lay the poore Draper a long time in prison, in which space, his Wife which before for daintinesse would not foule her fingers, nor turne her head aside, for feare of hurting the set of her neckenger, was glad to goe about and wash buckes at the Thames side, and to be a chare-woman in rich mens houses, her soft hand was now hardened with scouring, and in steade of gold rings vpon her lilly fingers, they were now fild with chaps,
20 prouoked by the sharpe lee, and other drudgeries.

At last, Master *Winchcombe* being (as you heard) chosen against the Parliament a Burgesse for the towne of *Newberie*, and comming vp to *London* for the same purpose, when hee was alighted at his Inne, hee left one of his men there, to get a Porter to bring his trunke vp to the place of his lodging.   Poore *Randoll Pert*, which lately before was come out of prison, hauing no other meanes of maintenance, became a Porter to carry burthens from one place to another, hauing an old ragged doublet, and a torne paire of breeches, with his hose out at the heeles, and a paire of old
30 broken slip shooes on his feete, a rope about his middle in stead of a girdle, and on his head an old greasie cap, which had so many holes in it, that his haire started through it : who assoone as hee heard one call for a Porter, made answer straight : heere master, what is it that you would haue carried ?

Mary (quoth hee) I would haue this Trunke borne to the *spread Eagle* at *Iuiebridge.*

You shall Master (quoth hee) but what will you giue mee for my paines ?

I will giue thee two pence.
40 A penny more and I will carry it (said the Porter) : and so being agreed, away he went with his burthen, till he came to the *spread Eagle* doore, where on a sudden espying Master *Winchcombe* standing, he cast downe the Trunke, and ran away as hard as euer hee could.

Master *Winchcombe* wondring what hee meant thereby, caused his man to runne after him, and so fetch him againe : but when hee saw one pursue him, hee ranne then the faster ; and in running, here hee lost one of his slip shooes, and then another :

euer looking behinde him, like a man pursued with a deadly weapon, fearing euery twinkling of an eye to bee thrust thorow. At last his breech, being tide but with one point, what with the haste hee made, and the weakenesse of the thong, fell about his heeles : which so shackled him, that downe hee fell in the streete all along, sweating and blowing, being quite worne out of breath : and so by this meanes the Seruing-man ouertooke him, and taking him by the sleeue, being as windlesse as the other, stood blowing and puffing a great while ere they could speake one to another.

Sirrah (quoth the Seruing man) you must come to my Master, you haue broken his Trunke all to peeces, by letting it fall.

O for Gods sake (quoth hee) let me goe, for Christs sake let mee goe, or else Master *Winchcombe* of *Newbery* will arrest mee, and then I am vndone for euer.

Now by this time *Iacke* of *Newbery* had caused his Trunke to bee carried into the house, and then he walked along to know what the matter was : and when he heard the Porter say that he would arrest him, hee wondred greatly, and hauing quite forgot *Perts* fauour, being so greatly changed by imprisonment and pouerty, hee said, Wherefore should I arrest thee ? tell me good fellow : for my owne part I know no reason for it.

O Sir (quoth hee) I would to God I knew none neyther.

Then asking him what his name was : the poore man falling downe on his knees, said : Good Master *Winchcombe* beare with me and caste mee not into prison : my name is *Pert*, and I do not deny but that I owe you fiue hundred pound : yet for the loue of God take pitty vpon mee.

When Master *Winchcombe* heard this, hee wondred greatly at the man, and did as much pitty his misery, though as yet hee made it not known, saying : Passion of my heart man, thou wilt neuer pay mee thus : neuer thinke being a Porter to pay fiue hundred pound debt. But this hath your prodigality brought you to, your thriftlesse neglecting of your businesse, that set more by your pleasure than your profit. Then looking better vpon him, he said : What, neuer a shooe to thy foote, hose to thy legge, band to thy necke, nor cap to thy head ? O *Pert*, this is strange : but wilt thou be an honest man, & giue me a bil of thy hand for my money ?

Yes sir, with all my hart (quoth *Pert*).

Then come to the Scriueners (quoth he) and dispatch it, and I will not trouble thee.

Now when they were come thither, with a great many following them at their heeles, master *Winchcombe* said : Hearest thou Scriuener ? this fellow must giue me a bill of his hand for fiue hundred pounds, I pray thee make it as it should bee.

The Scriuener looking vpon the poore man, and seeing him in that case, said to master *Winchcombe* : Sir, you were better to let it bee a Bond, and haue some sureties bound with him.

Why Scriuener (quoth hee) doest thou thinke this is not a sufficient man of himselfe for fiue hundred pound?

Truely Sir (said the Scriuener) if you thinke him so, you and I are of two mindes:

Ile tell thee what (quoth Master *Winchcombe*) were it not that wee are all mortall, I would take his word assoone as his Bill or Bond; the honesty of a man is all.

And wee in *London* (quoth the Scriuener) doe trust Bonds farre better than honesty. But Sir, when must this money bee paid?

10 Marry Scriuener, when this man is Sheriffe of *London*.

At that word the Scriuener and the people standing by laughed heartily, saying: In truth Sir, make no more adoo but forgiue it him: as good to doe the one as the other.

Nay, beleeue mee (quoth hee) not so: therefore doe as I bid you.

Whereupon the Scriuener made the Bill to be paid when *Randoll Pert* was Sheriffe of *London*, and thereunto set his owne hand for a witnesse, and twenty persons more that stood by, set to their hands likewise.

20 Then hee asked *Pert* what he should haue for carrying his trunk.

Sir (quoth hee) I should haue three pence, but seeing I finde you so kinde, I will take but two pence at this time.

Thankes good *Pert* (quoth he) but for thy three pence, there is three shillings: and looke thou come to mee to morrow morning betimes.

The poore man did so, at what time master *Winchcombe* had prouided him out of *Burchin-lane*, a faire sute of apparell, Mar-chant like, with a faire blacke cloak, and all other things fit to the

30 same: then hee tooke him a shop in *Canweek streete*, and furnisht the same shop with a thousand pounds worth of cloath: by which meanes, and other fauours that master *Winchcombe* did him, hee grew againe into great credit, and in the end became so wealthy, that while master *Winchcombe* liued hee was chosen Sheriffe, at what time he payed fiue hundred pounds euery penny, and after dyed an Alderman of the Citie.

Chap. X.

How *Iacke* of *Newberies* seruants were reuenged of their Dames tattling Gossip.

40 VPon a time it came to passe, when master *Winchcombe* was farre from home, and his wife gone abroad: That mistris many better, dame tittle, tattle, Gossip pintpot, according to her old custome, came to mistris *Winchcombes* house, perfectly knowing

of the good mans absence, and little thinking the good wife was
from home : where knocking at the gate, *Tweedle* stept out and
askt who was there ? where hastily opening the wicket, he suddainely discouered the full proportion of this foule beast, who
demanded if their mistris were within.

What mistres *Franke* (quoth hee) in faith welcome : how haue
you done a great while ? I pray you come in.

Nay, I cannot stay (quoth shee). Notwithstanding, I did call to
speake a word or two with your mistris, I pray you tell her that
I am here.   10

So I will (quoth hee) so soone as she comes in.

Then said the woman, What is she abroad ? why then farewell
good *Tweedle.*

Why what haste, what haste, mistris *Franke,* (quoth he) I ·pray
you stay and drink ere you goe. I hope a cuppe of new Sacke will
do your old belly no hurt :

What (quoth shee) haue you new Sacke already ? Now by my
honesty I drunke none this yeare, and therefore I doe not greatly
care if I take a taste before I goe : and with that shee went into
the wine-cellar with *Tweedle,* where first hee set before her a peece 20
of powdred beefe as greene as a leeke : And then going into the
kitchen, he brought her a peece of rosted beefe hote from the spit.

Now certaine of the maidens of the house, and some of the
yongue men, who had long before determined to bee reuenged of
this pratling huswife : came into the Cellar one after another, one
of them bringing a great peece of a gammon of Bacon in his hand :
and euery one bad mistris *Franke* welcome : and first one drunke
to her, and then another, and so the third, the fourth, and the
fift : so that mistresse *Frankes* braines waxt as mellow as a Pippin
at Michaelmas, and so light, that sitting in the Cellar, she thought 30
the world ran round.   They seeing her to fall into merry humours,
whetted her on in merriment as much as they could, saying,
Mistresse *Franke,* spare not I pray you, but thinke your selfe as
welcome as any woman in all *Newberie,* for we haue cause to loue
you, because you loue our Mistresse so well.

Now by my troth (quoth shee) lisping in her speech (her tongue
waxing somewhat too big for her mouth) I loue your Mistresse
well indeed, as if shee were mine owne daughter.

Nay but heare you (quoth they) she begins not to deale well
with vs now.   40

No my Lambs (quoth shee) why so ?

Because (quoth they) she seeks to barre vs of our allowance,
telling our Master, that hee spends too much in house-keeping.

Nay then (quoth shee) your Mistresse is both an Asse, and
a Foole : and though shee go in her Hood, what care I ? she is
but a girle to mee : Twittle twattle, I know what I know : Go too,
drinke to mee. Well *Tweedle,* I drinke to thee with all my heart :
why thou horeson, when wilt thou bee married ? O that I were

a yongue wench for thy sake : but tis no matter, though I be but a poore woman, I am a true woman.   Hang dogs, I haue dwelt in this towne these thirty winters.

Why then (quoth they) you haue dwelt heere longer than our Master.

Your Master (quoth shee) ? I knew your Master a boy, when he was calld *Iacke* of *Newberie*, I *Iacke*, I knew him calld plaine *Iacke* : and your Mistresse, now shee is rich, and I am poore, but its no matter, I knew her a draggle tayle girle, marke yee?

10   But now (quoth they) shee takes vpon her lustily, and hath quite forgot what shee was.

Tush, what will you haue of a greene thing (quoth shee)? Heere I drinke to you, so long as she goes where she list a gossipping : and its no matter, little said is soone amended : But heare you my masters, though mistresse *Winchcombe* goe in her Hood, I am as good as shee, I care not who tell it her : I spend not my husbands money in Cherries and Codlings, go too, go too, I know what I say well enough : I thanke God I am not drunke : Mistresse *Winchcomb*, mistresse ? No, *Nan Winchcombe*, I will call her

20 name, plaine *Nan* : what, I was a woman when she was sir-reuerence a paltry girle, though now shee goes in her Hood and Chaine of Gold : what care I for her ? I am her elder, and I know more of her trickes : nay I warrant you, I know what I say, tis no matter, laugh at me and spare not, I am not drunke I warrant : and with that being scant able to holde open her eyes, she be-ganne to nodde, and to spill the Wine out of the Glasse : which they perceyuing, let her alone, going out of the Cellar till shee was sound asleepe, and in the meane space they deuised how to finish this peece of knauery.

30   At last they all consented to lay her forth at the backe side of the house, halfe a mile off, euen at the foote of a Style, that who-soeuer came next ouer, might finde her : notwithstanding, *Tweedle* stayed hard by to see the end of this Action.   At last comes a notable Clowne from *Greeneham*, taking his way to *Newbery* : who comming hastily ouer the Style, stumbled at the woman, and fell down cleane ouer her.   But in his starting vp, seeing it was a woman, cryed out, Alas, alas.

How now, what is the matter (quoth *Tweedle*)?

O (quoth hee) here lies a dead woman.

40   A dead woman (quoth *Tweedle*) thats not so I trow, and with that hee tumbled her about :

Bones of me (quoth *Tweedle*) tis a drunken woman, and one of the Towne vndoubtedly : in troth it is a great pitty she should lye here.

Why doe you know her (quoth the Clowne)?

No not I (quoth *Tweedle*) neuerthelesse, I will giue thee halfe a groate, and take her in thy Basket, and carry her throughout the Towne, and see if any body know her.

Then said the other, let me see the money, and I will : For by the Masse, che earnd not halfe a groat this great while.

There it is (quoth *Tweedle*) : then the fellow put her in his Basket, and so lifted her vpon his back.

Now by the Masse shee stinkes vilely of Drinke, or Wine, or some thing. But tell me, What shall I say when I come into the Towne (quoth he)?

First (quoth *Tweedle*) I would haue thee so soone as euer thou canst get to the Townes end, with a lusty voyce to cry, O yes, and then say, Who knowes this woman, who? And though possible 10 some will say, I know her, and I know her; yet doe not thou set her downe till thou commest to the Market Crosse, and there vse the like wordes : and if any be so friendly, to tell thee where shee dwels, then iust before her doore cry so againe : and if thou performe this brauely, I will giue thee halfe a groat more.

Master *Tweedle* (quoth he) I knowe you well enough, you dwell with Master *Winchcombe*, doe you not? Ifaith if I doe it not in the nicke, giue mee neuer a penny :

And so away hee went, till hee came to the Townes end, and there he cryes out as boldly as any Bayliffes man, O yes, who 20 knowes this woman, who?

Then said the drunken woman in the Basket, her head falling first on one side, and then on the other side, Who co mee, who?

Then said he againe, Who knowes this woman, who?

Who co mee, who? (quoth shee) and looke how oft he spoke the one, shee spoke the other : saying still, Who co me, who co me, who? Whereat all the people in the streete fell into such a laughter, that the teares ranne downe againe.

At last one made answere, saying : Good fellow, shee dwels in the *North brooke street*, a little beyond Master *Winchcombes*. 30

The fellow hearing that, goes downe thither in all haste, and there in the hearing of a hundred people, cryes, Who knowes this woman, who?

Whereat her husband comes out, saying : Marry that doe I too well, God helpe mee.

Then said the Clowne, If you know her, take her : for I knowe her not but for a drunken beast.

And as her husband tooke her out of the Basket, she gaue him a sound boxe on the eare, saying, What you Queanes, do you mocke mee? and so was carried in. 40

But the next day, when her braine was quiet, and her head cleered of these foggy vapours, she was so ashamed of her selfe, that shee went not forth of her doores a long time after : and if any body did say vnto her, Who co me, who? shee would be so mad and furious, that shee would be ready to draw her knife and sticke them, and scold, as if she stroue for the best game at the cucking stoole. Moreouer, her pratling to mistresse *Winchcombes* folks of their mistresse, made her on the other side to fall out

with her, in such sort, that shee troubled them no more, eyther
with her company or her counsell.

Chap. XI.

How one of *Iacke* of *Newberies* maides
became a Ladie. `

AT the winning of *Morlesse* in *France*, the noble Earle of
Surrey being at that time Lord high Admirall of *England*,
made many Knights: among the rest was Sir *George Rigley*,
brother to Sir *Edward Rigley*, and sundry other, whose valours
10 farre surpassed their wealth: so that when peace bred a scarcitie
in their purse, and that their credits grew weake in the Citie, they
were enforced to ride into the Country, where at their friends
houses they might haue fauourable welcome, without coyne or
grudging.

Among the rest, *Iacke* of *Newberie* that kept a table for all
commers, was neuer lightly without many such guestes: where
they were sure to haue both welcome and good cheare, and their
mirth no lesse pleasing than their meate was plenty. Sir *George*
hauing lyen long at boord in this braue Yeomans house, at length
20 fell in liking of one of his maidens, who was as fair as she was
fond. This lusty wench hee so allured with hope of marriage,
that at length she yeelded him her loue, and therewithall bent her
whole study to worke his content: but in the end, shee so much
contented him, that it wrought altogether her owne discontent:
to become high, she laid her selfe so low, that the Knight
suddenly fell ouer her, which fall became the rising of her belley.
But when this wanton perceiued her selfe to be with childe, she
made her moane vnto the Knight in this manner.

Ah Sir *George*, now is the time to performe your promise, or to
30 make me a spectacle of infamy to the whole world for euer: in
the one you shal discharge the duety of a true knight, but in the
other shew your selfe a most periured person. Small honour will
it bee to boast in the spoyle of poore maydens, whose innocencie
all good Knights ought much rather to defend.

Why thou lewd paltry thing (quoth he) commest thou to father
thy bastard vpon me? Away ye dunghill carrion, away: Heare
you good huswife, get you among your companions, and lay your
litter where you list: for if you trouble mee any more, by heauen
I sweare, thou shalt dearely abide it: and so bending his browes
40 like the angry god of war, he went his wayes, leauing the childe-
breeding wench to the hazzard of her fortune, eyther good or bad.

This poore mayden seeing her selfe for her kindnesse thus cast
off, shedde many teares of sorrow for her sinne, inueighing, with

many bitter groanes, against the vnconstancie of loue alluring men. But in the end, when shee saw no other remedy, shee made her case knowne vnto her mistresse: who after she had giuen her many bitter checks and tants, threatning to turne her out of doores, shee opened the matter to her husband.

So soone as he heard thereof, hee made no more to doe, but presently poasted to *London* after Sir *George*, and found him at my Lord Admirals. What, master *Winchcombe* (quoth he) you are heartily welcome to *London*, and I thanke you for my good cheere. I pray you how doth your good wife, and all our friends 10 in *Barkshire*?

All well and merry, I thanke you good Sir *George* (quoth hee): I left them in health, and I hope they doe so continue. And trust me sir (quoth he) hauing earnest occasion to come vp to talke with a bad debtor, in my iourney it was my chance to light in company of a gallant widow: a Gentlewoman shee is, of wondrous good wealth, whom griesely death hath bereft of a kinde husband, making her a widow, ere she had been halfe a yeare a wife: her land, Sir *George*, is as well worth a hundred pound a yeare as one penny, being as faire and comely a creature, 20 as any of her degree in our whole countrey: Now sir, this is the worst, by the reason that she doubts her selfe to be with childe, she hath vowed not to marry these twelue moneths: but because I wish you well, and the Gentlewoman no hurt, I came of purpose from my businesse to tell you thereof: Now Sir *George*, if you thinke her a fit wife for you, ride to her, wooe her, winne her, and wedde her.

I thanke you good master *Winchcombe* (quoth he) for your fauour euer toward me, and gladly would I see this yongue widow if I wist where. 30

She dwelleth not halfe a mile from my house (quoth master *Winchcombe*) and I can send for her at any time if you please.

Sir *George* hearing this, thought it was not best to come there, fearing *Ioane* would father a childe vpon him, and therefore answered, hee had no leisure to come from my Lord: But (quoth he) would I might see her in *London*, on the condition it cost me twenty nobles.

Tush sir *George* (quoth Master *Winchcombe*) delayes in loue are dangerous, and he that will wooe a widow, must take time by the forelocke, and suffer none other to steppe before him, lest hee 40 leape without the widowes loue. Notwithstanding, seeing now I haue told you of it, I will take my Gelding and get me home: if I heare of her comming to *London*, I will send you word, or perhaps come my selfe: till when, adiew good Sir *George*.

Thus parted master *Winchcombe* from the Knight: and being come home, in short time he got a fair Taffety gowne, and a French hood for his mayde, saying: Come ye drabbe, I must be fayne to couer a foule fault with a fayre garment, yet all will not hide your great belly : but if I finde meanes to make you a Lady, what will you say then ?

O Master (quoth shee) I shall be bound while I liue to pray for you.

Come then minion (quoth her mistresse) and put you on this gowne and french hood : for seeing you haue lien with a.Knight, you must needs be a Gentlewoman.

The mayde did so : and being thus attyred, shee was set on a fayre Gelding, and a couple of men sent with her vp to *London*: and being well instructed by her master and dame what she should doe, she tooke her iourny to the Citie in the Tearme time, and lodged at the *Bell* in the *Strand*: and mistresse *Louelesse* must be her name, for so her Master had warned her to call her selfe : Neyther did the men that wayted on her, know the contrary ; for master *Winchcombe* had borrowed them of their Maister, to wayte vpon a friend of his to *London*, because hee could not spare any of his owne seruants at that time : notwithstanding, they were appointed for the Gentlewomans credite, to say they were her owne men. This being done, master *Winchcombe* sent Sir *George* a letter, that the Gentlewoman which he told him of, was now in *London*, lying at the *Bell* in the *Strand*, hauing great businesse at the Tearme.

With which newes Sir *Georges* heart was on fire, till such time as he might speake with her : three or foure times went he thither, and still she would not be spoken withall, the which close keeping of her selfe, made him the more earnest in his suite.

At length hee watcht her so narrowly, that finding her going forth in an euening, hee followed her, shee hauing one man before, and another behinde : carrying a verie stately gate in the streete, it droue him into the greater liking of her, being the more vrged to vtter his minde. And suddenly stepping before her, hee thus saluted her, Gentlewoman, God saue you, I haue often beene at your lodging, and could neuer finde you at leasure.

Why sir (quoth shee) (counterfeiting her naturall speech) haue you any businesse with me ?

Yes faire Widow (quoth hee) as you are a clyent to the law, so am I a sutor for your loue : and may I finde you so fauourable to let mee pleade my owne case at the barre of your beauty, I doubt not but to vnfold so true a tale, as I trust will cause you to giue sentence on my side.

You are a merry Gentleman (quoth shee) : but for my owne part, I know you not ; neuerthelesse, in a case of loue, I will bee no let to your sute, though perhaps I helpe you little therein. And therefore Sir, if it please you to giue attendance at my lodging, vpon my returne from the *Temple*, you shall know more of my minde, and so they parted.

Sir *George* receiuing hereby some hope of good happe, stayed for his deare at her lodging doore : whom at her comming shee friendly greeted, saying, Surely Sir, your diligence is more than the profit you shall get thereby: but I pray you how shall I call your name?

George Rigley (quoth hee) I am called, and for some small deserts I was knighted in *France*.

Why then Sir *George* (quoth shee) I haue done you too much wrong to make you thus dance attendance on my worthlesse person. But let mee bee so bold to request you to tell mee, how you came to know mee: for my owne part I cannot remember that euer I saw you before. 10

Mistris *Louelesse* (said Sir *George*) I am well acquainted with a good neighbour of yours, called Master *Winchcombe*, who is my very good friend, and to say the truth, you were commended vnto mee by him.

Truly sir *George* (said shee) you are so much the better welcome: Neuerthelesse, I haue made a vowe not to loue any man for this twelue moneths space. And therefore Sir, till then I would wish you to trouble your selfe no further in this matter till that time be expired: and then if I finde you bee not intangled to any other, and that by triall I finde out the truth of your loue, for 20 Master *Winchcombs* sake your welcome shall be as good as any other Gentlemans whatsoeuer.

Sir *George* hauing receiued this answer, was wonderous woe, cursing the day that euer he meddled with *Ioane*, whose time of deliuerance would come long before a twelue Moneth were expired, to his vtter shame, and ouerthrow of his good fortune: for by that meanes should hee haue Master *Winchcombe* his enemy, and therewithall the losse of this faire Gentlewoman. Wherefore to preuent this mischiefe, hee sent a Letter in all haste to Master *Winchcombe*, requesting him most earnestly to 30 come vp to *London*, by whose perswasion hee hoped straight to finish the marriage. Master *Winchcombe* fulfilled his request, and then presently was the marriage solemnized at the Tower of *London*, in presence of many Gentlemen of Sir *Georges* friends. But when hee found it was *Ioane* whom he had gotten with childe, hee fretted and fumed, stampt, and star'd like a diuell.

Why (quoth M. *Winchcombe*) what needs all this? Came you to my table to make my maide your strumpet? had you no mans house to dishonour but mine? Sir, I would you should well know, that I account the poorest wench in my house too good to 40 bee your whore, were you ten knights: and seeing you tooke pleasure to make her your wanton, take it no scorne to make her your wife: and vse her well too, or you shall heare of it. And hold thee *Ioane* (quoth hee) there is a hundred pounds for thee: And let him not say thou camest to him a begger.

Sir *George* seeing this, and withall casting in his minde what friend Master *Winchcombe* might bee to him, taking his wife by the hand, gaue her a louing kisse, and Master *Winchcombe* great thankes. Whereupon hee willed him for two yeares space to take his dyet and his Ladies at his house: which the Knight accepting, rode straight with his wife to *Newberie.*

Then did the Mistris make curtsie to the Maide, saying: You are welcome Madam, giuing her the vpper hand in all places.

And thus they liued afterward in great ioy: and our
King hearing how *Iacke* had matcht Sir *George*,
laughing heartily thereat, gaue him a
liuing for euer, the better to
10   maintaine my Lady
his Wife.

F I N I S.

The Gentle Craft.

A
DISCOURSE

Containing many matters of Delight, very
pleasant to be read:

shewing what famous men have been S H O O-
M A K E R S in time past in this Land, with
their worthy deeds and great Hospitality.

Set forth with Pictures, and variety of Wit and Mirth.

Declaring the cause why it is called the G E N T L E
C R A F T : and also how the Proverb first grew.

A Shoomakers Son is a Prince born. **T. D.**

With gentlenesse judge you,
At nothing here grudge you;
   The merry Shoomakers delight in good sport.
What here is presented,
Be therewith contented;
   And as you do like it, so give your report.

Haud curo invidiam.

LONDON, Printed for *John Stafford*, and are to be sold at his
house in Saint *Brides* Church-yard. 1 6 4 8.

To all the good Yeomen of the
GENTLE CRAFT.

YOu that the Gentle Craft professe, list to my words both
   more and lesse;
And I shall tell you many things, of worthy and renowned
   Kings,
And diuers Lords and Knights also, that were Shoomakers long
   a goe;
Some of them in their distresse, delighted in this businesse;
And some, for whom great wait was laid, did saue their liues
   by this same trade:
Other some, in sport and game, delighted much to learne the
   same.
No other Trade in all the Land, they thought so fit vnto their
   hand;
For euermore they stil did find that shoomakers bore a gallant 10
   mind:
Men they were of high conceit, the which wrought many a merry
   feat;
Stout of courage were they still, and in their weapons had great
   skill,
Trauellers by sea and land, each Country guise to vnderstand.
Wrong they wrought not any man, with reason all things did
   they scan:
Good houses keept they euermore, releeuing both the sicke and
   poore.
In law no mony would they spend, their quarrels friendly would
   they end.
No malice did they beare to any, but shew'd great fauour vnto
   many;
Offences soone they would forgiue, they would not in contention
   liue;
Thus in ioy they spent their dayes, with pleasant songs and
   roundelayes,
And God did blesse them with content; sufficient for them He 20
   sent;
And neuer yet did any know, a Shoomaker abegging goe:
Kind are they one to another, vsing each stranger as his brother.
Thus liu'd Shoomakers of old, as ancient Writers haue it told:
And thus Shoomakers still would be, so fame from them shall
   neuer flee.

To all courteous Readers, health.

HOw Saint *Hugh* was son vnto the renowned king of *Powis*,
a noble Brittaine borne, who in the prime of his yeares
loued the faire virgin *Winifred*, who was the only daughter of
Donwallo, which was the last king that euer reigned in *Tegina*,
which is now called *Flint-shire*. But she refusing all offers of
loue, was only pleased with a religious life. Her father was sent
to *Rome*, and died ; whose Lady left her life long before. This
Virgin therefore, forsook her fathers Princely Palace in *Pont Varry*,
10 and made her whole abiding in the most sweet pleasent valley of
Sichnaunt, and liued there solitarily and carelesse of all company
or comfort. It chanced that in Summers heat, this faire Virgin
being greatly distressed for lack of drink, and not knowing where
to get any, there sprang vp suddenly a Christall stream of most
sweet and pleasant water out of the hard ground, whereof this
Virgin did daily drink : vnto the which God himselfe gaue so
great a vertue, that many people, hauing beene washed therein,
were healed of diuers and sundry infirmities wherewith they were
borne. Moreouer, round about this Well where this Virgin did
20 vse to walke, did grow a kind of Mosse which is of a most sweet
sauour, and the colour thereof is as fresh in Winter as in Summer,
so that lying thereon, you would suppose yourselfe to be on a bed
of Down perfumed with most precious odours.

And what of all this ; Marry, read the booke and you shall
know ; but read nothing except you read all. And why so ?
Because the begining shews not the middle, and the middle shews
not the latter end.

And so farewell.

The pleasant History of S. *Hugh*; and first

of all, his most constant loue to
the faire Virgin *Winifred*.

Onquering and most imperious Loue, hauing seized on the
heart of young Sir *Hugh*, all his wits were set on worke, how
for to compasse the loue of the faire Virgin *Winifred*, whose disdain was the chiefe cause of his care, hauing receiued many
infinite sorrows for her sake: but as a streame of water being
stopt, ouerfloweth the bank, so smothered desire doth burst out
into a great flame of fire, which made this male-contented Louer 10
to seeke some meanes to appease the strife of his contentious
thoughts, whereupon he began to encourage himselfe:

Tush *Hugh*, let not a few froward words of a woman dismay
thee; for they loue to be intreated, and delight to be wooed,
though they would make the world beleeue otherwise: for their
denyals proceed more of nicenesse then niggardlinesse, refusing
that they would fainest haue. What if sometimes *Winifred* frown
on thee? yet her fauours may exceed her frowardnesse. The
Sunne is sometimes ouercast with clouds so that his brightnesse
is not seen. In wars the sorer the fight is, the greater is the glory 20
of the victory; and the harder a woman is to be won, the sweeter
is her loue when it is obtained: wherefore Ile once againe try my
fortune, and see what successe my sute shall find.

On this resolution sir *Hugh* returned to *Winifred*, greeting her
thus. Now faire Lady, hauing slept away the remembrance of
your sharp answers; I come againe in a new conceit, to reuiue an
old sute, and to see if the change of the day will yeeld a change
of dolours.

Truly Sir *Hugh* (quoth shee) if with the change of the day you
haue changed your opinion: your dolour will be driuen away well 30
enough: but as touching your suite, it shall be needlesse to
repeate it, because I am not willing to preferre it.

Stay there (quoth Sir *Hugh*) I will preferre it, so that you will
accept it.

Now (quoth she) I will accept it, if you will preferre it, in sending
it back to the place from whence it proceeded, and I would to
God I could send you away as soone as your suite.

Why then belike I am not welcome (said Sir *Hugh*).

Yes (quoth shee) as welcome to me, as a storme to a distressed
Mariner. I muse greatly that reason will not rule you, nor words 40
win you from your wilfulnesse: if you were as weary to wooe as I
am weary to heare you, I am perswaded that long since you would

haue ceased your vain suite. You think by these perswasions to turn my opinion; but as well you may think that you may quench fire with oyle: therefore I pray you, good Sir *Hugh*, be not so tedious vnto me, nor troublesome to your selfe.

Come, come (quoth he) all this will not serue your turn, ponder with thy selfe *Winifred*, that thou art faire, O that thou wert as fauourable; thy beauty hath bound me to be thy seruant, and neuer to cease, till I see another obtaine thee, or my selfe be possessed of my hearts content. Thou art a Kings daughter, and
10 I a Princes sonne, staine not the glory of true Nobility with the foule sin of obstinacy, but be thou as kind as thou art courtly, and gentle as thou art noble, and then shall our strife soone end.

Winifred perceiuing that the further off she was to grant loue, the more eager he was to desire it, shifted him off thus: Sir, although your ouerhastinesse driue me into the greater doubtfulnesse, yet let me intreat you, if you loue me, to giue me one months respite to consider on this matter, and it may be that vpon my better deliberation it shall be pleasing vnto you, and not at all discontent me.

20 Faire loue (quoth he) far be it from my heart to deny so kind a request; I am content to stay a month from thy sight, were it two or three, vpon condition, that thou wouldest then grant me thy good will; three months, although it be very long, yet it will come at last, and I could be content for that time to be dead for thy sake, insomuch that my life might be renewed by thy loue.

Nay (quoth *Winifred*) stay three months and stay foreuer: by this a Maid may see how ready men are vpon a light occasion to take long daies, whose loues are like a Fernebush, soone set one fire, and soone consumed: and seeing it is so, in faith Sir *Hugh*,
30 I doe meane to try you better before I trust you.

Pardon me faire *Winifred* (said Sir *Hugh*) if my tongue doe outslip my wit: in truth I speak but to please thee, though to displease my selfe; but I pray thee, let it not be three houres, nor three quarters of an houre, if thou wilt.

Nay, nay (quoth she) your first word shall stand: after three months come to me a gaine, and then you shall know my mind to the full, and so good Sir *Hugh* be gone: but if I doe euer heare from thee, or see thee betwixt this time and the time prefixed, I will for euer hereafter blot thy name out of my booke of Re-
40 membrances and neuer yeeld thee that courtisie which thou at this time so earnestly intreatest for.

Sir *Hugh* vpon these words departed betwixt hope and dread, much like to a man committing a trespasse, that stayed for the sentence of life or death.

O vnhappy man (quoth he) how hath my ouer slippery tongue lengthened the time of my sorrow? She of her selfe most courteously requested of me but one months stay, and I most willingly and vndiscreetly added thereto eight weeks more of misery, much like the Hind that hauing a knife giuen him to paire his nailes, did therewith murder himselfe. Now I could wish that the Sun had Eagles wings, swiftly to fly through the faire firmament, and finish six dayes in one dayes time.

With that he began to count the dayes and houres that were in three months, falling (in a manner) to dispaire with himselfe when he found them so many in number : and therewithall melancholily and sadly he went to his Fathers house, where his brother *Griffith* found by his countenance the perfect map of a pensiue louer : whereupon he said vnto him. 10

Why, how now brother? Hath *Winifreds* faire beauty so greatly wounded you, as you cannot speak a merry word to your freind, but sit in a corner, as if you were tonguelesse like a Stork ? Tush brother, women are like shaddowes, for the more a man follows them, the faster they run away : but let a man turn his course, and then they will presently follow him. What, man ? pluck vp a good heart, for there are more women now, then liued in the time of our old father *Adam*.

O (said *Hugh*) were there ten thousand times more then there are now, what were that to me, if *Winifred* be vnkinde ? Yet is 20 she the oyle that still maintaines the lamp of my light, and without her there is nothing comfortable to my sight.

Then (replyed *Griffith*) you are as much troubled in loue, as a Goat in an ague, and as blind as a Flie in October, that will stand still while a man cuts of his head, Come, goe ahunting with me, that will driue away your ouerfond conceits, and you shall see that these three months will come vpon you as a quarterday vpon a poore man that hath neuer a penney ready towards the payment of his rent.

CHAP. II. 30

How beautiful *Winifred* being ouer-much superstitious, forsook her fathers wealth, and liued poorely by a springing Fountain, from whence no man could get her to go; which Spring to this day is called *Winifreds* Well.

WInifred, who had but of late yeeres with her own father receiued the Christian Faith, became so superstitious, that she thought the wealth of the world for euer would haue been an heauy burthen for her soule, and haue drawne her mind from the loue of her Maker ; wherefore forsaking all manner of earthly 40 pomp, she liued a long time very poorely, hard by the side of a most pleasant, springing Well ; from which place neither her friends by intreaty, nor her foes by violence could bring her ; which

13. Stork] *1648 and all copies* stock ; but see Note.

Sir *Hugh* hearing, he went thither immediately after vnto her, which was the time limited by them both, and finding her mind altogether altered, he wondered not a little what she meant.   And when he approached near vnto the place where she sate, all suted in simple attire, he saluted her with these words.

All health to faire *Winifred*: I trust (my Deare) that now the Destinies haue yeelded a conuenient opportunity for me to finish my long begun sute, with the end of my former sorrowes.   Long and tedious hath the winter of my woes beene, which with nipping
10 care hath blasted the beauty of my youthfull delight, which is like neuer again to flourish, except the bright Sunshine of thy fauour doe renew the same : therefore (fair Loue) remember thy promise made vnto me, and put me no more off with vnpleasing delayes.

She (which all this while sat solemnly reading in her booke) lent little eare vnto his words ; which he perceiuing, pluckt her by the arme, saying : Wherefore answereth not my faire Loue to her dearest perplexed friend ?

What would you haue (quoth she ?)   Can I neuer be quiet for you ?   Is there no corner of content in this world to be found ?
20   Yes *Winifred* (said he) content dwels here or no where ; content me, and I will content thee.

If my content may be thy content, then read this book, and there rest content (said *Winifred*) and if thou refuse this, then think not to find content on earth.

Sir *Hugh* replied, What, is this all the reward I shall haue for obeying your heart-cutting commandment.   Haue I thus long hoped, and find no better hap ?   You wot well that it is now three long months since these eyes took comfort of thy beauty, and since that time that my bleeding heart hath receiued ioy in thy great
30 gentlenesse.

I haue forgot you quite (said she) ; what three moneths is that you speak of ?   For my part, I assure you that it is as far out of my mind as you are from the mount of *Calvary*.

Faire *Winifred* (quoth he) haue you forgotten me, and there-withall my Loue which was so effectually grounded vpon your good liking ?   You told me, that now I should receiue an answer to my content.

O Sir (quoth she) you haue stayed ouer-long, and your words are in my hearing as vnprofitable as snow in haruest ; my loue is
40 fled to heauen, from whence no earthly man can fetch it, and therefore build not on vain hope, nor do thou deceiue thy selfe by following an vnprofitable suit ; if euer I loue earthly man, it shall be thee, insomuch as thou hast deserued an earthly Ladies loue ; but my loue is settled for euer, both in this world, and in the world to come : and this I most earnestly intreat thee to take for a finall answer.

With that Sir *Hugh* turning his head a side, wept most bitterly, and in going a way he glanced his eye still back again after his

Loue, saying to himselfe: O vnconstant women, wauering and vncertain, how many sorrows are fond men drawn into by your wily inticements? who are also swallowed vp in the gaping gulf of care, while they listen after the heart-liking sound of your inchanting voices. O *Winifred*, full little did I think that so hard a heart could haue been shrowded vnder so sweet and louing a countenance: but, seeing that my good will is thus vnkindly requited, I will altogether abhor the sight of women, and I will seek the world throughout, but I will find out some blessed plot, where no kind of such corrupt cattell do breed. 10

Hereupon all in a hot hasty humour he made preparation for to go beyond the Seas, suiting himselfe after the nature of a melancholly man; and arriuing in *France*, he took his iourney towards *Paris*, which City (at that time) was well replenished with many goodly faire women, as well as *Britain*, though to his thinking nothing so louely, but neuerthelesse what they wanted in beauty, they had in brauery: which when Sir *Hugh* saw, he suddenly departed from that place, counting it the most pernicious place in the whole Countrey; and from thence he went into *Italy*, where he found such stately Dames and louely Ladies, whom nature had 20 adorned with all perfection of outward beauty, whose sight put him again in remembrance of his faire Loue, which, like fresh fuell newly augmented the flame of his burning desire, O (said he) how vnhappy am I to be haunted by these heart tormenting fiends, bewitching the eyes of simple men with Angel-like faces, and, like enchanting *Circes*, bringing them to a labyrinth of continuall woes.

O *Winifred*, thy peeuishnesse hath bred my dangers, and done thy selfe no good at all. Thou sitest weeping by a Christall streame, where is no need of water, while I wander vp and down, 30 seeking to forget thee; thou neuer remembrest me, hauing drawn the fountaine of mine eyes dry through thy discourteous disdain. Might I neuer see any of thy sex, my heart would be more at quiet, but euery place where I come puts me in mind of thy perfections, and therewithall renews my pain: but I will from hence as soon as possible I can, though not so soon as I would for feare lest these sweet Serpents should sting me to death with delight.

Hereupon he passed on so far, that at length he came to a City situated in the Sea, and compassed with the wild Ocean. Here (quoth sir *Hugh*) is a fit place for melancholly men; where it is 40 supposed no women do liue, insomuch that their delicate bodies cannot abide the salt sauour of the mounting waues: if it be so, there will I make my residence, counting it the most blessed place vnder heauen. But he was no sooner set on land, but he beheld whole troops of louely Ladies passing vp and down in most sumptuous attire, framing their gestures answereable to their beauties and comly personages.

Nay, now I see (quoth Sir *Hugh*) that the whole world is

infected with these deceiuing Syrens and therfore in vain it is for
me to seek for that I shall neuer find ; and therwithal sought for
some house wherein he might hide himself from them.   But, by
that time he was set to supper, comes a crue of Courtlike Dames
richly attired, and with wanton eyes and pleasent speech they
boldly sate down by him ; and perceiuing him to be a stranger,
they were not strange to allure him to their delight : wherefore
while he sat at meat, they yeelded him such mirth as their best
skill could afford ; and stretching their nimble fingers, playing on
10 their sweet sounding Instruments, they sang this ensuing song
with such cleare and quauering voices, as had been sufficient to
allure chast-hearted *Xenocrates* vnto folly ; and stil as they did
sing, Sir *Hugh* answered in the last line, insomuch as it seemed to
be a Dialogue between them ; and in this manner following, the
women began their song.

The Curtizans song of Venice.

Ladies. *Welcome to* Venice, *gentle courteous Knight,*
　　　　Cast off care, and entertain content.
　　　　If any here be gracious in thy sight,
20　　　　*Do but request, and she shall soon content:*
　　　　Loues wings are swift, then be not thou so slow ;
Hugh.　　*Oh that faire* Winifred *would once say so.*

Ladies. *Within my lap lay down thy comely head,*
　　　　And let me stroke those golden locks of thine,—
　　　　Looke on the teares that for thy sake I shed,
　　　　And be thou Lord of any thing is mine,—
　　　　One gentle looke vpon thy Loue bestow,—
Hugh.　　*Oh that faire* Winifred *would once say so.*

Ladies. *Embrace with ioy thy Lady in thine armes,*
30　　　　*And with all pleasures passe to thy delight :*
　　　　If thou doest think the light will work our harmes,
　　　　Come, come to bed, and welcome all the night ;
　　　　There shalt thou find what Louers ought to know,
Hugh.　　*Oh that faire* Winifred *would once say so.*

Ladies. *Giue me those pearles as pledges of thy Loue,*
　　　　And with those pearles the fauour of thy heart,—
　　　　Do not from me thy sugred breath remoue,
　　　　That double comfort giues to euery part :
　　　　Nay stay Sir Knight, from hence thou shalt not go.
40 Hugh.　*Oh that faire* Winifred *would once say so.*

　　When Sir *Hugh* had heard this song, and therewithall noted
their wanton gestures, he began to grow suspitious of their proffers,
and, thinking in himselfe, that either they sought his destruction,

43. sought *1675 &c.*: thought *1648*

as the Syrens did to *Vlysses* ; or that they intended to make
a prey of his purse, as *Lais* did of her louers : and therefore supposing some Adder to lie lurking vnder the fair flowers of his
proffered pleasures, he determined the next morning after (with
speed) to depart from the City. So when he had with good discretion auoided their company, while he lay tormented with
restlesse thoughts on his still tossed bed, began thus to meditate.

Now I wel see mine own vanity, that is as ill pleased with
womens fauor as their frowns ; how often haue I with heart sighing sorrow complained of womens vnkindnesse, making large 10
inuectiues against their discourtesies ?   And yet here where I find
women as kind as they are faire, and courteous as they are comely,
I runne into a world of doubts, and so suspitious of their faire
proffers, as I was earnest to winne *Winifreds* fauour.   It may be
(quoth he) that it is the nature of this gentle soyle to breed as kinde
creatures, as the Country of *Brittaine* breeds coy Dames.

Vndoubtedly, had my loue first taken life in this kind and
courteous Climate, she would haue beene as kind as they.   If
I mis-iudge not of their gentlenesse, because I haue alwayes beene
inured to scornfulnesse ; methinks they are too faire to be harlots, 20
and too bold to be honest ; but as they haue no cause to hate me
that neuer hurt them, so haue they little cause to loue me, being
a far stranger born, to them a man altogether vnknown.

But it may be that this time of the yeere is onely vnfortunate
for Louers ; as it is certainly known to all men, that euery season
of the yeere breeds a sundrie commoditie ; for Roses flourish in
June, and Gilly flowers in August, and neuer of them both doth
so in the cold Winter.   Such as seek for fruit on the saplesse trees
in the moneth of Ianuary, lose their labours as well as their longing : then why should I couet to gather fruits of loue, when I see 30
that loue is not yet ripe ?   Now let me obserue the season that
yeelds the sweetest comfort of loue-sick persons, and so I may
reape the ioyfull fruits of hearts content : I will therefore return
to my former Loue, hopeing now to find her as friendly, as at my
departure she was froward : I will once againe intreat her, and
speak her exceeding faire ; for with many drops the hardest stone
is pierc'd ; so also with many importunate intreaties a flinty heart
may be moued to some remorse.   I take no pleasure at all in any
place, but onely in her presence, with the which she continually
graceth a running streame ; far be it from her minde to kisse her 40
own shadow in the Chrystall spring, and to be in loue with her
own similitude ; for so she might be spoiled as *Narcissus* was : for
it is commonly seene, that sudden dangers follows fond opinions.

So with this and the like thoughts he droue out the night till
the Suns bright eye began to peep at his chamber window, at
which time dressing himselfe, he went to the water side, where he
found a ship ready to transport rich merchandize into the western
Ilands, in the which Sir *Hugh* became a passenger.   But when

they were put off to Sea, there arose so sudden a storme, and
of long continuance, that no man looked for life, but expected
euery moment present death, so that the Mariners quite forsooke
the tackle, and the Master the helme, committing themselues to
God, and their ship to the mercy of the swelling Seas, by whose
furious waues they were sometime tossed vp towards heauen, anon
thrown down to the deep of hell. In which extremity Sir *Hugh*
made this lamentation :

O vnhappy man, how eagerly doth mischance pursue me at my
10 heels ; for betwixt my Loue on the land, and danger of life on
the Sea, it hath made me the wretchedst man breathing on
earth.

Here we may see that miseries haue power ouer men, and not
men ouer miseries. Now must I die far from my friends and
be drenched in the deepe, where my body must feed the fishes
that swim in the rich bottom of the Sea. Therefore faire *Winifred,*
the chiefe ground of my griefs, here will I sacrifice my last teares
vnto thee, and poure forth my complaints.

O how happy should I count my selfe, if those fishes which
20 shall liue on my bodies food, might be meat for my Loue ! It
grieueth me much to think that my poore bleeding heart, wherein
thy picture is engrauen, should be rent in pieces in such greedie
sort ; but thrice accursed be that fish that first seteth his nimble
teeth thereon, except he swim therewith vnto my Loue, and so
deliuer it as a present token from me.

Had my troubled stars allotted me to leaue my life in the
pleasant valley of *Sichnant,* then no doubt but my Loue with her
faire hands would haue closed vp my dying eyes, and perhaps
would haue rung a peal of sorrowfull sighs for my sake.

30 By this time was the weather beaten Bark driuen by the shore of
Sicilie, where the men had safety of their liues, although with losse
of the ship, and spoile of their goods : but they had no sooner
shaken off their dropping wet garments on the shore, but that they
were asaulted by a sort of monstrous men that had but one eye
apiece, and that placed in the midst of their foreheads, with whom
the tempest-beaten Souldiers had a firce fight, in which many of
them were slain, and diuers of them fled away to saue themselues ;
so that in the end Sir *Hugh* was left alone to Fortune in a double
fray : and hauing at last quite ouercome all his aduersaries, he
40 went his way, and was so far entered into the dark wildernesse,
that he could not deuise with himselfe which way he should take
to get out, where he was so cruelly affrighted with the dreadfull
cry of fierce Lyons, Beares, and wilde Bulls, and many thousand
more of other dangerous and cruell, rauenous Beasts, which with
greedy mouthes ranged about for their prey, in which distresse
Sir *Hugh* got him vp into the top of a tree, and, being there, brake
out into this passion :

O Lord (quoth he) hast Thou preserued me from the great

perill and danger of the Sea, and deliuered me out of the cruell hands of monstrous men, and now sufferest thou me to be deuoured of wild beasts ? Alas, that my foule sins should bring so many sundrie sorrows on my head.

But for all this may I thank vnkinde *Winifred*, whose disdain hath brought my destruction. Wo worth the time that euer my eyes beheld her bewitching beauty. But hereby we may see that the path is smooth that leadeth to danger. But why blame I the blamelesse Lady ? Alas, full little did she know of my desperate courses in trauell. But such is the fury that hants 10 frantick Louers, that neuer feare danger vntill it fall, and light vpon their own heads.

But by that time that the day began to appeare, he perceiued an huge Elephant with stiffe joynts stalking towards him, and presently after came a fiery-tongue Dragon, which suddenly assaulted the peacefull Elephant in whose subtle encounter the wrathfull Dragon with his long, wringing taile did so shackle the hinder feet of the Elephant together, that, like a prisoner fast fettered in irons, he could not stir a foot for his life : what time the furious Dragon neuer left till he had thrust his slender head 20 into the Elephants long hooked nose, out of which he neuer once drew it, vntill by sucking the Elephants blood, he had made him so feeble and so weak, that he could stand no longer vpon his feet ; at which time the fainting Elephant with a greiuous cry, fel down dead vpon the Dragon : so with the fall of his weightie body burst the Dragon in peices, and so killed him ; whereby their bloods being mingled together, it stain'd all the ground where they both lay, changing the green grasse into a rich scarlet colour.

This strange fight betwixt these two beasts caused good Sir *Hugh* to iudge that Nature had planted betwixt them a deadly 30 hatred, the fire whereof could not be quenched but by shedding of both their hearts blood. Now when Sir *Hugh* saw that grim death had ended their quarrell, and perceiuing no danger neare, he came down from the tree, and sought to find out some inhabited Town : but being intangled in the woods, like the Centaure in his Labirinth, he could by no meanes get out, but wandred in vnknown passages leading him to many perils.

At last another Elephant met him, who according to his kind nature neuer left him till he had conducted him out of all danger, and brought him out of the Wildernesse into the way again ; 40 wherby sir *Hugh* at the length came in sight of a Post-town, where in foure dayes after he imbarked himselfe in a ship bound for *Brittaine*, and at last obtained the sight of his natiue Countrey, where he arriued in safetie, though in very poore sort, coming on shore at a place called *Harwich*, where for want of money he greatly lamented. And made much moan. But meeting with a merry Iourneyman-shoomaker dwelling in that town, and after some conference had together, they both agreed to trauell in the Countrey,

where we will leaue them, and speake of *Winifred*, and of her
great troubles and calamities.

Chap. III.

How faire *Winifred* was imprisoned, and condemned to
die for her religion: and how Sir *Hugh* became a
Shoomaker, and afterwards came to suffer death with
his Loue: showing also how the Shoomakers tools
came to be called Saint *Hughs* bones, and the trade of
shoo-making; *The Gentle Craft*.

10 ANon after that the doctrine of Christ was made known in
Brittaine, and that the worship of heathen Idols was forbidden, yet many troubles did the Christians endure by the
outragious bloodthirstinesse of diuers woluish Tyrants, that by the
way of inuasion set footing in this Land, as it fell out in the
dayes of *Dioclesian*, that with bloody minds persecuted such as
would not yeeld to the Pagan Law: amongst which the Virgin
Winifred was one, who, for that she continued constant in faith,
was long imprisoned.

During which time, Sir *Hugh* wrought in a shoomakers shop,
20 hauing learned that trade, through the courteous directions of
a kind Iourneyman, where he remained the space of one whole
yeere, in which time he had gotten himselfe good apparell, and
euerything comely and decent.   Notwithstanding though he were
now contented to forget his birth, yet could hee not forget the
beauty of his Loue: who although she had vtterly forsaken him,
yet could he not alter his affections from her, because, indeed
affections alter not like a pale-faced coward.   The wildest Bull
(quoth he) is tamed being tied to a Fig-tree, and the coyest Dame
(in time) may yeeld like the stone Charchædonis, which sparkles
30 like fire, and yet melts at the touch of soft wax.   Though Roses
haue prickles, yet they are gathered ; and though women seem
froward, yet they will shew themselues kind and friendly.   Neither
is there any wax so hard but, by often tempering, is made apt to
receiue an impression.   Admit she hath heretofore been cruell,
yet now may she be courteous.   A true hearted Louer forgets all
trespasses, and a smile cureth the wounding of a frown.   Thus,
after the manner of fond Louers, he flattered himselfe in his own
folly, and in the praise of his faire Ladie he sang this pleasant
Dity here following :

40   *The pride of* Brittain *is my hearts delight,*
           My Lady liues, my true loue to requite :
           And in her life I liue, that else were dead,
           Like withered leaues in time of Winter shed.

She is the ioy and comfort of my mind,
She is the sun that clearest sight doth blind,
The fairest flower that in the world doth grow,
Whose whitnesse doth surpasse the driuen snow.

Her gentle words more sweet than honey are,
Her eyes for clearnesse dims the brightest star.
O, were her heart, so kind as she is faire,
No Lady might with my true loue compare.

A thousand griefs for her I haue sustained,
While her proud thoughts my humble suit disdained 10
And though she would my heart with torments kill,
Yet would I honour, serue and loue her still.

Blest be the place where she doth like to liue:
Blest be the light that doth her comfort giue:
And blessed be all creatures farre and near,
That yeeld relief vnto my Lady dear.

Neuer may sorrow enter where she is,
Neuer may she contented comfort misse,
Neuer may she my proffered loue forsake;
But my good will in thankfull sort to take. 20

Thus feeding his fancy with the sweet remembrance of her beauty, being neuer satisfied with thinking and speaking in her praise, at length he resolued himselfe to go into *Flint-shire,* where he might sollicite his suit anew again : but coming neere to the place of her residence ; and hearing report of her troubles, he so highly commended her faith and constancy, that at length he was clapt vp in prison by her, and in the end he was condemned to receiue equall torment, for a triall of his own truth.

But during the time that they lay both in prison, the Iourneymen Shoomakers neuer left him, but yeelded him great reliefe 30 continually, so that he wanted nothing that was necessarie for him, in requital of which kindnesse he called them Gentlemen of the *Gentle Craft,* and a few dayes before his death, he made this song in their due commendations.

Of Craft and Crafts-men, more and lesse,
The Gentle Craft *I must commend*
Whose deeds declare their faithfulnesse,
And hearty loue vnto their friend:
The Gentle Craft, *in midst of strife,*
Yeelds comfort to a carefull life, 40

A Prince by birth I am indeed,
The which for Loue forsook this Land;
And when I was in extreme need,
I took the Gentle Craft *in hand,*

And by the Gentle Craft *alone,*
  Long time I liu'd being still vnknown,

Spending my dayes in sweet content,
  With many a pleasant, sugred Song:
Sitting in pleasures complement,
  Whilst we recorded Louers wrong:
And while the Gentle Craft *we vs'd,*
  True Loue by vs was not abus'd.

10
Our shoos we sowed with merry notes,
  And by our mirth expeld all mone:
Like Nightingales, from whose sweet throats,
  Most pleasant tunes are nightly blown;
The Gentle Craft *is fittest, then,*
  For poore, distressed Gentlemen.

Their minds do mount in courtesie,
  And they disdain a niggards feast:
Their bodies are for Chiualry,
  All cowardnesse they do detest.
For Sword and Shield, for bowe and Shaft,
20
  No man can stain the Gentle Craft.

Yea sundry Princes sore distrest,
  Shall seek for succour by this Trade:
Whereby their griefs shall be redrest,
  Of foes they shall not be afraid.
And many men of fame likewise
  Shall from the Gentle Craft *arise.*

If we want money ouer night,
  Ere next day noon God will it send,
30
Thus may we keep our selues vpright,
  And be no churl vnto our friend:
Thus do we liue where pleasure springs,
  In our conceit like petty Kings.

Our hearts with care we may not kill,
  Mans life surpasseth wordly wealth,
Content surpasseth riches still,
  And fie on knaues that liue by stealth:
This Trade therefore both great and small
  The Gentle Craft *shall euer call.*

40 When the Iourney-men Shoomakers had heard this song, and
the faire title that Sir *Hugh* had giuen their Trade, they engraued
the same so deeply in their minds, that to this day it could neuer
be razed out: like a remembrance in a Marble stone, which continueth time out of mind.

But not long after came that dolefull day, wherein these two

Louers must lose their liues, who like to meeke Lambs were led
to the slaughter : the bloody performance thereof was to be done
hard by that fair Fountain, where the Loue-despising Lady made
her most abode : and because she was a Kings daughter, the
bloody Tyrant gaue her the priuiledge to chuse her own death :
to the which she passed with as good a countenance, as if she had
been a fair young Bride prepared for marriage.

(*viz*) When they were come to the place of execution, and
mounted vpon the Scaffold, they seemed for beauty like two
bright stars, *Castor* and *Pollux* ; there they imbraced each other 10
with such chaste desires, as all thcse that beheld them, admired
to see how stedfast and firme both these Louers were, ready in
hearts and minds to heauen itself.

At what time the Lady turned her selfe to Sir *Hugh* and spake
to this effect : Now do I find thee a perfect Louer indeed, that
hauing setled thy affections aboue the skies, art readie to yeeld
thy life for thy Loue, who, in requitall thereof, will giue thee thy
life foreuer.

The loue of earthly creatures is mixed with many miseries, and
interlaced with sundrie sorrows ; and here grief shall abate the 20
pleasures of loue but be wel assured that ioy shall follow the
same.

Thou didst wooe me for loue, and now I haue won thee to
loue, where, setling both our selues vpon God His loue, we will
loue one another ; and in token of that heauenly loue receiue
of me I pray thee, a chaste and louing kisse from my dying lips.

Fair *Winifred* (quoth he) it is true indeed ; I neuer loued truly
vntill thou taughtest me to loue ; for then my loue was full of
discontent : but now altogether pleasing, and more sweet is the
thought thereof than any tongue can expresse. The thing that I 30
euer before called Loue, was but a shadow of loue, a sweetnesse
tempered with gall, a dying life, and a liuing death, where the
heart was continually tossed vpon the Seas of tempestuous
sorrows, and wherein the mind had no calme quietnesse : and
therefore blessed be the time that I euer learned this loue.

With that he was interrupted by the Tyrant who said, You are
not come hither to talk, but to die ; I haue sworn you both shall
die at this instant.

Thou Tyrant (said Sir *Hugh*) the verie like sentence is pronounced against thy selfe ; for Nature hath doomed thou shalt die 40
likewise, and albeit the execution thereof be something deferred,
yet at length it will come, and that shortly, for neuer did Tyrant
carrie gray hairs to the graue.

The young Lady desired first to die, saying to Sir *Hugh*, Come,
dear friend, and learn magnanimity of a Maide : now shalt thou
see a silly woman scorn death at his teeth, and make as small
account of his cruelty, as the tyrant doth of our liues ; and there-

46. as small *1675 &c.*: a small *1648*

withall stript vp her silken sleeues, and commited 'her Alabaster
arms into the executioners foule hands, hauing made choice to
die in bleeding : at what time, being pricked in euery vain, the
scarlet blood sprang out in plentifull sort, much like a precious
fountain lately filled with Claret wine.

And while she thus bled, she said : Here do I sacrifice my
blood to him that bought me, who by his blood washt away all
my sinnes. O my sweet Sauiour, thus were thy sides pierced for
my transgressions, and in this sort sprang thy precious blood
10 from thee, and all for the loue thou bearest to mankind : I feele
my heart to faint, but my soule receiueth strength, I come sweet
Christ I come. And therewithall her body fainting, and the blood
failing, like a Conduit suddenly drawn drie, the young Princesse
fell down dead, at what time a pale colour ouer-spread her faire
face in such comely sort, as if a heap of Roses had been shadowed
with a sheet of pure Lawn.

But it is to be remembred, that all the while the young Princesse
bled, her blood was receiued into certain basons, which being in
that sort saued together, the Tyrant caused it to be tempered with
20 poyson, and prepared it to be the last drink that Sir *Hugh* should
haue, saying ; That by her loue whom he so dearely loued he
should receiue his death. And thereupon, incontinently, without
any further delaying of time, he caused a cup of that most deadly
poysoned blood to be deliuered into his hands, who with a louely
and cheerfull countenance receiued the same and then vttered
his mind in this manner.

O thou cruell Tyrant (quoth he) what a poore spite is this to
inflict vpon a dying man, that is as carelesse how he dies, as
when he dies ; Easie it is for thee to glut me with blood, although
30 with blood thou art not satisfied. Sweet blood (quoth he) precious
and pure, how faire a colour dost thou cast before mine eyes ?
Sweet I say wast thou, before such time as this ill-sauouring poyson
did infect thee : and yet as thou art I nothing despise thee. O
my dear *Winifred*, full little did I think that euer I should come
to drink of thy heart blood.

My greedy eye, that glutton-like did feed vpon thy beauty, and
yet like the Sea was neuer satisfied, is now with thy gore blood
fully gorged. Now may I quench my thirsty desire with loue, that
like hot, burning coals set my heart in such an extreme heat, that
40 it could not be quenched before this time ; for if fair *Winifred*
could spare any loue from heauen, assuredly she left it in her blood ;
her sweet, heart blood I mean, that nourished her chast life : see,
here is a caudle to cool my vain affections. Far be it that any
true Louers should euer tast the like.

But this punishment haue the iust heauens poured vpon me,
for the preferring the loue of an earthly creature, before the loue
of an heauenly Creator ; Pardon, O Lord, the foule sins of
superstitious Louers, that while they make Idols of their Ladies,

they forget the honour of thy diuine Maiesty. Yet doth it do my heart much good to think that I must bury sweet *Winifreds* blood in my body, whose loue was lodged long ago in my heart : and therewithall drinking the first draught, he said, O Lord, me seemeth this portion hath a comfortable taste, far doth it surpasse that Nectar wherewith the gods were nourished.

Well (said the tyrant) seeing it pleaseth thee so well, thou shalt haue more; and therewith another cup of the same blood was giuen him to drink.

Yes come (quoth he) my thirst is not quenched ; for the first 10 draught gaue me but a taste of sweetnesse, and like a longing woman, I desire the rest; and with that he drank the second draught. The third being deliuered him, he took the cup into his hand, and, looking about, he said : Lo here I drink to all the kind Yeomen of the *Gentle Craft.*

I drink to you all (quoth he) but I cannot spare you one drop to pledge me. Had I any good thing to giue, you should soon receiue it : but my selfe the Tyrant doth take, and my flesh is bequeathed to the fowls, so that nothing is left but oneiy my bones to pleasure you withall ; and those, if they will do you any good, 20 take them : and so I humbly take my leaue, bidding you all farewell.

There with the last draught, he finished his life, whose dead carkasse after hanged vp where the fowls deuoured his flesh ; and the young Princesse was contemptuously buried by the Well where she had so long liued. Then had he the title of St. *Hugh* giuen him, and she of Saint *Winifred*, by which termes they are both so called to this day.

Chap. IV.

How the Shoomakers stole away Saint *Hughs* bones, and 30 made them working tools thereof, and the vertue that they found in the same: whereby it came, that when any man saw a Shoomaker trauelling with a pack at his back, they would presently say : There goes Saint *Hughs* bones.

VPon a time it chanced, that a company of Iourneymen Shoomakers passed along by the place where Saint *Hughs* dead body was hanging, and finding the flesh pickt cleane off from the bones, they entred thus into communication among themselues. 40

Neuer was Saint *Hugh* so bare (quoth one) to carry neuer a whit of skin vpon his bones ;

Nor thou neuer so bare (said another) to beare neuer a penny
in thy purse.   But now seeing you talk of Saint *Hugh*, it brings
me to remembrance of his Legacy that he gaue vs at his death :
What was that said the rest ?

Marry (quoth he) I will tell you, When the gentle Prince saw
that the cruelty of the time would not suffer him to be liberall to
his friends, but that his life was taken away by one, and his flesh
giuen to others, he most kindly bequeathed his bones vnto vs.

Tush (quoth another) that was but to shew his mind towards
10 the Shoomakers, because he had receiued of them so many
fauours : for alas, what can the dead mans bones pleasure the
liuing ?

No (quoth another) I can tell you there may be as great vertue
found in his bones, as the brains of a Weasill, or the tongue ot
a Frog.

Much like (answered the rest) but I pray thee shew vs what
vertue is in those things you speak of.

(Quoth he) I will tell you ; the braines of a Weasill hath this
power experientia docet, that if the powder thereof be mingled
20 with the runnet, wherewith women make their Cheese, no mouse
dares touch it : In like manner, the tongue of a water-frog hath such
great force in it, that if it be laid vpon the breast of any one
sleeping it will cause them to tell whatsoeuer you shall demand ;
for by that meanes *Dick Piper* knew he was a Cuckold.   Againe,
I know that those that are trauellers are not ignorant that whosoeuer puts but six leaues of Mugwort in his shooes, shall nere be
weary, though he trauell thirtie or fourtie miles on foot in a
forenoon.

That indeed, may be true (quoth one) for by the verie same
30 hearb my last Dame kept her Ale from sowring : and it is said
that where housleek is planted, the place shall neuer be hurt with
thunder : Pimpernel is good against Witchcraft ; and because my
sister *Ioan* carried alwayes some about her, Mother *Bumby* could
not abide her : Therefore what vertue a dead mans bones may
haue, we know not till we haue tryed it.

Why then (said the third man) let vs soon at night steal Saint
Hughes bones away, and, albeit the Tyrant will be displeased, yet
it is no theft ; for you say they were giuen vs, and therefore we
may the bolder take them ; And because we will turn them to
40 profit, and auoid suspition, we will make diuers of our Tools with
them, and then if any vertue do follow them, the better we shall
find it.

To this motion euery one gaue his consent, so that the same
night Saint *Hughes* bones were taken down, and the same being
brought before a sort of shoomakers, there they gaue their opinion ;
That it was necessary to fulfill the will of the dead, and to take
those bones in as good a part, as if they were worth ten thousand
pounds ; whereupon one stept out, and thus did say.

My friends, I pray you list to me,
And mark what S. Hughes *bones shall be.*

First a Drawer and a Dresser,
two wedges, a more and a lesser :
A pretty block three inches high,
in fashion squared like a Die,
Which shall be called by proper name,
a Heel-block, the very same.
A Hand-leather and a Thumb-leather likewise,
to pull out shoo-threed we must deuise ; 10
The Needle and the Thimble,
 shall not be left alone,
The Pincers and the pricking Aule,
 and the rubbing stone.
The Aule steele and tackes,
 the Sow-haires beside,
The Stirrop holding fast,
 while we sowe the Cow-hide,
The whetstone, the stopping-stick,
 and the paring knife : 20
All this doth belong
 to a Iourneymans life,
Our Apron is the Shrine,
 to wrap these bones in :
Thus shrowded we Saint Hugh
 in gentle Lambs skin.

Now all you good Yeomen of the *Gentle Craft,* tell me now
(quoth he) how like you this ?

As well (replyed they) as Saint *George* doth of his horse, for as
long as we can see him fight with the Dragon, we will neuer part 30
from this Posie.

And it shall be concluded, that what Iourney-man soeuer he be
hereafter, that cannot handle his Sword and buckler, his long
sword or a Quarter-staffe, sound the Trumpet, or a play vpon the
Flute, and bear his part in a three mans Song, and readily reckon
vp his Tools in Rime : except he haue born Colours in the field,
being a Lieutenant, a Sergeant or Corporall, shall forfeit and pay
a pottle of Wine, or be counted for a colt : to which they answered
all viua voce, Content content ; and then after many merry songs,
they departed. And neuer after did they trauell without these 40
tools on their backs : which euer since were called Saint *Hughes*
bones.

Chap. V.

How *Crispianus* and his brother *Crispine* the two sons
of the King of *Logria,* through the cruelty of the
Tyrant *Maximinus,* were fain in disguised manner to
seek for their liues safty, and how they were entertained by a shoomaker in *Feuersham.*

When the Romane *Maximinus* sought in cruell sort to
bereaue this Land of all her noble youth or youth of noble
blood; the vertuous Queen of *Logria* (which now is called *Kent*)
10 —dwelling in the city *Durouernum,* alias *Canterbury,* or the Court
of Kentishmen, hauing at that time two young sons, sought all the
meanes she could possible to keep them out of the Tyrant's claws;
and in this manner she spake vnto them:

My dear and beloued sons, the ioy and comfort of my age, you
see the dangers of these times, and the stormes of a Tyrants reign,
who, hauing now gathered together the most part of the young
Nobilitie, to make them slaues in a forraign Land, that are free-
born in their own Country, seeketh for you also thereby to make
a cleare riddance of all our born Princes, to the end he might
20 plant strangers in their stead.   Therefore (my sweet sons) take
the counsell of your mother, and seek in time to preuent ensuing
danger which will come vpon vs suddenly as a storme at sea, and
as cruelly as a Tyger in the wildernesse; therefore, suiting your
selues in honest habits, seek some poore seruice to shield you from
mischance, seeing necessity hath priuiledged those places from
Tyrannie.   And so (my sons) the gracious Heauens may one day
raise you to deserued dignitie and honour.

The young Lads seeing that their mother so earnest to haue
them gone, fulfilled her commandment, and, casting off their attire,
30 put homlie garments on, and, with many bitter tears took leaue of
the Queen their mother, desiring her before they went to bestow
her blessing vpon them.

O my sons (quoth she) stand you now vpon your ceremonies?
Had I leasure to giue you one kisse, it were something; the Lord
blesse you, get you gon, away, away, make hast I say, let not swift
time ouerslip you, for the Tyrant is hard by: with that she pushed
them out of a back doore, and then sets herselfe down to weep.

The two young Princes, which like pretty lambs went straying
they knew not whither, at length by good fortune, came to
40 *Feuersham,* where, before the dayes peep, they heard certain
shoomakers singing, being as pleasant as their notes, as they sat at
their businesse, and this was their Song,

Would God that it were Holiday,
  hey dery down down dery;
That with my Loue I might go play,
  with woe my heart is weary:
My whole delight, is in her sight,
  would God I had her company,
                    her company,
Hey dery down, down adown.

My Loue is fine, my loue is fair,
  hey dery down, down dery: 10
No maid with her may well compare,
  in Kent or Canterbury;
From me my Loue shall neuer moue,
  would God I had her company,
                    her company,
Hey dery down, down adown.

To see her laugh, to see her smile,
  hey dery down, down dery:
Doth all my sorrows clean beguile,
  and makes my heart full merry;   20
No griefe doth grow where she doth go.
  would God I had her company, &c.
Hey dery down, down adown.

When I do meet her on the green,
  hey dery down, down dery:
Methinks she looks like beauties Queen,
  which makes my heart full merry;
Then I her greet with kisses sweet,
  would God I had her company, &c.
Hey dery down, down adown.   30

My Loue comes not of churlish kind,
  hey dery down, down dery:
But bears a louing and courteous Mind,
  which makes my heart full merry;
She is not coy, she is my ioy,
  would God I had her company, &c.
Hey dery down, down adown.

Till Sunday comes farewell my dear,
  hey dery down, down dery;
When we do meet we'll haue good chear,   40
  and then we will be merry:
If thou loue me, I will loue thee,
  and still delight in thy company, &c.
Hey dery down, down dery.

The young Princes perceiuing such mirth to remain in so homely a cottage, iudged by their pleasant notes, that their hearts were not cloyed with ouer many cares, and therefore wished it might be their good hap to be harboured in a place of such great content.

But standing a long time in doubt what to do, like two distressed strangers, combating twixt hope and feare; at length taking courage, *Crispianus* knocking at the doore: What knaue knocks there (quoth the Iourneyman) and by and by down he takes his quarter staffe and opens the doore, being as ready to strike as speake, saying: What lack you? To whom *Crispianus* made this answer:

Good sir, pardon our boldnesse, and measure not our truth by our rudenesse; we are two poore boyes that want seruice, stript from our friends by the furie of these warres, and therefore are we enforced, succourlesse to craue seruice in any place.

What, haue you no friends or acquaintance in these parts to go to (said the Shoomakers) by whose means you might get preferment?

Alas Sir (said *Crispianus*) necessitie is despised of euery one, and misery is troden down of many; but seldome or neuer relieued: yet, notwithstanding, if our hope did not yeeld us some comfort of good hap, we should grow desperate through distresse.

That were great pitie (said the Shoomaker) be content, for, as our Dame tels our Master, A patient man is better then a strong man. Stay a while, and I will call our Dame to the doore, and then you shall heare what she will say.

With that he went in, and forth came his Dame, who beholding the said youths, said: Now alas, poore boyes, how comes it to passe that you are out of seruice? What, would you be Shoomakers, and learn the *Gentle Craft*?

Yes, forsooth (said they) with all our hearts.

Now by my troth (quoth she) you do look with honest true faces. I will intreat my husband for you, for we would gladly haue good boyes; and if you will be iust and true, and serue God, no doubt you may do well enough. Come in, my lads, come in.

Crispianus and his brother with great reuerence gaue her thanks; and by that time they had stayed a little while, down came goodman, and his wife hard by his heels, saying: husband, these be the youths I told you of, no doubt but in time they will be good men.

Her husband looking wishtly vpon them and conceiuing a good opinion of their fauors at length agreed that they should dwell with him, so that they would be bound for seuen years. The youths being contented, the bargain was soon ended, and so set to their business whereat they were no sooner setled, but that great search was made for them in all places; and albeit the Officers came to the house where they dwelt, by reason of their disguise they knew them not : hauing also taken vpon them borrowed names of *Crispianus* and *Crispine*.

Within a few days after, the Queen their mother was by the tyrant taken, and for that she would not confesse where her sonns were, she was laid in Prison in *Colchester* Castle, whereunto she went with as cheerfull a countenance as *Cateratus* did, when he was led captiue to *Rome* : and coming by the place where her sonnes sat at work, with a quick eye she had soon espied them ; and looke how a dying coal reuiues in the wind, euen so at this sight she became suddenly red : but, making signes that they should hold 10 their tongues, she was led along : whom seuen yeers after her sons did neuer see. But as men stand amazed at the sight of Apparitions in the ayre, as ignorant what successe shall follow ; euen so were these two Princes agast to see their own mother thus led away, not knowing what danger should ensue thereof.

Notwithstanding, they thought good to keep their seruice as their liues surest refuge : at what time they both bent their whole minds to please their Master and Dame, refusing nothing that was put to them to do, were it to wash dishes, scoure kettles, or any other thing, whereby they thought their Dame's fauour might 20 be gotten, which made her the readier to giue them a good report to their Master, and to do them many other seruices, which otherwise they should haue missed ; following therin the admonition of an old Iourney-man, who would alwayes say to the Apprentices :

> *Howsoeuer things do frame,*
> *Please well thy Master, but chiefly thy Dame.*

Now, by that time, these two young Princes had truly serued their Master the space of foure or fiue yeers, he was grown something wealthy and they very cunning in their trade ; whereby the house had the name to breed the best workmen in the Countrey ; 30 which report in the end prefer'd their Master to be the Emperours Shoomaker : and by this means, his seruants went to *Maximinus* Court euery day : but *Crispianus* and *Crispine* fearing they should haue been known, kept themselues from thence, as much as they could. Notwithstanding, at the last perswading themselues that Time had worne them out of knowledge, they were willing in the end to go thither, as well to hear tidings of the Queen their mother, as also for to seek their own preferment.

Chap. VI.

How the Emperours faire daughter *Vrsula*, fell in loue
with young *Crispine* coming with shooes to the Court;
and how in the end they were secretly married by a
blind Frier.

NOw among all the shoomakers men that came to the Court
with shooes, young *Crispine* was had in greatest regard with
the fair Princesse, whose mother being lately dead, she was the only
ioy of her father, who alwayes sought means to match her with
10 some worthy Romane, whose renown might ring throughout the
whole world.

But fair *Vrsula*, whose bright eyes had entangled her heart with
desire of the Shoomakers fauour, despised all proffers of loue, in
regard of him. And yet notwithstanding she would oft check
her own opinion, in placing her loue vpon a person of such low
degree, thus reasoning with her self.

Most aptly is the god of Loue by cunning Painters drawn blind,
that so equally shoots forth his fiery shafts : for had he eyes to
see, it were impossible to deal in such sort, as in matching fair
20 *Venus* with foule *Vulcan*, yoking the Emperiall hearts of Kings
to the loue of beggers, as he did to *Cofetua*, and as now in my selt
I find how mad a thing it would seem to the eyes of the world,
that an Emperors daughter should delight in the fauour of a
simple Shoomaker.

O *Vrsula*, take heed what thou dost, stain not thy royalty with
such indignity. O that *Crispines* birth were agreeable to his
person ! for in mine eye, there is no Prince in the world comparable to him : if then while he is clothed with these rags of
seruitude, he appear so excellent, what would he be were he in
30 Princely attire ! O *Crispine*, either thou art not as thou seemest, or
else Nature, in disgrace of Kings, hath made thee a shoomaker.

In these humours would the Princesse be often, especially at
Crispines approach, or at his departure ; For, as soon as euer he
came within her sight with shooes, a sudden blush like a flame of
lightning would strike in her face, and at his departure, an earthly
pale colour, like to the beams of the bright Sunne obscured by
coal-blacke clouds. But after many weary conflicts with fancy,
she fully resolued, at his next coming, to enter into communication
with him, but imagining his stay from Court ouer long, on the
40 sudden she sent presently for him, finding great fault in the last
shooes he brought her. At what time *Crispine* most humbly on
his knee greatly craued pardon for all such faults as she then had
found, promising amendment in the next shooes she should haue.

Nay (quoth she) Ile shew thee, they are too low something in the instep ; also the heel is bad, and besides that, they are too strait in the toes.

You shall haue a pair made (said he) shall fit you better, for none shall set a stitch in them but mine own self.

Do, said the Princesse, but let me haue them so soon as thou canst, and therewith *Crispine* departed.

The Princesse then all solitary, got her self into her Chamber, entred there into consideration, and found within her self great trouble and sorrow, while the tongue, the hearts aduocate, was not suffered to speak. At last she heard *Crispines* voice, enquiring 10 of the Ladies in the great Chamber for the Princesse, who answered, That hauing taken little rest the night before, she was now laid down to sleep, and therefore they willed him to come again some other time.

Asleep, replyed the Princesse ! I am not asleep, bid him stay : What hasty huswife was that which sent him hence ? Call him againe quickly I would aduise you.

And therefore changing melancholly into mirth, she arose vp from out of her bed, and, as a bright starre shooting in the Element, she swiftly got her forth to meet the shoomaker, whose faire sight 20 was to her as great a comfort as a Sunshine before a showre of raine.

How now (quoth she) hast thou brought me a pair of shooes ?

I haue (gracious Madam) quoth he.

Then (quoth the Princesse) come thy selfe and draw them on : therewith she sitting down, lifted vp her well proportioned legge vpon his gentle knee. Where, by that time her shooes were drawn on, she had prepared a good reward for her shoomaker and, giuing him an handfull of gold, she said : Thou hast so well pleased me in making of these shooes, that I cannot but reward thee in some good sort ; therefore Shoomaker, take this, and from hence- 30 forth let no man make my shooes but thy self. But tell me *Crispine*, art thou not in loue, that thou doest smug up thy selfe so finely, thou wast not wont to go so neatly : I pray thee tell me what pretty wench is it that is mistresse of thy heart ?

Truly, faire Madam (quoth he) If I should not loue, I might be accounted barbarous, for by natures course, there is a mutuall loue in all things : the Doue and the Peacock loue intirely, so doth the Turtle and the Popiniay : the like affection the fish Musculus beareth vnto the huge Whale, insomuch that he leadeth him from all danger of stony rocks ; and as among birds and fishes, so 40 amongst plants and trees the like concord is to be found ; for if the male of palme trees be planted from the female, neither of both prosper : and being set one neer another, they do flourish accord-ingly, imbracing with ioy the branches one of another. And for mine one part, I am in loue too : for first of all, I loue my Maker ; and next, my good Master and Dame : But as concerning the loue of pretty wenches, verily Madam, I am cleare : and the rather do I abstain from fixing my fancie on women, seeing many sorrowes do follow the married sort, for a dramme of delight hath a pound of pain.

That is (answered the Princesse) where contention setteth the house on fire, but where true loue remaines, there is no discontent : and what can a man more desire for this worlds comfort, but a vertuous wife, which is reported to be a treasure inestimable. Therefore *Crispine*, say thy mind, if I prefer thee to a wife, euery way deseruing thy loue, wouldst thou take it well ?

Truly Madam (said *Crispine*) if I should not accept of your good will, I should shew my selfe more vnmannerly than well nurtured : But seeing it pleaseth you to grace me with your Princely countenance, and to giue me libertie to speak my mind, this is my opinion : If I were to chuse a wife, then would I haue one faire, rich, and wise ; first, to delight mine eye : secondly, to supply my want, and thirdly, to gouern my house.

Then (said the princesse) her beauty I will referre vnto the iudgement of thine own eyes, and her wisedome vnto the triall of Time : but as concerning her portion, I dare make some report, because it well deserueth to be praised : For at her marriage thou shalt haue a bagge full of rare vertues with her.

Truly Madam (quoth *Crispine*) such coynes go not currant among Tannars : and I know, if I should go with it to the Market, it would buy me no soale-leather. Notwithstanding when I doe see her, I will tell you more of my mind.

The Princesse, taking him aside priuately, walking with him in a faire Gallerie, said ; in looking vpon me, thou mayest iudge of her, for she is as like me as may be.

When *Crispine* heard her say so, he right prudently answered : I had rather, Madam, she were your own selfe, than like yourselfe, and although my words fauour of presumption, yet, with your fauour, I dare boldly pronounce it, that I hold my selfe worthy of a Queen, if I could get her good will. And were it no danger to match with your Excellency so it should please you, it should not dislike me.

Then said the Princesse : Now shoomaker, I see thou hast some courage in thee : and doubt thou not, but if I were of that mind, but I would be as ready to guide thee from the dangerous rocks of my Fathers wrath, as the fish called Musculus is for the Whale : But couldst thou not be contented to die for a Ladies loue ?

No Madam (quoth he) if I could keep her loue and liue.

Then liue faire friend (answered she) enioy my Loue, for I will die rather than liue without thee.

Crispine hearing this, was stricken into an extasie of ioy, in such sort, as he wist not whether he were asleep or dreamed : But by that time he had summoned his wits together, with the plighting of his faith, he opened his estate and high birth vnto her, shewing all the extremities that he and his brother had been put vnto since

---

1. delight *1675 &c.*: light *1648*   21. go not *1675 &c.*: go out *1648*

the death of their royall Father, and of the imprisonment of the Queen, their Mother.

The which when faire *Vrsula* with great wonder heard, giuing him an earnest of her loue with a sweet kisse : she said ; My deare Loue, and most gentle Prince, euer did I think, that more than a common man was shrowded in these poore habiliments, which made me the bolder to impart my mind vnto thee, and now dread no more my Fathers wrath, for the fire thereof was long agoe quenched.

No, no (quoth *Crispine*) an Eagles thirst is neuer expelled, but 10 by blood. And albeit your father haue now (parhaps) qualified the heat of his fury by the length of time, yet if he should vnderstand of this my loue to thee, it would cause him to rake out of the ashes hot, burning coals of displeasure again : and then might my life pay a deare price for thy loue. Therefore (my deare *Vrsula*) I desire thee, euen by the power of that loue thou bearest to me to keepe secret what I haue shewed thee, nothing doubting but that in time I may find release of these miseries ; in the mean space we will be secretly married, by which holy knot we, as well in body as in heart, be vnseperately tied together. 20

To this *Vrsula* consented most gladly, and therevpon told him that she would meet him in her fathers Park, at any houre he would appoint ; which she might do the more easily, in respect she had a key to one of the Garden doores which gaue present passage into the Park. The day and houre being concluded vpon, they parted for this time, both of them indued with such content as in all their liues they neuer found the like.

And at this time there was in *Canterbury* a blind Frier that in many yeers had neuer seen the Sun ; to this man did *Crispine* go, thinking him the fittest Chaplain to chop vp such a marriage, 30 who, meeting with him at *Christ Church* one euening after the Antheme, broke with him after this manner.

Good speed good father : there is a certain friend of mine that would be secretly married in the morning betimes ; for which purpose he thinks you the fittest man to perform it in all the Cloyster : and therefore, if you will be diligent to do it, and secret to conceal it, you shall haue foure angels for your pains.

The Frier being fired with the desire of his gold, rubbing his elbow and scratching his crown, swore by the blessed Book that hung by his knee, that he would be both willing and constant to 40 keep it secret. Tush young man, you may trust me, I haue done many of these feats in my dayes. I know that youth are youth, but they would not haue all the world wonder at their doings : and where shall it be, said the Frier,

(Quoth *Crispine*) At Saint *Gregories* Chappell ; and because you shall not make your boy acquainted therewith, I my selfe will call you in the morning. Good father be not forgetfull to obserue the

38. fired *1675 &c.* : fixed *1648*

time, at two of the clock is the houre, and therefore look you be
ready when I shall call you.

I warrant you (replied the Frier :) and because I will not ouer-
sleep my selfe, I will for this night lie in my clothes, so that as
soon as euer you call, I will straight be readie.

Then father, I will trust you (quoth *Crispine*) and so departed.

When he came to his master, he made not many words, but so
soon as he had supt on Sunday at night, he went to his chamber,
and laid him down vpon his bed, making no creature in the house
10 priuy to his intent, not his own brother, his minde still running on
his faire Mistresse, and the happie houre that will tie them both in
one : neuer was there hunger-starued man that did long more for
the sweet approach of wholsome food than did *Crispine* for two a
clock.   And so soon as the silent night had drawn all things to
rest, *Crispine* got him vp, and to *Canterbury* goes he to meet his
rose-cheeked Lady in her Fathers Park, who also took hold of
Times forlock, and, like clear *Cynthia*, shaped her course to seek
out *Sol* in the Meridian.   But so soon as her searching eye had
spied him, she commended his vigilancie, saying he well obserued
20 his houre :

O my dear (quoth he) rich preys do make true men theeues :
but finding thee here so happily, I will fetch the Frier straight :

He had no sooner called at the Friers doore, but he presently
heard him : and groaping the way down, he opened the doore,
and along they went together : but the Frier, finding his iourney
longer than he expected, said, That either Saint *Gregories* Chappel
was remoued, or else he was not so good a foot man as he was
wont to be :

That is likely enough (said *Crispine* :) for how much the older
30 you are since you went this way last, so much the weaker you are
to trauell, but be you content, now we are at the last come to the
place, and therefore, good Frier, make what speed you may.

I warrant you (quoth he) and therewithall he puts his Spectacles
vpon his nose.

The fair Princesse perceiuing that, laughed heartily, saying,
Little need hath a blind man of a paire of Spectacles.

Truly Mistresse (said he) as little need hath an old man of
a young wife ; but you may see what vse is.   Though I be blind
and cannot see neuer a letter, yet I cannot say Masse without my
40 book and my Spectacles ;   And then he proceeded to solemnize
their marriage, which being finished, the Frier had his gold, and
home he was led :

In the mean time the Princesse stayed still in the Park for her
Bridegroom, where when he came on a bank of sweet primroses,
he pluckt the rose of amorous delight : and after the Princesse
came to her fathers Palace, and *Crispine* to his Masters shop.

CHAP. VII.

How *Crispianus* was prest to the wars, and how he
fought with *Iphicratis* the renowned Generall of the
Persians, who made warre vpon the Frenchmen:
shewing also the occasion that a Shoomakers son is
said to be a Prince born.

IN the mean time that *Crispine* was secretly busied about
his marriage, his brother *Crispianus*, the same night, with
many others, was prest to wars into the Countrey of *Gaul*, now
called *France*, which made his Master and Dame full of woe ; who 10
had committed to his gouernment the whole rule of his house.
And when *Crispine* came home, they told him what chance had
hapned.   And demanded where he had been ; they said they were
glad he had so well escaped.

Crispine excusing himselfe so well as he could, said he was
sorrie for his brothers sudden departure ; notwithstanding, the ioy
of his late marriage mitigated much of his sorrow : to whom, in his
brothers absence, his Master gaue the ouersight of his houshold,
which place he guided with such discretion, as thereby he got
both the good will of his Master, and the loue of the houshould ; 20
And as he sate one day at his work, he sung this song in commendation of marriage ; himselfe sung the Ditty, and his fellows bore
the burthen.

> *Among the ioyes on earth, though little ioy there be,*
> *hey down down adown, fine is the silken twist,*
> *Among the married sort much comfort I do see :*
> *hey down down adown, beleeue it they that list.*
> *He that is a married man hath beautie to embrace,*
> *hey down down adown, and therefore mickle wo :*
> *He liueth in delight, and is in happie case,* 30
> *hey down down adown, in faith we think not so.*
> *His wife doth dresse his meat, with euerything most meet,*
> *hey down down adown, fair women loue good chear :*
> *And when he comes to bed, she giues him kisses sweet,*
> *hey down down adown, for thanks he pays full dear*
> *A hundred honey sweets, he hath when that is done,*
> *hey down down adown, the truth is seldome known.*
> *He hath in a little time a daughter or a son,*
> *hey down down adown, God grant they be his own.*
> *A wife is euermore, both faithfull true, and iust,* 40
> *hey down down adown, 'tis more than you do know :*

21. commendation *1675 &c.*: communication *1648*

Her husband may be sure in her to put his trust,
hey down down adown, most are deceiued so.
While he doth ride abroad, she looks vnto his house,
hey down down adown, the finest cloth is torn:
And when he comes, she giues him brawn and sowse,
hey down down adown, and oftentimes the horn.

How now, what is that you say (quoth *Crispine*)?
Nothing (quoth they) but onely beare the burthen of your Song.
And surely we think it great pity that you are not married, seeing
10 you can sing so well in the praise of marriage.

Truly (quoth he) were it not for that holy Institution, what
would the world be but a brood of haplesse bastards ; like to the
cursed seed of *Cain*, men fit for all manner of villany, and such as
would leaue behind them a race of runnagates, persons that would
liue as badly as they are lewdly begotten.

The rest of the Iourney-men hearing him enter into such a deep
discourse of the matter, began therefore to demand many questions :
but seeing it appertaines not to our matter, weele leaue them to
their disputation : and in the mean space I will shew you some-
20 thing of *Crispianus*, who is now in *France*, with many other noble
Brittains, whom *Maximinus* sent thither to aid the Gauls against
the mightie force of *Iphicratis* the Persian generall, who had at
this time inuaded their Countrey with a great power.

The day of battel being appointed, the Armies met in the field,
at what time both the Generals like two Lyons filled with wrath
in their proud march viewed one another, breathing forth on both
sides words of disdain, and thus the Generall of the Gauls began.

Thou insulting Commander of the Easterne troups, how durst
thou set thy ambitious foot within our territories ? Cannot the
30 confines of *Persia* content thee, nor those conquered Kingdomes
alreadie in thy hand, but that with vnsatiable desire thou must
come to vsurp our right ? Know thou, that the vndaunted Gauls
do scorn thee : for albeit that *Alexander* like, thou seekest to
subdue the whole world, flattering thy selfe in thy fortunes, yet
neuer think that the son of a shoomaker shall bend our neck to a
seruile yoke. Therefore in our iust right we are come to giue thee
hire for thy pride, and by the force of our swords to. beat down
the Scepter of thy proud thoughts.

The renowned *Iphicratis* vpon these words made this replie :
40 Now may I report that the Gauls can do something, finding them
such good scoulds : But know this that I come not to raile, but
to reuenge those contemptuous speeches, and with the points of
sturdie Launces, to thrust them down your throats again. Indeed,
my fathers trade is a reproach vnto me, but thou art a reproach to
thy father : but thou shalt vnderstand that a Shoomakers son is a
Prince born, his fortune made him so, and thou shalt finde no
lesse.

And hereupon, the trumpets sounding to a charge, and the drums striking a alarum, there followed a sore and cruell fight : wherein *Crispianus* like a second *Hector* laid about him, hewing down his foes on euery side. Whose valiancy and Princely courage was noted of all the Gauls.

And this fierce fight ended with the nights approach, each Army tooke their rest. At what time the noble Generall of the Gauls sent for *Crispianus*, and receiuing him with sundrie kind imbracements in his tent, he demanded of what birth he was.

To whom *Crispianus* shaped his answer : Most worthie Generall, my birth is not meane, and by secrets lesse, but by trade I am a Shoomaker in *England*.

A Shoomaker (said the Generall !) If such fame wait vpon Shoomakers, and such magnanimity follow them, well were it for vs if all the people in the Kingdome were Shoomakers. And as great thanks I am to giue *Maximinus* for sending me such a Souldier, as he may be proud to haue such a subiect : and now right sorrie am I that euer I reproached famous *Iphicratis*, with his fathers trade, seeing I find it true, that Magnanimity and knightly Prowesse is not alwayes tied within the compasse of Noble blood. And for my own part, I will so honourably requite thy deseruings, that thou shalt blesse the time thou euer camest into these wars.

The next morning the Generals ioyned battell again, resoluing in this fight either by death or victory, to make an end of these troubles, where the Souldiers on each side stroue for the golden wreath of renown. The two Generals meeting in the battell, fought couragiously together ; in which bloody conflect the Prince of the Gauls was thrice by *Iphicratis*, vnhorsed, and as many times of *Crispianus* mounted again : but in the end the great Commander of the Eastern Armie so mightily preuailed, that he had seized on the person of the French Prince, and was carrying him captiue to his Colours.

But so highly was *Crispianus* fauoured of Fortune, that he and his fellows met him in the pride of his conquest : who then all besmeared in the Persian blood, set vpon *Iphicratis*, and so manly behaued himselfe, that he recouered the Prince again, and in despight of the Persians, brought him to his royall Tent ; in which encounter the noble *Iphicratis* was sore wounded, by reason whereof the Souldiers had rest for three or foure dayes : in which space *Iphicratis* sent to the Prince of Gauls, to know what kin he was that in such a valiant sort rescued him out of his hands ; saying, that if he would serue him, he would make him Ruler ouer a mightie Kingdome.

The French Prince sent him word, that it was a right hardie Brittaine, which had performed that honourable seruice : but no knight, though well deseruing greater dignity, but a Shoomaker in

33. him *1675 &c.* : *1648 omits*

England : and thus (quoth he) a Shoomakers son was by a Shoo-maker foiled.

When *Iphicratis* vnderstood this, he sent word again to the Gauls that for the fauour of that worthy man, he would not only cease the wars, but foreuer after be a friend to the Gauls : which ioyfull message when the French King vnderstood, most willingly he imbraced the vnlooked for tydings of happie peace : and there-upon made *Crispianus* a knight.

After the which there was a great feast ordained, whereunto 10 the renowned *Iphicratis* was inuited, and the two generals, with *Crispianus*, friendly met together. Thus the sowre war was ended with sweet feasting : and *Iphicratis* soon after departed out of the Countery with his Army, and neuer after annoyed them.

Then the French King, writing his Letter of thanks vnto the Emperour *Maximinus*, did therein certifie him of the Princely acts of *Crispianus*, whereby he was brought into the emperours fauour ; and with these letters *Crispianus* returned into *England*.

Chap. VIII.

How the Lady *Vrsula* finding her selfe to be with child,
20   made her great moan vnto her husband *Crispine*, and
how he prouided for her a secret place, where she
was deliuered.

IN the mean space the Lady *Vrsula* finding her selfe to be with child, and her vnknown husband coming one day with shooes vnto her, she made her moan vnto him, saying : O *Crispine*, how shall we do ? the time of my sorrow and shame draweth on ; I feel that liuing in my womb, which I fear will bring death vpon vs all :

Why my dear lady (answered he) art thou with child ? keep thy chamber close, and wittily excuse thy griefs, vntill I haue found 30 means to procure our safety.

But dost thou mean faithfully (said she) wilt thou not deceiue me, and for fear of my fathers wrath flie the country ? if thou shouldest do so, then were I the wretchedst Lady aliue. Forsake me not sweet *Crispine*, whatsoeuer thou doest, but take me with thee wheresoeuer thou goest : it is not my fathers frowns that I regard, so I may haue thy fauour : what do I care for a Princely Pallace : an homely Cottage shall content me in thy company. O my Loue, I will rather learn to spin hemp for thy shop-threed, than liue without thee in the greatest pleasure.

40   I will not leaue thee my dear Loue (quoth he) by that faith I vow, which I plighted to thee at our blessed marriage ; and therefore be contented, and it shall not be long before I return.

Leauing thus his sad lady, he came home and secretly brake

the matter vnto his dame, desiring her counsell in this his extremity.

What, how now (quoth she) hast thou got a Maid with child? Ah thou whorson villain, thou hast vndone thy selfe, how wilt thou do now? Thou hast made a faire hand; here is now sixteen pence a week beside sope and candles, beds, shirts, biggins, wastcoats, headbands, swadlebands, crosse-clothes, bibs, tailclouts, mantles, hose, shooes, coats, petticoats, cradle and crickets, and beside that a standing-stole, and a posnet to make the child pap: all this is come vpon thee, be sides the charges of her lying-in. 10 Oh *Crispine, Crispine,* I am heartily sorry for thee.

But, in good faith, if I knew the quean that hath brought thee to this folly; I would haue her by the face, I swear to you: for though I spake it before thee (*Crispine*) thou art a proper fellow, and thou mightest haue done full well if thou hadst had grace; God hath done his part on thee: and with that she began with kindnesse to weep. Whereupon her Husband, coming in, asked what she ailed:

Oh man (said she) *Crispine*!

Why, why, what of *Crispine*? Tell me. Why speakest thou not? 20 We shall lose a good seruant, so we shall.

What seruant shall we lose foolish woman (quoth he?) Tell me quickly.

O husband! by Cock and Pie I swear, Ile haue her by the nose.

Who wilt thou haue by the nose? What the Deuill, art thou mad, that thou wilt not answer me?

Crispine, who at his Masters coming shunned the roome, lending an eare vnto those words, went to his Master and said vnto him: Sir, these foure yeeres haue I serued you; and the fifth draws 30 neer to an end; and as I haue found you a good Master to me, so I trust you haue had no great cause to complain of me, though (through ignorance) I haue sometimes made offence: and knowing at this instant, no man so neer a friend vnto me as your selfe, I haue thought good to impart my secret counsell to you: something I presume vpon my Dames fauour: which made me open that vnto her, which now I wish I had not discouered. Notwithstanding, resting more vpon your discretion than her secrecie, I would desire your counsell in a matter that concerns me very neer.

Verily (said his master) if it be a thing wherein I may do thee 40 good, thou shalt find that I will not fall from thee in thy sorrows, and therefore be not abashed to declare thy mind, for I swear, if I may procure thee right, thou shalt put vp no wrong.

Why then Sir, thus it is (quoth he) my will running before my wit, I haue gotten a Maiden with child, and I wot not in this case what to do, that I might preserue the Maid from shame, and I my selfe from discredit: besides, I doubt, if it be known, it will cost me my life: therefore, in such case good master be secret.

Tush man feare not (quoth he) it is a matter of nothing : but
I pray thee, now tell me what wanton wagtaile is that thou hast
clapt thus vnder the apron ?

O Master (quoth he) the Kings faire Daughter *Vrsula* is my
Loue, and she it is that liues in care for my sake.

Passion of my heart, thou whorson Knaue (quoth his Master)
thou art a dead man. I maruell how the Deuill thou camest to
be so bold with her ? Surely thou hast drawn on her shooes on
Sunday, I may say, thou hast left so good a token behind : but in
10 truth my boy I commend thee that thou wouldest shoot at the
fairest.

Yea sir (quoth *Crispine*) and I haue hit the mark I trow, and
do verily beleeue, that none will shoot so neere again.

Nay swear not (said his master), many may aim at faire marks
and more then one man hits them now and then : but what
wouldst thou haue me to do in this case ?

My good master (quoth *Crispine*) the truth is, she is my wife ;
and the very same night my brother was prest to the warres,
I was married to her : and if you could tell me how she might be
20 deliuered of her burden without any suspition, I should not only
remain beholding to you while I liued, but would also gratifie your
kindnesse in such sort as would content you.

His Dame all this while listned to their talk, and when she
vnderstood he spake of the Kings daughter, and that he had
married her, she said, Now Gods blessing on thy heart *Crispine*,
that thou art so carefull for thy wife, but it maketh me wonder
she should marrie a Shoomaker ; and a poore fellow too.

Master and Dame (quoth *Crispine*), seeing I haue begun,
Ile shew you a further matter as strange as the other. The
30 necessitie of these times makes many Noble personages to mask
in simple habite, as *Iupiter* did in a shepherds weed ; and the
truth is, that Ladie *Vrsula* is not ignorant that by matching with
me she hath wedded a Prince : and you may say, that these fiue
yeeres two Princes haue serued you obediently, vnder the simple
borrowed names of *Crispine* and *Crispianus*. Our Royall Father
was slaine by the Emperour *Maximinus*, and the Queen our mother
yet lies imprisoned, and your poore house, and these leather
garments haue been our life of defence against the blood-thirsty
Tyrant. Now you see, that though there were hate towards vs in
40 the father, yet there is loue yeelded vs by the daughter. This
must be kept for a certain time from the knowledge of him, lest
our liues pay a dear ransome for our loues.

Well, *Crispine* (quoth his Dame) be of good cheare, for I haue
a deuice in my head, how to get thy Loue out of her fathers
Pallace, that she may be brought to bed in my own house, without
either hurt to thee, or dishonour to her, if thou wilt do as I wish
thee. When you do perceiue that she grows neere vnto the time
of her trauell, I would wish you to work such meanes as to set

some tree on fire late in the night, that standeth somewhat neere one of the Beacons vpon the Sea coast, whereby it will follow that such Watchmen as watch at our Beacons, supposing the Beacons at the Sea coast to be on fire, will set theirs on fire also. Then will there be a great hurly burly, with the preparation of men at Armes on all sides, to withstand the supposed foe, that which they shall neuer find : then (as you know) *Maximinus*, with his houshold will be in most fear, because he is most hated, that whilest he is abroad, the rest of his houshold will euery one of them seek for their own safegard, amongst the which, let faire *Vrsula* be one, 10 who, by that meanes singling her selfe alone, may take vp my house, and here she may be closely kept till she be deliuered, taking vpon her the name and habite of a simple woman.

But the truth of this matter (quoth *Crispine*) I doubt it will soone be perceiued and found out ; then how shall Ladie *Vrsula* do, for she will straight be missed.

Tush thats no matter (quoth his dame) and missed let her be, vntill such time as she is in a better case to go abroad againe ; so in such a tumult as then will be, they will suppose many things, that one mischance or other is befallen her : or if she be in health, 20 that she hath wandred into the woods or some other vncouth place, where she might best prouide for safety : and when she comes home again, I warrant thee *Crispine*, she shall be welcome.

Then said his Master, I like my wiues counsell well ; therefore by my consent put it in practice :

Whereunto *Crispine* consented and so making the Lady priuie to the purpose, at length it was put in execution, at what time there was crying out on all sides, Arme, Arme, Arme : our enemies are coming vpon vs. Where (quoth they ?) at *Rutupium* said one ; At *Aurugagus Castle*, said another : (quoth the third) it is at 30 *Doris* : I tell you (quoth the fourth) it is at *Duur* : And all this is but *Douer* (saith the fifth man) and at *Douer* it is vndoubt-edly, therefore haste, haste away : for neuer was there more need : so that *Maximinus* was almost at his wits end, as one not knowing which way to turn, the cries of the people came so thick, one after another. The waiting gentle women left the Princesse, and sought their own safetie. Thus while some were busie in carrying out the Kings treasure, others hiding the plate, and others the goods, *Vrsula* had an easie passage into the Shoomakers house.

The young Prince *Crispine* was gone with the rest of the town 40 towards *Douer*, where when they came there was nothing to do ; which when *Maximinus* saw, he was not a little glad the wars were so soon ended : But when he came to the Court and missed his daughter, there was posting vp and down in euery place to seek her, but all in vain, for no man could meet with her, for which he made a great lamentation, making a Proclamation throughout the whole Countrey, That whosoeuer could bring her to him, he should not onely haue a Princely reward, but also, if he were a man of

Noble blood, he should be honoured with the marriage of his
fair daughter. This was good news to *Crispine*, who was not to
learn to make profit thereof.

But by that time his Lady was light, *Crispianus* his eldest
brother arriued into *England* with great honour, as before you
haue heard. And before he went to the Court, he thought it good
to visit his old Master, who came also in good time to the christening of his brothers child, which when he with wonder beheld,
noting what a strange accident there was, that *Maximinus* daughter
10 should be his brothers wife. But after that he had in Princely
manner saluted the new deliuered Lady, taking the infant in his
arms, he kissed it, saying; Now I will say and swear (said he)
that a Shoomakers Son is a Prince born, ioyning in the opinion
of *Iphycratis*, and henceforth Shoomakers shall neuer let their
terme die.

Then turning to his Master and Dame (he said) how much dear
Master and Dame, are we bound to your fauours, that haue maintained our honors with our happinesse; for by that means, I
hope we shall make a ioyfull conclusion of our sorrowfull beginning,
20 and I will so work that the Emperour shall confirm what is alreadie
begun; I mean, the honour due to these Princely Louers, and,
together with our happy fortunes, procure our mothers liberty.

Hereupon within a short time after, he made preparation to the
Court, he attired himselfe in Princely manner, and with a most
knightly grace he deliuered to *Maximinus*, the King of Gauls letter,
where he certified the Emperor of the honourable deeds performed
by *Crispianus*, whereupon he receiued him to great fauour, and
said vnto him, Right renowned Knight, for the great honour thou
hast done me in *France*, I will honour thee with anything which
30 thou shalt command that standeth with the Maiesty and credit of
an Emperor to giue.

Then I beseech your Highnesse (quoth he) to grant me the life,
and liberty of my dear Mother, that late Queen of *Logria*.

Art thou her sonne? (said *Maximinus*) although thy father was
my foe, yet I must needs say, he was a couragious and warlike
Prince, thy suit is granted, and once I had a daughter was worthy
of thy loue, but vnconstant Fortune hath bereft me of that blisse :
but had it pleased the fair Heauens to haue left her me till this
day, I would haue made thee more honourable by her match :
40 But seeing that my wishing doth nothing profit thee, take hence
the richest Iewell I haue, and be thou next my selfe in authority :
with that he took from his own neck a Collar of most precious
Diamonds, and gaue it to *Crispianus*, saying, be thou as fortunate
as *Policrates*.

Chap. IX.

How fair *Vrsula* came before her father with *Crispine*
her husband, who was ioyfully receiued by him, and
in the end had his good will to confirme the marriage
betwixt them, whereupon there was great ioy on both
sides. And the Shoomakers in honour of this happy
day, made a ioyfull Song.

Within a certain space after, word was brought to the
Emperour, that his daughter was with a shoomaker come
to the Court; whereat *Maximinus* was stricken into a sudden ioy, 10
saying: An honourable Shoomaker may he be that hath brought my
fair daughter again, Welcome my sweet *Vrsula*, and in good time
welcome to thy father; and welcome also is this happy young man,
that hath so fortunately brought thee, and turning to *Crispianus*,
he said: Noble Sir Knight, take here my daughter to wife;

Not so, dear Father (quoth she) this man hath best deserued my
loue, that hath preserued my life, and his wife will I be.

Why *Vrsula* (said her Father) wilt thou darken the sun-shine of
my ioy, with the clouds of foule obstinacy, and yoke thy selfe
so vnequally? This man is a Prince. 20

And this mans son is another (quoth she).

That is strange (said the Emperour); can that child be a Prince,
whose father is but a Shoomaker?

Then answeared *Vrsula*, My Royall Father, a Shoomakers son
is a Prince born:

Most gracious Lord (quoth *Crispianus*) the very like sentence did
I hear the renowned *Iphicrates* pronounce to the King of Gauls,
when he vpbraided him with his birth:

With that *Crispines* Dame presented the child to the Emperour,
and fair *Vrsula* was very deligent to vncouer the childs face, and 30
held it to her Father.

Why daughter (quoth he) art thou not a shamed to honour a
base born brat so much? Hence with the Elfe, and therewithall
pusht it from him; whereat his daughters tears trickled down her
cheeks, and so kissing the child, gaue it again to the woman.

What (said *Maximinus*) dost thou loue the child so well, that
thou must kisse it, and weep for it?

I haue cause deare Father (quoth she) for that this childs mother
lay in my mothers belly.

At these words the Emperor suspected something, and demanded 40
of *Crispine* of what parentage he was. And then knowing that
he was *Crispianus* brother, all the controuersie was ended,
and their secret marriage confirmed openly, with great ioy and
triumph; at which time the Shoomakers in the same town made

Holiday: to whom *Crispine* and *Crispianus* sent most Princely gifts for to maintain their merriment.   And euer after vpon that day at night, the Shoomakers make great cheare and feasting, in remembrance of these two Princely brethren: and because it might not be forgotten, they caused their names to be placed in the Kalender for a yeerly remembrance, which you shall find in the moneth of October, about three dayes before the feast of *Simon* and *Iude*.

The Shoomakers song on *Crispianus* night.

10
*T*Wo *Princely brethren once there were,*
  right Sonnes vnto a King.
Whose father tyrant Maximinus
  to cruell death did bring:
Crispianus, *one was call'd,*
  the eldest of the two;
Crispine *was the others name,*
  which well had learned to wooe.
These brethren then were after fain,
  from fathers house to flie:
20
Because their foes, to spoil their liues
  in priuy wait did lie,
Into a kind shoomakers house,
  they suddenly stept in;
And there to learn the Gentle Craft,
  did presently begin.
And fiue yeers space they liued so,
  with great content of mind;
So that the Tyrant could not tell,
  whereas he shoud them find:
30
Though euery day to Court they came,
  with shooes for Ladies feet;
They were not known by their attire,
  they vs'd themselues so meet.
At length vnto the furious wars
  was Crispianus *prest:*
Whereas his knightly prowesse then
  he tryed aboue the rest.
But Crispine *found him better sport—*
  would I had Crispine *been:*
40
The Kings fair daughter Lou'd him well,
  as it was after seen.
The length of this fair Ladies foot,
  so well did Crispine *know,*
That none but he could please her mind,
  the certain truth is so.

25. presently *1675* &c.: present *1648*

Came he by night or else by day,
he was most welcome still;
With kisses sweet she did him pay,
and thanks for his good will.
So oft these Louers twaine did meet,
by day and eke by night:
That at the last the Lady said,
she should be shamed quite;
What was the matter, tell me true,
that so her sorrow bred? 10
Her Shoomaker most daintily
had got her maidenhead.
But he at length so wisely wrought,
as doth the Story tell:
Her fathers right good will he got,
and euerything was well.
And Crispianus *came again*
from warres victoriously:
Then Shoomakers made Holiday:
and therefore so will I. 20
And now, for Crispianus *sake,*
this wine I drink to thee,
And he that doth this mark mistake,
and will not now pledge me:
He is not Crispianus *friend,*
not worthy well I wot,
To haue a Lady to his Loue,
as Crispine *he hath got.*

Chap. X.

How Sir *Simon Eyer* being at first a Shoomaker, became 30
in the end Maior of *London*, through the counsell of
his wife: and how he broke his fast euery day on a
Table that he said he would not sell for a thousand
pounds: and how he builded *Leadon Hall.*

OUr English Chronicles do make mention that sometime
there was in the honourable City of *London* a worthy Maior,
known by the name of Sir *Simon Eyer*, whose fame liueth in the
mouths of many men to this day, who, albeit he descended from
mean parentage, yet, by Gods blessing, in the end he came to be
a most worthy man in the commonwealth. 40

This man, being brought young out of the North countrey, was
bound prentise to a Shoomaker, bearing then the name of the
Gentle Craft (as still it doth) his Master being a man of reason-

able wealth, set many iourney-men and prentises to work, who
followed their businesse with great delight, which quite excludeth
all wearinesse; for when seruants do sit at their worke like
Dromedaries, then their minds are neuer lightly vpon their
businesse; for it is an old prouerbe.

> *They proue seruants kind and good,*
> *That sing at their businesse like birds in the wood.*

Such fellows had this young Lad, who was not behind with
many Northern Iigs to answer their Southern Songs.   This youth
10 being the youngest prentise in the house, as occasion serued, was
often sent to the Conduit for water, where in short time he fell
acquainted with many other prentises coming thither for the same
intent.

Now their custome was so, that euery Sunday morning diuers
of these prentises did vse to go to a place neer the Conduit to
break their fast with pudding-pies, and often they would take
Simon along with them: but vpon a time it so fell out, that when
he should draw money to pay the shot with the rest, that he had
none, whereupon he merrily said vnto them: My faithfull friends,
20 and Conduit companions, treasurers of the water tankard, and
main pillers of the pudding house, I may now compare my purse
to a barren Doe, that yields the Keeper no more good than an
empty carkasse: or to a bad nut, which, being opened, hath neuer
a kernell: therefore, if it will please you to pardon me at this
time, and excuse me for my part of the shot, I do here vow vnto
you, that, if euer I come to be Lord Maior of this City, I will giue
a breakfast vnto all the printises in London.

We do take your word (quoth they) and so they departed.

It came to passe, that *Simon* hauing at length worn out his
30 yeers of Apprentiship, that he fell in loue with a maiden that was
neer neighbour vnto him, vnto whom at length he was married
and got him a shop, and labored hard daily, and his young wife
was neuer idle, but straight when she had nothing to do, she sat
in the shop and spun: and hauing liued thus alone a yeer or
thereabout, and hauing gathered something together, at length he
got him some printises, and a Iourney-man or two, and he could
not make his ware so fast as he could haue sold it, so that he
stood in great need of a Iourney-man or two more.

At the last, one of his seruants spying one go along the street
40 with a fardell at his back, called to his Master, saying, Sir, yonder
goes Saint *Hughs* bones, twenty pounds to a penney.

Run presently (quoth he) and bring him hither.

The boy running forth, called to the man, saying, Good fellow,
come hither, here is one would speak with you.

The fellow, being a Frenchman that had not long been in
England, turning about, said, Hea? what you sea? Will you

speak wed me : Hea ? What you haue ? tell me, what you haue, Hea ? And with that coming to the stall, the good-man askt him if he lackt work, We par ma foy (quoth the French-man).

Hereupon *Simon* took him in, and to worke he went merrily, where he behaued himselfe so well, that his Master made good account of him, thinking he had been a Bachelor, but in the end it was found otherwise.

This man was the first that wrought vpon the low cut shooe, with the square toe, and the latchet ouerthwart the instep, before which time in *England* they did weare a high shooe that reached 10 aboue the ankles, right after the manner of our husbandmens shooes at this day, saue onely that it was made very sharp at the toe turning vp like the tail of an Island dog : or as you see a cock carry his hinder feathers.

Now it is to be remembred, that while *Iohn Deneuale* dwelt with *Simon Eyer*, it chanced that a ship of the Ile of *Candy* was driuen vpon our Coast, laden with all kind of Lawns and Cambricks, and other linnen cloth : which commodities at that time were in London very scant, and exceeding dear : and by reason of a great leak the ship had got at Sea, being vnable to sail any 20 further, he would make what profit he could of his goods here.

And being come to *London*, it was *Iohn Deneuales* chance to meet him in the streets, to whom the Merchant (in the Greek tongue) demanded where he might haue lodging : for he was one that had neuer been in England before, and being vnacquainted, wist not whither to go : but while he spake Greek, *Iohn Deneuale* answered him still in French, which tongue the merchant vnderstood well : and therefore, being glad that he had met with one that could talk to him, he declared vnto him what tempests he endured at Sea, and also how his ship lay vpon the coast with such 30 commodities as he would sell.

Truly Sir (quoth *Iohn*) I am my selfe but a stranger in this Country and vtterly vnacquainted with Merchants, but I dwell with one in this City that is a very honest man, and it may be that he can help you to some that will deal with you for it, and if you think it good, I will moue him in it, and in the mean space, Ile bring you where you may haue a very good lodging ; tomorrow morning I will come to you again.

Sir (said the Merchant) if you please to do me that fauour, Ile not onely be thankfull vnto you for the same, but also in most 40 honest sort will content you for your pains : and with that they departed.

Now as soon as *Iohn* the Frenchman came home, he moued that matter vnto his Master, desiring him that he would do what he could for the Merchant. When his Master had heard each circumstance, noting therewith the want of such commodities in the Land, cast in his mind as he stood cutting vp his work, what were best to be done in this case, saying to his man *Iohn*, I will think vpon it betwixt this and the morning, and then I will tell you my mind: and therewithall casting down his cutting Knife, he went out of his shop into his Chamber, and therein walked vp and down alone very sadly, ruminating hereon: he was so far in his muse, that, his wife sending for him to supper two or three times, he nothing regarded the maids call, hammering this matter in his head:

At last his wife came to him, saying, Husband, what mean you that you do not come to supper? why speak you not man? Hear
10 you? good husband; come away, your meat will be cold: but for all her words he stayed walking vp and down still, like a man that had sent his wits a woll-gathering, which his wife seeing, puled him by the sleeue, saying, why, husband in the name of God, why come you not? wil you not come to supper to night? I called you a good while ago.

Body of me, wife (said he) I promise thee I did not hear thee.

No faith, it seemeth so (quoth she) I maruel whereupon your mind runneth.

Beleeue me wife (quoth he) I was studying how to make my
20 selfe Lord Maior and thee a Lady.

Now God help you (quoth she) I pray God make vs able to pay euery man his own, that we may liue out of debt and danger, and driue the Woolf from the doore, and I desire no more.

But wife (said he) I pray thee now tell me, Doest thou not think that thou couldest make shift to bear the name of a Lady, if it should be put vpon thee.

In truth Husband (quoth she) Ile not dissemble with you, if your wealth were able to beare it, my mind would beare it well enough.

30 Well wife (replyed he) I tell thee now in sadnesse, that, if I had money, there is a commodity now to be bought the gains, wherof would be able to make me a Gentleman foreuer.

Alas husband, that dignitie your Trade allows you already, being a squire of the *Gentle Craft*, then how can you be lesse than a Gentleman, seeing your sonne is a Prince borne?

Tush wife (quoth he) those titles do onely rest in name, but not in nature: but of that sort had I rather be, whose lands are answerable to their vertues, and whose rents can maintain the greatnesse of their minde:

40 Then sweet husband, tell me (said his wife) tell me, what commodity is that which you might get so much by? I am sure your self hath some money, and it shall go very hard but Ile procure friends to borrow one forty shillings, and beside that, rather then you should lose so good a bargain, I haue a couple of crowns that saw no Sun since we were first married, and them also shall you haue.

Alasse wife (said *Simon*) all this comes not neere that matter: I confesse it would do some good in buying some backs of leather, but in this thing it is nothing, for this is merchandize that is precious at this time, and rare to be had ; and I hear that whosoeuer will haue it must lay down 3,000 pounds ready money. Yea wife, and yet thereby he might get three and three thousand pounds profit.

His wife hearing him say so was inflamed with the desire thereof, as women are (for the most part) very couetous : that matter running still in her mind, she could scant finde in her heart to spare him time to go to supper, for very eagernesse to animate him on, to take that bargain vpon him.   Wherefore so soon as they had supt, and giuen God thanks, she called her husband, saying, 10 I pray you come hither, I would speake a word with you : that man is not alwayes to be blamed that sometimes takes counsell of his wife ; though womens wits are not able to comprehend the greatest things, yet in doubtful matters they oft help on a sudden.

Well wife, what mean you by this (said her husband ?)

In truth (quoth she) I would haue you to pluck vp a mans heart, and speedily chop vp a bargain for these goods you speak of.

Who I ? (quoth he), which way should I do it, that am not able for 3 thousand pounds, to lay down three thousand pence ?   20

Tush man (quoth she) what of that ? euery man that beholds a man in the face, knows not what he hath in his purse, and whatsoeuer he be that owes the goods, he will no doubt be content to stay a moneth for his money, or three weeks at the least : And, I promise you, to pay a thousand pounds a week is a pretty round payment, and, I may say to you, not much to be misliked of.

Now husband, I would haue you in the morning with Iohn the Frenchman to the Grecian Merchant, and with good discretion driue a sound bargain with him for the whole fraught of the ship, and thereupon giue him halfe a dozen Angels in earnest, and 30 eight and twenty dayes after the deliuery of the goods, condition to deliuer him the rest of his money.

But woman (quoth he) dost thou imagine that he would take my word for so weighty a masse of money, and to deliuer his goods vpon no better security ?

Good Lord (quoth she) haue you no wit in such a case to make shift ?   Ile tell you what you shall do : Be not known that you bargain for your own selfe, but tell him that you do it in the behalf of one of the cheif Aldermen in the City ; but beware in any case, that you leaue with him your own name in writing ; he being 40 a Grecian cannot read English : and you haue no need at all to shew *Iohn* the Frenchman, or if you should, it were no great matter, for you can tell well enough that he can neither write nor read.

I perceiue wife (quoth he) thou wouldest fain be a Lady, and worthy thou art to be one, that dost thus imploy thy wits to bring thy husband profit : but tell me, if he should be desirous to see the Alderman to confer with him, how shall we do then ?

Iesus haue mercy vpon vs (quoth she) you say women are fools, but me seemeth men haue need to be taught sometimes. Before you come away in the morning, let *Iohn* the Frenchman tell him that the Alderman himselfe shall come to his lodging in the afternoon : and, receiuing a note of all the goods that be in the ship, he shall deliuer vnto him a bill of his hand for the payment of his money, according to that time. Now sweetheart (quoth she) this Alderman shall be thine own selfe, and Ile go borrow for thee all things that shall be necessary against that time.

10 Tush (quoth her husband) canst thou imagine that he, seeing me in the morning, will not know me again in the afternoon?

O husband (quoth she) he will not know thee, I warrant thee : for in the morning thou shalt go to him in thy doublet of sheeps skins, with a smuched face, and thy apron before thee, thy thumbleather and hand-leather buckled close to thy wrist, with a foule band about thy necke, and a greasie cap on thy head.

Why woman (quoth he) to go in this sort will be a discredit to me, and make the Merchant doubtfull of my dealing : for men of simple attire are (God wot) slenderly esteemed.

20 Hold your peace good husband (quoth she) it shall not be so with you, for *Iohn* the Frenchman shall giue such good report to the Merchant for your honest dealing (as I praise God he can do no lesse) that the Grecian will rather conceiue the better of you than otherwise : iudging you a prudent discreet man, that will not make a shew of that you are not, but go in your attire agreeable to your trade. And because none of our folks shall be priuy to our intent, to-morrow weel dine at my cousin *Iohn Barbers* in *Saint Clements Lane*, which is not far from the *George* in *Lumbard-street*, where the merchant strangers lie. Now Ile be sure that all things 30 shall be ready at my cousin *Iohns* that you shall put on in the afternoon. And there he shall first of all with his scissers snap off all the superfluous hairs, and fashion thy bushy beard after the Aldermans graue cut : then shall he wash thee with a sweet Camphire Ball, and besprinkle thine head and face with the purest rose-water ; then shalt thou scoure thy pitchy fingers in a bason of hot water, with an ordinary washing Ball ; and all this being done, strip thee from these common weeds, and Ile put thee on a very fair doublet of tawny sattin, ouer the which thou shalt haue a cassock of branched damask, furred round about the skirts with 40 the finest foynes, thy breeches of black Veluet, and shooes and stockings fit for such array : a band about thy neck as white as the driuen snow, and for thy wrists a pretty pair of cuffs, and on thy head a cap of the finest black, then shalt thou put on a fair gown, welted about with Veluet, and ouerthwart the back thwart it shall be with rich foyne, with a pair of sweet gloues on thy hands, and on thy forefinger a great seale-ring of gold.

Thou being thus attired, Ile intreat my cousin *Iohn Barber*, because he is a very handsome young man, neat and fine in his apparell (as indeed all Barbers are) that he would take the pains to wait vpon you vnto the Merchants, as if he were your man, which he will do at the first, because one of you cannot vnderstand the other, so that it will be sufficient with outward curtesie one to greet another, and he to deliuer vnto you his notes, and you to giue him your Bill, and so come home.

It doth my heart good, to see how trimly this apparell doth become you, in good faith, husband, me seems in my mind, I see you in it already, and how like an Alderman you will look, when you are in this costly array. At your return from the Merchant, you shall put off all these clothes at my Cousins again, and come home as you did go forth. Then tell *Iohn* the Frenchman, that the alderman was with the Merchant this afternoon, you may send him to him in the morning, and bid him to command that his Ship may be brought down the Riuer : while she is coming about, you may giue notice to the Linnen Drapers, of the commodities you haue coming.

Enough wife (quoth he) thou hast said enough ; and, by the grace of God, Ile follow thy counsell, and I doubt not but to haue good fortune.

Chap. XI.

How *Simon Eyer* was sent for to my Lord Maiors to supper, and shewing the great entertainment he and his wife had there.

ANon after, supper time drew neer, she, making herselfe ready in the best manner she could deuise, passed along with her husband vnto my Lord Maiors house : and being entred into the great Hall, one of the Officers there certified my Lord Maior, that the great, rich Shoomaker and his wife were already come. Whereupon the Lord Maior in courteous manner came into the Hall to *Simon*, saying, You are most heartily welcome good Master *Eyer*, and so is your gentle bed-fellow. Then came forth the Lady Maiores and saluted them both in like manner, saying, Welcome, good Master *Eyer* and Mistresse *Eyer* both : and taking her by the hand, set her down among the Gentlewomen there present.

Sir (quoth the Lord Maior) I vnderstand you are a Shoomaker, and that it is you that hath bought all the goods of the great Argozy.

I am indeed, my Lord of the *Gentle Craft* (quoth he) and I praise God, all the goods of the great Argozy are mine own, when my debts are paid.

38. bought up *1675 &c.* : brought up *1648*

God giue you much ioy of them (said the Lord Maior) and I
trust you and I shall deal for some part thereof.

So the meat being then ready to be brought in, the guests were
placed each one according to their calling.   My Lord Maior
holding *Simon* by the hand, and the Lady Maiores holding his
wife, they would needs haue them sit neer to themselues, which
they then with blushing cheeks refusing, my Lord said vnto them,
holding his cap in his hand.

Master *Eyer* and Mistresse *Eyer*, let me intreat you not to be
10 troublesome, for I tell you it shall be thus : and as for those
Gentlemen here present, they are all of mine old acquaintance,
and many times we haue been together, therefore I dare be ʃthe
bolder with them : & albeit you are our neighbours also, yet I promise
you, you are strangers to my table, and to strangers common
courtesie doth teach vs to shew the greatest fauour, and therefore
let me rule you in mine house, and you shall rule me in yours.

When *Simon* found there was no remedy, they sat them down,
but the poore woman was so abashed, that she did eat but little
meat at the Table, bearing her selfe at the table with a comely
20 and modest countenance : but what she wanted in outward feeding,
her heart yeelded to, with inward delight and content.

Now, so it was, many men that knew not *Simon*, and seeing him
in so simple attire sit next my Lord, whisperingly asked one another
what he was.   And it was enough for *Simons* wife, with her eyes
and ears, to see and hearken after euerything that was said or
done.

A graue, wealthy Cittizen, sitting at the Table, spake to *Simon*,
and said, Sir, in good will I drink to your good health, but I
beseech you pardon me, for I know not how to call your name.

30 With that my Lord Maior answeared him, saying, his name is
Master *Eyer*, and this is the Gentleman that bought all the goods
that came in the black *Swan* of *Candy*, and, before God, though
he sit here in simple sort, for his wealth I do verily beleeue he is
more sufficient to bear this place than my selfe.   This was a man
that was neuer thought vpon, liuing obscure amongst vs, of none
account in the eyes of the world, carrying the countenance but of
a shoomaker, and none of the best sort neither, and is able to
deal for a bargain of fiue thousand pounds at a clap.

We do want many such shoomakers (said the Citizen) and so
40 with other discourse droue out supper.

At what time, rising from the table, *Simon* and his wife,
receiuing sundrie salutations of my Lord Maior and his Lady, and
of all the rest of the worshipfull guests, departed home to their
own house ; at what time his wife made such a recitall of the
matters ; how brauely they were entertained, what great chear was
there, also what a great company of Gentlemen and Gentlewomen
were there, and how often they drank to her husband and to her,
with diuers other circumstances, that I beleeue, if the night had

been six moneths long, as it is vnder the North pole, they would haue found talke enough till morning.

Of a truth (quoth she) although I sate closely by my Ladies side, I could eat nothing for very ioy, to heare and see that we were so much made of. And neuer giue me credit husband, if I did not hear the Officers whisper as they stood behind me, and all demanded one of another, what you were, and what I was: O (quoth one) do you see this man? mark him well, and marke his wife well, that simple woman that sits next my Ladie: what are they? What are they (quoth another)? Marry this is the rich Shoomaker 10 that bought all the goods in the great Argozy: I tell you there was neuer such a Shoomaker seen in London since the City was builded. Now by my faith (quoth the third) I haue heard much of him to-day among the Merchants in the street, going between the two Chains: Credit me husband, of mine honesty this was their communication. Nay, and do you not remember, when the rich Citizen drank to you (which craued pardon because he knew not your name) what my Lord Maior said? Sir (quoth he) his name is Master *Eyer*, did you mark that? and presently thereupon he added these words: this is the Gentleman that bought, and so 20 forth. The Gentleman vnderstood you, did you heare him speake that word?

In troth wife (quoth he) my Lord vttered many good words of me, I thank his honour, but I heard not that.

No (quoth she.) I heard it well enough: for by and by he proceeded further, saying, I suppose though he sit here in simple sort, he is more sufficient to beare this charge than my selfe. Yea (thought I) he may thank his wife for that, if it come so to passe.

Nay (said *Simon*) I thank God for it.

Yea, and next him you may thank me (quoth she). And it did 30 her so much good to talk of it, that I suppose, if she had liued till this day, she would yet be prating thereof, and if sleep did not driue her from it.

And now seeing that *Simon* the Shoomaker is become a merchant, we will temper our tongues to giue him that title, which his customers were wont to do, and from henceforth call him master *Eyer*, who, while he had his affairs in hand, committed the Gouernment of his shop to *Iohn* the Frenchman, leauing him to be guide to his other seruants, by meanes of which fauour *Iohn* thought himselfe at that time to be a man of no small reputation. 40

30. quoth she *1675* &c. : quoth he *1648*

Chap. XII.

How *Iohn* the Frenchman fell in loue with one of his
Mistrisse Maids: and how he was crossed through
the craft of *Haunce* the Duchman.

AT the same time there was dwelling in the house, a iolly lusty
wench, whose name was *Florence,* whom *Iohn* the Frenchman
loued dearly well, and for her onely sake he brought many a good
bottle of wine into the house, and therewithall so soon as their
master and mistresse were gone to bed, they would oftentimes
10 make merrie amongst themselues ; which *Haunce* a Iourney-man
in the same house perceiueing, sought to crosse them as much as
in him lay, thereby to bring his own purpose the better to passe,
which was to ioyn the maidens fauours to his own affection.

And because the Frenchman had greatest gains vnder his
Master, and being thereof no niggard when he had got it, the
maids did most delight in him, and little esteemed the Duchman,
though his good will were as great towards her as the other : for
they could not be in any corner of the house together, nor could
they meet in any place abroad, but the Duchman would still watch
20 them.

Vpon a time, *Florence* being at Market, her Loue *Iohn* went
forth of the shop to meet her, and *Haunce* stayed not long behind,
who at length espied them, and heard his fellow *Iohn* questioning
with her in this sort.

What *Florence,* what haue you in your basket ? hea, let me see
what you buy.

Marrie, *Iohn* (quoth she) I haue bought Beefe and Mutton,
and other things.   Come, come, must you peep in my basket
(quoth she) away, for shame away.

30   Be Got, *Florence,* me will see a little : ha, ha ! *Florence,* you
buy the pudding hea ? You loue de puddings ? *Florence* hea ?

Yea, Sir (quoth she) what if I do loue puddings? what care you?

Of my tra, *Florence,* if I be your husband me will giue you
pudden, shall warren.

My husband (quoth she ?) in faith Sir, no, I mean not to marrie
a Frenchman.

What *Florence,* de Frenchman be de good man : but *Florence,*
me will giue you a pinte of wine by my treat.

O, I cannot stay now, I thank you, *Iohn.*

40   What (quoth he) *Florence,* no stay with your friend?   I shall
make you stay a little time.

And so with that, taking her by the hand, into the Tauern they
go, and *Haunce* the Duchman following them, and sate close in

42. they go *1675 &c.*: then go *1648*

the next roome, and by that means he heard all that they said, and that they appointed the next Sunday to go to *Islington* together, and there to be merry : and so, the maid hasting away, they departed.

Well (quoth *Haunce* secretly to himselfe) it shall go hard but Ile disappoint you.

Sunday in the afternoon being come, *Iohn* the Frenchman, according to his appointment, went before to *Islington*, leauing *Florence* to come after, with another Maid which dwelt in the same house, whilest he prepared good chear for their coming : and the 10 more to make her merrie, he hired a noise of musitians to attend their pleasure.

And as it after happened, his fellow *Haunce* preuented this sport, who watching in the fields for *Florence*, at length he spied her coming : to whom he said, Well met fair *Florence*, your friend *Iohn* hath changed his mind, for whereas he appointed you to meet him at *Islington*, you shall lose your labour so to do, for he is not there.

No ? how so (said *Florence*) ?

The reason is this (said *Haunce*) so farre as I can vnderstand 20 by him, he thinks you are verie fickle and inconstant, and because it was his chance this morning, to see you speak to a young man that passed by, he saith verrily, that you are a maruellous great dissembler : and in this humour he is gone I know not whither.

And is it euen so (said *Florence*) ? Ile tell thee what *Haunce*, because he hath made thee priuie to his mind, I will shew thee somewhat of mine. Doth he suspect me because I did but speake to one ? Nay, if he be so iealous now, what will he be hereafter ? And, therefore insomuch that it is so, let him go to the Deuill, he shall very well find, that I will set as light by him, 30 as he doth by me. Did the knaue get leaue of my Mistris for me to come abroad this day, and doth he now serue me thus ? Well, this shall teach me wit, in faith, and so she turns back again.

Nay (quoth *Haunce*) seeing you are now abroad, let me intreat you to go to *Hogsdon*, and I will bestow a messe of cream vpon you.

In the end she was won, and as they walked together, *Haunce* spake thus vnto her : I know not what cause *Iohn* the Frenchman hath giuen you, to bear him so good will, as I perceiue you do, but in my mind, he is a far vnmeet match for you. And thus 40 much I know, he is of a very mistrustfull nature, a wauering mind, and deceitfull heart, he did professe great good will to you in outward shew, but I haue heard him speak most shamefully of you behind your back, making his vaunts, that he had you at a beck of his finger, and how that for a pint of Wine he could cause you to follow him vp and down ouer all the Citie, *Florence*, I am a fool to tell you thus much, it may be you will scarce beleeue it, and, for my part, I will not vrge you thereunto : but

in troth, look what I tell you, it is for good will, because I haue
been sorrie to see you abused.

I thank you good *Haunce* (quoth she) I may beleeue it well
enough : but from henceforth I know what I haue to do : I confesse
indeed, that I haue drunk with him abroad, but it was at his own
earnest intreaty, neither could I euer be quiet for the knaue, he
doth so follow me vp and down in euery place ; but, seeing, I know
his dissimulation to be such, if I do not requite him in his kind,
trust me no more : and now I am heartily sorrie that I was so
10 foolish as to follow him this day at his appointment : but seeing
he hath serued me thus, he shall not know of my coming out of
doors, and therefore good *Haunce*, do not tell him that you met
me this day in the fields.

Nay in faith, *Florence* ; (quoth he) I will not onely be secret
to thee, but will also from henceforth acquaint thee with all my
proceedings.

And hauing eaten their creame, *Haunce* brought her some part
of the way homeward : and, taking his leaue of her, he went back
to see if he could meet with *Iohn* the Frenchman, who hauing
20 stayed at *Islington* for *Florence* vntill almost night, and she not
coming, he and the Musicians together were faine to eat vp the
meat, without more company, which caused *Iohn* the frenchman to
swear like a Turk.

And as he was coming homeward ouer the fields chaffing and
fretting to himselfe, who should he meet withall but *Haunce* the
Duchman : who said to him : What *Iohn*, who thought to meet
you here ?

Here thou seest I am now (said *Iohn*) : but when came you
from home?

30 Marry but euen now (quoth *Haunce*).

And who is at home (said *Iohn*) ?

The other answered, there was no body but their mistresse, and
the maid *Florence*, with the rest of the houshold.

Is *Florence* at home (said *Iohn*) ? The Deuill take her for me, she
hath maid a right fool of me indeed.

How so (quoth *Haunce*) ? Then the other in a great chafe, said :
Be Got shall be reuenged, *Florence* mock an me too mush, too
mush she make me beleeue she loue me, and me tink so too, and,
be Got, she make me a Iack Fool.

40 When *Haunce* heard him say so, he said : Alas good *Iohn*, she
loue thee ? If you think so, you are greatly deceiued : for she is
the scoffingest quean in *London* : And I haue heard her behind
your back, to mock and flout you, saying : Doth shitten *Iohn* think
that I will marry him ? In faith Sir no.

When the Frenchman heard this, he stampt like a mad-man,
and bit his thumb, saying : Mordue me shall be reuenged, be Got :
shitten *Iohn*? call a shitten *Iohn*, hea? A de put in corroyn, a
meshant, shitten *Iohn*, no better name but shitten *Iohn*?

It is as I tell you (quoth *Haunce*) : and moreouer, she said she scorned to come after you to *Islington*, saying, she would see you hanged first.

Well be no matter ; she no loue me, me no loue she, but me shall go home, me shall, and beat as a stockfish.

Nay, do not so (said *Haunce*) but let her alone : for it is no credit for you to beat a woman : and besides that, if you should, our Master would turn you out of doores ; therefore be quiet a while, and be secret in that I haue told you, then shall you see how she vseth you.   10

In this humour they departed : at what time, *Iohn*, full of melancholy, stood frowning by the fire side : and as the Maid went vp and down the house about her businesse, he cast looks on her, as fierce as a Panther ; but she, by reason of the Duchmans tale to her, shews her selfe as scornfull as he was currish, and not once cast her eye towards him, and thus they droue out the time of a senight or a fortnight.

Chap. XIII.

How Master *Eyr* was called vpon to be Sheriffe of *London*, and how he held his place with worship.   20

IN this space master *Eyer* following his businesse, had sold so much of his Merchandize as paid the Grecian his whole money : and yet had resting to himselfe three times as much as he had sold, whereof he trusted some to one Alderman, and some to another, and a great deal amongst substantiall Merchants ; and for some had much ready money, which he imployed in diuers merchandizes : and became Aduenturer at Sea, hauing (by Gods blessing) many a prosperous voiage, whereby his riches dailie increased.

It chanced vpon a time, that being in his study, casting vp his accounts, he found himselfe to be clearely worth twelue or thirteen 30 thousand pounds, which he finding to be so, he called his wife to him, and said :

The last day I did cast vp my accounts, and I finde that Almighty God of his goodnesse hath lent me thirteen thousand pounds to maintain vs in our old age, for which his gracious goodnesse towards vs, let vs with our whole hearts giue his glorious Maiesty eternall praise, and therewithall pray vnto him, that we may so dispose thereof, as may be to his honour, and the comfort of his poore members on earth, and aboue our neighbours may not be puffed vp with pride, that, while we think on our wealth, we 40 forget God that sent it to vs, for it hath been an old saying of a wise man, that abundance groweth from riches, and disdain out of abundance : of which God giue vs grace to take heed, and grant vs a contented mind.

So soon as he had spoken this, they heard one knocking hastily at doore, whereupon he sent *Florence* to see who it was, the Maiden, coming again, told her Master it was one of my Lord Maiors Officers that would speake with him.   The Officer being permitted to come in, after due reuerence, he said, Sir, it hath pleased my Lord Maior with the worshipfull Aldermen his brethren, with the counsell of the whole communaltie of the honourable City, to chuse your worship Sheriffe of *London* this day, and haue sent me to desire you to come and certifie your minde therein, 10 whether you be contented to hold the place or no.

Master *Eyer* hearing this, answered he would come to his Honor and their worships incontinent, and resolue them what he was minded to do ; and so the Officer departed.

His wife, which all this while listned to their talk, hearing how the case stood, with a ioyfull countenance meeting her husband, taking him about the neck with a louing kisse, said, Master Sheriffe, God giue thee ioy of thy name and place !

O wife (quoth he) my person is far vnworthy of that place, and the name far exceeds my degree.

20   What, content your selfe, good husband (quoth she) and disable not your selfe in such sort, but be thankfull vnto God for that you haue, and do not spurn at such promotion as God sendeth vnto you : the Lord be praised for it, you haue enough to discharge the place whereunto you are called with credit : and wherefore sendeth God goods, but therewithall to do him and your Countrey seruice ?

Woman (quoth he) Soft fire makes sweet mault : For such as take things in hand rashly, repent as suddenly : to be Sheriffe of *London* is no little cost.   Consider first (quoth he) what house I ought to haue, and what costly ornaments belong thereunto, as : 30 hanging of Tapistry cloth of Arras, and other such like, what store of Plate and Goblets of Gold, what costly attire, and what a chargeable train, and that which is most of all, how greatly I stand charged beside, to our Soueraigne Lord, the King, for the answering of such prisoners as shall be committed to my custody, with an hundred matters of such importance, which are to such an Office belonging.

Good Lord husband (quoth she) what need all these repetitions ? You need not tell me it is a matter of great charge : notwithstanding, I verily think many heretofore haue with great credit 40 discharged the place, whose wealth hath not in any sort been answerable to your riches, and whose wits haue been as mean as your own : truly Sir shall I be plain ?   I know not anything that is to be spoken of, that you want to performe it, but only your good will : and to lack good will to do your King and Countrey good were a signe of an vnworthy Subiect, which I hope you will neuer be.

Well wife (said her husband) thou dost hold me here with prittle prattle, while the time passeth on, tis high time I were gone to *Guild-Hall*, I doubt I shall appear too vnmannerly in causing my Lord Maior and the rest to stay my leisure.

And he hauing made himselfe ready, meet to go before such an assembly as he went vnto, he went out of doores, at what time his wife called after him, saying : and holding vp her finger. Husband, remember, you know what I haue said : take heed you dissemble not with God and the world, look to it Husband.

Go too, go too, get you in (quoth he) about your businesse, and so away he went.

So soon as he was gone out of sight, his wife sent one of his men 10 after him to *Guild Hall*, to hearken and hear, whether her husband held his place or no : and if he do, bring me word with all possible speed.

I will, mistresse (quoth her man).

Now, when Master *Eyer* came to *Guild-Hall*, the Lord Maior and his brethren bade him heartily welcome, saying Sir, the communaltie of the City, hauing a good opinion of you, haue chosen you for one of our Sheriffes for this yeer, not doubting but to find you a fit man for the place.

My good Lord (quoth he) I humbly thank the City for their 20 courtesie and kindnesse, and would to God my wealth were answereable to my good will, and my ability were able to bear it. But I find my selfe insufficient ; I most humbly desire a yeers respite more, and pardon for this present.

At these words, a graue Commoner of the City standing vp, with due reuerence spoke thus vnto the Maior : my good Lord, this is but a slender excuse for master *Eyer* to make ; for I haue often heard him say, and so haue diuers others also, that he hath a Table in his house whereon he breaks his fast euery day, that he will not giue for a thousand pounds : Wherefore (vnder your 30 Lordships correction) in my simple iudgement, I think he that is able to spare a thousand pounds in such a dead commodity is very sufficient to be Sheriff of *London*.

See you now (quoth my Lord) I muse, Master *Eyer*, that you will haue so lame an excuse before vs, as to take exceptions, at your own wealth, which is apparantly proued sufficient ; you must know, Master *Eyer*, that the Commons of *London* haue searching eyes, and seldome are they deceiued in their opinion, and, therefore looke what is done, you must stand to it.

I beseech you, my Lord (quoth Master *Eyer*) giue me leaue to 40 speak one word. Let it be granted, that I will not giue my Table whereon I breake my fast for a thousand pounds, that is no consequence to proue it is worth so much, my fancy to the thing is all : for doubtlesse no man here would giue me a thousand shillings for it when they see it.

All is one, for that (quoth my Lord Maior) yet dare I giue you as much wine as you will spend this yeer in your Shriualrie to let me haue it.

My good Lord (quoth he) on that condition I will hold my place, and rest no longer troublesome to this company.

You must hold (said my Lord) without any condition or exceptions at all in this matter ; and so they ended.

The Assembly being then broken vp, the voice went Master *Eyer* is Sheriffe, Master *Eyer* is Sheriffe.   Whereupon the fellow that Mistresse *Eyer* sent to obserue how things framed, ran home in all haste, and with leaping and reioycing said : Mistresse, God giue you ioy, for you are now a Gentlewoman.

10   What (quoth she) tell me sir sawce, is thy Master Sheriffe, or no ? and doth he hold his place ?

Yes Mistresse, he holds it now as fast as the stirrop doth the shooes while we sow it.

Why then (quoth she) I haue my hearts desire, and that I so long looked for, and so away she went.

Within a while after came her husband, and with him one of the Aldermen, and a couple of wealthy Commoners, one of them was he that gaue such great commendations of his Table, and comming to his doore, he said, You are welcome home good Master 20 Sheriffe.

Nay, I pray you, come in and drink with me before you go. Then said he, Wife bring me forth the pasty of Venison, and set me here my little Table, that these Gentlemen may eat a bit with me before they go.

His wife which had been oft vsed to this terme, excused the matter, saying ; The little Table ! Good Lord husband, I do wonder what you will do with the little Table now, knowing that it is vsed already ? I pray you good Husband, content your selfe, and sit at this great Table this once.   Then she whispered him in the eare, 30 saying ; What man, shall we shame ourselues ?

What shame ? (quoth he) tell not me of shame, but do thou as thou art bidden ; for we are three or foure of vs, then what do we troubling the great table ?

Truly (answered she) the little table is not ready now good husband, let it alone.

Trust me we are troublesome guests (said the Aldermen), but yet we would fain see your little Table, because it is said to be of such prize.

Yea, and it is my mind you shall (quoth Master *Eyer*), therefore 40 he called his wife again, saying, good wife, dispatch and prepare the little Table : for these Gentlemen would fain haue a view of it.

Whereupon his wife, seeing him so earnest, according to her wonted manner, came in : and setting her selfe down on a low stool, laid a fair Napkin ouer her knees, and set the platter with the pasty of Venison thereupon, and presently a chear was brought for Master Alderman, and a couple of stools for the two commoners, which they beholding, with a sudden and hearty laughter, said : Why Master Sheriffe, is this the table you held so deare ?

Yes truly (quoth he).

Now verily (quoth they), you herein haue vtterly deceiued our expectation.

Euen so did you mine (quoth he) in making me Sheriffe : but you are all right welcome, and I will tell you true, had I not thought wondrous well of you, you had not seen my table now. And I think, did my Lord Maior see it as you do, he would repent his bargain so hastily made. Notwithstanding I account of my table neuer the worse.

Nor haue you any cause (quoth they) and so after much pleasant talk, they departed, spreading the fame of master Sheriffes little Table over the whole City.

But you must now imagine, that a thousand cares combred the Sheriffe, in prouiding all things necessary for his office : at what time he put off his Shoomakers shop to one of his men, and set vp at the same time the signe of the black Swan swiming vpon the sea, in remembrance of that ship, that first did bring him his wealth, and before that time, the sign of the black swan was neuer seen or known in any place in or about the City of *London.*

Chap. XIIII.

How *Haunce* hauing circumuented *Iohn* the Frenchmans Loue, was by him and others finely deceiued at the Garden.

NOw at that time *Iohn* the frenchman, and fair *Florence* were both at variance, as you heard before, by the Duchmans dealing, by which subtilty he sought means to win fauour for himselfe, which *Iohn* the Frenchman perceiued, and therefore went about, not only to preuent him, but to take reuenge on him for his deceitfulnesse. And meeting *Florence* as she went into the Garden for flowers, he began to talk thus vnto her. What, *Florence*, you go to the Garden ?

And how then (quoth she) what haue you to say to that ?

Me sea nothing, but you be discontent ; you no speak a me, you no look a me ; nor you no drink with me, nor noting, ah *Florence*, how chance dat ?

Go get thee hence, prating fool (quoth she) I drink with thee ? Thou shalt be pie-peckt first.

Pie-peck ? What be pie-peckt a hea ? Be Got *Florence*, you make me a Iack-nape, you mock a me, and call me shitten *Ian*, and you be so proud, because *Haunce* loue you, dat shall be maruell, but and if you call me shitten *Iohn* any more, par my foy, shall not put vp, shall not take at your hands.

Who told you, that I called you shitten *Iohn* (quoth *Florence*) I neuer called you so.

No *Florence*! you no call a me shitten *Iohn*? a so meshant
villain pulard *Haunce* tell a me so.

I neuer said so (quoth *Florence*), but *Haunce* told me that you
made your boast that I was at a beck of your finger; and that
you could make me follow you vp and down the whole City for
a pinte of Wine; no, I would you should well vnderstand, I will
not follow a better man than you.

Of my fet *Florence*, me neuer say so.

No? Yes (quoth she) but you did, I can tell you by a good
10 token, for that very time that I should haue met you at *Islington*,
you said it, and made me a fool to come ouer the fields to you,
and when all came to all, you sent *Haunce* to tell me you were
gone there hence long agone.

Ah cet toking, *Haunce* (quoth *Iohn*) be des ten bon, tis true,
for me tarry, dere more den one, two, tree hour, and had prouide
shapon, de rabit, de creame, de pudding-pie, and twenty ding more.

Well howsoeuer it was, I am sure I was made an asse betwixt
you, and for that cause I will beware how I shew kindnesse again
to any: therefore, *Iohn* I pray you be gone, and seek some other
20 company, for you shall not go with me.

No (said *Iohn*)? Well den, adieu, *Florence*, and so they departed.

Now it is to be vnderstood, that *Haunce* had promised *Florence*
to meet her in the Garden, and to bring with him a bottle of
Wine, and there in the presence of a maid or two more, to make
themselues sure together: and she for that purpose, had carryed
with her a good corner of a Venison pasty. But there was an
English-Iourney-man in the house called *Nicholas*, that vnderstood
thereof, who, meeting with *Iohn* the Frenchman, he made him
priuie thereunto, saying; Trust me *Iohn*, if thou wilt be ruled by
30 me, we will not onely disappoint this match, but also with their
good chear make ourselues merry. *Iohn*, who was glad and ready
to do the Duchman any iniury, consented to follow *Nicholas* his
counsell in any thing.

Then (quoth *Nicholas*) it shall be thus: I will go to the Garden,
and stay for *Haunce* his coming with the Wine, and, in the meane
space do thou hide thy selfe vnder one of the hedges of the
Garden on the other side, and with thee take a couple of pots,
and let the one be empty, and the other filled with water, and when
Haunce is come into the Garden with his bottle of Wine (now he
40 will not let me see it by his good will) notwithstanding, Ile
obserue well where he doth set it down, and then I will finde
the meanes, while they are busie in toying and talking, to conueigh
the bottle of Wine through the hedge to thee, and likewise the
Venison: then, emptying the bottle, thou shalt fill it with water,
and thrusting it through the hedge again, it shall be set where
first it was found, which being done, thou shalt hastily rap at the
Garden doore, at what time they shall be told that it is my
Master or Mistresse, which they hearing will be in such a maze,

that on a sudden they will not know which way to turn themselues, especially for the conueying away of *Haunce*: Now when
you haue knockt twice or thrice, and that you heare no body
come to the doore, get you away, and stay for me at the Rose in
Barking, and there we will drink vp their Wine, eat vp the Venison :
and this being done weele laugh them to scorn.

Truly *Nicholas* (quoth *Iohn* the Frenchman) this will be braue,
and thereupon they prepared themselues to do the feat. *Nicholas*
therefore got him into the Garden, and by and by after comes
Haunce with the bottle of Wine, who knocking at the Garden 10
doore was straight let in : but seeing *Nicholas* there, he secretly
set his bottle in a corner : but *Nick*, who had as searching eyes as
Argus in his businesse, quickly did as before he had determined,
and instead of Wine set the bottle down again, where he first
found it full of water,

Then comes *Iohn*, and lustily knocks at the doore.

There is our Master and Mistresse (quoth *Nicholas*).

Alas (quoth *Florence*) what shall we do for *Haunce*? then rapt
he at the doore again, Alas (quoth she) get you ouer the hedge.

Shall I open the doore (quoth *Nick*?)   O no, said *Florence*, 20
not yet good *Nick*.

With that he knockt more hastily : Anon, anon (quoth she).
Hence *Haunce*: Go to the doore *Nick*.

Who is there (quoth he)?   And with that opening the doore
found iust no body.   Truly *Florence* (said he) they are gone
whosoeuer they were.   God be with you, I can stay no longer.

When he was departed, the Maids wished that *Haunce* had
been there again.   Alas, poore fellow (quoth they) is he gone,
and left his bottle behind him?

Marry I am glad that it is no worse (quoth *Florence*): And 30
now, that the Wine is here, we will drink it for his sake, and I
haue here a morsell of Venison, that will giue it a good relish :
and therewithall looking for it, she found the cloak, but the meat
gone.   Now, a vengeance one it (quoth she) one skuruie Cur or
other hath got into the Garden and took away the meat !

O God, what ill luck is that (quoth the Maid :) a murren one
that Cur that got it : but seeing it is gone, farewell it.

Well (said *Florence*) here is the wine yet, I know it is excellent
good : for he told me he would bring a bottle of the best Renish
Wine that could be bought in *London* : and I am certain he is as 40
good as his word.   But beleeue me *Ioane*, he is as kind hearted
and as louing a fellow as euer professed loue to any : I assure you
that here is a cup of Wine that the King might drink thereof : but
how shall we do for a glasse ?

Weele drink it out of the bottle (said *Ioane*).

Not so (quoth *Florence*) I do loue to see what I drink, and
therefore Ile borrow a glasse at the next house.

22. she : he *1648 &c.*

And while she goes for a glasse (said *Ioane* to her selfe) Ile haue a taste of it before she returns again : and then setting her hand vnto the bottle, and the bottle to her mouth she drank a good draught, and finding it to be something thin in the going down, she said to *Besse* that sat by : Credit me now, but for the name of Wine, I haue drunk as good water.

It is Renish Wine (quoth *Besse*) and that is neuer strong.

It may be made of rain well enough (quoth *Ioane*).

At which words *Florence* entred with a glas : and powring it out
10 into the glasse, she extolled the colour, saying, see what a braue colour it hath, it is as clear, I do assure you, as rock water : and therewithall drinking it off, she said, it drinks very dead : Of a troth (quoth she) this is but bad Wine, it is euen as dead as a doore naile : and so filling the glasse again, she gaue it vnto *Besse*.

She tasting thereof, said : Passion of me, this is plain water.

Water (said *Ioane* ?) Is it water ? Let me taste of it once again : by my Maiden-Head, it is water indeed (quoth she).

Water (said *Florence*) you haue played the drabs in drinking out the Wine, and filling the bottle again with water.

20 Of my faith (quoth *Ioane*) you say not true in so saying : I would you did vnderstand, we played not the drabs in any such sort, but *Haunce* rather played the Knaue, that brought vs water instead of Wine.

Nay (quoth *Florence*) I dare swear for him that he would not serue you so for all the wealth my Master is worth. And I am perswaded it was no body but your selues that did it : but, in faith you might haue dealt so with another, and not with me.

Nay then (quoth they) you need not to serue vs so, to cause vs drink water instead of Wine : and we would you should think,
30 although you be Master Sheriffes Maid, we loue our mouths as well as you do yours for your life, and it was but an homely recompence for our good will, I tell you true : neither do we care how little we come to be thus deluded.

Go too, go too (said *Florence*) you are like to Penelopes puppy, that doth both bite and whine, I know you well enough.

Know vs (quoth *Ioane*). What do you know by vs ? we defie you for anything you can say by vs. Know vs ? Nay it were well if thou didst know thy selfe ; and hearest thou ? though thou hast thy companions to meet thee at thy pleasure, and we haue
40 not : no, know vs ? we are known to be as honest as thou art, or else we should be sorry ; and so she departed in a chafe.

Now *Iohn* the Frenchman and *Nicholas*, hauing eaten the Venison and drunk vp the wine, came back again time enough to hear all this strife, whereat they greatly reioyced. But so soon as *Florence* did meet with *Haunce* again, she kept no small stir for mocking her with a bottle of water, about the which they fell at variance, in such sort that they were not friends for a long time after.

But during the time that *Haunce* was out of fauour *Nicholas*
sought the Maids frendship by all the means he might, but in
vain was his pains spent therein: for, although *Florence* (out-
wardly) seemed much displeased, yet *Haunce* had her heart still,
and in processe of time obtained great fauour; the matter was
grown so foreward, that the performance of their marriage was
forthwith appointed, which they intended should be celebrated at
the Abbey of Grace on *Tower hill.* Notwithstanding, this matter
was not kept so close, but that their secret dealings were known,
and *Nicholas,* purposing to deceiue the Duchman, made *Iohn* the 10
Frenchman priuie thereunto, saying; *Iohn,* it is so, that this night,
at midnight Masse, *Florence* and *Haunce* do intend secretly to be
married, and they haue appointed the Frier to do it so soon as the
Tapers are all put out, because they will not be seen of any:
Therefore *Iohn,* if now you will be my friend, I do not doubt but
to marry her my selfe, and so to giue the Duchman the slampam,
and bore him through the nose with a cushin.

Ha (quoth *Iohn*) be Got me shall do as you sea, and therefore
Nicholas tell me what you do.

Marry *Iohn* (quoth he) you know the Duchman loueth to drink 20
well, and by that he loueth weele cause him to lose his Loue; for
we will get him out to the Tauern, and there cause him to be disguised, that he shall neither be able to stand nor go.

Iohn the Frenchman hearing this, scratched his head, and
rubbing his elbow, said, Ma foy, *Nicholas,* dis be de fine trick:
how shall we get him forth a doores?

Excellent well (quoth *Nicholas*) for there is a new Iourney-man
come to Town with Sir *Hughs* bones at his back, and you know
that we, being of the *Gentle Craft,* must go giue him his welcome,
and I will tell *Haunce* thereof, who being now very iocund, by 30
reason that his marriage is so neer, will not deny to come, I know.
Therefore you and the stranger Iourney-man shall go before to the
Tauern, and then I will go fetch him.

A beene, content, content (said *Iohn*).

And so to the Tauern he hasted with the strange man. Anon
comes *Nicholas* and *Haunce,* and with them two or three Iourney-
men more, and all to the new Iourney-man: sitting down, they
got *Haunce* in the midst, called for wine lustily, and such varieties,
as the Duchman was soon set packing; for euery one sought to
ouercharge him, and, being himselfe of a good kind to take his 40
liquor, spared not to pledge euery man. At what time, in the
midst of his cups, being well whitled, his tongue ran at random
(as wine is the bewrayer of secrets) so it proued by him, for there
he opened to his companions all his whole mind, saying My
hearts, for all I sit here I must be a married man ere morning.

---

23. nor go *1675 ; 1648 apparently introduces foreign matter which breaks off
at the end of the page,* nor go, and while he lies parbraking his minde, hearing
this, scratched his head &c., *as in text.*

God giue you ioy (quoth they).

But who shall you marry (said *Nick*).   *Florence*?

Yea *Florence* (said the Duchman) that is the Lasse that I do loue, and all the world cannot deceiue me of her now, I am the man that must haue her Maidenhead, and this night we must be married at the Abbey of Grace ; and if you be good fellows, go with me to Church ; will you go with me?

Will we ged with thee? (said *Iohn* Frenchman) that we will.

O *Iohn* (said *Haunce*) I haue wiped your nose, and *Nicks* too,
10 you must weare the willow Garland.

Well, what remedy (quoth they) it is the better for you.

But in faith *Haunce*, seeing it is so (quoth *Nick*) weele haue one pottle of Wine more, that we may drink to the health of your fair Bryde.

Ile pledge her, if it be a gallon (quoth *Haunce*).

Be my fet and trot (said *Iohn*) weele haue a gallon. Hea Drawer, where be you?   I pray you bring me a gallon of de best Claret, and a gallon of de best Sack, shall make merry i'fet : What *Florence* be marry and I no know?

20   But by the time that this wine was drunk, *Haunce* was laid vp for walking any more that night.   When *Nick* perceiued that, he stole suddenly out of the Tauern, and went to meet *Florence* at the appointed place : but *Iohn* quickly missed him, knew straight whereabout he went, got him presently to the Constable of the Postern gate and told him, that *Nick* had laid a man for dead in *Tower street*, and that he was gone to saue himselfe vnder the priuiledge of the Abbey of Grace ; but (quoth he) if you will go along, I shall bring him out with fair words vnto you, and then I desire you to clap him vp to answer this matter in the morning.

30   But where dwell you (said the Constable)?

I do dwell with Master Alderman *Eyer* (quoth *Iohn*) and there you shall haue me at all times.

The Constable did as *Iohn* bade him, and commited *Nicholas* to prison.   In the mean space, *Florence* and an old woman of *Tower street* said that they did go to a womans labour, and by that means they passed along by the watch, and to the Abbey of Grace they came.   They had not long been there, but that *Iohn* Frenchman meeting them, said, *Florence*, well met, here is a fit place to finish that I haue long looked for :

40   *Iohn* (quoth she) thou art like an euill spirit that must be coniured out before a body shall get any quietnesse, vrge not me vpon any such matters, for you be not the man I looke for, and therefore, as taking little pleasure in your presence, as of your proffers, I would be very glad to see your back.

What (said *Iohn*) haue you no compassion vpon a poore man? you be hard-hearted indeed.

But as he was vttering these speeches, it was his wiues chance to hear his tongue, being newly come from the Barge at *Billinsgate*, and at that time going toward Saint *Katherines* to see if she could meet with some of her Countrey folks that could tell her any tydings of her husband; but as I said, hearing his tongue, and knowing him by his speech, she said : What, *Iohn Deneuale?* My husband *Iohn Deneuale?* What make you wed pretty wence hea ?

At which words *Iohn* was stricken into such a dump, that he wist not what to say : notwithstanding, hearing *Florence* to ask if she was his wife, he answered and said, Yea.

O thou dissembling fellow (quoth she) is it euen so? Didst thou say thou wast a Batcheller, seeking to marry me, and hast a 10 wife aliue? Now fie on thee : O good Lord, how was I blest to escape him : nay, now I see that *Haunce* may haue a wife in *Flaunders* too, although he be here : and therefore, by the grace of God, I will not marry a stranger.

O (quoth *Iohn*) I thought my wife had been dead, but seeing she is aliue, I will not lose her for twenty thousand crowns.

So *Florence* departed and left *Iohn* with his wife.

Now, *Haunce* neuer waking vntill it was next day at noon ; when he saw he had ouerslept himself, being very sorry, he went home, not knowing how to excuse his folly to *Florence* ; 20 whom she vtterly forsook, as well in regard of his drunkennesse, as for that being a stranger, he might, like *Iohn* Frenchman, haue another wife liuing. But *Nicholas* (that all this while lay in prison) being brought before Aldermann *Eyer*, rehearsed the truth, and, crauing pardon for his offence, was without more ado deliuered. And *Florence* being called before him, he made vp the match between her and his man *Nicholas*, marrying them out of his house with credit, giuing them a good stock to begin the world withall : also for *Iohn* Frenchman he did very much, and shewed himselfe a good Master to his man *Haunce*, and to all the rest of his 30 seruants.

Chap. XV.

How Master Alderman *Eyer* was chosen Lord Maior of *London*, and how he feasted all the prentises on Shroue tuesday.

WIthin a few yeers after, Alderman *Eyer* being chosen Lord Maior of *London*, changing his copy, he became one of the worshipfull Company of Drapers, and for this yeer he kept a most bountifull house. At this time it came into his mind what a promise once he made to the Prentises, being at breakfast with 40 them at their going to the Conduit, speaking to his Lady in this wise : Good Lord (quoth he) what a change haue we had within these thirty yeers? And how greatly hath the Lord blessed vs since that ? blessed be his Name for it.

I do remember, when I was a young Prentise what a match I
made vpon a Shroue tuesday morning, being at the Conduit,
among other of my companions; trust mee wife (quoth he) tis worth
the hearing, and Ile tell thee how it fell out.

After we had filled our Tankards with water, there was some
would needs haue me set down my Tankard, and go with them
to breakfast (as many times before I had done) to which I consented : and it was a breakfast of Pudding-pies. I shall neuer forget it. But to make short, when the shot came to be paid, each one
drew out his money but I had not one peny in my purse, and credit
I had none in the place ; which when I beheld, being abashed,
I said; Well my Masters, do you giue me my breakfast this time;
and in requitall thereof, if euer I be Maior of *London*, Ile bestow a
breakfast one all the Prentises of the City : these were the words, little
thinking, (God wot) that euer it should come to passe : but such was
the great goodnesse of our God, who setteth vp the humble, and pull-
eth down the proud, to bring whom he pleaseth to the seat of Honour.
For as the scripture witnesseth, Promotion cometh neither from the
East nor from the West, but from him that is the giuer of all good
things, the mighty Lord of heauen and earth. Wherefore wife, seeing God hath bestowed that vpon me that I neuer looked for ; it is
reason that I should perform my promise : and being able now,
Ile pay that which then I was not able to do : for I would not
haue men say that I am like the Ebon-tree, that neither beares
leafes nor fruit. Wherefore wife, seeing that Shroue tuseday is so
neer at hand, I will vpon that day fulfill my promise, which vpon
that day I made.

Truly (my Lord) (quoth she) I will be right willing thereunto.

Then answered my Lord, as thou dost loue me, let them want
neither Pudding-pies nor Pancakes, and look what other good
chear is to be had, I will referre all to your discretion.

Hereupon great prouision was made for the Prentises breakfast :
and Shroue tuesday being come, the Lord Maior send word to the
Aldermen, that in their seuerall Wards they should signifie his
mind to the Citizens, to craue their fauours that their Prentises
might come to his house to breakfast, and that for his sake they
might play all the day after. Hereupon it was ordered that at the
ringing of a Bell in euery Parish, the Prentises should leaue work
and shut vp their shops for that day, which being euer since
yeerly obserued, it is called the Pancake Bell.

The Prentises being all assembled, my Lord Maiors house was
not able to hold them, they were such a multitude, so that besides
the great Hall, all the Gardens were set with Tables, and in the
backside Tables were set, and euery other spare place was also
furnish'd : so that at length they were al placed and while meat
was bringing in, to delight their eares, as well as to feed their
bodies, and to drown the noise of their pratlings, Drums and
Trumpets were pleasantly sounded : that being ended, the waits

of the City, with diuers other sorts of Musick played also to beguile the time, and to put off all discontent.

After the first seruice, were all the Tables plentifully furnished with Pudding-pies and Pancakes, in very plentifull manner ; and the rest that remained was giuen to the poore. Wine and Ale in very great measure they had giuen, insomuch that they had no lack, nor excesse to cause them to be disordered. And in the midst of this their merriment, the Lord Maior, in his Scarlet gown, and his Lady in like manner went in amongst them ; bidding them all most heartily welcome, saying vnto them, that his promise 10 so long ago made, he hath at length performed. At what time they (in token of thankfulnesse) flung vp their Caps, giuing a great shout, and incontinently they all quietly departed.

Then after this, Sir *Simon Eyer* builded *Leaden-Hall*, appointing that in the midst thereof, there should be a Market place kept euery Munday for Leather, where the Shoomakers of *London*, for their more ease, might buy of the Tanners without seeking any further.

And in the end, this worthy man ended his life in *London* with great Honour.

A new loue Sonnet. 20

Maide.

All hayle sweet youth, fair Venis graft,
    Cheife Master of the Gentle Craft,
How comely seemes thou in my sight,
    Like *Phebus* in the heauens bright,
That neuer was in *Cupids* pound,
    Or from his shaft receiud a wound ;
For by thy mirth it doth appeare
    Thy minde is free from griefe and care.

Shoomaker. 30

Faire Maid, you speak no more but truth,
    For why the freedome of my youth,
I value at too high a rate,
    To linke myselfe with any mate ;
There is no comfort on the earth,
    Compared to a freeborne mirth,
When fairest beauties me orethwart,
    I look the better to my heart.

When beauteous Nymphs do me surprize,
    I shut the Casements of mine eyes, 40
For he is a fond and foolish Elfe,
    That loues a maid losing himselfe,
To fall in loue is such a thing,
    From whence sometimes doth mischiefe spring,
I wish well vnto women-kind,
    But for to wed I haue no minde.

Maide.

What if your Casements chance to ope,
  And giue affection so much scope,
As to encounter with a Dame,
  Why then methinks it were a shame,
For you to loue and not to speake,
  And by degrees the Ice to break :
But if you speak and so obtaine,
  Then haue you found your heart againe.

10 It were a shame for Maids to woe,
  But men may speak and so may you,
If that occasion offerd be,
  God Cupids blind and cannot see,
But shoots at randome here and there,
  O therefore *Edmond,* haue a care,
At vnawares you may be hit,
  No pollicy can hinder it.

But O vnhappy women kinde,
  That toxicated are in minde,
20 And know not how to vent the same,
  Without the losse of our good name,
They count vs bold if now and than,
  We do but look vpon a man,
And look we may, but dare not speak,
  Much lesse our mindes vnto them break.

Shoomaker.

Would I were worthy for to know
  The cause of this your griefe and wo,
For why, your words and looks declare,
30 Your minde is ouercharg'd with care,
If that your heart be fled away,
  And it be taken for a Stray,
The man that hath it Ile perswade
  To take some pity on a Maid.

This young man struck this faire maid mute,
  She wanted one to pleade her Sute,
Faine would she speak, but was afraid,
  This is the case of many a Maid,
He was the man whom she loud best,
40 Her heart did lodge within his breast,
Although to him it was vnknown
  Vntill at last he lost his owne.

  38. case *1675 &c.* : cause *1648*

Cupid the god of loue came downe,
  And on this young Man cast a frown,
He bent his bowe and sent a dart,
  That struck the young Man to the heart,
And, cause the Maid should win the prize,
  He opened the Shoomakers eyes,
So when her beauty he beheld,
  He gladly yeelded vp the field.

With folded Armes along he walkt,
  And thus vnto himselfe he talkt,   10
O what are we that vainly trust
  In our weak strengths that are but dust;
I durst haue sworne no liuing wight,
  Could moue me from my sweet delight,
But now I see and feele the smart,
  Mine eyes too soon deceiue my heart.

He that before was grown so stout,
  And strong enough to keep loue out,
Is vanquisht now and made to yeeld,
  And did both win and lose the field;   20
He conquerd her to him vnknown,
  She conquerd him, made him her own:
Thus Maids with men are dallying still,
  Till they haue brought them to their will.

Alas (quoth he) how am I crost,
  Beholding her, my selfe Iue lost;
Now beauty is become a snare,
  The which hath brought me to dispaire;
If she no other man had loud,
  I might haue hope she might be moud;   30
But she another doth affect,
  And I must dye without respect.

She noting of his passion then,
  As Maids will do that loue young Men;
And finding the occasion fit,
  Mark here a wily wenches wit;
Delayes proue dangerous she knew,
  And many Maids haue found it true:
Thus in her selfe resolud to speak,
  Shee vnto him her mind did break.   40

(Quoth she) young man, it is your lot,
  The god of loue hath laid a plot,
The net was spread, the bird is caught,
  And I haue found the thing I sought:
Though Men are strong and Women weak,
  Stout hearts will yeeld before theyl break;
And Women sometimes win the field
  When men are willing for to yeeld.

With that the Nimphs and Rurall Swaines,
  Come straightway tripping ore the plaines.
The Satyres made them Pipes of Reeds,
  And brought in Musick more then needs;
The Syrens sung such songs of mirth,
  That brought King *Oberon* from the earth;
The Fairies with their Fairy king,
  Did dance about them in a ring:

Chorus.

10   All health and happinesse betide,
  The Shoomaker and his sweet bride,
Lo thus we sing and thus we dance,
  Till we haue brought loue in a trance,
Thus pleasures sweet this couple grace,
  Both linckt together in sweet imbrace,
The neighboring hils and dailes resound,
  With Eccho of our pleasant sound.

Whilst thus they sung their Roundelayes,
  God *Cupid* crownd their heads with bayes,
20   The bride lookt like the Queen of *May*,
  The Shoomaker led her away,
Where now they liue in quiet peace,
  And loue doth more and more increase,
Thus loue you see, can finde a way,
  To make both Men and Maids obey.

How a Shoomakers widdow fell in loue with her man.

These three years *Iohn* I haue been deep in loue,
  And nere till now had time my mind to moue,
Speak, Canst thou loue me though I am thy Dame?
30   I would not haue thee daunted, Fie, for shame.
Old prouerb, spare to speak and spare to speed,
  Thou wantst a wife and I a husband need.

His Answer.

Mistris I am in loue as well, tis true,
  But to speak truth, in truth I loue not you,
I haue a Maid in Chase, as sweet a Lasse,
  In my conceit I think, as euer was:
Pray then, forbeare, it neuer shall be said
  I took a widdow and forsook a Maid.

40   Reader obserue whats written by the Poet,
  Women and Maids loue men, but few will shew it.

F I N I S.

14. *1675 ; 1648 omits this line.*

THE
GENTILE
CRAFT.

The second Part.

Being a moſt merrie and pleaſant
Hiſtorie, not altogether vnprofitable nor
any way hurtfull: verie fit to paſſe away the te-
diouſneſſe of the long winter evenings.

By *T. D.*

Newly correcded and augmented.

Haud curo invidam.

LONDON,
Printed by *Elizabeth Parſlow*, dwelling neere

To the Master and Wardens of the worshipfull company of the Cordwaynors

in London, all continuance of health and perfect brotherly affection.

ONce more hath good will emboldened me, to present vnto your Worships my worthles labour, to manifest the good affection I beare to this fraternity: and finding, you lent a gentle looke on the first part of this History, I haue beene the more bolde to proffer you the second: for hauing bound my selfe by promise to performe it: and you perhaps clayming promise as a debt, expecting payment, I bent all my study to keepe touch: whereupon I tender this small trifle vnto you, onely crauing at your worships hands, a good opinion of my poore endeuours. And albeit this pamphlet doth not minister matter worthy your graue view: yet in regard of the subiect, I trust you will deigne to esteeme it, sith so well as I could, though not so well as I would, I haue sought herein to procure your delight: and although you finde not all the men spoken of, which is promised in the first part, yet thinke it no faintnes in me, but fault of good instruction: and againe, for as much as these men here mentioned were all of this Citie (whose story grew longer then I supposed) and the other of the country: I thought good so to breake off, and to defer their story to another time, when I may more perfectly speake thereof In the meane space I commend your Worships to the protection of the most highest.

Your Worships in all he may.

T. D.

To the Courteous Readers
health.

GEntle Reader, you that vouchsafe to cast curteous lookes into this rude Pamphlet, expect not herein to find any matter of light value, curiously pen'd with pickt words, or choise phrases, but a quaint and plaine discourse best fitting matters of merriment, seeing wee haue herein no cause to talke of Courtiers or Scholers. Notwithstanding, if you find your selfe 'quer charged with melancholy, you may perhaps haue here a fit medicine to purge that
10 humour, by conferring in this place with Doctor *Burket :* or if you meet with round *Robin*, he may chance ryme it away. I tell you among Shoomakers is some solace, as you shall see by *Tom Drums* entertainment, and other mad merry prankes playd by the Greene-King of S. Martins. If that will not suffice, you may, in meeting with *Anthony now now*, haue such a fit of mirth, with his firking Fiddle, that it shall be a great cause to expell choler. And so I leaue you to your owne liking, whether you will enter to see this sport or no : stand backe, I pray, roome for a Gentleman, for you cannot come in vnder a groat.

Containing the History of *Richard*
Casteler: and the first of his loue.

THE louely Maidens of the Citty of *Westminster*, noting what
a good husband *Richard Casteler* was and seeing how
diligently hee followed his businesse, iudged in the end he
would proue a rich man : for which cause many bore him very
good affection, and few there was that wished not themselues to
be his wife : insomuch that he hauing the custome of all the
pretty Wenches in the Citty, by that meanes knew the length of 10
euery Maidens foot so well, that he aboue all other best pleased
them. On the Sundayes when he came into the Church, the
Maides eyes were so firmely fixed on him that hee could neither
looke forward, backeward, nor on any side, but that he should be
sure to haue a winke of one, a smile of another, the third would
giue a nod : and to be briefe, they would all cast on him such
gracious lookes, that it was easie to guesse by their outward countenance, their inward good will.

And when in his Holy-dayes attire he past along the streets,
the Maidens (after their businesse was done) standing at their 20
Masters doores and spying him, would say thus one to another :
Now verily, there goes a proper ciuill young man, wise & thrifty :
yea such a one as in time will proue wondrous wealthy, and
without all doubt, will come to great credit and preferment.

These and the like words would they vse of him continually,
whereby he had among them such a generall good opinion, that,
as he stood a dayes at his cutting boord, he should be sure to
haue twenty cursies made him in an houre, by Maidens that past
vp and downe : some would bestow on him dainty, sweet nose-
gayes, of the fairest flowers they could find, and other some would 30
bring him handkerchers of Cambrick, and diuers such like fauours,
well bewraying their friendship towards him.

But among many that secretly affected him, I will onely tell
of twaine, because aboue all the rest, their merriments doe onely
remaine in memorie, the one of them was called *Margaret* of the
spread-Eagle, but more commonly knowne by the name of long
Meg of Westminster. The other was a proper neat wench named
Gillian of the George, both of them as wily as they were witty,
who among all the Maides in *Westminster* were reputed to

5. a good a husband *1639*   11. aboue] about *1639*

be the best seruants ; hauing therefore good wages, they maintained themselues gallantly, and therwithall so honestly, that no
man could quip them with bad liuing, though afterward it fell out
otherwise, as in this historie you shall heare.

Margaret was a maiden, borne in *Lancashire*, in height and
proportion of body passing the ordinary stature of women, but
there-withall very comely, and of amiable countenance, her
strength was agreeable to her stature and her courage as great as
them both : she was of a quicke capacitie, and pleasant dis-
10 position, of a liberall heart, and such a one as would be sodainely
angry, and soone pleased, being readier to reuenge her wrongs by
weapons, then by words : and therein did shee differ from the
nature of other women, because shee could not abide much
brabling : and so heedfull was shee of her behauiour in her
yonger yeeres, that, her good properties far exceeding her portion,
she was wooed by diuers, but would be won by none, for the man
whom shee most loued least thought vpon her.   And albeit shee
manifested her good will by diuers meanes, yet did *Richard* little
regard it, hauing his mind nothing bent vnto marriage, by meanes
20 whereof *Margaret* grew into such sad conceits as changed her
chery cheekes into a greene wan countenance, in-somuch that
euery one wondred to see her pensiueries.

At last it chanced that *Margaret* hauing occasion to go into
London, it was her good fortune to meet with *Gillian* of the
George whom her mistres had sent thither to buy Comfets and
Carawayes, with diuers other sweet meates, for that they had
a banket bespoken by diuers gallant Courtiers, which that night
appointed to come thither : but so soone as *Margaret* spied her,
she smiled, saying : *Gillian* now in good sadnes, wel met, (if thou
30 beest met a maid.)

And ill met (quoth shee) not meeting so good a maid as my
selfe.

Tush (said *Margaret*) it is good for vs to thinke well of our
selues, for there is enough that think ill of vs.

Mary I defie them (quoth *Gillian*) that thinks ill of me, and
I respect as little their speech, as they do my profit.   For a woman
with a good life, feares no man with an euill tung.

If you bee so hot (quoth *Margaret*) where the wind blows so
cold, what will you be by that time supper is ready, where the
40 fire will be as fierce as your choller is great ? and mistake mee
not, good *Gillian*, though I said men think ill of vs, I meane not
thereby that any goe about to blemish our good names ; but
I suppose they thinke not so wel of vs as they might do that doe
not loue vs so well as to marry vs.

Nay (said *Gillian*) if that be all, I am at a good point ; for
though my maiden-head be somewhat burdensom to beare, yet
I had rather keepe it, then bestow it on a bad husband : but
though I say it, though I be but a poore wench, I haue choise of

husbands enough, and such as I am assured in my conscience, would both loue me well, and keepe me gallantly.

Wherefore then doe you not marry (quoth *Margaret*)? in my opinion it is the most pleasingst life that may be, when a woman shall haue her husband come home and speake in this sort vnto her. How now Wife? how dost thou my sweetheart? what wilt thou haue? or what dost thou lacke? and therewithall kindly embracing her, giues her a gentle kisse, saying: speake my prettie mouse, wilt thou haue a cup of Claret-wine, White-wine, or Sacke to supper? and then perhaps he carues vnto her the leg ₁₀ of a Capon, or the wing of a Chicken, and if there be one bit better then other, shee hath the choise of it: And if she chance to long for anything by and by it is sent for with all possible speed, and nothing is thought too deare to doe her good. At last hauing well refresht themselues, she sets her siluer whistle to her mouth, and calles her maid to cleare the boord: then going to the fire, he sets her on his knee, and wantonly stroking her cheeke, amourously hee chockes her vnder the chin, fetching many stealing toutches at her rubie lips, and so soone as he heares the Bell ring eight a clocke, he calles her to goe to bed ₂₀ with him. O how sweet doe these words sound in a womans eares? But when they are once close betweene a paire of sheetes, O *Gillian* then, then.

Why what of that (quoth she)?

Nay nothing (saith *Margaret*) but they sleep soundly all night.

Truly (quoth *Gillian*) there be many wiues, but few that meete with such kind husbands: but seeing you aske me why I marry not, in troth *Meg* I would tell thee, if I had time to stay: but I feare I haue stood too long pratling here already, and there-fore farewell good *Meg*, when I see thee againe, thou shalt know ₃₀ more of my mind.

Nay *Gillian*, heare you (quoth she) go but a little way with me, and I will goe home with you as straight as a line, for I haue nothing to buy but a score of Quinces, and couple of Pomegranets, and that shall be done in a trice.

Gillian was contented for her good companies sake to stay a while, and as soone as *Margaret* had made her market, they settled themselues to goe homeward, where by the way *Gillian* entred into this communication.

You did euen now demand a question of me, and very desirous ₄₀ you were to know why I did not marry when I was so well offered: Trust me *Margaret*, I take you to be my friend, which makes me the more willing to vnfold my fancy, being as well perswaded of your secresie as I am of your amity, and there-vpon I am the more willing to make you copartner of my counsailes. Fire in straw will not be hidden, and the flames of affection wil burst forth at length, though it be long kept vnder. And truth it is that I haue forsaken good matches, for I might haue had Master *Cornelius* of the Guard if I would, who as you know is wealthy, and therwithall of very good conuersation, yet there was one thing made me refuse his kind offer.

What was that (quoth *Margaret*) I pray thee tell?

(Quoth she) he loued not me so well but I loued another tenne times better, and therefore it is not good for handes to ioyne, where hearts agree not. No *Meg*, no, there is a youth in our street that nearer touches my heart and better pleases my mind, notwith-standing he shall go namelesse, for it is an old prouerb, two may 10 keep counsell if one be away.

Nay then (quoth *Meg*) if you dare not trust me, tell no further, notwithstanding, I haue had credit in as great matters as yours, for many a man hath put his life in my hands, & found no hurt thereby, and as many women haue commited their secrets to me, as men haue ventured their bodies with me.

Go to *Margaret*, you are disposed to iest (said *Gillian*) but sweare by thy Maidenhead that thou wilt neuer bewray my liking, nor preuent me in my loue, & I will shew thee all.

Nay fie, do not so (quoth *Margaret*) shew not all, for shame, least 20 more see it then my selfe, for so may they blush at thy boldnes, and nothing commend thy modesty: but it is happy that I haue a maidenhead left to sweare by: else I perceiue I should know nothing of thee.

No, trust me (quoth *Gillian*) for such a one as cannot keepe her Maidenhead, wil neuer keep a secret, and that made *Katherine* of the Crane to be such a blab: but now *Meg* I will proceed to the matter. What doe you thinke by *Richard* of the Rose, the wakeful cock of *Westminster*?

Oh, he (quoth *Meg*) is that the man? there is no reason I should 30 thinke amisse of him that euery man commends: neuerthelesse, he is no body in respect of riches, being but a yong housekeeper of one yeares standing, a man (God wot) vnacquainted with the worlds guise, and, to speake truth, nothing comparable to Master *Cornelius*.

I will tell thee what (quoth *Gillian*) that man which needeth neither to flatter with his friends, nor borrow of his neighbours hath riches sufficient: and hee is most poore that hath least wit, by which arguments I am able to prooue, that the Cock is as wealthy as he is wary, for he will sure be beholding to no body, or 40 to as few as he may, and it is al wayes to be noted that men of such mindes doe neuer proue beggers.

Margaret hearing *Gillian* so stoutly to take *Richards* part, perceiued by her vehement speeches the great affection she bore to him, and finding that she was sick of her owne disease, *Margaret* sought means to remoue the cause of her griefe, & thereby thrust her selfe into the greater sorrow: And the policy she vsed most herein, was to speak altogether in *Richards* dispraise, seeking thereby to dislodge her loue, and the more firmely to plant her owne, whereupon she vttered her mind in this sort.

Well *Gillian*, seeing you beare so good an opinion of *Richard* of the Rose, I would not for a bushel of Angels seek to disswade you : but because you request my opinion how I like the man, in troth I will tell thee my mind without fraud or flattery : I confesse that *Richard* is a gentle young man, curteous and kind, diligent about his businesse, and wary in his dealings, which argues good husbandry. Notwithstanding, I like not these ouer-couetous fellowes, of such greedy mindes, such penny fathers and pinch-fistes, that will not part from the paring of their nailes nor the dropping of their nose, if they thought it would yeeld them but the fourth part of a farthing. Tell me I pray thee, what ioy should a woman haue with such a churle, that would grudge at every halfe-penny that is laid out, that in a whole yeare would not leaue a farthing worth of mustard vnwritten in his booke : And such a one I feare will this Cocke proue, for me thinkes hee lookes with a hungry nose, and, howsoeuer you think of him, I know not but I verily feare, though hee be a Cocke by name, hee will neuer proue a Cock of the game. Againe he is but a dwarfe in respect of a man, a shrimpe, a Wren, a hop of my thumbe, such a one as a baby might hide in a wrinkle of their buttocks.

Well *Meg* (quoth shee) you are priuiledged to speake your pleasure, but should another thus mistearme him, I would teare her face : I tell thee true I had rather haue a winner then a waster, a sparer, then a prodigall spender : for when a man in his youth, hath gotten something with paine, he may the better spend it in his age with pleasure, and farre better it is hee should be thought couetous, then carelesse ; his stature and proportion of body pleases me well enough, for it is no matter how great hee is, but how good hee is.

But *Margaret* seeing our talk hath indured so long, that it hath brought vs both home, let vs at our parting be mindfull of our promises, to keepe secret whatsoeuer hath been said, for little knowes the young man the depth of my mind, and therefore would I keepe it close, till I saw some signe of good will proceeding from him, for it becommeth not maidens to be woers, though willingly they could wish to wed where they best fancie, and so farewell sweet *Margaret*.

Adue gentle *Gillian* (quoth *Margaret*) vntill our next meeting, when I hope I shall further vnderstand of your proceedings in your loue.

When *Meg* had thus vnderstood her mind, and saw how the matter went, she sought all meanes possible to preuent her, as hereafter shall be shewen.

<hr>

10. pinchfoistes *1639*

Chap. II.

How *Margaret* requested *Richard* to the eating of a
Posset at night: And how her Masters buttocks was
scalded therewith.

IT chanced that against Whitsontide, *Margaret* stood in need
of a new paire of Shooes: Therefore in a morning betimes
she came to *Richard* of the Rose to bespeake them aforehand, and
the more to declare her kindnes, and to win his good will, she
carried with her a bottle of excellent good Muskadine, which one
10 of the Yeomen of the Kings wine seller had bestowed vpon her:
and to make it relish the better, she carried with her a dainty
peece of powdred beefe, and the tender carkasse of a cold Capon,
and thus plesantly began to greet him. All health to the kind
cocke of *Westminster*, that with the Larke greetes the Sun rising with
a cheerefull note, and mounts aboue many to the loue of pretty lasses.
Tell me (quoth she) thou bonny Lad, wilt thou take the length of
my foote, and make me a good payre of shooes against Sunday?
That I will *Margaret* (quoth he) therefore let me see thy foote:
There is both my foote and leg (said *Meg*) I am not ashamed
20 to shew either of them, for I am not legged like a Crane nor footed
like a Flie, and therewith lift vp her cloathes to the knee, whereat
Richard smiling said, a little higher *Meg* and shew all:
Whereupon she sodainly replied in this sort: soft, *Richard* not
so, for I will tell thee one thing.

> *Euery Carter may reach to the garter,*
> *A Shoomaker he may reach to the knee,*
> *But he that creepes higher shall aske leaue of me.*

Good reason (quoth *Richard*) leaue is light, which being
obtained a man may be bold without offence, but this onely is my
30 griefe, I haue neuer a Last in my shop long enough for thy foot:
Then I would they were all fired (quoth *Meg*) He that will be
counted a good workman must haue tooles to fit all persons, and
I muse that you which striue to be counted excellent, will want
necessaries: Fie *Richard* fie, thou shouldest neuer be vnprouided
especially for women.
Well *Meg* (quoth he) be contented, consider you are a woman
of no ordinary making, but as in height thou ouerlookest all, so in
the length of thy foot thou surpassest all; therefore I must haue a
paire of Lasts made for the nonce, and that shall be done out of hand.
40 I tell thee *Dicke* (quoth shee) as high as I am, I am not so high
as *Paules* nor is my foot so long as *Graues-end* Barge.
Notwithstanding (quoth *Richara*) a paire of Lasts to fit thy foot
will cost as much as a hundred of fagots which will not be bought
vnder ten groats:

If they cost a crown (quoth *Meg*) let me haue them ; what man, rather then I will goe without shooes I will beare the charge thereof my selfe, and in token that I mean troth, take there the money, thou shalt find me no *Crinkler*, but one that will reward cunning to the vttermost : I loue not to pinch for a peny, or stand vpon tearmes for two pence, if I find my shooes good I will not shrinke for a shilling ;

In troth (quoth *Richard*) franke customers are worthy of good ware, and therefore *Meg* doubt not, for thou shalt haue as good a shoe as euer was drawne vpon womans foote.   10

God a mercy for that, sweet *Dicke* (quoth shee) and seeing thou saist so, I will bestow this bottle of wine on thee to breakfast, beside that, I haue brought here a modicome that will proue as good a shooing-horne to drawe downe a cup of Muskadine, as may be : and therewithall shee pluckt out her powdred beefe, and her colde Capon ;

Richard seeing this, with thankes to *Margaret* for her meat, reacht out a couple of ioyne stooles, and after that they had laid a cloth thereon, they downe did sit, at which time many merry speeches did passe betweene them. And at that very time there was in 20 the same shoppe, amongst a great many other men a pleasant iorney man called round *Robin*, being a wel trust fellow short and thicke, yet very actiue and pleasantly conceited : for singing hee was held in high reputation among all the Shoomakers in *Westminster*, and he would scant speake anything but in rime. This jolly companion seeing them bent so well to their breakfast, and nothing at all to respect him, in the place where he sate cast out these merry speeches vnto them.

> *Much good doe it you masters, and well may you fare,*
> *Beshroe both your hearts and if you do spare :*   30
> *The wine should be nought as I judge by the smell,*
> *And by the colour too I know it full well.*

Nay faith (quoth *Meg*) thats but a jest,

> *Ile sweare (quoth* Robin) *tis none of the best.*

Tast it (quoth *Meg*) then tell me thy mind :

> *Yea marry (quoth* Robin) *now you are kind.*

With that *Margaret* filling a cup brim full, gaue it into his hand saying : Now tast it *Robin* and take there the cup.

> *Nay hang me (quoth* Robin) *if I drinke it not vp.*

By my Maiden-head (quoth *Margaret*) I see that thou art a 40 good fellow : and to haue thee drinke it vp, is the thing that I craue.

> *Then sweare (quoth* Robin) *by the thing you haue,*
> *For this to sweare I dare be bold :*
> *You were a maid at three yeares old.*

> *From three to foure, fiue, sixe, and seauen,*
> *But when you grew to be eleuen,*
> *Then you began to breed desire ;*
> *By twelue your fancy was on fire :*
> *At thirteene yeares desire grew quicke,*
> *And then your maiden-head fell sicke :*
> *But when you came vnto fourteene,*
> *All secret kisses was not seene :*
> *By that time fifteene yeares was past,*
> 10 *I guesse your maiden-head was lost.*
> *And I pray God forgiue me this,*
> *If thinking so I thinke amisse.*

Now by my honesty (quoth *Meg*) you doe me mighty wrong to thinke so ill of me: for though indeed I confesse, I cannot excuse my selfe, for women are not Angels, though they haue Angels faces : for to speake the truth, might I haue had my owne hearts desire when time was, I would rather haue chosen to lye with a man then a maid, but such merry motions were out of my mind many a deere day agoe, and now I vow that a maiden I will die.

> 20 *By this wine (quoth* Robin) *I dare sweare you lye,*
> *For were I as my master by this good light,*
> *You would leese your maiden-head ere twelue a clock at night.*
> *With high derry derry,*
> *If it be not gone already.*

Nay (quoth *Margaret*) your Master scornes me, he keeps all his gownes for *Gillian* of the George : a pretty wench I confesse, hauing a proper body but a bad leg, she hath a very good counte nance but an ill coulour, and you talk of desire, but her desire I doubt will bring her the greene sicknesse, if your master like a good 30 Phisition giue her not a medicine against that malady :

Why *Margaret* (quoth *Richard*) hath she told you so much of her mind, that you know her griefe so well ?

It may be she hath (quoth *Margaret*) but whether she did or no, it is sufficient that I know so much : But I thinke (quoth *Margaret*) you are not so besotted to make any account of a Tallow cake.

> *No, faith (quoth* Robin) *a nut-browne girle,*
> *Is in mine eye a Diamond and a Pearle :*
> *And shee that hath her cheekes cherry red,*
> *Is euer best welcome to a young mans bed.*

40 Certainly (quoth *Richard*) which is the best or worst I know not yet, nor doe I meane hastily to proue ; And as *Gillian* of the George, as she hath no reason to hate me, so she hath no cause to loue me : but if she doe, it is more fauour then I did euer merit at her hand, and surely were it but in regard of her good will, I am not to scorne her nor for her fauour to feed her with floutes, but

for her good thoughts of me to think well of her, though not so well as to make her my wife :

Well said Master (quoth *Robin*).

> *In this sort grind you still,*
> *So shall we haue mo sackes to mill.*

Trust me (quoth *Margaret*) I speake not this so much to disgrace *Gillian*, as for the regard I haue to your credit: but to make an end of *Gillian* and this iest altogether, let me entreat you soone at night to come to our house ; and thinke this, though your cheere chance to be small, your welcome shall be great. I know that this Summer (and especially against these holy-daies) you will worke till ten, and I promise you by eleuen I will haue as good a posset for you as euer you did taste on in your life. My master is an old man and he commonly goes to bed at nine, and as for my mistris, I know where she will be safe till midnight masse be ended, so that for an houre we may be as merry as pope *John* : what say you *Richard* (quoth she) Will you come?

In troth, *Margaret* (quoth he) I heartily thank you for your good will, I would willingly come but I loue not to be from home so late.

> *I thinke so (quoth* Robin) *least you should misse* Kate,
> *But take my counsell, when you are with* Meg :
> *Suppose you haue got fine* Kate *by the leg.*

Robin (said he) thou art so full of thy rime, that often thou art without reason : thou seest that *Margaret* hath been at cost with vs to-day, and it is more then good manners to charge her further, before we haue made amends for this : and beside that, late walking in the euening brings young men into much suspition.

Tush (quoth *Margaret*) once and vse it not, is not such a matter : therefore sweet *Richard* you shall come, and you shall not say me nay, therefore I charge you on paine of displeasure not to faile, and forget not to bring round *Robin* with you, and so farewell.

> *No, faith (quoth* Robin) *it shall not need,*
> *I am bidden already and so God speed.*

Who bad thee (quoth *Margaret*)?

> *What are thy wits so vnsteady ?*
> *You did bid me (quoth* Robin) *haue you forgot already ?*

Why then I pray thee good *Robin* (said *Meg*) do not forget in any case, and put thy Master in mind thereof if he should chance to change his opinion, or ouerslip the time through greedines of work, for, ifaith *Robin* if thou bring him along with thee, I will thinke the better of thee while I liue :

Why then (quoth he).

> *And as I am no knight,*
> *We will come to eate the posset soone at night.*

Now *Margaret* was no sooner gone, and *Richard* at his cutting boord, and *Robin* set on his stoole, but in comes *Gillian* of the George bringing in her aporne the corner of a Venison Pastie, and a good deale of a Lambe pye, who with a smyling countenance entring the shop, bidding *Richard* good morrow, askt if he had broke his fast?

Yes verily (quoth *Richard*) I thank long *Meg*, we haue beene at it this morning, and had you come a little sooner you had found her heere, for she went away but euen now, and I verily thinke
10 she is scant at home yet.

> *Tis a lusty wench* (quoth Robin) *gentle and kind,*
> *And in truth she beares a most bountifull mind.*

Gillian hearing *Robin* to enter into *Megs* commendations, began to grow jealous of the matter : out vpon her foule stammell (quoth she) he that takes her to his wife shall be sure of flesh enough, let him get bread where he can : tis such a bold betrice, she will acquaint her selfe with euery bodie.   Notwithstanding this I will tell you, *Richard*, the lesse she comes in your company, the more it will be for your credit.   And howsoeuer she deserues it, God
20 knowes, I cannot accuse her, but I promise you, she hath but a hard report among many.   But letting her rest as she is, see here what I haue brought you, and with that she gaue him the Venison and the rest, and drawing her purse, she would needs send for a quart of wine.   *Richard* sought to perswade her to the contrary, but she would not be intreated ; what man, quoth she, I am able to giue you a quart of wine.

Thats spoke like an Angell (quoth *Robin*).

> *And this I doe thinke,*
> *If you be able to giue it, we be able to drinke.*

30 Hereupon the wine was fetcht, and so they sate them downe to their meate, at what time they fed not so heartily on the Venison pasty, but *Gillians* eye fed as greedily on *Richards* fauour : & as soone as the wine was come, she pluckt out of her pocket a good peece of sugar, & filling a glasse of wine tempered wel therwith, she drank to him saying : here, *Richard*, to all that loue you and me, but especially to him whom I loue best :

Let it come (quoth *Richard*) I will pledge him, whosoeuer it be.

> *So will I* (quoth Robin) *without any faile,*
> *Were it the best* Hipocras, *I would turn it ouer my naile.*

40 Then *Gillian* looking round about, spoke to this effect : verily *Richard*, heere is a pretty house, and euery thing hansome by Saint *Anne*; I see nothing wanting but a good wife to keep all things in his due kind :

Whereunto *Robin* made this answer.

> *Now speake thy conscience, and tell me good* Gill,
> *Wouldst not thou be that good wife, with a good will?*

Who I ? alas (quoth she) your Master scornes me, he looks for a golden girle, or a girle with gold, that might bring him the red ruddocks chinking in a bag, and yet possible he were better to haue one with lesse money, and more huswifery : for my owne part I thanke God, and in a good time may I speake it, I would not come to learne of neuer a woman in *Westminster* how to deale in such affaires :

I thinke no lesse (quoth *Richard*) and therefore I pray God send you a good husband, and one well deseruing so good a wife :

With that *Gillian* fetcht a great sigh, saying : Amen I pray 10 God, for it is a sinfull thing to leade a sinfull life, except :

Nay, say your mind, speake your mind (quoth *Richard*) :

Why (quoth she) it is written, that we shall giue an account for euery idle word, and that ill thoughts are as bad as wanton deeds :

It is true (quoth *Richard*)

Then God helpe vs all (quoth *Gillian*) but if I were married, I should remoue a great many of them.

Why then, marry me (quoth *Robin*) and thereby preuent the perill of bad thoughts :

Harke, in thy eare *Robin* (quoth she) I would thy Master 20 would say as much and then he should soone know my mind.

> *Ha, ha (quoth* Robin) *ifaith, you drab,*
> *And would you haue him to stampe the crab ?*

Why what is the matter (quoth *Richard*)?

Nay nothing (quoth *Gillian*) but that I was bold to jest with your man, and I hope you will not be offended if he and I talke a word or two.

There is no reason I should (quoth *Richard*) and therefore conferre at your pleasure, and the whilest I will be busie with the Lambe pye. 30

Then *Gillian* rounding *Robin* in the eare, spoke in this sort vnto him. I perceiue you can spie day at a little hole : you may see *Robin*, loue is like an vnruly streame that will ouer-flow the banks if the course be once stopt, as by my speeches no doubt you haue noted : neuerthelesse how forcible soeuer fancy is, it is thought small modesty in a maiden to lay open her heart in those cases, but I am of opinion that affection growing as strong in a woman as a man, they ought to haue equall priuiledge, as well as men to speake their minds. *Robin,* I take thee to be an honest fellow, and it is the part of a man in cases of honest loue 40 to assist poore maidens : counsell, the key of certainty ; which makes me to require both thy counsaile and help. In truth *Robin* to be plaine, I loue thy Master with all my heart : and if thou wouldst be so much my friend to break the matter vnto him and therewithall to procure his good liking to me, I would bestow on thee as good a sute of apparell as euer thou wast master of in thy life :

Whereunto *Robin* answered, saying,

> *Heers my hand* Gillian, *at thy request*
> *Ile make a vow Ile doe my best,*
> *But for my apparell grant me this,*
> *In earnest first to giue me a kisse.*

There it is (quoth *Gillian*) and I doe protest, that vpon that blessed day, when he giues his happy consent to be my husband, at the deliuery of thy apparell I will make that one kisse twenty, and hereupon shaking hands, they came to the table and set them downe againe.

Richard marking all, said nothing, but at her approach to the boord tooke the glasse and drunk to her, giuing her thankes for her cost and kindnes : she gladly accepting the same, bending her body instead of cursie, tooke it at his hands, and with a winke drunk vnto *Robin*, and so taking her leaue of them both as light as a Doe she ran speedily home.

So soone as she was gone, *Robin* told his Master it was the pleasantest life in the world to liue a Batcheler, during which time he could neither want good cheere nor good company :

I mary (quoth *Richard*) but what I get one way I spend another way, while I passe the time in trifling about nothing : you see (quoth he) here is a forenoone spent to no purpose, and all by the means of a couple of giglets, that haue greater desire to be playing with a man then to be mindfull to follow their busines : but if I liue I will sodainly auoid both their delights and their loues. I tell thee *Robin*, I account their fauours full of frawd and their inticements daungerous, and, therefore a man must not be won with faire words as a fish with a baite.

Well Master (quoth *Robin*) all is one to me, whether you loue them or loath, but yet soone at night let not the posset be forgot.

Beleeue me (quoth *Richard*) if I rest in the mind I am in now, I meane not to be there at all.

O then you will loose her loue (quoth *Robin*) for euer and euer Amen :

That (said his Master) is the onely thing that I request, for the loue of a shroe is like the shadow of a cloude that consumeth as soone as it is seene, and such loue had I rather loose then find.

> *But yet (quoth* Robin) *this once follow my mind.*
> *Though by her loue you set but light,*
> *Let vs eate the posset soone at night :*
> *And afterward I will so deale,*
> *If you will not my trickes reueale :*
> *That they shall trouble you no more,*
> *Though by your loue they set great store :*
> *For, one another they shall beguile,*
> *Yet thinke themselues well pleasd the while.*

Verily (quoth his Master) if thou wilt doe so, I wil be *Megs* guest for this once, and happy shall I thinke my self to be so well rid of them :

Hereupon being resolued, they plyde their worke hard till the euening, and when the Sunne was crept vnder the earth, and the Stars vp in the skies, *Richard* hauing his shop window shut in, and his doores made fast, he with his man *Robin* tooke their direct way to the spread Eagle, where they no sooner knockt at the doore, but *Margaret* came downe and let them in, with such a cheerefull countenance, as gaue perfect testimony of their welcome.

Now *Richard* (quoth she) I will witnesse you are a man of your word, and a man that hath a respect of his promise : I pray you hartily come neere, for to haue you come in my office, is my desire :

But tell vs first (quoth Robin) *was your office neuer a fire ?*

Yfaith no (quoth she) you see the kitchin is large and the chimney wide :

But how many rookes (quoth Robin) *hath the goodnes of your kitchin tride ?*

I know not (said *Meg*) how many or how few :

Trust me (quoth Robin) *I thinke euen so.*

Goe to (quoth *Meg*) I smell out your knauery, and guesse at your meaning, but taking it to be spoken more for mirth, then for malice, I let them passe. Then taking *Richard* by the hand, she bad him sit downe, saying : Good *Richard* think yourselfe welcome, for in troth I haue neuer a friend in the world that can be better welcome :

I thank you good *Margaret* (said he).

I thank her still (quoth Robin) *with thanks of euery degree,* *For you that haue all the welcome, shall giue all thanks for mee.*

Why *Robin* (q. *Meg*) be not offended for thou art welcome to me.

Ifaith (quoth he) you bid me welcome when you haue nothing else to do.

Herewithall *Margaret* very neately laying the cloth, with all things necessary, set a dainty minst pie on the boord, piping hote, with a great deale of other good cheere, and hauing sent another maid of the house for a pottle of wine, they fell to their meat merrily, whereof when they had eaten and drunk, *Margaret* stepping from the boord went to reach the posset, but while she had it in her hands she sodainly heard one comming down the stairs :

Gods precious (quoth she) my Master comes, what shift shall we make to hide the posset, if he chance to see it, we shall haue

more anger than ten possets are worth. With that she quickly whipt into the yard and set the posset downe vpon the seat in the priuy-house, thinking it there safest out of sight, for her Master being an old crabbed fellow, would often steale downe to see what his maids were a doing, but God wot that was not the cause, for the old man, being raised by the loosenes of his body, came hastily downe to pay tribute to *Ajax*, where when he was come, he clapt his buttocks into the posset, wherewith being grieuously scalded, he cried out saying, alacke, alacke, help maids, help, or I
10 am spoild foreuer ; for some spirit or diuell in the foule bottome of the priuie hath throwne vp boyling leade vpon my buttocks, and in this case like one dauncing the trench more he stampt vp and downe the yard, holding his hips in his hands :

Meg that better knew what the matter was then her master, ran into the house of office with a spit in her hand, as if she had beene purposed to broch the diuell, and there casting the well spiced posset into the midst of the puddle, taking the bason away, said, how now Master, what is the matter, who hath hurt you, or are you not hurt at all ?

20 Hurt (quoth her master) I tell thee *Meg*, neuer was man thus hurt, and yet I am ashamed to shew my hurt :

Bring me a Candle (quoth *Meg*) I tell you, Master, it is better all should be shewen, then all should be spoyled : and there with casting by his shirt, spied both his great cheekes full of small blisters, whereupon she was faine with all possible speed to make him a medicine with sallet oyle and houseleeks, to asswage the fury of an vnseene fire. And by meanes of this vnhappy chance, *Richard* with his man was faine secretly to slip away, and to goe home without tasting the posset at all : which was to *Robin* no small
30 griefe, and yet they could both of them scant stand for laughing, to thinke how odly this ieast fell out.

> *I am (quoth* Robin) *forty yeares old and more,*
> *Yet did I neuer know posset, so tasted before:*
> *I thinke his eyes in his Elbowes he had,*
> *To thrust his arse in the posset, or else he was mad.*

His master answering said, beleeue me *Robin*, I neuer knew the like in my life, but by the grace of God I will neuer goe there no more to eate a posset : and so going to bed they slept away sorrow till morning.
40 At what time *Margaret* comming thither told them she was very sorie they were so suddenly broke from their banket ; but, Yfaith, *Richard* (quoth she) another time shall make amends for all.

CHAP. III.

How the Cocke of *Westminster* was married to a Dutch
maiden, for which cause Long *Meg*, and *Gillian* of
the George wore willow Garlands.

RIchard *Casteler* liuing a long time a Batchelor in *West-minster*, after many good proffers made vnto him, refusing
all, hee at last linked his loue to a young Dutch maiden
dwelling in *London*, who besides that, was of proper personage,
and comely countenance, and could doe diuers pretty feates to get
her owne liuing. To this pretty soule went *Richard* secretly a 10
wooing, who for halfe a yeare set as light by him, as hee did by the
Maidens of *Westminster*, And the more hee was denyed, the more
desirous hee was to seeke her good will, much like to an vnruly
patient, that most longes after the meate hee is most forbidden :
and such is the fury of fond Louers, to esteeme them most
precious, that are to them most pernitious : he scornfully shunnes
such as gently seekes him, and wooes her earnestly that shakes
him off frowardly : but while he was thus busied to make himselfe
blessed by matching with a Mayden in *London*, round *Robin* cast
in his mind how to set the Maydens wittes a worke in *Westminster*, 20
which he effected as occasion was offred in this sort.

Margaret and *Gillian* comming often by the shop, cast many a
sheepes eye to spye out their beloued friend, and after they had
many times mist him from his busines, they thought either that
he was growne loue-sick or lazie : but knowing him a man to be
mightily addicted to the getting of money, judged that it was not
idlenes, that withdrew him from his busines, but rather that he
was gone a wooing to one pretty wench or other, for louing hearts
haue euer suspicious heades and jealousie is copartner with
affection : whereupon *Margaret* entred into these speeches with 30
round *Robin.*

I muse much (quoth *Meg*) where your Master layes his knife a
boord now adayes, for seldome or neuer can I see him in his
shop : trust me, I doubt, he is become thriftles, and will proue but
a bad husband in the end : tell me *Robin* (said she) I pray thee
say where doth the Cocke crow now ?

> *Not so (said* Robin) *my Master will not that allow,*
> *I must not shew his secrets to one or other :*
> *Therefore you shall not know it though you were my mother,*
> *Yet thus much by thy speech I plainly do see,* 40
> *Thou thinkst not so well of him as he thinks on thee.*

Margaret, hearing round *Robin* rime to so good purpose,
asked if hee knew his Masters minde so much ? truly (quoth shee)
if I wist he bore any spark of loue toward me, it should neither goe

vnregarded nor vnrewarded, therefore sweet *Robin* let me know whereupon thou speakest; feare not my secrecie, for I will rather loose my life then bewray his loue.

Heereupon *Robin* said that his Master was very well affected towards her, and that if it were not that *Gillian* of the George did cast searching eyes into his actions, he would long ere this haue vttred his mind: but (quoth *Robin*) he is so haunted by that female spirit, that he can take no rest in no place for her, and therefore the more to quiet his mind, he hath left his shop to my charg, and betaken himselfe to wander the Woods so wild.

These words vttered by *Robin* made *Margarets* heart leape in her belly: wherefore taking gently her leaue of him, she thus began to meditate on the matter: Now doe I well see that the tongue of a wise man is in his heart, but the heart of a foole is in his tongue: and, *Richard* (quoth she) hast thou borne me such secret good will and would neuer let me know it? Iwis, iwis, soone would thy sorrow be asswaged if thou soughtest remedie at my hand: well though the fire be long supprest, at length it will burst into a flame, and *Richards* secret good will, at last will shew it selfe, till when I will rest my selfe contented, thinking it sufficient that I know he loues me: and seeing it is so, I will make him sue and serue, and daunce attendance after me: when he is most curteous, I will be most coy, and as it were scorning his proffers, and shunning his presence, I will make him the more earnest to intreat my fauour: when he sayes he loues me, I will laugh at him, and say he can faine and flatter well: if he affirme he be grieued through my disdaine, and that the lacke of my good wil hath been his greatest sorrow, I will say alas good soule, how long haue you been louesick? pluck out thy heart man and be of good cheere, there is more maids then Malkin: though I doe lightly esteeme thee, there are some that perhaps will better regard both thy griefe, and thy good will, and therefore good *Dicke* trouble me no more.

Thus must maides dissemble least they be counted too curteous and shewing themselues ouerfond, become the lesse fauoured, for a woman's loue being hardly obtained, is esteemed most sweet, therefore we must giue our louers an hundred denials for fashion sake, though at the first we could find in our hearts to accept their proffered pleasures.

Thus in a iolly humor *Margaret* ietted home, flattering herselfe in her happy fortune, in which delight we will leaue her, and make some rehearsall of *Gillians* ioy: who, comming in the like manner to *Robin*, asking for his Master, was certified by him, that for her sake onely he liued in such sorrow, that he could not stay in his shop, and therfore was faine to driue away melancholy by marching abroad.

O Gillian (quoth he) had it not bin for two causes, he would long ere this haue vttered his mind vnto thee, for he loues thee aboue measure:

Yfaith (quoth *Gillian*) is it true (*Robin*) that thou dost tell me?

Doubt not of that (quoth he) doe you think that I will tell you a lye? I should gaine nothing by that, I am sure: if then you will beleeue me you may; if not, chuse, I meane not to intreat you thereto:

Nay good *Robin* (quoth she) be not angry, though I credit thy speeches, yet blame me not to aske a question.

Aske what you will (quoth *Robin*) I respect it not, and I may chuse whether I will answere you or no: Swounds, now I haue opened my masters secret, you were best blab it through all the towne.

Nay good *Robin* that is not my mind (quoth *Gillian*) but I beseech thee, let me know those two causes that keepes thy Master from vttering his mind:

Nay soft, there lay a straw for feare of stumbling (quoth *Robin*). Hold your peace *Gillian*, it is not good to eate too much hony, nor to gorge you with too much gladnes: let it suffice that you know what you know.

Nay good sweet *Robin* (quoth she) I pray thee make it not dainty now to tell me all, seeing you haue begun: the day may come that I may requite thy curtesie to the full:

Say you so, *Gillian* (quoth hee)? now by good *Crispianus* soule I sweare, were it not that I am in hope you will proue kind to my Master, and be a good Mistresse to vs when you are married, I would not vtter one word more, no not halfe a word, nor one sillable.

Well *Robin* (quoth she) if euer I come to command in thy masters house, and to carry the keys of his Cubberts gingling at my sides, thou shalt see I will not keepe a niggards Table, to haue bare platters brought from the boord, but you shall haue meate and drinke plenty, and be vsed as men ought to be vsed in all reasonable manner. And whereas you seeme to make doubt of my kindnesse toward thy Master, ha *Robin*, I would thou knewest my heart.

Robin hearing this, told her this tale, that his master loued her intyrely and would long since haue vttered his mind, but for two reasons: the first was, that he could neuer find fit oportunity to doe it, because of Long *Meg*, whose loue to him was more then he could wish and such as he would gladly remoue if he might: for (saith *Robin*) though my Master do not care a straw for her, yet she casts such a vigilant eye vpon him, that if he do but speake, or looke vpon any, she by and by poutes and lowres, and many times inveyes against the parties with disgracefull termes, which is to my Master such a griefe, that he is faine to keepe silent, what otherwise should be shown: and the second reason is this, that because he is not so wealthy as he could wish himselfe, you would disdaine his sute, and make no account of his good will.

Who I (quoth *Gillian*)? now by these ten bones it was neuer my mind to say him nay. I tell thee *Robin* I doe more respect his kindnes then his goods: he is a proper youth and well conditioned, and it is far better to haue a man without money, then money without a man.

Why then good *Gillian* (quoth *Robin*) harken hither three dayes hence, and you shall heare more, but in the meane space looke you play mum-budget, and speake not a word of this matter to any creature.

10 I warrant thee *Robin* (quoth she) and so away she went being as glad of this tydings as her Master was of a good Term:

Now when his Master came home, his man *Robin* asked him how he sped in his suit?

Verily (quoth he) euen as Cookes doe in baking of their pies, sometimes well, sometimes ill. *London* Maids are wily wenches: on *Sunday* my sweetheart was halfe won, but now I doubt she is wholy lost. Now she is in one mind, by and by in another, and to be briefe, neuer stedfast in anything.

Tush Master (quoth *Robin*) stoop not too much to a thistle, but 20 take this comfort, that what one will not, another will. I tel you Master, Crabs yeeldes nothing but verjuice, a sower sauce good for digestion but bad to the taste, and these nice minions are so full of curiosity, that they are cleane without curtesie: Yet well fare the gallant girles of *Westminster*, that will doe more for a man than he will doe for himselfe.

What is that (said his Master)?

Mary (quoth he) get him a wife ere he is aware, and giue two kisses before he calles for one.

That indeed is extraordinary kindnes (quoth *Richard*) but their 30 loues are like braided wares, which are often showne, but hardly sold.

Well Master (quoth *Robin*) you know your two old friends, *Meg* and *Gillian*:

I, what of them (quoth *Richard*)?

In troth (quoth he) I haue made them both so proud, that they prance through the streets like the Kings great horses: for I haue made them both beleeue that you loue them out of all cry.

And I beshroe thy heart for that (quoth *Richard*) for therein thou dost both deceiue them, and discredit mee: I assure thee I 40 like not such jesting.

> *Now gip* (*quoth* Robin) *are you grieud ot my talke?*
> *And if you be angry I pray you goe walke.*
> *Thus you doe neuer esteeme of a man,*
> *Let him doe for you the best that he can.*

Richard hearing his man so hot, pacified him with many cold and gentle speeches, wishing, if he had begun any iest, that he should finish it with such discretion, that no reproach might grow thereby vnto him, and then he would be content : whereupon *Robin* proceeded in this sort.

Vpon a time *Margaret* according to her wonted manner came thither, whom *Robin* perswaded that his Master was newly gone into *Tuttle field*, and that he left word if she came she should doe so much as to meet him there : but (quoth he) take heed in any case least *Gillian* of the George spie you, and so follow to the place where my Master attends your comming, who I dare sweare would not for all the Shooes in his shop it should be so : and therefore good *Margaret* if you chance to see her, goe not 10 forward in any case, but rather lead her a contrary way, or make some queint excuse, that she may leaue your company, and not suspect your pretence.

Tush (quoth *Margaret*) let me alone for that, if she follow me she were better no, for, Ifaith, I will lead her a dance shall make her weary before she haue done, and yet shall she goe home as very a foole as she came forth, for any goodnesse she gets at my hand : and therefore farewell *Robin* (quoth she) for I will trudge into *Tuttle fields* as fast as I may.

But looke (quoth Robin) *you loose not your Maiden-head by* 20 *the way.*

Robin presently thereupon runnes vnto *Gillian*, saying what cheere *Gillian* how goes the world with all the pretty wenches here ? it is a long while since I haue seene you.

Ifaith, *Robin* (quoth they) we rub out with the rest, but what is the news with thee ?

Small news (quoth Robin) *yet somewhat I haue to say,*
All Maides that cannot get husbands must presently marry,
They that cannot stay,
But heare you, Gillian *a word by the way.* 30

And with that (rounding her in the eare) he told her that incontinent it was his Masters mind that she should meet him in *Tuttle fields*, charging her if she met *Margaret* of the Spread Eagle, that she should in no case goe forward but turne her steps some other way, for (quoth he) my Master cannot abide that great rounsefull should come in his company.

For that let me alone (quoth *Gillian*) but trust me *Robin*, it could not haue come in a worse time this tweluemoneth, for this day haue we a mighty deale of worke to doe, beside a great bucke that is to be washt : 40

Why then let it rest till another time (quoth *Robin*) :

Nay (quoth she) hap what hap will, I will goe to him, sith so kindly he sent for me ; and thereupon making her selfe quickly ready, into *Tuttle fields* she got, where at last she espied *Margaret* with a hand-basket in her hand, who as sodainly had got

33. Spread Eagle] Crane *1639*

a sight of her, and therefore made a shew as if she gathered hearbs in the field. I wis that craft shall not serue your turne (quoth *Gillian*) I will gather hearbs as fast as you, though I haue as little need of them as your selfe.

But in the mean time *Robin* got him home, and hartily laught to see what paines these wenches tooke for a husband. O (quoth he) what a merry world is this, when Maids runnes a madding for husbands, with hand-baskets in their hands? now may I well sweare what I haue seene.

10
   Two Maides runne as fast as they can,
   A mile in the fields to meet with a man.

Then how can men for shame say that Maidens are proud, disdainfull or coy, when we find them so gentle, that they will run to a man like a Falcon to the Lure, but alas poore soules, as good were they to seek for a needle in a bottle of hay, as to search for *Richard* of the Rose in *Tuttle fields*: but hereby doe I know their minds against another time, if my Master should chance to request their company.

20
Thus did round *Robin* deride them when he found their fondness to be such: but to leaue him to his humor, we will returne to the Maids that were so busie in picking vp hearbs in the fields: when *Meg* saw that *Gillian* would not away, at last she came vnto her, asking what she made there?

Nay what doe you here (quoth she)? for my owne part I was sent for to seeke Harts-ease, but I can find nothing but sorrel:

Alack good soule (quoth *Meg*) and I come to gather thrift, but can light on nothing but thistles, and therefore I will get my waies home as fast as I can:

In doing so you shall doe well (quoth *Gillian*) but I mean to get some Harts-ease ere I goe away:

30
Nay *Gillian* (quoth she) I am sure I shall find thrift as soone as you shall find Harts-ease, but I promise you I am out of hope to find any to-day.

I pray you get you gone then (quoth she).

What would you so faine be rid of my company (quoth *Meg*)? for that word I meane not to be gone yet: Ifaith *Gill* I smell a rat.

Then (quoth she) you haue as good a nose as our gray Cat: but what rat do you smell, tell me? I doubt I doubt if there be any rat in the field, you would faine catch him in your trap, if you knew how; but Ifaith *Meg*, you shall be deceiued as cunning as you are.

40
Then belike (qd. *Meg*) you would not haue the rat taste no cheese but your owne:

All is one for that (said *Gillian*) but wheresoeuer he run I would haue him creep into no corner of yours:

Your wordes are mysticall (quoth *Meg*) but if thou art a good wench, let us goe home together:

Not so (said *Gillian*) as I came not with you, so I meane not to goe with you.

No (quoth *Meg*)? before God I sweare I will stay as long as thou for thy life.

In troth (quoth she) I will make you stay till midnight then.

Yea (quoth *Meg*)? now, as sure as I liue I will try that.

And in this humor sometimes they sat them downe, and sometimes they stalkt round about the field, till it was darke night, and so late, that at last the watch met with them, who contrary to *Gillians* mind, tooke paines to bring them both home together: at what time they gaue one another such priuie flouts, that the watchmen tooke no little delight to heare it : But their Mistresses that had so long mist them from home though they were very angry with their long absence, yet were glad they were come againe. And asking where they had been so long, the watchmen answered, that the one had beene to seeke Harts-ease, and the other to gather thrift and therefore that they should not blame them for staying so long to get such good commodities : Verily (quoth their Mistresses) we will not, for no maruell if they stayed out till midnight about such matters, seeing we haue sought it this seuen yeares and could neuer find it : and in this sort this iest ended.

Within a while after this, *Richard* through his long woing, had gotten the good will of his sweet-heart, and therefore making all things ready for his marriage, the matter being known through *Westminster*, *Margaret* and *Gillian* had tydings thereof with the soonest, who comming vnto *Richard*, said he was the most false and vnconstant man in the world.

Haue I (quoth *Meg*) set my whole mind vpon thee to be thus serued ?

Nay (quoth *Gillian*) haue I loued thee so deerly, and indured such sorrow for thy sake, to be thus vnkindly cast off?

And I (quoth *Meg*) that neuer thought any thing too much for thee, that loued thee better then my life, that was at all times ready at thy call, and ready to run or goe at thy commandement to be so vndeseruedly forsaken, grieues not my heart a little :

Nay (quoth *Gillian*) could you make me leaue my worke to waite vpon thee in *Tuttle-fields* ?

Nay did I waite there halfe a day together (quoth *Meg*) at thy request to be thus mockt at thy hand ? Now I wish it from my heart, if thou marriest any but me, that thy wife may make thee as errant a Cuckold as *Iack Coomes*.

So you are very charitable (quoth *Richard*) to wish me no worse then you meane to make your husband : but when did I request thee to come into *Tuttle-fields* ?

What haue you so weake a memory (quoth she)? I pray you aske your man round *Robin* whether it were so or no :

Well (quoth *Robin*) how then ? wherefore did you not speake with him at that present ?

You know it comes in an houre, comes not in seuen yeare,
Had you met him at that instant you had married him cleare.

A vengeance take her (quoth *Meg*) I could not meete him for *Gillian.*

And I could not meet him for *Margaret*, a morin take her (qd. *Gillian*).

Richard perceiuing by their speech there was a pad lying in the straw, made this reply. It is a strange thing to see how you will blame me of discourtesie, when the whole fault lyes in your
10 selues : had you come at the appointed time, it is likely I had marryed one of you, seeing my minde was as well addicted to the one as to the other :

Why may it not be yet (quoth they) if it please you ?

Not so (said *Richard*) you speake too late, Men gather no grapes in Ianuary, my wine is already prouided, and my wife prepared : therefore I thanke you both of your good wills, though I be constrained of force to forsake you.

The maidens, being herewith struck into their dumps, with water in their eyes, and griefe in their hearts went home, to whom *Robin*
20 carryed two Willow garlands, saying

You pretty soules that forsaken be,
Take here the branches of the Willow tree,
And sing loues farewell ioyntly with me.

Meg being merily inclined, shooke off sorrow in this sort, and gently taking the willow Garland, said : wherefore is griefe good ? can it recall folly past ? no : can it helpe a matter remedilesse ? no : can it restore losses, or draw vs out of danger ? no : what then ? can griefe make vnkind men curteous ? no : can it bring long life ? no : for it doth rather hasten our death, what then can it do : can
30 it call our friends out of their graues ? no : can it restore virginity if we chance to lose our maidenhead ? no : Then wherefore should I grieue ? except I went to kill myselfe : Nay seeing it is so, hang sorrow, I will neuer care for them that care not for me, and therefore a Figge for the Cocke of *Westminster* : by this good day I am glad I haue scapt him, for I doe now consider I should haue neuer tooke rest after foure a clocke in the morning, and alas, a young married wife would be loath to rise before eight or nine : beside that I should neuer haue gone to bed before ten or eleuen, or twelue a clocke at night by that meanes, what a deale of time
40 should I haue lost aboue other women : haue him quoth you ? now God blesse me, I sweare by *Venus*, the faire goddesse of sweet loue, in the minde I am in, I would not haue him, if he had so much as would lie in *Westminster* Hall. And therefore *Robin* this Willow garland is to me right heartily welcome and I will goe with thee to *Gillian* presently, and thou shalt see vs weare them rather in triumph then in timerous feare.

40. aboue] about *1639*

Well said, in good sadnes (quoth *Robin*) thou art the gallantest girle that euer I knew.

But when she came to *Gillian*, *Robin* staid for her at the staire foot : they found her sicke in her bed, fetching many sore sighes, to whom *Margaret* spake in this manner.

Why, how now, *Gillian*, what, sicke abed ? now fie for shame, plucke vp a good heart woman, let no man triumph so much ouer thee, to say thou gauest the Crow a pudding, because loue would let thee liue no longer : be content (quoth she) and take courage to thee, death is a sowre crabbed fellow.

Ah no (quoth *Gillian*) death is sweet to them that liue in sorrow, and to none should he be better welcome then to me, who desires nothing more then death to end my miseries :

What now (quoth *Margaret*) whose Mare is dead ? art thou a young wench, faire and comely, and dost thou despaire of life ? and all for loue, and all for loue. O fond foole worthy to weare a coate with foure elbowes, this were enough if there were no more men in the world but one, but if there were two, why shouldst thou languish, much lesse knowing there is so many to be had.

O (quoth *Gillian*) what is all the men in the world to me now I haue lost *Richard*, whose loue was my life.

I pray thee rise (quoth *Meg*) and let vs go drinke a quart of Sacke to wash sorrow from our hearts.

O (quoth shee) I cannot rise if you would giue me a hundred pound, nor will I rise for any mans pleasure :

What (quoth *Meg*) if your father sent for you, would you not goe to him ?

No (quoth she).

Would you not goe to your mother ?

No.

But what if your brethren requested you to rise ?

Yfaith I would not (quoth she) :

Say that some of the Kings Gentlemen intreated your company ?

Neuer prate, I would not goe to the best Lord in the Land (qd. *Gillian*) nor to no man els in the world :

No (quoth *Meg*) I am sure you would.

(Quoth she) if I doe, say I am an errant queane, and count me the veriest drab that euer trod on two shooes.

Nay (quoth *Meg*) seeing you say so, I haue done, I was about to tell you of a matter, but I see it is to small purpose, and therefore Ile keep my breath to coole my pottage.

A matter (said *Gillian*)? what matter is it sweet *Meg* tell me ?

No, no (quoth she) it is in vaine, I would wish you to couer your selfe close, and keepe your selfe warme, least you catch an ague, and so good night *Gillian*.

Nay, but *Meg* (quoth she) good *Meg* if euer thou didst loue me, let me know what this matter is that you speake of, for I shall not be in quiet till I know it :

Tush tis but a trifle, a trifle (quoth *Meg*) not worth the talke : your sweetheart *Richard* hath sent his man *Robin* for you, and, as he tels me he hath a token to deliuer you.

What (quoth *Gill*) is that true? Where is *Robin*? why comes he not vp?

Truly (quoth *Meg*) he counts it more then manners to presse into a Maides chamber : beside he would be loath to giue any cause of suspition to any of your fellowes, to thinke Ill of him or you, for now a dayes the world is growne to such a passe, that if
10 a Maide doe but looke merrily vpon a young man, they will say straight, that either she shall be his wife, or that she is his harlot : but if they see a man come into a womans chamber, they will not sticke to sweare that they haue been naught together ; for which cause *Robin* intreated me to come vnto you, and to certifie you that hee stayed at the three-Tunnes for your comming : but seeing you are a bed I am sorry I haue troubled you so much, and therefore farewell good *Gillian*.

O stay a little good *Meg* (quoth she) and I will goe along with you : and with that on she slipt her petticoate, and made such
20 hast in dressing her selfe that she would not stay the plucking on of her stockings nor the drawing on of her shooes :

Why, how now *Gillian* (quoth *Meg*) haue you forgot your selfe? remember you are Ill and sicke a bed :

Tush (quoth shee) I am well enough now :

But if you goe foorth to-night you are an arrant drab and a very queane (quoth *Meg*) :

Tush tis no matter for that (said *Gillian*). Griefe hath two tongues, to say and to vnsay, and therefore I respect not what you prate, and therewithall shee ran downe the stayres after *Margaret*,
30 who got *Robin* to goe before to the three-Tunnes, where when *Gillian* came, she asked him how his Master did, and what his errand was to her.

Soft : First let vs drinke (quoth Robin*) and then let vs talke,*
That we cannot pay for, shall be set vp in chalke.

You speak merrily (quoth *Margaret*) whatsoeuer you meane, but I would I could see the wine come once, that I may drink a hearty draught ; for sorrow they say is dry, & I find it to be true.

Then drinke hard (quoth Robin*) and bid sorrow adue.*

40 Thus when they had whipt off two or three quarts of wine, *Gillian* began to grow as pleasant as the best, and would needs know of *Robin*, what it was he had to say to her ;

Nothing, quoth he, but to doe my Masters commendation, and to deliuer you his token.

This token (quoth *Gillian*)? What, a Willow garland? is the matter so plaine? is this the best reward hee can giue me for all my good will ; had he nobody to flout but mee?

Yes by my faith (quoth *Meg*) it was his minde that I should beare you company, therefore, looke what he sent to you, he did the like to mee, and that thou maiest the better belieue me, see where it is.

O intollerable iniury (quoth *Gillian*) did I take paines to rise and come out of my warme bed for this? O how vnfortunate haue I beene aboue all other in the world? Well, seeing I cannot recall what is past, I will take this as a iust penance for my too much folly; and if *Margaret* will agree, we will weare these dis-dainfull branches on his marriage day to his great disgrace, though to our continuall sorrow.

Content (quoth *Meg*) all is one to mee, looke what thou wilt allow, I will not dislike, and so paying the shot, away they went.

At length, when the marriage day was come, and that the Bride in the middest of her friends was set downe to dinner, *Margaret* and *Gillian*, attyred in red Stammell petticoats, with white linnen sleeues, and fine Holland Aprons, hauing their Willow garlands on their heads, entred into the Hall singing this song :

> *When fancie first framd our likings in loue,*
>   *sing all of greene Willow :*
> *And faithfull affection such motion did moue,*
>   *for Willow, Willow, Willow.*
> *Where pleasure was plenty we chanced to be,*
>   *sing all of greene Willow :*
> *There were we enthrald of our liberty,*
>   *and forced to carrie the Willow garland.*

> *This young man we liked and loued full deere,*
>   *sing all of greene Willow :*
> *And in our hearts-closset we kept him full neere,*
>   *sing Willow, Willow, Willow.*
> *He was our hearts-pleasure and all our delight,*
>   *sing all of greene Willow,*
> *We iudgd him the sweetest of all men in sight,*
>   *Who giues vs vnkindly the Willow garland.*

> *No cost we accounted too much for his sake,*
>   *sing all of greene Willow :*
> *Fine bands and handkerchers for him we did make,*
>   *sing Willow, Willow, Willow :*
> *And yet for our good will, our trauell and paine,*
>   *Sing all of greene Willow :*
> *We haue gotten nothing but scorne and disdaine ;*
>   *as plainly is proud by this Willow garland.*

> *Then pardon our boldnesse, thou gentle faire Bride,*
>   *sing all of greene Willow :*
> *We speake by experience of that we haue tride,*
>   *sing Willow, Willow, Willow.*

Our ouer much courtesie bred all our woe.
sing all of greene Willow :
But neuer hereafter we meane so to doe,
For this onely brought vs the Willow garland.

Their song being thus ended, the Bride said she was heartily
sorry for their hard fortune in loue, greatly blaming the Bridegroom for his vnkindnes ;

Nay, do not so (quoth *Meg*) for you shal find him kind enough
soon at night : but seeing he hath disappointed me in this sort, it
10 shall go hard, but I will make shift to lose my maiden-head as
soone as you shall lose yours, and you shall make good haste, but
I wil be before you.   O God (quoth she) haue I been so chary to
keep my honesty, and so dainty of my maiden-head that I could
spare it no man for the loue I bore to hard-hearted *Richard*, &
hath he serud me thus ?   Well *Gillian* (quoth she) let vs go, neuer
wil I be so tide in affection to one man again while I liue ; what a
deale of time haue I lost and spent to no purpose since I came to
London ? and how many kinde offers haue I forsaken, & disdain-
fully refused of many braue Gentlemen, that would haue bin glad
20 of my good will ?   I thinke I was accurst to come into his
company : Well, I say little, but henceforward hang me if I refuse
reason, when I am reasonably intreated ; trust me, I would not for
a good thing, that my friends in the country should know that one
of my ripe age, bone and bignesse hath all this while liud in
London idly, like an vnprofitable member of the common-wealth ;
but if I liue, they shall heare that I will be better imployd, and
so adue good *Gillian*.

Thus *Margaret* in a melancholy humor went her waies, and in
short time after, she forsooke *Westminster*, & attended on the
30 Kings army to *Bullio*, and while the siege lasted, became a
landresse to the Camp, and neuer after did she set store by her
selfe, but became common to the call of euery man, till such time
as all youthfull delights was banished by old age, and in the end
she left her life in *Islington*, being very penitent for all her former
offences.

Gillian in the end was well married, and became a very good
house-keeper, liuing in honest name and fame till her dying
day.

Chap. IV.

40 How round *Robin* and his fellowes sung before the King.

THe Kings Maiesty hauing royally won the strong town of
Bullen, victoriously he returned & came into *England*, and
according to his accustomed manner, lying at his Palace of
Whitehall, diuers of the Nobility, passing vp and down *West-*

minster, did many times heare the Shoomakers iournymen singing ; whose sweet voyces and pleasant songs was so pleasing in the eares of the hearers, that it caused them to stay about the doore to hearken thereunto : *Robin* aboue the rest, declared such cunning in his song, that he euer obtained the chiefest praise ; and no maruell, for his skill in pricksong was more then ordinary, for which cause the Singing-men of the Abbey did often call him into the Quire.

Now you shall vnderstand, that by their often singing in the Shop, the iourneymen of that house were noted aboue all the men 10 in *Westminster*, and the report of their singing went far and neer, in so much that at the last, the Kings Maiesty had knowledge thereof, who, hearing them so greatly commended, caused them to be sent for to the Court. Whereupon round *Robin* and his foure fellows made themselues ready, and their Master being of a good mind, against the day that they should goe before our King, he suted them all at his owne proper cost, in doublets and hose of crimson Taffety, with black Veluet caps on their heads, and white feathers ; on their legs they had fine yellow stockings, pumps and pantofles on their feet : by their sides each of them wore a faire sword ; and in this 20 sort being brought before his Maiesty, vpon their knees they craued pardon for presuming to come into his royall presence :

The King, seeing them to be such proper men, & attyred in such Gentleman-like manner, bad them stand vp : Why my Lords (quoth he) be these the merry-minded Shoomakers you spake of ?

They are most dread Soveraigne (said they) ;

Certainly (said our King) you are welcome euery one, but who among you is round Robin ?

> *My Liege (quoth* Robin) *that man am I,* 30
> *Which in your Graces seruice will liue and die :*
> *And these be my fellowes euery one,*
> *Ready to waite your royall Grace vpon.*

How now, *Robin* (said our King). What, canst thou rime ?

> *A little my Liege (quoth he) as I see place and time.*

His Grace laughing heartily at this pleasant companion, told him that he heard say he could sing well.

> *Trust me (quoth* Robin) *at your Graces request*
> *You shall well perceiue we will doe our best.*

Hereupon the King sate him downe, where many great Lords 40 and Ladies of high estate attended on his Highnesse. And being in the Christmas time, after the master of merry disports had performed all his appointed pastimes, *Robin* with his fellowes had liberty to declare their cunning before our King, but the Maiesty of his Princely presence did so amate them, that they were quite dashd out of countenance, which his Grace perceiuing, gaue them

many gracious words of encouragement, whereupon they began in
this sort, singing a song of the winning of *Bullen.*

The Song of the winning of *Bullen* sung before the King by round *Robin* and his fellowes.

I N the moneth of October
  Our King he would to Douer :
    By leaue of Father and the Sonne :
A great armie of men,
Well appointed there was then,
10   *Before our noble King to come ;*

The valiant Lord Admirall,
He was captaine Generall,
    Of all the royall Nauie sent by Sea :
The sight was worthie to behold,
To see the ships with shining gold,
    And Flags and Streamers sailing all the way.

At Bullen *then arriuing,*
With wisdome well contriuing :
    The armed men were set in battle ray ;
20 *And* Bullen *was besieged round,*
Our men with Drum and Trumpets sound,
    Before it marchd couragious that day.

Then marke how all things chanced,
Before them was aduanced
    The royall Standard in the bloodie field ;
The Frenchmen standing on the walls,
To them our English Heralds calls,
    Wishing in time their Citie for to yeeld.

Our King hath sent to proue you,
30 *Because that he doth loue you,*
    He profferd mercy, if you will imbrace :
If you deny his kinde request,
And in your obstinacie rest,
    Behold you bring your selues in wofull case.

(Quoth they) wee doe deny you,
And flatly we defie you,
    Faire Bullen *is a famous Maiden towne ;*
For all the deeds that hath beene done,
By conquest neuer was she won,
40   *She is a Lady of most high renowne.*

When they so vnaduised,
His proffer had despised,
    Our Ordinance began to shoote amaine ;

Continuing eight houres and more,
For why our King most deeply swore,
* Her* Maiden-head *that he would obtaine.*

When thus his Grace had spoken,
Hee sent her many a token,
* Firie balls, and burning brazen rings :*
Faire, broad arrowes sharpe and swift,
Which came among them with a drift,
* Well garnishd with the gray goose wings.*

This Maiden towne that lately 10
Did shew herselfe so stately,
* In seeking fauour, many teares she shed :*
Vpon her knees then fell she downe,
Saying, O King of high renowne,
* Saue now my life, and take my maiden-head.*

Lo, thus her selfe she ventred,
And streight her streets wee entred,
* And to the market place we marched free :*
Neuer a French-man durst withstand,
To hold a wepon in his hand, 20
* For all the gold that euer hee did see.*

Their song being ended, our King cast them a purse with fifty faire angells for a reward, commending both their skill and good voyces, and after much pleasant communication, they had liberty to depart ; and when they came home, they told to their Master all their merriment before the King, and what reward his Grace had bestowed on them ; and powring the gold downe vpon the Table, the same being truly told by their Master, euery mans share came iust to five pound apiece. Which, when round *Robin* saw, he swore he would bestow a supper vpon his Master and 30 Mistresse that night, though it cost him two angels ; which his fellowes hearing, and seeing *Robins* liberall heart to be such, said they would ioyne with him, and laying their money together, would haue all the Shoomakers in *Westminster* to beare them company.

Content (quoth Robin) *with all my heart ;*
And twenty shillings I will spend for my part :
And as I am true man, and sung before our King,
As much shall each of you spend before our parting.
So shall we haue musicke and gallant cheere, 40
Secke and Sugar, Claret wine, strong Ale and Beare.

This being concluded, they met all together at the signe of the Bell, where they were so merry as might be, at what time *Robin* began to blame his Master, that had not in three yeeres space gotten his Mistresse with childe.

Hold thy peace (quoth he) all this while I haue but iested, but when I fall once in earnest, thou shalt see her belly will rise like a Tun of new Ale: thou knowst I am the Cocke of *Westminster*.

I (quoth Robin) *you had that name,*
More for your rising, than your goodnesse in Venus *game.*

The company at this laughd heartily, but seuen yeeres after this iest was remembred; for in all that space had not his wife any child: Wherefore *Robin* would often say, that either his Master was no perfect man, or else his Mistresse was in her in-
10 fancy nourished with the milk of a Mule, which bred such barren-nesse in her; for till her dying day she neuer had child.

And after they had liued together, many yeeres, at last, *Richard Casteler* dyed, and at his death he did diuers good and godly deeds: among many other things he gaue to the City of *Westminster* a worthy gift to the cherishing of the poore inhabitants for euer. He also gaue toward the reliefe of the poore fatherlesse children of *Christs Hospitall* in *London*, to the value of forty pound land by the yeere; and in the whole course of his life he was a very bountifull man to all the decayed housekeepers of that place,
20 leauing behind him a worthy example for other men to follow.

Chap. V.

The pleasant Story of *Peachey* the famous Shoomaker of Fleet-street in *London*.

MVch about this time, there liued in *London* a rich Shoomaker, and a gallant housekeeper; who, being a braue man of person, bore a mind agreeable thereunto, and was therefore of most men called lusty *Peachey*: hee kept all the yeere forty tall men on worke, beside Prentises, and euery one hee clothed in tawny coats, which he gaue as his liuery to them, all with black
30 caps and yellow feathers; and euery Sunday and holiday, when this gentleman-like Citizen went to Church in his black gown garded with Veluet, it was his order to haue all his men in their liueries to wait vpon him, with euery man his sword and buckler, ready at any time, if need required.

It came to passe vpon S. *Georges* day, that this iolly Shoomaker (being seruant to the Duke of *Suffolk*) went to the Court with all his men after him, to giue attendance vpon his noble Master, which some yong Gentlemen, more wanton than wise, beholding & enuying his gallant mind, deuised how they might picke some
40 quarrell, thereby to haue occasion to try his manhood:

(Quoth they) Did you euer know a shoomaker, a sowter, a cobling companion, braue it so with the best, as this fellow doth? see with what a train of hardie squires he goes, what squaring lads

they be : they look as if they would fight with *Gargantua*, and make
a fray with the great Turk, and yet I durst lay my life they dare
scantly kill a Hedgehog : mark him I pray, I warrant you there
is neuer a Knight in this countrey that goes with so great a train.

Swounes (quoth one) it were a good sport to draw, & try what
they can do.

My Masters be aduised (quoth another) and attempt nothing
rashly : I tell you this fellow is a hardy Coine, he is a currant
mettle yfaith, and whensoeuer you try him, Ile warrant you shall
finde he will not flie a foot.   10

With that comes by lusty *Tom Stuteley* and *Strangwidge*, two
gallant Sea Captaines, who were attired all in Crimson Veluet, in
Marriners wide slops that reacht to the foot, in watched silk thrumb
hats and white feathers, hauing Pages attending with their weapons,
who seeing a cluster of Gentlemen in hard communication at the
Court gate, askt what was the matter ?

Marry Captaine (quoth they) we are all beholding to yonder
lusty Gallant that hath so many waiting on him with Tawny Coats :

Sblood, what is he (quoth *Stutely*) ?

He seemes to be a gallant man (said *Strangwidge*) whatsoeuer 20
he be : and were it not I see him in the Duke of *Suffolks* liuerie,
I should haue taken him by his train to be some Lord at the
least :

Nay (quoth *Stutely*) he is some Knight of good liuing.

Gentlemen (quoth they) how your iudgements deceiue you : it
is certaine he is as good a Shooemaker as any is in *Fleetstreet*.

What ? is he but a Shooemaker (quoth *Stutely*) ? O how that
word makes me scratch my elbo :   Can a Shooemaker come to the
Court with more Seruingmen at his heeles then Captaine *Stutely* ?
See how it makes my blood rise : O the passion of my heart, how 30
the villaine squares it out ? see, see, what a company of handsome
fellowes follow him, it is twenty pound to a penny but they were
better borne then their Master :

Not so (quoth the Gentleman) but I think their birth and
bringing vp was much alike, for they be all Shooemakers & his
stoole companions :

Now, by this iron and steell (quoth *Stutely*) were it not that he
is attendant on the good Duke, I would haue him by the eares
presently. I will lay an hundred pound, and stake it downe
straight, that Captaine *Strangwidge* and I will beat him and all 40
his forty men.

The Gentlemen being ready to set this match forward, greatly
commended the Captaines high courage : notwithstanding they
would not hazard their money on such a desperate match.

Well Gentlemen (quoth they) you say he dwels in *Fleetstreet*,
and that he is a Shoomaker, neuer trust vs more if we become not
his customers, but the crossest customers shall he finde vs that
euer came to his shop for shooes.

Nay (quoth *Stuteley*) we will bespeak Boots of him, & thus we will raise our quarrell : when they are made, if they come not on easie and sit on our legs neatly, we will make them pluck them off againe, & presently we will beat them in peeces about his pate, which if he seeme to take in dudgin, and with his men follow vs into the street for reuenge, if we make them not leap before vs like Monkies, and force them run away like sheep-biters, let vs lose our credits and Captainships for euer.

But what if you should chance to kill any of them (said the
10 Gentlemen) :

Swounes (quoth they) what care we, we are bound to sea on a gallant voyage, wherein the King hath no small venture, and without vs it cannot go forward, so that it is not the death of twenty men can stay vs at home, and therefore when they should be seeking of vs in *Fleetstreet*, we would be seeking out the Coast of *Florida*.

You say well Captaines (quoth they) and, no doubt if you do any such thing we shall heare of it : for the report thereof will be famous through *London*.

20 Within a while after *Stutely* and *Strangwidge*, hauing thus determined, came into *Fleetstreet*, and making inquiry for *Peachies* shop, they were by euery man directed to the house : where, when they were come, they called for the goodman of the house : the foreman of the shop demanded what their will was ?

Why knaue (quoth they) what carest thou, let vs speak with thy Master.

Gentlemen (quoth he) if you lack any such commodity as we make, you shall finde me sufficient to serue you, for to that end hath my Master set me in the shop.

30 Why, Iack-sauce (quoth *Stutely*) you whorson peasant, know you to whom you speak ?

The fellow being very cholerick, and somewhat displeased at these disdainfull speeches, made him this round answer : Ask you to whom I speak (quoth he) ?

I, goodman flat-cap (said *Strangwidge*) we ask to whom you speak ?

Sir (quoth he) I speak to a Veluet foole, a silken slaue that knowes not how to gouerne his tongue :

With that *Stutely* swore like a madman and presently drew out
40 a dudgin haft dagger that he had by his side, and began to lay at the fellow, which one of his fellowes seeing, flung a Last at his head and feld him to the ground : *Strangwidge* thereupon drew his sword, but by that time the fellow had took downe his sword and buckler, which hung in the shop hard at hand, and therewith so well defended himselfe, that *Strangwidge* could do him no hurt : and by that time *Stutely* recouering crald vp againe.

But *Peachie* hearing a great hurly burly in the shop, came forth

32. chtleeick *1639*

and demanded the cause of the quarrell? his seruants told him
that those Gentlemen had giuen the Iourneymen very ill words:

How can they chuse but speak ill (quoth *Peachie*) for it may be
they neuer learnd to speak well: whereupon he went vnto them
saying; how now, Captaines, how grew this quarrell twixt you
and my men?

Thy men (quoth *Stutely*)? thy Roags, and thy selfe is no better
that brings them vp:

Sir (quoth *Peachie*) you wrong me too much, and get you
quickly from my doore, or, by this sunne that shines, ile set you 10
packing, & therefore neuer think to outface me with great looks,
for I tell thee *Stutely* and *Strangwidge* both, did you look as big
as the Deuill I feare you not. And you forgot your maners too
much to giue me such base tearms, for I would you well knew.I
keepe forty good fellowes in my house, that in respect of their
manhood may seeme to be your equals.

O intollerable Comparison (quoth *Stutely*) flesh and blood
cannot beare such abuse. Ile tell thee what (quoth he) if we two
beat not thee and thy forty men, I durst be hangd vp at thy doore.

Fie, fie, tis too much oddes (quoth *Peachy*) dare you two take 20
ten? nay dare you fight with fiue?

Take that and try (quoth *Strangwidge*) and therewithall gaue
him a sound blow on the eare:

Nay this is too much (quoth *Peachy*) put vp this and put vp all:
Stutely and *Strangwidge* (quoth he) if you be men, meet me in
Lincolnes Inne-fields presently:

Content (quoth they) & thereupon went their wayes.

Peachie fetching straight his sword and buckler, calld his man
Iohn Abridges to go with him, charging all the rest not to stir out
of doores, and so into the fields they went, where immediately 30
they met with these lusty Caueliers. The Captaines seeing him
come only with one man, askt if there were all the helpe he had?

I will request no more (quoth *Peachie*) to swinge you both out
of the fields.

Brag is a good Dog (quoth *Stutely*) but tell vs, hast thou made
thy Will and set thy house in order?

What if I haue not (quoth *Peachie*)?

Why then (quoth *Strangwidge*) for thy wife and childrens sake
go home againe and do it, or else get more aide about thee to
preserue thy life. 40

Why how now Master (quoth *Iohn Abridges*) come you into the
field to fight with women? why these be two disguised butter
whores ile lay my life, that haue more skill in scoulding then in
fighting: but heare you (quoth he) if you be men, leaue your foule
words, and draw your faire weapons, and, because I will spare
your middle peece, if I strike a stroke below the girdle, call me
Cut:

Sblood shall we be thus out-braued (quoth *Stutely*)? and therewith drawing their weapons, they fell to it lustily, where *Peachie* and his man laid so brauely about them, that they beat both the Captaines out of breath, in which fray, *Stutely* was wounded in the head, and *Strangwidge* in the sword arme, but at last they were parted by many Gentlemen that came in good time to preuent further mischiefe.

The Captaines got them straight to the Surgion, & *Peachie* with his man went directly home: and while they were a dressing,
10 *Peachie* hearing how they were hurt, sent to *Stutely* a kerchiefe by one of his men, and by another a scarffe to *Strangwidge*, by the third he sent a bottle of *Aqua vitae*, wishing them to be of good cheare, for hee intended to be better acquainted with them ere long. The Captaines finding these fauours to be but flouts, were more grieued thereat, then at their hurt, and therefore, with many disdainfull speeches, they refused his profferd curtesie.

And you shall vnderstand that afterward *Peachies* men by two and two at a time, did often meet and fight with them, and so narrowly would they watch for them, that they could be in no
20 place in peace, insomuch that the Captaines found fighting work enough, & a great deale more then willingly they would, whereby they receiued many scarres and wounds in the body, so that lightly they were neuer out of Surgions hands. Vpon a time it chanced that, being vpon the point of their voyage, and shortly to go to sea: *Stuteley* and *Strangwidge* hauing beene at the Court, and newly come from my Lord-Admirals lodging, before they came to *Charing-crosse*, they were encountred by a couple of *Peachies* men, who presently drew vpon them, and laid so freely about, that the two Captaines were glad at length to house them-
30 selues for their refuge.

Now a plague on them (quoth *Stuteley*) shall we neuer be in quiet for these quoystrels? neuer were we so ferrited before, swownes we can no sooner look into the streets, but these shoo-makers haue vs by the eares: a pox on it that euer we medled with the rascals: sblood they be as vnluckie to be met, as a Hare on a iorney, or a sergeant on a Sunday morning, for euer one mischiefe or other followes it, Captaine *Strangwidge* (quoth he) there is no other shift but to seek their friendship, otherwise we are in danger euery houre to be maimed, therefore, to keep our
40 lims sound against we go to Sea, tis best to finde meanes to quiet this grudge.

Then (said *Strangwidge*) it were good to do so, if a man knew how: but you may be sure they will not easily be intreated, seeing we haue so mightily abused them in speech.

Thus they cast in their mindes diuers times by what meanes they might be reconciled: and albeit they sent diuers their friends vnto Master *Peachie*, and by his men, yet they would not yeeld, nor giue consent to be appeased, nor to put vp such wrong as they had receiued without further reuenge : so that the Captaines were at length constrained to make sute to the Duke of *Suffolk* to take vp the matter : who most honorably performed their request : and so the grudge ended betwixt them, to the great credit of Master *Peachie*, and all his men.

Chap. VI.

How *Harrie Neuell*, and *Tom Drum* came to serue *Peachey* of *Fleetstreet*.

THe fame of *Peachey* running through *England* by meanes of the frayes which he and his men had with *Stuteley* and 10 *Strangwidge*, it made many of that occupation desirous to come and dwell with him, for beside that he was a tall man of his hands, he was also an excellent good workman, & therewithall a bountifull house keeper. Among many other that was desirous of his seruice, there was one called *Tom Drum*, that had a great minde to be his man, a very odde fellow, and one that was sore infected with the sin of cogging : this boasting companion, sitting on a time sadly at work in his Masters shop at *Petworth*, and seeing the Sun shine very faire, made no more to doe but suddenly shrowded vp S. *Hughes* bones, & taking downe his pike-staffe, clapt his pack at 20 his back, and called for his Master, who, comming into the shop, and seeing his man prepared to be prauncing abroad, demanded what the matter was that he followed not his businesse.

O Master (qd. he) see you not how sweetly the Sun shines, & how trimly the trees are deckt with green leaues ?

Well & how then (quoth his Master) ?

Marry sir (quoth he) hauing a great mind to heare the small birds sing, and seeing the weather fitter to walk then to work, I called you forth to take my leaue and to bid you farewell, I hope sir, I haue no wager in your hand. 30

Why no (quoth his Master) thou wilt be sure to take an order for that, and therefore seeing thou wilt be gone, adue.

God be with you good master (quoth he) and farewell all good fellowes of the gentle craft, and therewith he departed.

The iourneymen of the Towne hearing that *Tom Drum* went away, according to their ancient custome they gathered themselues together to drink with him, and to bring him out of town : and to this intent vp they go with him to the signe of the Crowne, where they parted not till they had drunk a Stand of Ale drie.

Which being done, they bring him a mile on his way, carrying 40 a gallon of beere with them : & lastly there once againe they drink to his good health, and to *Crispianus* soule : and to all the good fellowes of *Kerbfoord* : which being done, they all shook him by the hand, and with hallowing and whooping, so long as they can see him, they bid him a hundred times farewell.

So soone as he was gone out of their whooping, the sweat reeking in his hand, and the Ale in his head, he trips so light in the highway, that he feeles not the ground he goes on : and, therefore, being in a merry vaine, and desirous to driue out the weary way, as he walks he begins thus pleasantly to sing

10
> *The Primrose in the greene Forrest,*
>   *the Violets they be gay :*
> *The double Dazies and the rest,*
>   *that trimly decks the way,*
> *Doth moue the spirits with braue delights,*
>   *whose beauties Darlings be :*
> *With hey tricksie, trim goe tricksie,*
>   *vnder the greenewood tree.*

The singing of this song awaked a young Gentleman whom sorrow had laid asleepe on a greene bank by the high wayes side. Who hauing vnaduisedly displeased his Parents, in a cholerick
20 humour departed from them, betaking himselfe to trauell, thereby to try how fortune would fauour him abroad : but hauing now spent all his money, he was in a wofull taking, not knowing what to do, for neuer had he beene brought vp to any trade, whereby he might be able to get a penny at his need. Wherefore being in this distresse, he was fully purposed to go to *London*, and there to learne some occupation, whereby he might keep himself a true man, and not to be driuen to seek succour of his friends.

Now therefore when he heard *Tom Drum* so trimly tune it on the way, raising himselfe from the sad ground, he awaited his
30 comming, at whose sudden sight *Tom Drum* started like one that had spied an Adder : & seeing him prouided with a good sword and buckler, supposed he had beene one that waited for a fat purse : for which cause he began thus to enter parly with him.

Good fellow (quoth he) God giue you good morrow, but ill speed.

Why saist thou so (quoth *Harrie*)?

Because (said *Tom*) by the good light of the day thou maist see to passe beside me, and that by thy speeding ill, I may speed the better :

40 What hast thou such store of money (quoth *Harrie*) that thou art loath to lose it ?

No by my faith (quoth he) I haue so little that I cannot spare it : for I assure thee all my store is but one poore pennie, and that thou maist see vnder my little finger.

Why then (quoth *Harrie*) if I were minded to assault thee, it should be more to rob thee of thy manhood then thy money : but tell me what pack is that thou bearest at thy back ?

Marry they be Saint *Hughes* bones :

Saint *Hughes* bones (quoth *Harrie*) what is that ?

A kind of commodity (said *Tom*) which I cannot misse, for they be my working tooles.

I pray thee (said *Harrie*) what occupation art thou ?

Sir (quoth he) I am a Goldsmith that makes rings for womens heeles :

What meanest thou by that (said *Harrie*) ?

I am (quoth *Tom*) of the Gentle Craft, vulgarly called a Shoo-maker.

The happier thou art (quoth *Harrie*) that thou hast a trade to liue by, for by that means thou carriest credit with thee in euery place : but tell me good friend what is thy name, and how far dost thou trauell this way ?

Sir (quoth he) I trauell to the next towne, but my iorney is to *London*, & as for my name, I am not ashamed to shew it : For my name is a Nowne substantiue that may be felt, heard, or vnderstood, and to speak the truth I am called : whoe there I trust, sir you ask for no hurt, you are no Bayliffe nor Bayliffs man, are ye ?

No not I (said *Harrie*).

Gods blessing on you (quoth he) I loue you the better : for I was neuer so fraid lest my Hostesse of the *George* in *Petworth* had sent you for to arrest me, for I think I owe her some ten Groats of the score, set vp in very faire Chalk, as one of the principals of her house is able to testifie : but I pray God send her meat, for I verely think I shall neuer send her monie.

But yet (quoth *Harrie*) I know not how to call your name :

Verily (said he) I am called *Thomas Drum* or *Tom Drum*, chuse you whether :

Well *Thomas* (quoth *Harrie*) I perceiue thou art a man & a good fellow ; therefore I will not be strange to open my need vnto thee. I haue beene vnto my parents vntoward, and more then that, not knowing when I was well, wilfully I came from them : and now that I haue spent all my money and worne myselfe out of credit, I haue vtterly vndone my selfe, for I am not worth a groat, nor no man will trust me for two pence.

Why then (quoth *Tom*) thou art not worth so much as goodman *Luters* lame nagge, for my Lord of *Northumberlands* huntsman would haue giuen halfe a Crowne for him to haue fedde his dogges : notwithstanding be of good cheere, if thou wilt goe to *London* with me, I will beare thy charges, and, Ifaith, at the next towne we will be merry and haue good cheere.

Alas (quoth *Harry*) how can that be, seeing you haue but one penny ?

I tell thee what (quoth *Tom*) wert thou a Shoomaker as I am, thou mightst goe with a single penny vnder thy finger, and trauell all *England* ouer, and at euery good towne haue both meate and drinke and lodging of the best, and yet haue thy penny in store, as when we come to *Gilford* you shall soone see.

Beleeue me (quoth *Harry*) that is more then any tradesmen in *England* els can doe.

Tush (quoth *Tom*) shoomakers will not see one another lacke, for it is our vse if wee know of a good fellow that comes to towne, wanting either meate or money, and that he make himselfe knowne, he shall neede to take no further care, for he shall be sure that the iorneymen of that place will not onely giue him kinde 10 welcome, but also prouide him all things necessary of free cost: And if he be disposed to worke among them, he shall haue a Master prouided by their meanes, without any sute made by himselfe at all.

Verily (quoth *Harry*) thou dost rauish me with the good report of thy passing kind and curteous trade, and I would spend part of my gentle bloud, to be of the gentle Craft: and for thy curtesie, if thou wouldst teach it mee, I would annoint thee a gentleman foreuer:

Wilt thou say and hold (quoth *Tom*)?
20 Or els hang me (said *Harry*):
Then (said he) annoint me a Gentleman, and I will shape thee for a Shoomaker straight.

Thereupon *Harry* tooke his knife, and, cutting his finger, all to smeared *Tom-Drums* face with his bloud, that hee made him looke like the Image of *Bred-streete* corner, or rather like the *Sarazines-head* without *New-gate*.

Tom Drum, seeing him doe so, said he might by that means as well annoint him a Ioyner, as a Gentleman.

Nay (said *Harry*) I do not deceiue thee I warrant thee, seeing 30 this blood did spring from a Gentleman, if thou wilt not beleeue me, aske all the men in the towne-Malin, and they will say the like.

Well, Ile take thy word (quoth *Tom*). And therefore looke that presently thou strip thy selfe, for I will cast thee in a Shoomakers mould by and by:

Harry perceiuing his meaning did what he willed, and so he was suted in *Toms* attire, and *Tom* in his; so that *Harry* bore the pike staffe and Saint *Hughes* bones: and *Tom* swaggered with his sword and buckler; and comming in this sort to *Gilford*, they were both taken for shoomakers and very hartely welcomed by 40 the iorneymen of that place, especially *Harry*, because they neuer saw him before: And at their meeting they askt him and if he could sing, or sound the Trumpet, or play on the Flute, or recon vp his tooles in rime, or manfully handle his pike staffe, or fight with a sword and buckler?

Beleeue me (quoth *Harry*) I can neither sound the Trumpet, nor play on the Flute: and beshroe his nose that made me a shoomaker, for he neuer taught me to recon vp my tooles in rime nor in prose.

Tom hearing him say so : told them that he made him of an old seruing man a new shoomaker :

When was that (quoth they).

Marry (saith he) when I was annointed a Gentleman, I thinke this face can shew, that I haue gentle blood about me :

Why then (quoth they) thou art but a painted Gentleman, but we must account this young man wise, that to auoid misery betakes himselfe to follow mistery, for cunning continueth when fortune fleeteth, but it will be hard for such as neuer were brought vp to the bodily labour to frame their fine fingers to any course 10 faculty.

Not a whit (quoth *Harry*) for labour by custome becommeth easie.

Thou saist true (said *Tom*). I durst lay a good wager I haue made more shooes in one day then all the iorneymen here haue done in a month :

With that one of the iorney-men began to chafe, saying, how many a paire of shooes hast thou made in a day ?

I made, quoth *Tom*, when the daies were at longest, eight score paire of shooes in one day. 20

O monstrous detestable lye (quoth they) and thereupon one ran into the chimney and cried, come againe *Clement*, come againe.

Whom calst thou (quoth *Tom*) ?

I call *Clement carry lye*, that runnes Poste betwixt the Turke, and the Deuill ; that he may take his full loading ere he goe, for the best iorneyman that euer I knew, neuer made aboue ten paire in a day in his life : and I will lay my whole yeeres wages with thee, that thou canst not make twenty paire in a day as they ought to be : I should be ashamed but to doe as much as another, and I neuer saw him yet that could out worke me, yet dare not I take 30 vpon me to make a doozen paire of shooes in a day : but it is an old saying, they brag most that can doe least.

Why thou Puppie (quoth *Tom*) thou house Doue, thou Cricket, that neuer crept further then the chimney corner, tell me what Countries hast thou trauelled ?

Far enough (quoth he) to proue as good a work-man as thou art :

I deny that (quoth *Tom*) for I haue been where I haue seene men headed like Dogs, and women of the same shape, where if thou hadst offered them a kisse, they would haue beene ready to haue snapt off thy nose ; othersome I haue seen, that one of their legs 40 hath been as good as a penthouse to couer their whole bodies, and yet I haue made them shooes to serue their feet, which I am sure thou couldest neuer do : nay, if thou wilt go with me, if thou seest me not make an hundred paire of shooes from sunrising to sunsetting ; count me worse then a stinking Mackrell.

Now verily thy talke stinkes too much (quoth they) and if thou canst do so, neuer make further iorney, but try the matter heere.

I tell you (quoth *Tom*) I cannot try it in *England*, nor yet in

France, Spaine, or *Italy,* nor in any part of the lowe countries, nor in high *Germany, Sweathland,* or *Polonia.*

We think no lesse (quoth they) nor in any part of the world beside.

Yes (quoth *Tom*) I can do it as we trauell to *Russia,* for there euery day is fiue and fiftie of our dayes in length : nay Ile tell you further, quoth *Tom,* in some parts of the world where I haue been, it is day for halfe a yeare together, and the other halfe yeare is continually night : and goe no further, quoth he, but into the 10 further part of *Scotland,* and you shall find one day there (in the month of Iune) to be foure and twenty houres long, and therefore, my Masters while you liue, take heed how you contrary a traueller, for therein you shall but bewray your owne ignorance, and make yourselues mocking stockes to men of knowledge.

And trauellers (quoth they) vncontrouled, haue liberty to vtter what lies they list.

Masters tell me (quoth *Tom*) were you not borne in *Arcadia?*

No (quoth they) but why aske you?

Because (said *Tom*) that countrey doth more abound in plenty 20 of Asses, where they swarme as thicke as Bees in *Cicily* :

We haue cause to giue you thanks (quoth they) for calling vs Asses so kindly :

Not so (said *Tom*) I did but aske a question ; but seeing you are so cunning, tell mee what Countrey breeds the best Hides, and Leather, and from whence haue we the best Corke?

Our best Corke comes from *Portugall* (qd. they) but the best Leather grows in our owne land :

I deny it (quoth *Tom*) there is I confesse good Corke in *Portugall,* but the best grows in *Sparta* ; but for Hides and Lether there is 30 none comparable to that in *Siciona* : where I haue made a man a paire of shooes that hath lasted him a twelue month to toyle in euery day. O tis a gallant Countrey, for I tell you what, there is neuer a shoomaker in *England* that kept so many men as I did at that time.

Then said the rest, thou speakest thou knowest not what : Master *Peachy* of *Fleet-streete* keeps continually forty men a work, and the green-King of *Saint-Martins* hath at this time little lesse then threescore iourney men.

That is pretty well (quoth *Tom*) but what say you to him that 40 for halfe a yeere together, kept waiting on him aboue a hundred men that neuer did him stitch of work? this was a shoomaker of some account :

But who was that (quoth they)?

Marry (quoth *Tom*) simple though I stand heere, it was my selfe, and yet I neuer made brags of it.

O what a shamelesse lyer art thou (quoth they) we neuer knew thee able to keep one man.

39. That is] Then is *1639*

Now, by this bread (said *Tom*) you do me mighty wrong, & were it not that ye be all of this gentle Craft, which science I doe so greatly loue and reuerence, this Iron and steele should make it good vpon your flesh, for I tell you once againe, I haue beene Master of an hundred men, and put sixteene score to the hundred :

I pray you tell vs (quoth they) what men were they?

What men were they (quoth *Tom*) they were vermin :

In troth (quoth they) we thought as much, and we commend you for telling truth, and we suppose if you were well searcht we should find twenty vermin waiting on you still. But tell vs *Tom,* art thou minded to be Master *Peachies* man?

I am (quoth he) except he will make me his fellow.

By the Masse (quoth they) then wert thou best to haue thy wards ready, and thy hilts sure, for he receiues no seruant before he tries his man-hood ;

So much the better (quoth *Tom*) and for that purpose I poste vp to *London.*

Thus hauing had at *Gilford* very good cheere, the iourney-men of the towne paid for all, and beside gaue them money in their purses to spend by the way ; and so toward *London* they went with all speed.

C H A P. V I I.

How the wilde Knight Sir *Iohn Rainsford* for burying a Massing Priest aliue, was faine to leaue his Lady and forsake his house, till he had obtained his pardon of the King: who meeting with *Henry Neuell,* and *Tom Drum,* went with him to serue *Peachy* of *Fleet-street,* where for a while he became a Shoomaker.

YOu shall vnderstand that at this time there liued a gallant Knight called Sir *Iohn Rainsford,* who was for his courage and valiant heart inferiour to few men liuing : he kept a bountifull house, and a braue company of tall men to waite vpon him. To all the poore round about where he dwelt, he was very charitable, releeuing them daily both with money and meate ; he was a famous Courtier, and in great fauour with the King, and the onely thing that disgraced his vertues, was this, that he was something wild in behauiour and wilfull in his attempts, often repenting sadly what he committed rashly.

It came to passe vpon a time that as this couragious Knight was riding home to his own house, there was at a certaine village, a corps carried to be buried, the deceased father of fiue small children and the late husband of a wofull Widdow, whose pouerty was such, that she had no money to pay for his buriall : which thing Sir *Iohn* the parish Priest doubting, would not by any meanes doe his duty to the dead man, except he might first haue his money.

The Widdow and her children, with many teares intreated him to do his office, but he would not be perswaded, saying? What you beggers, would you haue me open my sacred lips to inuocate and call vpon the King of Heauen to receiue thy husbands soule, and to perswade our great Grandmother the earth to wrap his cold
10 body in her warme bosome, for nothing? I tel thee, no : first shall his soule frie in the flames of purgatory, till it be as thin as a pancake, and his body remaine aboue ground till the Crowes haue pickt his carrion carkasse to the bare bones : and therefore leaue your puling, and prate no more, least you make me as chollericke as a quaile ;

And therewithall, as he was going away, the poore Widdow falling on her knees, pluckt him by the gowne, saying : good Sir *Iohn*, for sweet Saint *Charity*, say one *Ave Maria*, or one *Pater noster*, and let my poore husbands corps be couered, though it be
20 but with one handfull of holy ground.

Nay dame (quoth he) do you remember at the last shrift how you serued me? you would not : no forsooth you would not : and now good Mistris I will not : no penny, no *Pater Noster*, that is flat : I pray you now see if your honesty be sufficient to keepe your husband from the Crowes. I thought a time would come at length to cry quittance for your coynes : and with that word away he went.

The poore Widdow seeing his obstinacy, with a heauy heart turned into the high wayes side, which was hard adioyning to the
30 Church-yard, and there she and her children wofully begged of the passers by some money to bury their fathers dead body.

At last Sir *Iohn* came riding with all his men, of whom the poor Widdow in this manner began to aske his almes :

Good Sir (quoth she) if euer womans misery mooued your heart to pitty, giue me one penny for Gods sake, toward the burying of my poore husband : in like manner the children cried, saying, one penny for Christ his sake, good Master one penny.

Sir *Iohn*, hearing their lamentable cry, and seeing the dead corps lying there, askt why the Priest did not bury it?
40 O Sir Knight (quoth she) I haue no money to pay for the buriall, and therefore the Priest will not doe it.

No (quoth Sir *Iohn*)? by Gods blessed mother I sweare Ile make him bury the dead or Ile bury him aliue : whereupon he willed one of his men presently to goe to the Parsonage for the Priest, and to bring him thither immediately. His men did so, and foorth came Sir *Iohn*, in his gowne and corner cap, roughly demanding who would speake with him?

That would I (quoth Sir *Iohn Rainesford*) : therefore tell me, how comes it to passe, that according to order you put not this dead corps into the pit?

Sir (quoth he) because according to order they will not pay me for my paines.

Aboue all men (quoth Sir *Iohn*) Priestes should respect the poore and charitably regard the state of the needy, because they themselues doe teach charity to the people, and perswade men vnto works of mercy : and therefore Sir *Iohn*, seeing good deeds are meritorious, doe you win heauen by this good work, let the dead possesse their due :   10

I so they shall (said the Priest) so I may not loose my due : for I tell you further, I count it little better then folly, to fill my soule with pleasure by emptying my purse with coine :

Wilt thou not bury him (said the Knight) :

No not without money (said the Priest) ;

I pray thee (said the Knight) let me intreat thee for this time to doe it, because the woman is poore.

Then let me intreat you to pay me (quoth the Priest) because you are rich.

Sir *Iohn Rainsford* seeing him stand so peremptory on his 20 points, swore a deep oath, that it were best for him to bury him, or (quoth he) Ile bury thee ;

Bury me (said the Priest) a fig for you, and bury blind bayard when he is dead, or the dogs that your Hauks will not eate.

The Knight at these words being maruelous angry commanded his men to take him vp & cast him into the graue : his men made no more to do, but presently vpon their Masters word tooke vp the Priest, and, wrapping him round in his gowne, put him quicke into the graue, and the rest cast earth vpon him as fast as they could, at what time the Priest cried out, hold, hold, for Gods sake, 30 let me rise and I will bury him.

Nay soft (quoth the Knight) thou art not like to rise, no rising heere before the generall resurrection, that thou shalt rise to iudgement.

And therefore quicke as he was they buried him, which being done, he commanded the Sexton to make another graue for the dead man, and sending for another Priest he askt him if he wold bury the dead without money, who, making twenty legs, shiuering and shaking with feare, answered : I forsooth, with all my heart, for they are knaues and no Christians that will not doe it.   40

Now when the dead man was buried, the Knight gaue the poore Widdow an angell in gold to comfort her and her children, and so rode his way.

When he came home, he told his Lady what he had done ; who greatly grieuing thereat, wisht he had paid for twenty burials, rather then he had made that one buriall.

Tis done now (said the Knight) and vndone it cannot be againe, though with griefe I should kill my selfe.

Now you shall vnderstand that the Deane of the Dioces, hauing word hereof, rode vp presently to *London* and made a great complaint thereof vnto the King, which when his grace had considered, he was very wroth thereat, and therefore sent down pursuants to apprehend the Knight, but he before had forsaken his house, and wandred in disguise vp and downe the Countrey. His Lady in the meane space made great suite for his pardon, being therein assisted by diuers great Counsellors, and Noble Lords, who much lamented the Knights case: notwithstanding 10 they could hardly forbeare laughing many times when they thought vpon this mad pranke.

But as Sir *Iohn* disguisedly wandred, he chanced twixt *Gilford* and *London* to light in the company with *Harry Neuell* and *Tom Drum*: But *Harry*, vewing him well in the face, discried by his countenance what he was, and maruelling much to see him in such distresse, made himselfe not known, but sounded him in this sort.

Sir (quoth he) whither do you wander this way, or to what place trauell you?

20 Gentle youth (quoth he) fitly dost thou aske me whither I wander, seeing, indeed, we doe all but wander in this vale of misery: dost thou demand whither I trauell? nay, rather aske wherefore I trauell, or wherewith I trauell? and then could I soone answer thee:

Sbones (quoth *Tom*) I durst lay a haporth of Ale, that the Peasant is in labour with loue.

Nay (quoth Sir *Iohn*) hadst thou said I trauelled with griefe, and that I was in labour with sorrow, then hadst thou said right, for I may say to thee, I haue had a sore labour continually this month 30 in paine, and yet is not the time of my deliuerance come, wherein I should be freed from this vntoward child of care: thou didst thinke I was in loue, O would to God it were so, for while I was in loue my dayes ran foorth in plesant houres, but I am cast off like a lumpe of earth from the gardiners spade: I loue, but I am not beloued, but rather hated and despised.

Tush (quoth *Tom*) bridle these foolish passions, for Ile tell thee what, hunger asswageth loue, and so doth time, but if thou be not able to doe any of these, then to take an halter, which if thou doest vse as it ought, if euer thou complaine more of sorrow or 40 care, neuer trust my word for a cupple of blacke puddings.

Belike (said Sir *Iohn*) thou hast been some hangman that thou art so cunning in the nature of an halter: but howsoeuer thou accountest it good, yet it is an Ill word foure times a yeer at *Newgate*, and as small comfort is it to me to heare it rehearst at this time.

Indeed (said *Harry*) these are vnsauory tearmes to be spoken to a sorrowfull man: neither haue any of vs great cause to be merry at this meeting, considering the hard cases wee are in, that are both masterlesse, and moneylesse, which if God doe not soone send vs, will cause our sodaine misery.

With that the Knight turning his head, pluckt his hat to his eyes to hide the teares that trickled down his face, saying, O my masters, want of money cannot make a man miserable, if he haue health and liberty, to worke for his liuing, but indeed, the frownes of a good Master, the displeasure of a good Master, the hate of a good Master, may easily make a seruant miserable, as by mine own experience I haue seen, & to my grief but lately felt.

What man, be blith (said *Tom*) and neuer grieue so much for the Ill will of a Master.   God keepe me from being of thy mind, for if I should haue grieued at the Ill will of euery Master that I haue serued, I verely thinke I should haue kild a proper man long ere this ; for I am sure I haue had as many Masters as there are Market townes in *England*.

And yet perhaps (quoth *Harry*) none so good a Master as his was.

Neuer did man speake truer word, said the Knight, for he was to me good kind and liberall, but howsoeuer he hath banisht me his house, yet shall my heart serue him while I liue : now doth it come in my mind, how happy they are that liue in his fauour : how blessed they be that enioy his presence ; O were my head once againe shadowed vnder his faire roofe, it would expell all vnquiet thoughts, which like milstones presseth downe my hearts comfort.

What, would you goe dwell with him againe (quoth *Tom*)? fie, what a base mind doe you beare ; were it to me, by this flesh and bloud, I would rather run as far as *Ierusalem* to seeke a Master.

Tom, *Tom* (said the Knight) I know this, wealth makes men lofty, but want makes men lowly, and commonly gentle.   Masters haue proud seruants, but had I beene as wise, as I was wilfull, I might haue led a happy life, but if teares might satisfie for mine offence, I would quickly recouer his fauour.

Hereupon the wofull Knight would haue parted their company, but *Harry*, secretly conferring with him had knowledge how his griefe grew, and making themselues known the one to the other, agreed to goe to *London* together, and there to try what fortune would befall them.

The Knight tooke great comfort by this conference, and hauing store of gold about him, made them great cheere at *Kingstone*, and in the end was content to take their counsaile : and comming into *Fleet-streete*, Tom Drum brought them to *Peachies* house, where such meanes was made : that at last vpon the tryall of their manhood, they were all entertained ; and so well *Peachy* liked of Sir *Iohn* that he vowed he should not be his man, but his fellow.

Within short time after, the French-men had landed in the Ile of *Wight*, about two thousand men of warre, who burned and spoyled the Country very sore, for which cause the King had made ready an army of men to goe thither.   *Peachy* at his owne proper cost, set forth thirty of his owne seruants, well armed at all essayes, and himselfe as Captaine ouer them mustred before the King: who liked so well of them, that he chose out seauen of that company for his owne Guard; at what time Sir *Iohn*, in disguised manner shewed there such good seruice, that thereby he won his Maiesties high fauour, and was by him most graciously pardoned. *Peachy* was hereupon made the King's Shoomaker, who liued long after in great fauour and estimation, both with his Maiesty & all the honourable Lords of the Court.

10

Chap. VIII.

Of *Tom Drums* vants, and his rare intertainment at Mistris *Farmers* house, the faire Widdow of *Fleet-street.*

THere liued in *Fleet-streete* at this time a faire Widdow, who was famous for her beauty, as she was esteemed for her wealth; she was beloued of many Gentlemen and sued vnto by diuers Cittizens, but so deepe was the memory of her late husband ingrauen in her heart, that she vtterly refused marriage leading a sober and solemne life.

20 *Harry Neuell* hauing his heart fired with the bright beams of this blazing Comet, sought all meanes possible to quench the heate thereof with the floudes of her fauourable curtesie: and lacking meanes to bring himselfe acquainted with so curious a peece, bewrayed by his outward sighs, his inward sorrows: which vpon a time *Tom Drum* perceiuing, demanded the cause of his late conceiued griefe, saying, How now *Hall*, what wind blowes so bleake on your cheekes now? tell me mad wag, hath *Cupid* and you had a combate lately? why lookest thou so sad? hath the blind slaue giuen thee a bloody nose, or a broken head?

30 Oh, no *Tom* (quoth he) that little tyrant aimes at no other part but the heart, therefore tis my heart, and not my head that bleeds.

With whom *Hall*, with whom art thou in loue, tell me man? it may be I may pleasure thee more in that matter then my Lord Maior: therefore, Ifaith *Harry* say who is it? neuer be afraid man to vnbuckle your Budget of close counsell to me, for if I bewray your secrets call me dogs-nose and spit in my face like a young kitling. I tell thee *Harry*, I am holden in greater account among women then you are aware, and they will more willingly
40 shew their secrets to me then to their ghostly father.

But art thou so in fauour with fine wenches (quoth *Harry*)?

Ifaith Sir I (quoth *Tom*) and I tro I haue not liued thus long, but I know how to make a woman loue me, by a cunning tricke that I haue : I durst lay my life, I will make a dozen maids runne after me twenty miles for one nights lodging, striuing, who should first bestow her maiden-head on me.

That tricke surpasses of all that euer I heard (quoth *Harry*).

Nay (quoth *Tom*) Ile tell thee once what a merry pranke I plaid, God forgiue me for it : vpon a time, on a Saterday in the morning, I went into *East-Cheape* of purpose to spie what pretty wenches came to Market, where I saw a great many as fresh as flowers in May, tripping vp and down the streets with handbaskets in their 10 hands, in red stammell petticoates, cleane neckerchers and fine holland aprons as white as a Lilly : I did no more but carry the right leg of a Turtle vnder my left arme, and immediately the wenches were so inamoured with my sight that they forsooke the butchers shops, and inticed me into a Tauerne, where they spent all the money they should haue laid out at Market, onely to make me merry : and neuer had I so much to doe, as to be rid of their company, where they were ready to fall together by the eares, for the kisses they would haue bestowed vpon me.

But it may be (quoth *Harry*) your art would faile me now, to 20 help your friend at a dead lift :

Not so (said *Tom*) and therefore if there be any in this street that thou hast a mind vnto, thou shalt carry but the head of a dead crow about thee, & it shall be of force to bring her to thy bed, were it fine Mistres *Farmer* herself.

But art thou acquainted with her (quoth *Harry*) or dost thou thinke thou couldst prefer a friend to her speech ?

I (quoth *Tom*). Why I tell thee I am more familiar with her then with *Doll*, our kitchen-drudge : why man, she will doe anything at my request, nay, I can command her in some sort, for 30 I tell thee she will not scant be seene in the street, though some would giue her twenty pound for euery step, and I did but slightly request her to walke into the fields with me, and straight she went, and I neuer come into the house, but I haue such entertainment as no man hath the like : for as soone as euer she sees me set footing on her checkquerd pauement, presently with a smiling looke, she meetes me halfe way, saying, what my friend *Tom-Drum*? honest *Thomas*, by my Christian soule, hartily welcome : then straight a chair and a cushion is fetcht for me, and the best cheere in the house is set on the table, and then sitting downe by my side 40 in her silken gowne, she shakes me by the hand and bids me welcome, and so laying meate on my trencher with a siluer forke she wishes me frolicke, at what time all the secrets of her heart she imparts vnto me, crauing my opinion in the premises.

I assure thee (said *Harry*) those are high fauours, well be-wraying the great friendship that she beares thee, and I much maruell that thou, being a young man, wilt not seeke a wife that is so wealthy, and so make thy selfe famous, by marrying Mistris

Farmer, for it is likely she could well a way to make him her husband, to whom she opens her hearts secrets.

Tis true (quoth *Tom*) and I know that if I spoke but halfe a word she would neuer deny me: nay she would spend ten of her twelue siluer Apostles, on condition I would vouchsafe to be her husband. But wot you what *Harry*, it is well known, though Lillies be faire in shew, they be foule in smell, and women, as they are beautifull so are they deceitfull: beside, Mistris *Farmer* is too old for me.

10 Too old (quoth *Harry*)? why man she is not so old as charing Crosse for her gate is not crooked nor her face withered: but were she an hundred yeare old, hauing so strong a body and so faire a face, she were not in my opinion much to mislikt: yet in my conscience I thinke, since first her faire eyes beheld the bright sunne, she neuer tasted the fruites of twenty flourishing Somers: nor scant felt the nipping frostes of nineteene cold winters, and therefore her age need be no hurt to her marriage.

Ile tell thee my mind (quoth *Tom*) after a woman is past six-teene yeeres old, I will not giue fifteene blew buttons for her: but
20 tell me *Harry*, dost thou like her? if thou dost, say so, and I will warrant her thy owne.

Gentle *Tom Drum* (quoth *Harry*) the true figure of vnfained friendship, and the assured Map of manhood, doe but prefer me to her acquaintance, and I will request no greater curtesie.

Here is my hand (quoth *Tom*) it shall be done, and on Thursday at night next we will goe thither, and then thou shalt see whether *Tom Drum* can command anything in Mistresse *Farmers* house or no.

The day being thus set downe, *Harry* had prepared himselfe
30 a faire sute of apparell against the time, and beside had bought certaine giftes to bestow on the faire Widdow: *Tom Drum* in like sort had drest himselfe in the best manner he might, still bearing *Harry* in hand that none in the world should be better welcome then he to the Widdow: which God wot was nothing so, for she neuer respected him but onely for the shooes he brought her: but you shall see how it fell out.

The day being come, *Tom* taking *Harry* by the hand, and comming to the Widdows doore, took hold on the Bell and rung thereat so lustily, as if he had beene bound seauen yeares Prentise
40 to a Sexton: whereupon one of the Prentises came straight to the doore, saying who is there?

Sirra (quoth *Tom Drum*) tis I, open the doore;

The fellow seeing it to be *Tom Drum*, with a frown askt him what he would haue? who answered, he would speake with his Mistris.

My Mistris is busie (quoth the fellow) cannot I doe your errand?

No marry can you not (quoth *Tom*) I must speak with her my selfe:

Then stay a little (quoth the boy) and I will tell, and with that in he went, leauing *Tom* still at the doore, where they sate till their feet waxt cold before the boy returned.

By the Masse (quoth *Harry*) whatsoeuer your credit with the Mistris is I know not, but the curtesie is small that is shewen you by her man :

Tush (quoth *Tom*) what will you haue of a rude vnmannerly boy? If any of the Maids had come to the doore, we had beene long ere this brought to their Mistris presence : therefore once againe I will vse the help of the Bell-rope. 10

At his second ringing, out comes one of the Maids, saying with a shrill voyce : who the Diuell is at the doore, that keepes such a ringing?

Why, you queane (quoth he) tis I.

What *Tom Drum* (quoth shee) what would you haue?

I would speak with your mistresse (quoth he) :

Trust me (said the maid) you cannot speake with her now, she is at supper with two or three that are sutors ; Master Doctor *Burket* is one, and Master Alderman *Iaruice* the other :

Tut (quoth *Tom*) tell me not of sutors but tell her that I am 20 here, then good enough.

Well, I will (quoth shee) and with that, claps to the dore againe, and keepes them still without.

This geare workes but ill-fauouredly yet (said *Harry*) and you are little beholding either to the men, or to the maids, for ought that I see, that will not shew you so much fauour to stay within dores.

Tis no matter, *Harry* (quoth he) but if their Mistresse should know this she would swinge their coats lustely for it :

And with that one of the boyes, opening the doore, told *Tom* 30 that his mistresse wold haue him send vp his errand.

Sblood (quoth he) is she so stately that she will not come downe? I haue seene the day when she would haue bin glad to haue spoken with me :

I (quoth the fellow) it may be so, when you haue brought her a new paire of shoes, that hath pincht her at the toes.

Come *Harry* (said *Tom*) I will take the paines for this once to goe vp to her.

By my faith but you shall not (said the fellow) : and therefore keepe you backe, for you come not in here : 40

Tom Drum seeing himselfe thus disgracd before his fellow *Harry* (being very angry) askt if this were the best entertainment that they could affoord their Mistresses Friends? And there- withall began to struggle with them: which their mistresse hearing, started from the table, and suddenly came to see what the matter was, who being certified of *Tom Drums* sawcinesse began thus sharpely to check him,

Why, fellow (quoth she) art thou mad, that thus vnciuilly thou behauest thyself? what hast thou to say to me, that thou art thus importunate?

No hurt (quoth he) but that this gentleman and I would haue bestowed a galland of wine to haue had three or foure houres talke with you.

I tell thee (said she) I am not now at leasure, and therefore good honesty trouble me no more: neither is it my wont to be won with wine at any time;

Gods Lord (quoth he) are you grown so coy? if you and I were 10 alone I know I should finde you more milde: what must no man but Doctor *Burket* cast your water? is his Phisicke in most request? well I meane to be better entertained ere I goe, for there is neuer a Flemming of them all shall out face me, by the morrow Masse I sweare.

Mistris *Farmar* seeing him so furious, answered he should haue present entertainment according to his desert; whereupon she made no more to doe, but quietly went to her seruants, and willed them to thrust him out by the head and shoulders: which presently they performed. But *Harry* was by her very modestly answered, 20 that if he had occasion of any speech with her, the next day he should come and be patiently heard and gently answered: with which words after she had drunke to him in a gobblet of Claret wine, he departed, and, going home, he told *Tom Drum* he was highly beholding to him for his curtesie in preferring his sute to Mistris *Farmer*:

Surely (quoth hee) you are in very high fauour with the faire woman, and so it seemed by your great entertainment: I pray thee *Tom*, tell me how tasted the meat which she set on thy trencher with her siluer forke: and what secret was that shee told 30 in thy eare? trust me, thou art precious in her eies, for she was as glad to see thee, as one had giuen her a rush, for when after many hot wordes she heard thee draw thy breath so short, she for very pitty tumbled thee out into the street to take more ayre:

Well (quoth *Tom*) floute on, but I am well enough serued, Ile lay my life, had I not brought thee with me, neuer a man should haue had more welcome then I: and now I consider with my selfe that it did anger her to the heart when she saw I was pur-posed to make another co-partner of her presence: but it shall teach me wit while I liue, for I remember an old saying, loue and 40 Lordship brookes no fellowship.

But when this matter was made known to the rest of the iorneymen, *Tom Drums* entertainment was spoke of in euery place, insomuch that it is to this day a prouerb amongst vs, that where it is supposed a man shall not be welcomed, they will say he is like to haue *Tom Drums* entertainment. And to auoid the flouts that were daily giuen him, poore *Tom Drum* forsooke *Fleet-street*, and at last went into *Scotland*, being prest for a Drummer at *Muskelbrough* field, where the noble Duke of

Sommerset & the Earle of *Warwick* were sent with a noble army, where Englishmen and Scots meeting, there was fought a cruell battle, the victory whereof fell to the Englishmen : at what time there was slaine of the Scots to the number of 14 Thousand, and fifteene hundred taken prisoners, where we will leaue *Tom Drum* till his returne, making mention how *Harry Neuell* behaued him-selfe in the meane space in *London.*

Chap. IX.

How *Harry Neuell* wooed Mistris *Farmer* and deceiued Doctor *Burket*: and how they were both beguiled by a Prentice that dwelt in the house, who in the end married her.

Istris *Farmer* fiering the hearts of many with her beauty, was wondrously wooed by Doctor *Burket*, who would giue vnto her diuers rich gifts, the which though they were faire and costly, yet Mistris *Farmer* would hardly accept them, but euen what he in a manner by perforce constrained her to take, least by his cunning he should insert therein some matter more then ordinary, that might mooue any motion of loue, contrary to her naturall inclination :

Vpon a time *Harry Neuell* comming thether, and finding the Doctor very diligent to breed the Widdows content, whereby he greatly hindred his proceedings, cast in his mind how he might disburden the house of the Doctor and get opportunity to prefer his owne sute. At last lighting on a deuice fit for the purpose, in this sort he delt with the doctor ;

There was an Egyptian woman that at *Black-wall* was in trauell with child, and had such hard labour, that she was much lamented among all the wiues that dwelt thereabout. *Harry Neuell* com-ming that way, and hearing thereof, thought it a fit matter to imploy Doctor *Burket* about, while in the meane space he might the better bewray his affection to the Widdow.

Whereupon he sent one to him attyred like a seruing man, booted and spurd, who comming to the Widdows house all in a sweate, laid load on the doore demanding for Master Doctor :

What would you with him (quoth one of the Maids)?

Marry (quoth he) my Lady *Sunborne* hath sent for him in all post hast, and therefore I pray you let me speake with him.

I will presently doe your errand (said the maid) whereupon running vp she told him that my Lady *Sunborne* hath sent a messenger in very great hast to speake with him. Doctor *Burket*, hearing that and being well acquainted with the Lady *Swinborne*, took leaue of the Widdow & went to the messenger, saying how now good fellow, what would my good Lady haue with me?

Sir (said the messenger) she would desire you if euer you did tender the life of a Lady, to make no delay, but presently to put your selfe a horse-back & come to her, for she is wondrous sick:

I am sory for that (said the Doctor); & surely I will make all speed possible to come to her: whereupon the Doctor tooke horse and immediatly went with the seruingman.

10   *Harry* hearing of his departure, came to the Widdow with a smiling countenance and thus merily began to wooe her.

Now Mistris *Farmer*, happy it is that a yong man once in a moneth may find a moment of time to talk with you: truth it is that your good graces haue greatly bound me in affection to you, so that onely aboue all the women in the world I haue setled my delight in your loue, & if it shall please you to requite my good will with the like kindnesse, I shall account my birthday blessed, & remaine your faithfull friend for euer.

Gentle man (quoth she) for your good will, I thank you, but I 20 would haue you vnderstand, that the lesse you loue me, the better I shall like you, for your delights & mine are not alike, I haue setled my fancy on a single life, being a Widdow vnmeete to marry, & vnapt to loue; once indeed I had learned that lesson, but my schole master being vntimely dead that taught me, I grew forgetfull of all those principles & then I swore neuer to follow that study more: wherefore if you will become a faithfull friend to me, let me be assured thereof by this, that from henceforth you will not any more trouble me with this matter, & thereby you shall bind me to think the better of you while I know you: & doe 30 not think I speak this of any affection proceeding from myself to any other, or for the desire of any benefit proferred by any other to me.

Faire Mistris (quoth *Harry*) I know it is the custome of women to make their denials vnto their louers, & strictly to stand on nice points, because they will not be accounted easily won, or soone entreated: alack deere Dame, consider nature did not adorne your face with such incomparable beauty, & framed euery other part so full of excellency, to wound men with woe, but to worke their content. Wherefore now in the *Aprill* of your yeares, and the sweet 40 summer of your dayes, banish not the pleasures incident to bright beauty, but honour *London* streets with the faire fruite of your womb & make me blessed by being father to the issue of your delicate body; & though your beauty as the spring doth yet yearely grow, yet in the black winter of old age it will not be so, & we see by daily experience, that flowers not gathered in time rot & consume them selues: wherfore in my opinion you should doe the world intollerable wrong to liue like a fruitlesse figtree.

Nay then Sir (quoth she) I perceiue you will grow troublesome, and shew your selfe no such man as you professe your selfe : and seeing among many I request but one thing at your hands, and you refuse to doe it for my sake, I may say your frindship is more in words then in works ; wherefore I perceiue I must be constrained to call my Maid for a cup of voyding beere ere you will depart.

Nay Mistris (quoth he) I will saue you that labour, seeing your loue commands me ; & I pray God grant you a more fauourable mind at our next meeting, & with these words he departed.

Now you shall vnderstand that this gallant Widdow had in her house a very proper youth which was one of her aprentices, who had a long time borne his Mistris great good will : whereupon he became so diligent & carefull about all things committed to his charge, that thereby he won much commendations among all the neighbors, & was for the same highly esteemed of his Mistris : who after he had long concealed his grief, at last vnburdened himselfe of some sorrow, by making a friend priuy to his passions, who comforted him in this sort :

Tush man (quoth he) what though she be thy Mistris & thou her prentise, be not ashamed to shew thy affection to her : she is a woman wise & modest, and one that howeuer she answers thy demand, will not think worse of thee for thy good will : therefore try her, thou knowest not how fortune may fauour thy sute, and the worst is she can but say thee nay :

O (quoth he) if I were out of my years, I could haue some heart to wooe her, but hauing yet three quarters of a yeere to serue, it may be some hindrance to my freedome if she should proue froward.

Tush stand not on those tearms (said his friend *Francis*) she will neuer requite a kindnes with such discurtesie, and therefore *William*, proue not a foole by being too fearefull.

O my deare friend *Francis* (quoth he) how can I suppose I should speed well, seeing she disdains Doctor *Burket*, and refuses Master Alderman, & will shew no countenance to gallant Master *Neuell* ;

What a bad reason is this (quoth *Francis*) some cannot abide to eate of a Pig : some to taste of an Eele, othersome are sicke if they see but a Crab, and diuers cannot away with cheese ; yet none of them all but doe liue by their victuals ; euery man hath his fancy, & euery woman will follow her own mind, and therefore, though she find not an Alderman or a Doctor for her diet yet she may think *William* her man a fit morsell for her own tooth.

I wis (quoth *William*) thy reasons are good, and I haue aduantage aboue all other suters to follow my sute, being in the house daily with her, and euery euening when they are away : beside she hath appointed me this after noone to come to her Closet, that I may shew her my reckoning and accounts & in what sort her state standeth : wherefore seeing I haue such occasion, I will no longer trifle out the time : but so soon as that businesse is ended put my selfe to the hazard of my happy fortune : wherefore good *Francis* farewell till I see thee againe, & how I speed, at our next meeting thou shalt know.

The time at last being come that Mistris *Farmer* had appointed to haue her books cast ouer, getting into her closet shee whistled for her Maid, & bad her call vp *William* ; (quoth she) let him bring his books of account with him :

The maid did as her Mistris commanded, & vp comes *William* 10 with his books vnder his armes : & after he had very reuerently don his duty to his Mistris, she bad him sit downe saying, now *William* let me see these reckonings iustly cast vp, for it is long since I haue cast an eye into mine estate.

Mistris (quoth he) doubt not but your estate is good and your accounts iustly kept for I haue had as great regard thereto as the goods had been my owne.

Therein (quoth she) I am the more beholding to thee, neither shal thy true seruice goe vnrewarded if I liue ; or if I dye thou shalt not be altogether forgotten.

20 These kind speeches greatly comforted *Williams* heart, where-vpon he fell to his reckonings roundly, till, his mind running too much on his Mistris beauty, sometimes he would misse and count three-score, and foure-score, nine-score.

Nay there you faile (quoth his Mistris) and ouer-tell forty, for three and foure is but seauen.

Tis true indeed Mistris (said he) and three times seauen is iust fiue and twenty.

I tell thee (quoth she) tis but one and twenty, what fellow, begin you to dote in your yong yeares ?

30 O my deere Mistris (said he) blame me not if I doe so, seeing your sweet presence hath made farre wiser then my self to dote : O my good Mistris pardon my presumption, for being thus bold to vnburden my hearts griefe vnto you, my hearty loue to your sweet selfe is so great, that except you vouchsafe fauourably to censure, and kindly to iudge thereof, that the sorrowes of my mind will wound my very soule, and make my life loathsome vnto me.

Wherefore my good Mistris, despise not your poore seruant, but yeeld vnto him such succour, as may prolong his dayes with 40 many blessed houres.

His Mistris obscuring her beauty with lowring browes, (like foggy vapours that blot the sky) made him this answer : How now Sirra ? hath my too much mildnesse made you thus sawcy ? can you set your loue at no lower a pitch, but you must mount to be Master of your Mistris ?

No Mistris (quoth he) no master, but your seruant for euer.

Goe to, leaue your prating (quoth she) or I will breake thy head I sweare, haue I refused as thou seest, a graue and wealthy

Alderman that might make me a Mistris of worship and dignity, and denied master Doctor of his request, who as thou knowest is at this day esteemed the cunningest Physition in *London*, and diuerse other honest and well landed Gentlemen, and among the rest young Master *Neuell*, who as some say, is descended of a noble house, and whose loue I dare sweare is to me most firmely deuoted, so that in my heart I am perswaded he loues the ground the better that I tread on : & should I (I say) forsake all these to make my foot my head, and my seruant my superiour, to marry thee which art a Prentice boy? 10

Nay Sir (quoth she) seeing you are grown so lusty, tis time to tame you and looke to your steps : therefore I charge you leaue the shop and get you into the kitchin to help the Maid to washe the dishes and scowre the Kettles ; and whereas since my husbands decease I haue giuen foure nobles a yeare to a water bearer, I will make thee saue me that charges, for it is well seene, that too long the water Tankard hath beene kept from thy lazy shoulders, and if thou scornest to doe this, get where thou wilt ; but if thou wilt remaine with me, so long as thou hast a day to serue thou shalt be thus imployed. 20

Hereupon she called vp her man *Richard* to supplie his place, and to be fore-man of the shop, gracing him with the keyes of the counting house ; which *William* seeing, sadly went out of her sight, wofully to himselfe bewayling his hard fortune, but yet such was his loue to his Mistris, that he rather chose to be drudge in her kitchin, then to change her seruice for any other. All the seruants in the house much mused at this alteration : but to no creature did his Mistris tell the cause thereof, but kept it secret to her selfe : toward the euening, foorth he must needs goe for water, at what time he wanted no flouts of all his fellows, nor of many of 30 the neighbors seruants : where meeting with his friend *Francis*, discoursed to him the whole cause of his disgrace : he greatly chafing thereat, perswaded him neuer to endure such base drudgery, but rather to seeke preferment in some other place. Notwithstanding *William* would not follow his counsell, but rather chose patiently to abide all brunts.

Night being come, and supper ended, *William* was set to performe his penance for his presumption in loue, that is to say, to scrape the trenchers, scowre the kettles and spits, and to wash vp the dishes : which he went about with such good will, that it 40 seemed to him rather a pleasure then a paine.

His Mistris closset, joyning to the kitchin, had a secret place therein to look into the kitchin, where closely sitting, she earnestly beheld her man how he bestirred himselfe in his busines : Wherevpon she entered into this consideration with her selfe. Now fie for shame, how Ill doth it beseeme me to set so handsome a youth to such drudgery ? if he bore a man's mind he would neuer indure it, but being of a base and seruile condition, he doth easily indure

the yoake of seruitude, and yet I am too blame so to thinke, for if he had stubbornly disobeyed my commandement, how could I otherwise iudge, but that in pride and disdaine he thought himselfe too good to be at any direction : some seruants would in such a case haue giuen me many foule words, and rather malepartly set me at nought and forsake my seruice, then to haue indured the tearms of disgrace that he hath done by this means : but heereby it is euident that loue thinks nothing too much. Well *Will* (quoth she) the vertue of thy mind shall breed better
10 thoughts in thy Mistris, which shall make her reward thy good will in a large measure : see, see, how neately he goes through his work, how handsomely he handles euerything : and surely well may I suppose that he which is so faithfull a seruant, would certainly proue a kind husband, for this hath beene no slender triall of his constant heart.

With that hearing the Maid and some other of the seruants talke with him, she lending a heedfull eare to their speech, heard them speake to this purpose :

Good Lord *William* (quoth one) I maruell much that you,
20 being of so good parents and hauing so little a while to serue, will be thus vsed at her hands? it were too much if you were but this day bound prentice, to be set to such slauery :

I sweare (quoth another) I haue three times longer to serue then you and if she should bid me doe as thou dost, I would bid her doe it herselfe, with a morin :

Ile tell you what (quoth the third) Ile be plaine and vse but few words, but I would see my faire Mistris with the black Deuill before I would doe it.

Well well my masters (quoth *William*) you are mad, merry wags
30 but I take it as great fauour done me by my Mistris thus to imploy me, that thereby I might haue knowledge how to decke vp a kitchen that meeting with a bad huswife to my wife, I know how to instruct her in houshold affaires :

I care for no such fauour (said he).

Their Mistris hearing all, said nothing but determined to try them all what they would doe ere it were long wherefore being now greatly affectioned to her man, couered her loue with such discretion, that none could perceiue it : For Master Doctor being newly returned, came thither puffing and blowing, saying he was
40 neuer so serued since he was borne ; (quoth he) since I was here, I haue at least ridden an hundred miles with an arrant knaue that carried me I knew not whether : he rode with me out of *Bishopsgate* foorth right as far as *Ware*, and then compassing all *Suffolke* and *Norfolke*, he brought me backe againe through *Essex*, and so conducted me to *Black-wall* in *Middlesex* to seeke out my Lady *Swinborne*, my good Lady and Mistris : at last I saw it was no such matter, but the villaine being disposed to mocke me, brought me to a woman Egiptian, as blacke as the great Diuell, who lay

in child-bed and was but deliuered of a child of her owne colour: to the which in despite of my beard they made me be God-father, where it cost me three crownes, and I was glad I so escaped, and who was the author of all this deceipt but Master *Neuell*? but if euer I come to giue him Phisicke, if I make him not haue the squirt for fiue dayes, count me the veriest dunce that euer wore veluet cap.

Master Doctor (quoth she) I am very sorie you were so vsed, notwithstanding to make Master *Neuell* and you friends I will bestow a breakefast vpon you to morrow, if it please you to accept 10 my offer.

Faire Widdow (quoth he) neuer a one in the world would haue vrged me to be friends with him but your selfe, and I am contented for your sake to doe it: and thus till next morning he took his leaue.

Next day as soone as she was vp she called vp one of her men saying, Sirra run quickly, take a basket and fetch me a bushel of oysters from Billinsgate;

The fellow frowning said, I pray you send another, for I am busie in the shop. 20

Why knaue (quoth she) Ile haue thee goe.

(Quoth he) make a drudge of some other and not of me, for to be plaine I will not goe.

No (quoth she) Call me *Iohn* hither:

When he came, she desired him very gently to fetch her a bushel of oysters.

Why Mistresse (quoth he) my friends sent me not here to be a Porter to fetch Oisters from *Billingsgate*. I tell you true, I scorne you should require any such matter of me.

Is it true (quoth she)? very well, I will remember this when you 30 forget it.

Thus, when she had tried them all, she called her man *William*, saying: sirra goodman scullian take the great close basket, and fetch me a bushell of oysters from *Billinsgate*, & look you tarry not.

I will forsooth Mistris (quoth he) & presently away he went with such good will as none could go with better, being maruellous glad that she would request anything at his hands.

When he was come againe, with a smiling countenance she said, what *Wilkin* art thou come already? it is well done, I pray 40 thee bring some of them vp into my Closset, that I may taste how good they be:

Yes forsooth (quoth *William*) and after her he went, the Maide likewise carried vp a couple of white manchets, and with a Diaper napkin couered the table.

Now Maid (quoth she) fetch me a pint of the best red wine: I will forsooth (said the Maid).

24. Iohn] Richard *1639: but cf. p. 200 l. 41.*

Mistris (said *William*) if it please you, I will open your Oysters
for you ;

I pray you, do (quoth she) :

Then taking a towell on his arme, and a knife in his hand,
being glad he had gotten so good an office, shewed himselfe so
feat and expert in his occupation, that he opened as fast as his
Mistresse could eat.

Beleeue me *William* (quoth she) you are nimble at an oyster,
and quick in caruing vp shell-fish, though dull in casting vp
10 accounts, I pray thee tell me how many shels are in three and
thirtie oysters ?

Threescore and six (said *William*) :

You are a witty youth (quoth she) if thy speech be true it must
then needs follow that I haue eaten three and thirty oysters, haue
also deuoured threescore and six shels, which is too much for
one womans breakfast in a cold morning in conscience, and
therefore I had need quickly to giue ouer, least I break my belly
with oyster shels : whereupon she cald her maid, saying : come
hither *Ioane,* and bring me a goblet of wine that I may wash
20 *Williams* shels from my stomack.

Indeed Mistris (quoth he) if you take my words so, I spoke
without book :

It is true (quoth she) for they are alwaies without that are
neuer within, and either thy knowledge is small, or thy blindnesse
great, or oyster shels very soft, that I should eat so many and
neuer feele one : for surely, if there be threescore and six
oystershels in three and thirty oysters, there must needs be as many
more in three and thirty oysters : and to affirme my words true,
behold here the shels that were out of the oysters, now shew me
30 those that were within the oysters.

William, seeing his Mistris thus pleasant, began to gather some
courage to himselfe, and therefore thus vttered his mind : Deare
Mistris, needs must I proue both blinde in sight, and dull in
conceipt, while your faire eyes that giues light to the Sunne
obscure themselues, and dark the glory of their shine, when I seek
to receiue comfort thereby : and the want of your good will makes
my wits so weak, that like a barren tree it yields no fruit at all.

True (quoth she) : three times seuen is iust fiue and twenty : but
tell me what is the cause that moues thee to desire my fauour,
40 and to request my good will ?

Good Mistris pardon me (quoth he) and I will tell you :

Whereupon she replied, saying, trust me *William,* my pardon is
easier to be gotten then the Popes, and therefore be not afraid to
proceed.

Why then my deare Mistris, seeing you haue so graciously
granted liberty to my hearts aduocate, to pleade at the bar of your
beauty, and to open the bill of my complaint : know this, that hope
against hope perswaded me to labour for your loue, that gaining

the same I might be called a blessed man by winning such a wife.

What *Will* (quoth she) art thou not ashamed, that such a youth as thy selfe, a lad, a stripling, a prentice boy, should in the ignorance of his age, cumber himselfe with the cares of the world, and wantonly take a wife, that knowes not how to guide himselfe ? I tell thee fellow, first learne to thriue, and then wiue.

O my deare Mistris (said *William*) let not pleasant youth which is the glory of many be a disgrace to me : neither without triall deere Mistris disable not my manhood, which now I take to be in his chiefe prime.

Nay (quoth she) if thou wilt haue thy manhood tried, prepare thy selfe for the warres, and purchase honour by beating down our countries foes, and so shalt thou weare the golden wreath of honour foreuer.

In troth Mistris (quoth he) I had rather haue my manhood tried in another place.

Yfaith where (quoth shee) ?

By my troth (said he) in your soft bed, which is far better then the hard field :

Why thou bold knaue (quoth she) it were a good deed to make you a bird of *Bridewell* for your saucinesse.

Beleeue me Mistris (quoth he) I am sorie you should be offended, rather will I get me into a corner and die through disdaine, then stay in your sight and grieue you, and with that away he went.

She seeing him so hastily depart, called him againe saying : *William* come hither, turne againe you faint-hearted coward, what, art thou afraid of *Bridewell* ? vse thy selfe well, and I will be thy friend :

The young man that with these words was reuiued like a sick man out of a dead sound, turning merrily to his Mistris, gaue her a kisse, saying : on that condition I giue you this.

How now sir (quoth she) I called you not back to be so bold : in good sadnesse do so againe, and I will giue you on the eare.

Nay, Mistris (quoth he) if that be all the danger, take then another, and lay me on the eare (so I may lay you on the lips) and spare not :

Nay, then (said his Mistris) I see my too much softnesse makes thee saucy, therefore for feare thou shouldest catch a surfet, I charge thee on paine of loues displeasure, to get you downe about your businesse, and see that all things be in readinesse against my friends come : why goe you not ? what stand you in a maze ? pack I say and be gone.

And thus my deare Mistris (quoth he) parts my soule out of Paradise, and my heart from heauens ioy : notwithstanding you command and I consent and alwayes let me finde fauour, as I am forward to follow your precepts, and therewithall away he went.

He was no sooner gone, but she hauing determined what to

do, sent for her friends, at what time the Alderman comming
thither, and Master Doctor, she had also inuited Master *Peachie*
and his Wife, and with them came gallant young *Neuill.*

When they were all set at the table, after they had well tasted
of the delicates there prepared : Mistris *Farmer* told them for two
causes she had requested their companie that day to breakfast :
the one was, that master Doctor and young *Neuill* might be made
friends : and the other that in their sight she might make her
selfe sure to her husband, that they might be witnes of their vowes.

10   The companie said, they should be very glad to see so good
a work performed : whereupon shee calling vp all her men seruants,
spake to this purpose. My good friends and kinde neighbours,
because I will haue none ignorant of that which is to be effected,
I haue presumed to bring my seruants into your presence, that
they also may beare record of the reconciliation betwixt Master
Doctor and Master *Neuill,* and therefore my Masters, if your
hearts consent to an unitie, declare it by shaking hands, that it
may not bee said, that my house was the breeder of brawles, and
on that condition I drink to you both : the Gentlemen both

20   pledged her, and according to her request ended the quarrell.

When this was done, she merrily told them, that among her
men she had chosen her Master : albeit quoth she, this matter may
seeme strange in your sight, and my fancie too much ruled by
follie, yet this my determination I purpose by Gods grace to follow,
hoping it shall breed no offence to any in the companie, in such
a chance to make mine own choice.

Her man *Richard,* & the rest that supposed themselues most
graced by her fauours, began at this speech to look something
peart, and all the companie held opinion that she bore the best

30   minde to the foreman of her Shop : for first of all turning her
speech to him, she said : *Richard* come hither, thou hast greatly
to praise God for making thee so proper a man, thou art a neat
fellow, and hast excellent qualities, for thou art not proud, nor
high minded, but hast a care to thy businesse, and to keepe the
Shop : and because I haue committed great matters into thy
hands, I pray thee go downe and look to thy charge, for I haue
nothing more to say to thee at this time.

The fellow at these words lookt as blew vnder the eyes, as a stale
Codshead vnder the gill : and going downe the staires shook his

40   head like one that had a flea in his eare.

Now come hither *Iohn* (quoth she) I must needs say thou art
come of good parents, & thou knowst they bound thee not Prentice
to fetch oysters from *Billinsgate* like a Porter, nor to haue thy
daintie fingers set to drudgerie, therefore good *Iohn* get you downe
after your fellow, for here is nothing for you to doe at this time.

Her man *William,* that all this while was playing the scullion
in the kitchin was then sent for, who comming before the company
with his face all begrimd, and his cloathes all greasie, his Mistris

spake in this manner What a slouenlie knaue comes here ? were not this a fit man think ye to be Master of this house and Lord of my loue ?

Now by my troth (said Mistris *Peachie*) I neuer saw a more vnhandsome fellow in my life : fie how hee stinkes of kitchin stuffe : what a face and neck hath he ? a bodie might set Leekes in the very durt of his lips. I thinke in my conscience three pound of Sope, & a barrell of Water is little enough to scowre him cleane : the like flowts vsed all the rest at poore William, to which his Mistris made this answer. 10

Good Lord my masters, how much do your sights deceiue you ? in my sight he looks the loueliest of them all, hauing a pleasant countenance, and a good grace, and so pleasing is he in euery part to my sight, that surely if hee will accept of mee for his wife, I will not refuse him for my husband : her friends looking one vpon another, and maruelling at her speech, thought verily she had but iested, till such time she took him by the hand, and gaue him a kisse.

Whereupon *William* spake thus vnto her : faire Mistris, seeing it hath pleased you, beyond my desert, and contrarie to my 20 expectation, to make me so gracious an offer, worthie I were to liue a beggar if I should refuse such a treasure : and thereupon I giue you my heart and my hand :

And I receiue it (quoth she) for it is thy vertue and true humilitie that hath conquered my former conceipts, for few men would haue wonne a wife as thou didst.

No, how did he win you (said *Harrie Neuill*) ?

By fetching oysters from *Billingsgate* (quoth she) which I know you would not haue done, seeing all the rest of my seruants scornd to do it at my request : 30

Sblood (quoth *Harrie*) by feching of oysters : I would haue fetcht oysters, and mustles, and cockles too, to haue got so good a bargaine.

The Alderman and the Doctor lookt strangely at this matter : neuerthelesse seeing it was not to be helpt, they commended her choice, saying it was better for a man in such a case, to be fauourable in a womans eyes, then to haue much gold in his coffers.

Then did she set her black man by her white side, and calling the rest of her seruants (in the sight of her friends) she made them 40 do reuerence vnto him, whom they for his drudgerie scorned so much before : so the breakfast ended, she wild them all next morning, to beare him companie to Church, against which time, *William* was so daintily trickt vp, that all those which beheld him, confest he was a most comely, trim, and proper man, and after they were married, they liued long together in ioy and prosperous estate.

Harrie Neuill became so grieued hereat, that soone after he went

from Master *Peachie*, and dwelt with a Gold smith, and when he
had beene a while there, committing a fault with his Masters
daughter, he departed thence and became a Barber-Surgion : but
there his Mistris and he were so familiar, that it nothing pleased
his Master, so that in halfe a yeare he sought a new seruice and
became a Cook : and then a Comfetmaker dwelling with master
Baltazar, where after he grew something cunning, hauing done
some shrewd turne in that place, he forsooke that seruice, and
became a Smith, where their maide *Iudeth* fell so highly in loue
10 with him that he for pure good will which he bore her, shewed his
Master a faire paire of heeles : and then practised to be a Ioyner,
where he continued till hee heard his Father was sick, who for his
abominable swearing had cast him from his fauour, but after he
had long mist him, and that he could heare no tidings of his
vntoward and wilde wanton Sonne, hee sent into diuers places to
enquire for him, and at last, one of his seruants lighted where he
was, by which meanes he came to his father againe :
   Who in a few yeares after, leauing his life, this sonne *Harrie*
became Lord of all his lands : and comming vpon a day to *London*
20 with his men waiting vpon him, he caused a great dinner to be
prepared, and sent for all those that had been his masters and
mistresses : who being come, he thus began to commune with
them My good friends, I vnderstand that a certaine kinsman of
mine was sometimes your seruant, and as I take it, his name was
Harrie Neuell : who as I heare, vsed himselfe but homely toward
you, being a very wilde and vngracious fellow, the report whereof
hath beene some griefe to me, being one that alwayes wisht him
well : wherefore look what damage he hath done you I pray you
tell me, and I am content with reason to see you satisfied, so that
30 he may haue your fauours to be made a freeman.
   Surely sir (said *Peachie*) for mine own part I can say little, saue
only that he was so full of loue, that he would seldome follow his
businesse at his occupation : but that matter I freely forgiue and
will not be his hindrance in any thing.
   Marry sir (said the Goldsmith) I cannot say so : for truly sir he
plaid the theefe in my house, robbing my daughter of her maiden-
head, which he nor you is neuer able to recompence, though you
gaue me a thousand pound, yet, I thank God she is married and
doth well.
40   I am the glader of that (said the Gentleman) and for that fault
I will giue toward her maintenance forty pound.
   The Barber hearing him say so, told him that hee had iniured
him as much, and had beene more bold a great deale then became
him, whereby (quoth he) I was made a scorne among my neighbours.
   Tush you speake of ill will (said the Gentleman) if your wife will
say so I will beleeue it :

16. his seruants lighted] this seruants lighed *1639*

To which words the woman made this answer, Good sir, will you beleeue me there was neuer so much matter, the youth was an honest faire conditioned young man, but my husband bearing a naughty iealous minde, grew suspicious without cause, onely because he saw that his seruant was kinde and gentle vnto me, and would haue done any thing that I requested : notwithstanding I haue had many a fowle word for his sake, and carried some bitter blowes too, but all is one, I am not the first woman that hath suffered iniury without cause :

Alas good soule (said the Gentleman) I am right sorry for thy griefe, and to make thee amends, I will bestow on thee twentie Angels, so your husband will not take it in dudgin ;

The woman with a low cursie gaue him thanks, saying : truly sir I am highly beholding to you, and truly I shall loue you the better because you are so like him.

The smith likewise for his maide said all that he might, to whose marriage the Gentleman gaue twentie pound :

Thus after hee had fully ended with them all, hee made himselfe knowne vnto them, at what time they all reioyced greatly, and then after he had bestowed on them a sumptuous dinner, they all departed. And euer after, this Gentleman kept men of all these occupations in his own house, himself being as good a workman as any of them all.

Chap. X.

Of the greene king of S. *Martins* and his merry feats.

THere dwelt in S. *Martins* a iolly Shooemaker, hee was commonly called the Greene king, for that vpon a time he shewed himselfe before King *Henry*, with all his men cloathed in greene, he himselfe being suted all in greene Satten. He was a man very humorous, of small stature, but most couragious, and continually he vsed the Fencing-schoole. When he went abroad, he carried alwayes a two handed sword on his shoulder, or vnder his arme : he kept continually thirtie or fortie seruants, and kept in his house most bountifull fare : you shall vnderstand that in his young yeares, his father dying, left him a good portion, so that he was in great credit and estimation among his neighbours, and that which made him more happie, was this, that God blest him with the gift of a good wife, who was a very comely young woman, and therewithall very carefull for his commoditie : but he whose minde was altogether of merriment, little respected his profit in regard of his pleasure : insomuch that through his wastefull expence he brought pouertie vpon himselfe ere he was aware, so that he could not do as he was accustomed : which when his daily companions perceiued, they by little and little shund his company, and if at

any time he passed by them, perhaps they would lend him a nod,
or giue him a good morrow and make no more a doe.

And is it true (quoth the Greene king) doth want of money part
good company, or is my countenance chaunged, that they do not
know me? I haue seene the day when neuer a knaue of them all,
but would haue made much of my dog for my sake, and haue
giuen me twenty salutations on a Sunday morning, for one poore
pint of Muskadine: and what, hath a thred bare cloake scarde all
good fellowship? why though I haue not my wonted habites,
10 I haue still the same heart: and though my money be gone, my
mind is not altred: why then what Iacks are they, to reiect mee?
I, I, now I finde my wiues tale true, for then she was wont to say,
Husband, husband, refraine these trencher flies, these smooth
faced flatterers, that like drones, liue vpon the hony of your labour
and sucke away the sweetnes of your substance. I wis, I wis, if
once you should come in want, there is not the best of them all,
that would trust you for ten groates: by which saying Ile lay my
life she is a witch, for it is come as iust to pas as *Marlins*
prophesie; fie, I would the other day but haue borrowed 12 d. &
20 I tride 13 frinds, & went without it: it being so, let them go hang
themselus, for I wil into *Flanders*, that is flat, and leaue these slaues
to their seruill conditions, where I will try if a firkin barrell of butter
bee worth a pot of strong beere, and a loade of *Holland* cheese better
then a gallon of *Charnico*: and if it be, by the crosse of this sword,
I will neuer staine my credit with such a base commodity againe.

With that he went to his wife, saying: woman dost thou heare?
I pray thee looke well to thy busines till I come againe: for
why? to driue away melancholy, I am minded to walke a mile or
twaine:
30   But husband (quoth she) were you there where you layd your
plate to pawne? I pray you is it not misused? and is it safe?

Woman (quoth he) I was there, and it is safe I warrant thee,
for euer comming into thy hands againe, thou knowest I borrowed
but twentie marke on it, and they haue sold it for twentie pound:
tis gone wife, tis gone.

O husband (quoth she) what hard fortune haue we, to be so ill
delt withall? and therewithall she wept.

Fie (quoth he) leaue thy weeping, hang it vp, let it goe, the best
is, it neuer cost vs groate: were our friends liuing that gaue vs
40 that, they would giue vs more: but in vaine it is to mourn for
a matter that cannot be helpt, farewell wife, looke to thy house and
let the boyes plie their worke.

The greene king, hauing thus taken his leaue, went toward
Billingsgate, of purpose to take Barge: where by the way hee met
with *Anthony* now now, the firkin Fidler of *Finchlane*:

What master (quoth he) well met, I pray whither are you walking?
and how doe all our friends in saint *Martins*? Will you not haue
a crash ere you goe?

Yfaith, *Anthony* (quoth he) thou knowest I am a good fellow, and one that hath not been a niggard to thee at any time, therefore if thou wilt bestow any musick on me, doe ; and if it please God that I return safely from *Flanders* againe, I will pay thee well for thy paines ; but now I haue no money for musick.

Gods-nigs (quoth *Anthony*) whether you haue money or no, you shall haue musick, I doe not allways request coyne of my friends for my cunning : what, you are not euery body, and seeing you are going beyond sea, I will bestow a pinte of wine on you at the Salutation :
10

Saist thou so *Anthony* (quoth he) in good sooth I will not refuse thy curtesie, and with that they stept into the Tauern; where *Anthony* cald for wine : and drawing forth his Fiddle began to play, and after he had scrapte halfe a score lessons he began to sing.

When should a man shew himselfe gentle and kinde,
When should a man comfort the sorrowfull minde?
 O Anthony *now, now, now.*
 O Anthony *now, now, now.*
When is the best time to drinke with a friend? 20
When is it meetest my money to spend?
 O Anthony *now, now, now.*
 O Anthony *now, now, now.*
When goes the King of good fellowes away?
That so much delighted in dauncing and play?
 O Anthony *now, now, now.*
 O Anthony *now, now, now.*
And when should I bid my Master farewell?
Whose bountie and curtesie so did excell?
 O Anthony *now, now, now.* 30
 O Anthony *now, now, now.*

Loe ye now Master (quoth he) this song haue I made for your sake, and, by the grace of God when you are gone I will sing it euery Sunday morning vnder your wiues window, that she may know we dranke together ere you parted :

I pray thee do so (said the Greene king) and do my commendations vnto her, and tell her at my returne I hope to make merry.

Thus after they had made an end of their wine, and paid for the shot, *Anthony* putting vp his Fiddle departed, seeking to change musicke for money : while the Greene king of Saint *Martins* 40 sailed in *Grauesend* Barge. But *Anthony* in his absence sung this song so often in Saint *Martins*, that thereby he purchast a name which he neuer lost till his dying day, for euer after men called him nothing but *Anthony* now now.

But it is to be remembered that the Green kings wife became so carefull in her businesse, and gouerned her selfe with such wisdome in all her affaires, that during her husbands absence she did not

onely pay many of his debts, but also got into her house euerything that was necessary to be had, the which her diligence won
such commendations, that her credit in all places was verie good,
and her gaines (through Gods blessing) came so flowing in, that
before her husband came home, she was had in good reputation
with her neighbours : and hauing no need of any of their fauours,
euery one was ready to proffer her curtesie, saying good neighbour
if you want anything tell vs, and looke what friendship we may doe
you, be sure you shall find it.

10   I neighbour (quoth she) I know your kindnesse and may speake
thereof by experience : well may I compare you to him that
would neuer bid any man to dinner, but at two of the clocke in
the after noone, when he was assured they had fild their bellies
before, and that they would not touch his meate, except for
manners sake : wherefore for my part I will giue you thankes,
when I take benefit of your proffer.

Why neighbour we speake for good will (quoth they) :

Tis true (quoth shee) and so say they that call for a fresh quart
to bestow on a drunken man, when they know it would doe him
20 as much good in his bootes as in his belly.

Well neighbour (quoth they) God be thanked that you haue no
cause to vse friends.

Mary Amen (quoth shee) for if I had, I think I should finde
few here.

These and the like greetings were often betwixt her and her
neighbors ; til at last her husband came home, & to his great
comfort found his estate so good, that he had great cause to
praise God for the same, for a warme purse is the best medicine
for a cold heart that may be.   The greene king therefore bearing
30 himselfe as braue as euer he did, hauing sworne himselfe a
faithfull companion to his two hand-sworde, would neuer goe
without it.

Now, when his auncient acquaintance saw him again so gallant,
euery one was ready to curry fauour with him, and many would
proffer him the wine.   And where before they were wont scornefully
to thrust him next the kennell, and nothing to respect his pouerty,
they gaue him now the vpper hand in euery place, saluting him
with cap and knee : but he remembring how sleightly they set by
him in his neede, did now as sleightly esteeme their flattery, saying :
40 I cry you mercy, me thinkes I haue seene your face, but I neuer
knew you for my friend.

No (quoth one) I dwell at *Aldersgate*, and am your neere
neighbor,

And so much the worse (said the Greene king) :

Wherefore (quoth the other) ?

Because (said he) I thinke the place meete for an honester man.

I trust sir (said his neighbour) you know no hurt by me.

Nor any goodnes (quoth the greene king) but I remember you

are he, or one of them of whom once I would haue borrowed fortie pence, yet could not get it, if thereby I might haue saued fifty liues : therefore goodman hog, goodman cog, or goodman dog, chuse you which, scrape no acquaintance of me, nor come any more in my company, I would aduise you, least with my long sword I crop your cowards legs, and make you stand, like Saint *Martins* begger, vpon two stilts.

The fellow hearing him say so, went his wayes, and neuer durst speake to him afterward.

Chap. XI.

How the Greene King went a walking with his wife, and got *Anthony* now now to play before them, in which sort hee went with her to *Bristow*.

THe Green king being a man that was much giuen to goe abroad, his wife vpon a time, thus made her mone to him : good Lord husband (quoth she) I thinke you are the vnkindest man aliue, for as often as you walke abroad, you were neuer the man that would take me in your company : it is no small griefe to me, while I sit doating at home, euery Sunday and Holy-day, to see how kindely other men walke with their wiues, and louingly beare them company into the fields, that thereby they may haue some recreation after their weekes weary toyle : this pleasure haue they for their paines, but I poore soule could neuer get such curtesie at your hands : either it must needs be that you loue me but little, or else you are ashamed of my company, and I tell you true you haue no reason either for the one or the other.

Certainly wife (said hee) I should be sorrie to driue any such conceit into thy head, but seeing you find your selfe grieued in this kinde, let me intreat thee to be content, and then thou shalt perceiue that my loue is not small toward thee, nor my liking so bad to be ashamed to haue thee goe by my side : Thursday next is Saint *Iames* day, against which time prepare thy selfe to goe with me to the faire, where, by the grace of God, Ile bestow a fat Pig vpon thee, and there I meane to be merry : and doubt not but I will walke with thee till thou art weary of walking.

Nay (quoth shee) I should neuer be weary of your company, though I went with you to the Worlds end :

God a mercy for that wife, quoth hee, but so doing I doubt I should trie you a very good foote-woman, or a bad flatterer.

Thus it past till Thursday came, in the meane season meeting with two or three other shoomakers, he asked them if they would walke with him and his wife to Saint *Iames* faire :

29. then] when *1639*

That wee will with all our hearts :

But will you not like flinchers flie from your words (quoth he)?

To that (they said) if they did they would forfeit a gallon of wine.

Tush (said the greene king) talke not to me of a gallon of wine, but will you bee bound in twenty pound a peece to performe it ?

Why what needs bands for such a matter (quoth they)? we trust you will take our wordes for more then that.

My masters (said the greene king) the world is growne to that
10 passe, that words are counted but wind, and I will trust you as little on your word as Long *Meg* on her honesty : therefore if you will not be bound, chuse, I will make no account of your company.

The men hearing him say so, knowing him to be a man of a merry mind, after their wits were all washt with wine, to the Scriueners they went, and bound themselues in twenty pound according to his request. They had no sooner made an end of this merry match, but as they stumbled into another Tauerne, who should they meet but *Anthony* now now : who as soon as he spide the green King smiling with a wrie mouth, he ioyfully imbract
20 him with both his hands, saying : what my good master well met, when came you from the other side the water ? by my troth you are welcome with all my heart.

God a mercy good *Anthony* (quoth he) but how chance you come no more into Saint *Martins*?

O Master (quoth he) you know what a dainty commoditie I made at your parting to *Grauesendbarge*?

Yes mary (said the greene king) what of that ?

Why (quoth he) by singing it vnder your window, all the merry shoomakers in Saint *Martins* tooke it by the toe, and now they
30 haue made it as common as a printed Ballad, and I haue gotten such a name by it that now I am called nothing but *Anthony* now now.

Why Master ile tell you, it hath made me as well acquainted in Cheapeside as the cat in the creame-pan : for as soone as the Goldesmiths wiues spie mee, and as I passe along by the Marchants daughters, the apes will laugh at me as passes : beside that all the little boyes in the streets will run after mee like a sort of Emits. *Anthony* now now, sayes one: *Anthony* now now, another: good Lord, good Lord, you neuer knew the like : heare ye master,
40 I am sure that song hath gotten mee since you went more pence then your wife hath pins : and seeing you are come againe, I will make the second part very shortly.

But hearest thou, *Anthony* (said he)? if thou wilt come to me on Saint *Iames* his day in the Morning, thou shalt walke with vs to the faire, for I meane to make merry with my wife that day :

Master (quoth he) by cock and pie I will not misse you. And thus after they had made *Anthony* drinke, he departed.

Saint *Iames* his day at last being come, he cald vp his wife betimes, and bad her make ready, if she would to the faire : who very willingly did so : and in the meane space her husband went to his cubbert, and tooke thereout forty faire soueraignes, and going secretly to one of his seruants, he willed him to take good heed of his house, and to see that his fellowes plide their businesse : for (quoth he) I goe with my wife to Saint *Iames* faire, and perhaps you shall not see vs againe this sennight :

Well Master said the fellow, I will haue regard to your busines I warrant you.

Wherewith he cald his wife, saying : come wife will you walke ? 10 With a good will husband (quoth she) I am ready :

With that *Anthony* now now, began to scrape on his treable viall, and, playing a huntsup, said good morrow master good morrow, foure a clocke and a faire morning.

Well said *Anthony* (quoth he) we be ready for thy company, therefore along before, and let vs heare what musicke you can make.

Fie husband (quoth she) take not the Fidler with you, for shame : Tush be content (quoth he) Musicke makes a sad mind merrie :

So away they went, and at Saint *Giles* in the fields he met the 20 rest of his company : well found, my masters (quoth he) I perceiue you haue a care of your bonds :

So away they went with the Fidler before them, & the Greene king with his two hand sworde marching like a master of fence going to play his prize : when they came to the high way turning downe to *Westminster*, his wife said : yfaith husband we shall come to the faire too soone, for Gods sake let vs walke a little further.

Content wife (quoth he) whereupon they went to *Kensington*, where they brake their fast, and had good sport by tumbling on 30 the greene grasse, where *Anthony* brake his Fiddle, for which cause the Greene king gaue him ten shillings, and willed him to goe back and buy a new one.

And now my friends (quoth he) if you will walke with mee to *Brainford* I will bestow your dinner vpon you, because I haue a minde to walke with my wife ?

They were content, but by that time they came there, the woman began to wax somewhat wearie, & because the day was farre spent before they had dined, they lay there all night : where he told his friends that the next morning he would bring his wife 40 to see the George in *Colebrook*, and then would turne home : but to be briefe, when he came there, he told them flatly he meant to goe to Saint *Iames* his faire at *Bristow* : for (quoth he) my wife hath longed to walke with me, and I meane to giue her walking worke enough.

But sir (quoth they) we meane not to goe thither :

Before God but you shall (quoth hee) or forfeit your band.

The men seeing no remedy, went along to *Bristow* on foote,

whereby the poore woman became so weary, that an hundred times she wisht she had not come foorth of doores: but from that time till she died, she neuer intreated her husband to walke with her againe.

An hundred merry feates more did he, which in this place is too much to be set downe. For afterward *Tom Drum* comming from the winning of *Mustleborow*, came to dwell with him, where he discoursed all his aduentures in the wars: and according to his old cogging humor, attributed other mens deeds to himselfe, for
10 (quoth he) it was I that killed the first Scot in the battell, yet I was content to giue the honour thereof to Sir *Michaell Musgraue*, notwithstanding (quoth he) all men knowes that this hand of mine kild *Tom Trotter*, that terrible traytor, which in despite of vs, kept the Castell so long, & at last as he cowardly forsooke it, and secretly sought to flye, with this blade of mine I broacht him like a roasting pigge. Moreouer, Parson *Ribble* had neuer made himselfe so famous but by my meanes. These were his daily vaunts, till his lies were so manifest that hee could no longer stand in them.
20 But after the Greene king had long liued a gallant housekeeper, at last being aged and blinde, he dyed, after he had done many good deedes to diuers poore men.

F I N I S.

THOMAS
OF
READING.

OR,

The fixe worthie Yeomen
of the West.

Now the fift time corrected and enlarged
By *T. D*

LONDON,
Printed by W. I. for T. P.
1 6 2 3.

The pleasant Historie of the sixe
worthy Yeomen of the West.

IN the dayes of King *Henry* the first, who was the first King that instituted the high Court of Parliament, there liued nine men, which for the trade of Clothing, were famous throughout all England. Which Art in those daies was held in high reputation, both in respect of the great riches that thereby was gotten, as also of the benefite it brought to the whole Common-wealth: the yonger sons of Knights & Gentlemen, to whom their Fathers would leaue no lands, were most commonly preferred to learn this 10 trade, to the end that therby they might liue in good estate, & driue forth their daies in prosperity.

Among all Crafts this was the onely chiefe, for that it was the greatest merchandize, by the which our Countrey became famous through all Nations. And it was verily thought, that the one halfe of the people in the land liued in those daies therby, and in such good sort, that in the Common-wealth there were few or no beggers at all: poore people, whom God lightly blesseth with most children, did by meanes of this occupation so order them, that by the time that they were come to be sixe or seuen yeares of 20 age, they were able to get their owne bread: Idlenesse was then banished our coast, so that it was a rare thing to heare of a thiefe in those daies. Therefore it was not without cause that Clothiers were then both honoured and loued, among whom these nine persons in this Kings daies were of great credit, viz. *Tho. Cole* of *Reading*, *Gray* of *Glocester*, *Sutton* of *Salisburie*, *Fitzallen* of *Worcester*, (commonly called *William* of *Worcester*) *Tom Doue* of *Excester*, and *Simon* of *South-hampton*, alias *Supbroath*: who were by the King called, The sixe worthy Husbands of the West. Then were there three liuing in the North, that is to say, *Cutbert* 30 of *Kendall*, *Hogekins* of *Hallifax*, and *Martin Byram* of *Man-chester*. Euery one of these kept a great number of seruants at worke, spinners, carders, weauers, fullers, dyers, sheeremen, and rowers, to the great admiration of all those that came into their houses to behold them.

Now you shall vnderstand, these gallant Clothiers, by reason of their dwelling places, separated themselues in three seuerall com-panies: *Gray* of *Glocester*, *William* of *Worcester*, and *Thomas* of *Reading*, because their iourney to *London* was all one way, they conuersed commonly together. And *Doue* of *Excester*, *Sutton* of 40 *Salisburie*, and *Simon* of *South-hampton*, they in like sort kept company the one with the other, meeting euer all together at

Bazingstoke : and the three Northerne Clothiers did the like, who commonly did not meet till they came to Bosome Inne in *London*.

Moreouer, for the loue and delight that these Westerne men had each in others companie, they did so prouide, that their Waines and themselues would euer meet vpon one day in *London* at *Iarrats* Hall, surnamed the Gyant, for that hee surpassed all other men of that age, both in stature & strength : whose merriments and memorable deedes, I will set downe vnto you in this following discourse.

10 **How King *Henry* sought the fauour of all his subiects, especially of the Clothiers.   CHAP. I.**

THis King *Henry*, who for his great learning and wisdome was called *Beauclarke*, beeing the third Son to the renowned Conquerour : after the death of his brother *William Rufus*, tooke vpon him the gouernement of this Land, in the absence of his second brother *Robert* Duke of *Normandie*, who at this time was at wars amongst the Infidels, and was chosen King of *Ierusalem*, the which he, for the loue he bare to his owne countrey, refused, and with great honour returned from the holy Land ; of whose comming

20 when King *Henrie* vnderstood, knowing hee would make claime to the crowne, sought by all meanes possible to winne the good will of his Nobilitie, and to get the fauor of the Commons by curtesie : for the obtaining whereof hee did them many fauours, thereby the better to strengthen himselfe against his brother.

It chanced on a time, as he, with one of his sonnes, and diuers of his Nobilitie, rode from *London* towards *Wales,* to appease the fury of the Welshmen, which then began to raise themselues in armes against his authority, that he met with a great number of Waines loaden with cloath, comming to *London*, and seeing them

30 still driue one after another so many together, demaunded whose they were :

The Waine-men answered in this sort : *Coles* of *Reading* (quoth they.)

Then by and by the King asked another, saying : Whose cloth is all this ?

Old *Coles* (quoth he) :

And againe anone after he asked the same question to others, and stil they answered, Old *Coles*,

And it is to be remembred, that the King met them in such

40 a place, so narrow and streight, that he with the rest of his traine, were faine to stand as close to the hedge, whilest the carts passed by, the which at that time being in number aboue two hundred, was neere hand an houre ere the King could get roome to be gone : so that by his long stay, he began to be displeased, although the

admiration of that sight did much qualifie his furie ; but breaking out in discontent, by reason of his stay, he said, he thought Old *Cole* had got a Commission for all the carts in the country to cary his cloth.

And how if he haue (quoth one of the Wain men) doth that grieue you good sir?

Yes, good sir (said our King) what say you to that?

The fellow seeing the King (in asking that question) to bend his browes, though he knew not what he was, yet being abasht, he answered thus : Why sir, if you be angry, no body can hinder you; for possible sir, you haue anger at commaundement.

The king seeing him in vttering of his wordes to quiuer and quake, laughed heartily at him, as well in respect of his simple answere, as at his feare : and so soone after the last Wain went by, which gaue present passage vnto him and his Nobles : and thereupon entring into communication of the commoditie of cloathing, the King gaue order at his home returne, to haue Old *Cole* brought before his Maiestie, to the intent he might haue conference with him, noting him to be a subiect of great abilitie : but by that time he came within a mile of *Stanes*, he met another company of waines in like sort laden with cloth, whereby the King was driuen into a further admiration : and demanding whose they were, answere was made in this sort :

They be goodman *Suttons* of *Salisbury*, good sir : and by that time a score of them were past, he asked againe, saying : whose are these ;

Suttons of *Salisburie* (qd. they) and so still, as often as the King asked that question, they answered, *Suttons* of *Salisburie*.

God send me many such *Suttons* (said the King).

And thus the farther he trauelled Westward, more Waines and more he met continually : vpon which occasion he said to his Nobles, That it would neuer grieue a King to die for the defence of a fertile Countrie and faithfull subiects. I alwaies thought (quoth he) that *Englands* valor was more than her wealth, yet now I see her wealth sufficient to maintaine her valour, which I will seeke to cherish in all I may, and with my sword keepe my selfe in possession of that I haue, Kings and Louers can brooke no partners : and therefore let my Brother *Robert* thinke, that although hee was Heire to *England* by birth, yet I am King by possession. All his fauourers I must account my foes, and will serue them as I did the vngratefull Earle of *Shrewsbury*, whose lands I haue seized, and banisht his body.

But now we will leaue the King to his iourney into *Wales*, and waiting his home returne, in the meane time tell you the meeting of these iolly Clothiers at *London*.

How *William* of *Worcester*, *Gray* of *Gloucester*, and old
  Cole of *Reading*, met altogether at *Reading*, and of
  their communication by the way as they rode to
  London.   CHAP. 2.

WHen *Gray* of *Glocester*, and *William* of *Worcester* were
      come to *Reading*, according to their custome, they alwaies
called olde *Cole* to haue his companie to *London*, who also duely
attended their comming, hauing prouided a good breakefast for
them : and when they had well refreshed themselues, they tooke
10 their horses and rode on towards the Cittie : and in their iourney
William of *Worcester* asked them if they had not heard of the earle
of *Moraigne* his escape out of the land :
    What is he fled (qd. *Gray*)?
    I muse much at this matter, being in such great regard with the
King as he was : but I pray you, do you not know the cause of his
going (qd. *Cole*)?
    The common report (quoth *Gray*) is this, that the couetous
earle, who through a greedy desire, neuer left begging of the King
for one thing or other, and his request being now denied him, of
20 meere obstinacie and wilfull frowardnesse, hath banished himselfe
out of the land, & quite forsaken the Countrey of *Cornwall*, hauing
made a vow neuer to set foote within *England* againe, and as
report goeth, he with the late banisht Earle of *Shrewsbury*, haue
ioyned themselues with *Robert* duke of *Normandie*, against the
King, the which action of theirs hath inflamed the Kings wrath,
that their Ladies with their Children are quite turned out of doores
succorlesse and friendlesse, so that as it is told me, they wander
vp and downe the countrie like forlorne people, and although
many doe pittie them, yet few doe releeue them.
30   A lamentable hearing (qd. *William* of *Worcester*) and with that
casting their eies aside, they espied *Tom Doue* with the rest of his
companions come riding to meete them, who as soone as they were
come thither, fell into such pleasant discourses, as did shorten the
long way they had to *Colebroke*, where alwaies at their comming
towards *London* they dined : and being once entred into their Inne,
according to olde custome, good cheere was prouided for them :
for these Clothiers were the chiefest guests that trauailed along the
way : and this was as sure as an act of Parliament, that *Tom Doue*
could not digest his meat without musicke, nor drinke wine without
40 women, so that his hostesse being a merrie wench, would oftentimes call in two or three of her neighbours wiues to keepe him
company ; where, ere they parted, they were made as pleasant as
Pies.
    And this being a continuall custome amongst them when they

came thither, at length the womens husbands beganne to take exceptions at their wiues going thither: whereupon great controuersie grew betweene them, in such sort, that when they were most restrayned, then they had most desire to worke their willes:

Now gip (quoth they) must we be so tied to our taske, that we may not drinke with our friends? fie, fie, vpon these yellowe hose, will no other die serue your turne? haue wee thus long bin your wiues, and doe you now mistrust vs? verily you eate too much salt, and that makes you grow cholericke, badde liuers iudge all others the like, but in faith you shall not bridle vs so like asses, but wee will goe to our friends, when we are sent for, and doe you what you can.

Well (quoth their husbands) if you be so head-strong, we will tame you: it is the duty of honest women to obey their husbands sayings.

And of honest men (quoth they) to thinke well of their wiues; but who doe sooner empeach their credite, then their husbands, charging them, if they doe but smile, that they are subtile; and if they doe but winke, they account them wiley, if sad of counten- ance, then sullen: if they bee froward, then they are counted shrewes: and sheepish if they bee gentle: if a woman keepe her house, then you will say shee is melancholy, if shee walke abroad, then you call her a gadder; a Puritane, if shee be precise: and a wanton, if she be pleasant: so there is no woman in the world that knowes how to please you: that we thinke our selues accurst to be married wiues, liuing with so many woes. These men, of whose company you forewarne vs, are (for ought that euer we saw) both honest and courteous, and in wealth farre beyond your selues: then what reason is there, why we should restraine to visit them? is their good will so much to be requited with scorne, that their cost may not be counteruailed with our company? if a woman be disposed to play light of loue, alas, alas doe you thinke that you can preuent her? Nay wee shall abide by it, that the restraint of libertie inforceth women to be lewd: for where a woman cannot be trusted, she cannot thinke her selfe beloued, and if not beloued, what cause hath she to care for such a one? therefore husbands, reforme your opinions, and doe not worke your owne woes, with our discredit. The Clothiers, we tell you, are iolly fellowes, and but in respect of our curtesie, they would scorne our company.

The men hearing their wiues so well to plead for themselues, knew not how to answere, but said, they would put the burden on their consciences, if they deale vniustly with them, and so left them to their owne wills. The women hauing thus conquered their husbands conceits, would not leaue the fauour of their friends for frownes, and as aboue the rest *Tom Doue* was the most pleasantest, so was he had in most reputation with the women, who for his sake made this Song:

Welcome to towne, Tom Doue, Tom Doue,
 The merriest man aliue,
Thy company still we loue, we loue,
 God grant thee well to thriue,
And neuer will depart from thee,
 For better or worse, my ioy,
For thou shalt still haue our good will,
 Gods blessing on my sweet Boy.

This song went vp and downe through the whole country, and
10 at length became a dance among the common sort, so that *Tom
Doue,* for his mirth and good fellowship, was famous in euery
place.

Now when they came to *London,* they were welcome to the host
Iarrat the Gyant, and assoone as they were alighted, they were
saluted by the Merchants, who waited their comming thither, and
alwaies prepared for them a costly supper, where they commonly
made their bargaine, and vpon euery bargaine made, they still
vsed to send some tokens to the Clothiers wiues. The next
morning they went to the hall, where they met the Northern
20 Clothiers, who greeted one another in this sort.

What, my Masters of the West, well met: what cheere? what
cheere?

Euen the best cheere our Merchants could make vs: (quoth
Gray.)

Then you could not chuse but fare well (quoth *Hogekins*):

And you be weary of our company, adieu (quoth *Sutton*):

Not so, said *Martin,* but shall wee not haue a game ere wee
goe?

Yes faith for an hundred pounds.

30 Well said, old *Cole* (said they): and with that *Cole* and *Gray*
went to the dice with *Martin* and *Hogekins*; and the dice running
on *Hogekins* side, *Coles* money beganne to waste.

Now by the Masse (quoth *Cole*) my mony shrinks as bad as
Northerne cloth.

When they had played long, *Gray* stept to it, and recouered
againe the money that *Cole* had lost. But while they were thus
playing, the rest being delighted in contrarie matters, euery man
satisfied his owne humour.

Tom Doue called for musicke, *William* of *Worcester* for wine,
40 *Sutton* set his delight in hearing merry tales, *Simon* of *South-hampton*
got him into the kitchin, and to the pottage pot hee goes, for he
esteemed more a messe of pottage, then of a vension pastie. Now
sir, *Cutbert* of *Kendall* was of another minde, for no meat pleased
him so well as mutton, such as was laced in a red petticoate.
And you shall vnderstand, that alwaies when they went to dice,
they got into *Bosomes* Inne; which was so called of his name that
kept it, who being a foule slouen, went alwaies with his nose in his
bosome, and one hand in his pocket, the other on his staffe,

figuring forth a description of cold winter, for he alwaies wore two coates, two caps, two or three paire of stockings, and a high paire of shooes, ouer the which he drew on a great paire of lined slippers, and yet would oft complaine of cold, wherfore of all men generally he was called Old Bosome, and his house *Bosomes* Inne.

This lump of cold ice had lately married a yong wife, who was as wily as she was wanton, and in her company did *Cutbert* onely delight, and the better to make passage to his loue, he would often thus commune with her : I muse good wife (quoth he).

Good wife (quoth she) ? Verily sir, in mine opinion, there is none good but God, and therefore call me Mistresse.

Then said *Cutbert*, Faire Mistris, I haue often mused, that you being a proper woman, could find in your heart for to match with such a greazie Carle as this, an euill mannered mate, a foule lump of kitchin stuffe, and such a one as is indeede, a scorne of men ; how can you like him that all women mislikes ? or loue such a loathsome creature ? me thinks verily it should grieue you to lend him a kisse, much more to lie with him.

Indeed sir (quoth she) I had but hard fortune in this respect, but my friends would haue it so, and truly my liking and my loue toward him are alike, he neuer had the one, nor neuer shall get the other : yet I may say to you before I married him, there were diuers proper young men that were sutors vnto me, who loued mee as their liues, and glad was he that could get my company, those were my golden dayes, wherein my pleasure abounded, but these are my yeres of care and griefe, wherein my sorrowes exceede. Now no man regards me, no man cares for me, and albeit in secret they might beare mee good will, yet who dares shew it ? and this is a double griefe, he carries ouer me so iealous a minde, that I cannot looke at a man, but presently hee accuseth me of in- constancie, although (I protest) without cause.

And in troth (qd. *Cutb.*) he should haue cause to complaine for somewhat, were I as you.

As sure as I liue, and so he shall (quoth she) if he doe not change his byas.

Cutb. hearing her say so, beganne to grow further in requesting her fauour, wishing he might be her seruant and secret friend, and the better to obtain his desire, he gaue her diuers gifts, insomuch that she began something to listen vnto him : and albeit she liked well of his speeches, yet would she blame him, and take him vp very short sometimes for the same, till in the end, *Cutbert* shewed himselfe to be desperate, saying hee would drowne himselfe rather than liue in her disdaine.

O my sweet heart not so (qd. shee) God forbid I should be the death of any man : Comfort thy selfe, kind *Cutbert*, and take this kisse in token of further kindnesse, and if thou wilt haue my fauour, thou must be wise and circumspect, and in my husbands sight I would alwaies haue thee to find fault with my doings, blame my bad huswifries, dispraise my person, and take exceptions at euery thing, whereby he will be as well pleased, as *Simon* of *Southhampton* with a messe of pottage.

Deere Mistresse (quoth he) I will fulfill your charge to the vttermost, so that you will not take my iest in earnest.

Shee answered, Thy foulest speeches I will esteeme the fairest, and take euery dispraise to be a praise from thee, turning each word to the contrarie : and so for this time adieu, good *Cutb.* for supper time drawes nere, and it is meet for me to looke for my
10 meat.

With that down comes old Bosome, calling his wife, saying, Ho *Winifred*, is supper readie? they haue done playing aboue : therefore let the Chamberlaine couer the Table.

By and by husband (qd. she) it shall be done straight way.

How now my Masters who wins (qd. *Cutb.*).

Our mony walkes to the West (qd. *Martin*) : *Cole* hath woone li. of me, and *Gray* hath gotten well :

The best is (qd. *Hogekins*) they will pay for our supper :

Then let vs haue good store of Sacke (qd. *Sutton*).
20 Content (said *Cole*) for I promise you, I striue not to grow rich by dice-playing, therefore call for what you wil, I will pay for all.

Yea (said *Simon*) ! Chamberlaine, I pray thee bring a whole bottle of pottage for me.

Now *Tom Doue* had all the fidlers at a becke of his finger, which follow him vp and down the citie, as diligent as little chickens after a hen, and made a vow, that there should want no musicke. And at that time there liued in London a musician of great reputation, named *Reior*, who kept his seruants in such costly garments, that they might seeme to come before any Prince. Their coates were
30 all of one colour ; and it is said, that afterward the Nobilitie of this Land, noting it for a seemely sight, vsed in like maner to keepe their men all in one liuerie. This *Reior* was the most skilfullest musician that liued at that time, whose wealth was very great, so that all the Instruments whereon his seruants plaid, were richly garnished with studdes of siluer, and some gold : the bowes belonging to their Violines were all likewise of pure siluer. He was also for his wisedome called to great office in the cittie, who also builded (at his owne cost) the Priory & Hospitall of Saint *Bartholomew* in *Smithfield*. His seruants being the best consorts
40 in the Citie, were by *Tom Doue* appointed to play before the young Princes.

Then supper being brought to the bord, they all sat down, and by and by after comes vp their host, who tooke his place among them : and anone after, the good-wife in a red peticote and a wastcoate, comes among them as white as a Lilly, saying, My Masters, you are welcome, I pray you be merry.

Thus falling close to their meate, when they had well fed, they found leysure to talke one with another : at what time *Cutb.* began thus to finde fault, Ywis, my hoast (quoth he) you haue a wise huswife to your wife, heere is meate drest of a new fashion : God sends meate, and the diuell sends cookes.

Why what ails the meate (quoth she) serues it not your turne? better men then your selfe are content withall, but a paultrie companion is euer worst to please.

Away, you sluttish thing (qd. *Cutb.*) your husband hath a sweet iewell of you : I maruell such a graue ancient man would match himselfe with such a young giglot, that hath as much handsomenes in her, as good huswifry, which is iust nothing at all.

Well sir (saide shee) in regard of my husbands presence I am loth to aggrauate anger, otherwise I would tell thee thy owne.

Goe to, what neede all this (quoth the company)? in good faith, *Cutbert,* you are too blame, you find fault where none is.

Tush, I must speake my mind (quoth *Cutbert*) I cannot dissemble, I trust the good man thinkes neuer the worse of me : so I haue his good will, what the foule euill care I for his wifes.

Enough (quoth *Tom Doue*) let vs with musicke remoue these brabbles, we meane to be merry, and not melancholy.

Then said olde *Cole,* Now trust me, *Cutbert,* we will haue your hostesse and you friends ere we part : here woman I drinke to you, and regard not his words, for he is babbling wheresoeuer he comes.

(Quoth the woman) nothing grieues me so much, as that hee should thus openly checke mee, if he had found any thing amisse, he might haue spied a better time to tell me of it then nowe, ywis hee neede not thrust my bad huswifrie into my husbands head, I liue not so quietly with him, God wot : and with that she wept.

Come *Cutb.* (quoth they) drinke to her, and shake handes and be friendes.

Come on, you puling baggage (quoth he) I drinke to you, here will you pledge mee and shake hands?

No, (quoth shee) I will see thee choakt first, shake hands with thee? I will shake hands with the diuell assoone.

Goe to (said her husband) you shall shake hands with him then : If you will not shake hands, ile shake you : what, you young huswife?

Well husband (said she) it becomes a woman to obey her husband, in regard whereof, I drink to him.

Thats well said (quoth the company) : & so she tooke her leaue and went downe.

And within a while after, they paid the shot, and departed thence to *Iarrats* Hall, where they went to their lodging ; and the next day they tooke their way homeward all together : and comming to *Colebrooke,* they tooke vp their lodging, and it was *Coles* custome to deliuer his money to the goodwife of the house to keepe it till morning, which in the end turned to his vtter destruction, as hereafter shall be shewed.

How *Grayes* wife of *Glouester*, with one or two more of
her neighbours went to the Faire, where seruants
came to be hired, and how she tooke the Earle of
Shrewesburies Daughter into her seruice.   Chap. 3.

IT was wont to be an old custome in *Gloustershire*, that at
a certaine time in the yeare, all such young men and Maidens
as were out of seruice, resorted to a faire that was kept neere
Gloucester, there to be readie for any that would come to hire
them, the yong men stood all on a row on the one side, & the
10 Maidens on the other. It came to passe, that the Earle of
Shrewsburies daughter, whose Father was lately banished, being
driuen into great distresse, and weary with trauaile, as one whose
delicate life was neuer vsed to such toyle, sate her downe vpon the
high way side, making this lamentation.
    O false and deceitfull world (quoth she)! who is in thee that
wishes not to be rid of thee, for thy extremities are great? Thou
art deceitfull to all, and trustie to none.   Fortune is thy treasurer,
who is like thy selfe, wauering and vnconstant, she setteth vp
tyrants, beateth downe Kings : giueth shame to some, and renowne
20 to others : Fortune giueth these euils, and we see it not : with her
hands she toucheth vs, and we feele it not, she treades vs vnder
foote, and we know it not : she speakes in our eares, & we heare
her not : she cries aloud, and we vnderstand her not : And why ?
because we know her not, vntill miserie doth make her manifest.
    Ah my deare father, well maist thou do.   Of all misfortunes it
is most vnhappy to be fortunate : and by this misfortune came my
fall.   Was euer good Lady brought to this extremity? What is
become of my rare Iewels, my rich aray, my sumptuous fare, my
waiting seruants, my many friends, and all my vaine pleasures?
30 my pleasure is banisht by displeasure, my friends fled like foes,
my seruants gone, my feasting turned to fasting, my rich array
consumed to ragges, and my iewells deckes out my chiefest
enemies : therefore of all things the meanest state is best, pouerty
with suretie, is better than honour mixed with feare : seeing God
hath allotted me to this misery of life, I will frame my heart to
embrace humility, and carry a mind answerable to my misfortunes,
fie on this vaine title of Ladiship, how little doth it auaile the
distressed ?   No, no, I must therefore forget my birth and parentage, and think no more on my fathers house, where I was
40 wont to bee serued, now will I learne to serue, and plaine *Meg* shall
be my name, good Lord grant I may get a good seruice, nay any
seruice shall serue, where I may haue meate, drinke, and apparel.
    She had no sooner spoke these words, but she spied a couple
of Maidens more comming towards her ; who were going to the

faire : and bidding her good morrow, asked her if she went to the faire.

Yea mary (qd. she) I am a poore mans child that is out of seruice, and I heare that at the Statute, folkes do come of purpose to hire seruants.

True it is (said the Maidens) and thither go we for the same purpose, and would be glad of your company.

With a good will, and I am right glad of yours (said she) beseeching you good Maidens, you will doe me the fauour, to tell me what seruice were best for me : for the more too blame my parents, they would neuer put me forth to know any thing.

Why what can you doe (quoth the maidens) can you brew and bake, make butter and cheese, and reape corne well?

No verily (said *Margaret*) but I would be right glad to learne to doe any thing whatsoeuer it be :

If you could spin or card (said another) you might do excellent well with a clother, for they are the best seruices that I know, there you shall bee sure to fare well, and so liue merrily.

Then *Margaret* wept saying alas, what shall I do? I was neuer brought vp to these things.

What can you doe nothing (quoth they)?

No truly (quoth she) that is good for any thing, but I can read and write, and sowe, some skill I haue in my needle, and a little on my Lute : but this, I see will profit me nothing.

Good Lord (quoth they) are you bookish? wee did neuer heare of a Maide before that could reade and write. And although you can doe no other thing, yet possible you may get a seruice, if you can behaue your selfe manerly.

I pray you (qd. another) seeing you are bookish, will you doe so much as to reade a loue-letter that is sent me, for I was at a friends of mine with it, and he was not at home, and so I know not what is in it.

I pray you let me see it (quoth *Margaret*) and I will shew you. Whereupon she readeth as followeth.

> O Ienny *my ioy, I die for thy loue,*
> *And now I heare say that thou dost remoue :*
> *And therefore,* Ienny, *I pray thee recite,*
> *Where shall I meete thee soone at night.*
>
> *For why, with my Master no more will I stay,*
> *But for thy loue I will runne away :*
> *O* Ienny, Ienny, *thou puttest me to paine,*
> *That thou no longer wilt here remaine.*
>
> *I will weare out my shooes of Neats Leather,*
> *But thou and I will meete together,*
> *And in spight of Fortune, Rat, or Mouse,*
> *Wee will dwell together in one. house.*

For who doth not esteeme of thee,
Shall haue no seruice done of me :
Therefore good Ienny *haue a care,*
To meete poore Fragment *at the faire.*

Now alas, good soule (quoth *Ienny*) I think he be the kindest young man in the world.

The rest answered, that he seemed no lesse.

And surely it appeareth that he is a pretty wittie fellow (quoth one of them) how finely he hath written his letter in rime, trust 10 me, I will giue you a good thing, and let me haue a copy of it to send to my sweet heart :

That you shall with all my heart : & so comming to the faire, they tooke vp their standing.

Within a while after, goodwife *Gray* of *Gloucester* came thither to store herselfe of diuers commodities : and when shee had bought what she wold, she told her neighbor she had great need of a Maid seruant or twaine : therefore (qd. she) good neighbor goe with me, and let me haue your opinion.

With a good wil (said her neighbor) and together they went, 20 and looking and viewing the Maidens ouer, she tooke speciall notice of *Margaret*.

Beleeue me (quoth she) there stands a very proper Maiden, and one of a modest and comely countenance.

Verily (said her neighbor) so she is, as euer I looked vpon.

The Maiden seeing them to view her so well, was so abashed, that a scarlet colour ouerspred her lilly cheeks, which the woman perceiuing came vnto her, and asked if she were willing to serue.

The Maid with a low curtesie, and a most gentle speech, answered it was the onely cause of her comming.

30 Can you spinne or card (said good-wife *Gray*) ?

Truly Dame (said she) though my cunning therein be but small, my goodwill to learne is great, and I trust, my dilligence shall content you.

What wages will you take (quoth goodwife *Gray*) ?

I will referre that (said *Margaret*) to your conscience and courtesie, desiring no more then what I shall deserue. Then asking what country woman she was, the Maiden wept, saying, Ah good Dame, I was vntimely borne in Shropshire, of poore parents, and yet not so needie as vnfortunate, but death hauing 40 ended their sorrowes, hath left me to the crueltie of these enuious times, to finish my Parents Tragedie with my troubles.

What Maiden ! (qd. her dame) haue you a care to doe your busines, and to liue in Gods feare, and you shall haue no care to regard fortunes frownes, and so they went home together.

Now, so soone as the goodman saw her, hee asked his wife where she had that Maiden. She said, at the Faire.

Why then (quoth he) thou hast brought al the Faire away, and

I doubt it were better for vs, to send the Faire to another Towne, then to keepe the Faire here.

Why man (quoth she) what meane you by that?

Woman, I meane this, that she will proue a Loadstone, to draw the hearts of all my men after her, and so we shal haue wise seruice done of all sides.

Then said his wife, I hope, husband, *Margaret* will haue a better care both to her owne credit, and our commodity then so, and so let her alone to looke to such matters.

Is thy name *Margaret* (quoth her Master)? proper is thy name to thy person, for thou art a pearle indeed, orient, and rich in beautie.

His wife hearing him say so, began to change her opinion: What husband (quoth she) is the winde at that doore? Begin you to like your maid so well? I doubt I had most need to looke to your selfe: before God, I had rather then an angell I had chosen some other: but heare you maid; you shall packe hence, I will not nourish a snake in my bosome, and therefore get you gone, I will none of you, prouid a seruice where you may.

The Maiden hearing her say so, fell downe one her knees, and besought her, saying, O sweet dame, be not so cruel to me, to turne me out of doores, now: alas, I know not where to go, or what to do, if you forsake me. O let not the fading beauty of my face dispoyle me of your fauour: for rather then that shall hinder my seruice, this my knife shall soone disfigure my face, and I will banish beautie as my greatest enemy. And with that, her aboundant teares stopped her speech, that shee could not vtter one word more.

The woman seeing this, could not harbour any longer, nor could her Master stay in the roome for weeping.

Well, *Margaret* (said her dame) (little knowing that a Lady kneeled before her) vsing thy selfe wel I will keepe thee, and thou shalt haue my good will, if thou gouerne thyselfe with wisedome; and so she sent her about her businesse.

Her husband comming to supper, said. How now wife, art thou so doubtfull of mee, that thou hast put away thy Maiden?

I wis (qd. she) you are a wise man, to stand praising of a Maidens beauty before her face:

& you a wise woman (qd. he) to grow iealous without a cause.

So to supper they went, and because *Margaret* shewed her selfe of finest behauiour aboue the rest, she was appointed to waite on the table. And it is to be vnderstood, that *Gray* did neuer eate his meat alone, but still had some of his neighbors with him, before whom he called his maid, saying, *Margaret*, come hither. Now because there was another of the same name in the house, she made answere.

I call not you Maiden (qd. he) but *Margaret* with the lilly white hand.

After which time she was euer called so.

How the Kings Maiestie sent for the Clothiers, and of the sundry fauours which he did them.   CHAP. 4.

KIng *Henry* prouiding for his voyage into *Fraunce*, against
King *Lewis* and *Robert* Duke of *Normandie* his owne brother,
committed the gouernment of the Realme in his absence, to the
Bishop of *Salisbury*, a man of great wisedome and learning, whom
the King esteemed highly, and afterward he thought good to send
for the chiefe Clothiers of *England*, who according to the Kings
appointment came to the Court, and hauing licence to come
10 before his Maiestie, he spake to this effect.

The strength of a King is the loue and friendship of his people,
and he gouernes ouer his Realme most surely, that ruleth iustice
with mercy : for he ought to feare many, whom many do feare :
therfore the gouernors of the Common-wealth ought to obserue
two speciall precepts : the one is, that they so maintain the profit
of the Commons, that whatsoeuer in their calling they doe, they
referre it thereunto : the other, that they be alwaies as well carefull
ouer the whole Common-wealth, as ouer any part thereof ; lest
while they vphold the one, the other be brought to vtter decay.

20 And forasmuch as I doe vnderstand, and haue partly seene, that
you the Clothiers of *England* are no small benefit to the wealth
publike, I thought it good to know from your owne mouthes, if
there be any thing not yet graunted that may benefit you, or any
other thing to be remoued that doth hurt you.

The great desire I haue to maintaine you in your trades, hath
moued me hereunto.   Therefore boldly say what you would haue
in the one thing or the other, and I will grant it you.

With that, they all fell downe vpon their knees, and desired God
to saue his Maiestie, and withall, requested three daies respite to
30 put in their answere : which was graunted.   And thereupon they
departed.

When the Clothiers had well considered of these matters, at
length they thought meete to request of his Maiestie for their first
benefite, that all the Cloth-measures through the Land might be
of one length, whereas to their great disaduantage before, euery
good towne had a seuerall measure, the difficulty thereof was such,
that they could not keepe them in memory, nor know how to
keepe their reckonings.

The second thing whereof they found themselues grieued, was
40 this, that the people would not take crackt money, though it were
neuer so good siluer ? whereupon it came to passe, that the
Clothiers and diuers others receiuing great summes of money, do
take among it much crackt money, it serued them to no vse,
because it would not goe currant, but lay vpon their hands without profit or benefit, whereof they prayed reformation.

The third was a griefe, whereof *Hodgekins* of *Halifax* com-playned, and that was, That whereas the towne of *Halyfax* liued altogether vpon Cloathing, and by the reason of false borderers, and other euill minded persons, they were oft robbed, and had their Clothes carried out of their fieldes, where they were drying, That it would please his Maiestie to graunt the towne this priuilege, That whatsoeuer he was that was taken stealing their Cloth, might presently without any further tryall be hanged vp.

When the day of their appearance approached, the Clothiers came before the King, and deliuered vp their Petition in writing, 10 which his Maiestie most graciously perusing, saide, hee was ready to fulfill their request : and therefore for the first point of their Petition, he called for a staffe to be brought him, and measuring thereupon the iust length of his owne arme, deliuered it to the Clothiers, saying. This measure shall bee called a yard, and no other measure throughout all the Realme of *England* shall be vsed for the same, and by this shall men buy and sell, and we will so prouide, that whosoeuer he be that abuseth our subiects by any false measure, that he shall not onely pay a fine for the same to the King, but also haue his body punished by imprisonment. 20

And as concerning the second point of your Petition, because of my sudden departure out of the Land, I know not better how to ease you of this griefe (of crackt money) this decree I make, because they account crackt money not currant, I say, none shal be currant but crackt money. And therefore I will giue present charge, that all the money thorow the Land shall be slit, and so you shall suffer no losse.

But now for your last request for the towne of *Halifax*, where by theeues your Clothes are so often stolne from you, seeing the lawes already prouided in that case, are not sufficient to keepe 30 men in awe, it is indeed high time to haue sharper punishment for them.

With that *Hodgekins* vnmannerly interrupted the King, saying in broad Northerne speech, Yea gude faith, mai Liedge, the faule eule of mai saule, giff any thing will keepe them whiat, till the karles be hanged by the cragge. What the dule care they for boaring their eyne, sea lang as they mae gae groping vp and downe the Country like fause lizar lownes, begging and craking?

The King smiling to heare this rough-hewen fellow made this reply : Content thee *Hodgekins*, for we will haue redresse for all : 40 and albeit that hanging of men was neuer seene in *England*, yet seeing the corrupt world is growne more bold in all wickednesse, I thinke it not amisse to ordain this death for such malefactors : and peculiarly to the towne of *Hallifax* I giue this priuiledge, That whosoeuer they finde stealing their Cloth, being taken with the goods, that without further iudgment, they shall be hanged vp.

Thus (said our King) haue I granted what you request, and if hereafter you find any other thing that may be good for you, it shall be granted ; for no longer would I desire to liue among you, then I haue care for the good of the Common-wealth, at which word ended, the King rose from his royall throne, while the Clothiers on their knees prayed for both his health, and happy successe, & shewed themselues most thankefull for his highnesse fauour.   His maiestie bending his body towards them, said that at his home returne, he would (by the grace of God) visit them.

How the Clothiers had prouided a sumptuous feast for the Kings sonnes, Prince *William* and Prince *Richard*, at *Gerrards* Hall, shewing also what chaunce befell *Cutbert* of *Kendall* at that same instant.   CHAP. 5.

THe Clothiers departing from the Court in a merry mind, ioyfull of their good successe, each one to other praised and magnified the Kings great wisedome and vertue, commending also his affability and gentle disposition, so that *Hodgekins* affirmed on his faith, that hee had rather speake to his Kings Maiestie, then to many Iustices of peace.

Indeed (said *Cole*) he is a most mild and mercifull Prince, & I pray God he may long raigne ouer vs.

Amen said the rest.

Then said *Cole*, My Masters, shall we forget the great curtesie of the Kings sonnes, those sweet and gentle Princes, that still shewed vs fauour in our suite? in my opinion, it were reason to gratifie them in some sort, that we may not vtterly bee condemned of ingratitude : wherefore (if you thinke good) wee will prepare a banquet for them at our hoast *Garrats*, who as you know, hath a faire house, and goodly roomes : Besides, the man himselfe is a most couragious mind and good behauiour, sufficient to entertain a Prince : his wife also is a dainty fine Cooke : all which considered, I know not a fitter place in *London*.

Tis true (quoth *Sutton*) and if the rest be content, I am pleased it shal be so.

At this they all answered, Yea, for (quoth they) it will not be passing forty shillings a peece, and that we shall recouer in our crackt money.

Being thus agreed, the feast was prepared.

Tom Doue (quoth they) we will commit the prouiding of musicke to thee :

And I (said *Cole*) will inuite diuers of our Merchants and their wiues to the same.

That is well remembred (said *Gray*).

Vpon this they called to the hoast and hostis, shewing their determination, who most willingly said, all things should be made ready, but I would haue two daies liberty (said the good wife) to prepare my house and other things.

Content (said the Clothiers) in the meane space we will bid our guests, and dispatch our other affaires.

But *Simon* of *Southampton* charged his hostise, that in any case she should not forget to make good store of pottage.

It shall be done (quoth she).

It is to be remembred, that while this preparation was in hand, that *Cutb.* of *Kendall* had not forgot his kindnes to his hostisse of *Bosomes* Inne. Therefore finding time conuenient when her husband was ouerseeing his haymakers, he greeted her in this sort, Sweet hostesse, though I were the last time I was in towne, ouer bold with you, yet I hope it was not so offensiue to you, as you made shew for.

Bold, my *Cutb.* (quoth she)? thou hast vowed thy selfe my seruant: and so being, you are not to be blamed for doing what I wild you. By my honestie, I could not chuse but smile to my selfe, so soone as I was out of their sight, to thinke how prettily you began to brabble.

But now (quoth he) we will change our chidings to kissings, and it vexeth mee that these cherry lippes should be subiect to such a Lobcocke as thy husband.

Subiect to him (quoth she)! In faith sir, no, I will haue my lips at as much liberty as my tongue, the one to say what I list, and the other to touch whom I like: In troth, shall I tell thee, *Cutb.* the churles breath smels so strong, that I care as much for kissing of him, as for looking on him: t'is such a mis-shapen mizer, and such a bundle of beastlinesse, that I can neuer thinke on him without spitting. Fie vpon him, I would my friends had carried me to my graue, when they went with me to the Church, to make him my husband. And so shedding a few dissembling teares, she stopt.

What my sweet Mistrisse (quoth he) weepe you? Nay sit downe by my side, and I will sing thee one of my country Iigges to make thee merry.

Wilt thou in faith (quoth shee?)

Yes verily (said *Cutbert*):

And in troth (quoth she) if you fall a singing I will sing with you.

That is well, you can so suddenly change your notes (quoth *Cutbert*) then haue at it.

    Man.   *Long haue I lou'd this bonny Lasse,*
             Yet durst not shew the same.
    Wom. *There in you proue your selfe an Asse,*
    Man.   *I was the more to blame.*
          Yet still will I remaine to thee,
             Trang dilly do, trang dilly:
          Thy friend and louer secretly,
    Wom. *Thou art my owne sweet bully.*

Man. *But when shall I enioy thee,*
         delight of thy faire loue?
Wom. *Euen when thou seest that fortune doth,*
         all manner lets remoue.
Man. *O, I will fold thee in my armes,*
         Trang dilly do, trang dilly,
         And keepe thee so from sudden harmes,
Wom. *Thou art my owne sweet bully.*

Wom. *My husband he is gone from home,*
         you know it very well.
Man. *But when will he returne againe?*
Wom. *In truth I cannot tell.*
         If long he keepe him out of sight,
         Trang dilly do, trang dilly,
         Be sure thou shalt haue thy delight.
Man. *Thou art my bonny lassie.*

While they were singing this song, her husband being on a sudden come home, stood secretly in a corner and heard all, and blessing himselfe with both his hands, said, O abhominable dissimulation, monstrous hypocrisie, and are you in this humour? can you braule together and sing together? Well (quoth he) I will let them alone, to see a little more of their knauery. Neuer did Cat watch Mouse so narrowly, as I will watch them: And so going into the Kitchin, hee asked his wife if it were not dinner time.

Euen by and by, husband (quoth she) the meat will be ready.

Presently after comes in *Hodgekings* and *Martin*, who straight asked for *Cutbert* of *Kendall.* Answere was made, that he was in his Chamber. So when they had called him, they went to dinner: then they requested that their host and hostesse would sit with them.

Husband (said she) you may goe if you please: but as for me, I will desire pardon.

Nay, good wife, goe vp (said her husband). What woman, you must beare with your guests.

Why husband (qd. she) do you thinke that any can beare the flirts & frumps, which that Northerne tike gaue me the last time he was in towne; now God forgiue me, I had as liefe see the diuell as to see him: therefore good husband goe vp your selfe, and let me alone, for in faith, I shall neuer abide that Iacke while I liue.

Vpon these words away went her husband, and though he said little, hee thought more. Now when he came vp, his guests bade him welcome.

I pray you sit downe, good mine hoast (quoth they) where is your wife? what will she sit with vs?

No verily (said he) the foolish woman hath taken such a displeasure against *Cutbert*, that she sweares she will neuer come in his company.

Is it so (said the other)? then trust mee we are well agreed : and I sweare by my fathers sale (qd. hee) that were it not meere for good will to you, then loue to her, I would neuer come to your house meere.

I beleeue it well (said old *Bosome*). And so with other communication they droue out the time, till dinner was ended.

After they were risen, *Martin* & *Hodgekins* got them forth about their affaires, but *Cut.* tooke his host by the hand, saying, My 10 host, ile go talk with your wife ; for my part I thought we had bin friends : but seeing her stomack is so big, and her heart so great, I will see what she will say to me ; and with that hee stept into the kitchin, saying, God speed you hostise.

It must be when you are away then (said she).

What is your reason (said the other)?

Because God neuer comes where knaues are present.

Gip goodly draggletaile (qd. he) had I such a wife, I would present her tallow-face to the deuell for a candle

With that she bent her browes, and like a fury of hell began to 20 flie at him, saying, Why you gag-tooth iacke, you blinking companion, get thee out of my kitchin quickly, or with my powdred beefe broth, I will make your pate as bald as a friers.

Get me gon (quoth hee)? thou shalt not bid me twice : out you durty heeles, you will make your husbands haire growe through his hood I doubt :

And with that he got him into the Hall, and sat him downe on the bench by his hoast, to whom he said : Tis pittie, my Oast, that your aged yeeres that loues quietnesse, should be troubled with such a scolding queane. 30

I, God helpe me, God helpe me (quoth the old man) and so went towards the Stable : which his wife watching, suddenly stept out and gaue *Cutbert* a kisse.

Within an houre after, the old man craftily called for his Nag to ride to field : but assoone as he was gone, *Cutbert* and his Hostesse were such good friends, that they got into one of the Warehouses, and lockt the doore to them : but her husband hauing set a spie for the purpose, suddenly turned backe, and called for a capcase which lay in the Warehouse. The seruant could not find the key by any meanes. Whereupon hee called to haue the 40 locke broke open. Which they within hearing, opened the doore of their owne accord.

So soone as her husband spied her in that place, with admiration he said : O the passion of my hart, what do you here? what you two that cannot abide one another? what make you so close together? is your chiding and rayling, brabling, and brauling, come to this? O what dissemblers are these !

Why, my host (qd. *Cutbert*) what need you take the matter so hotte? I gaue a Cheese to my country man *Hodgekins*, to lay vp, and deliuered it to your wife to be kept; and then is it not reason, that she should come and seeke me my Cheese?

O (quoth the old man) belike the dore was lockt, because the cheese should not run away.

The doore (said his wife) vnknown to vs clapt to it selfe, and hauing a spring locke, was presently fast.

Well huswife (qd. he) I will giue you as much credit as a Crocadile, but as for your companion, I will teach him to come 10 hither to looke cheeses.

And with that he caused his men to take him presently, and to bind him hand and foote. Which being done, they drew him vp in a basket into the smoky louer of the hall, and there they did let him hang all that night, euen till the next day dinner time, when he should haue beene at the banquet with the princes: for neither *Hodgekins* nor *Martin* could intreat their inflamed hoast to let him downe.

And in such a heate was he driuen with drawing him vp, that he was faine to cast off his gownes, his cotes, and two paire of his 20 stockings, to coole himselfe, making a vow he shold hang there 7. yeares, except the kings sonnes came in person to beg his pardon, which most of all grieued *Cutbert*. When *Cole* and the rest of the Westerne Yeomen heard hereof, they could not chuse but laugh, to thinke that he was so taken tardy.

The yong princes hauing giuen promise to be with the clothiers, kept their houre, but when all the rest went to giue them entertainment, *Simon* was so busie in supping his pottage, that he could not spare so much time. Which when the princes saw, with a smiling countenance they said, Sup *Simon*, theres good 30 broath,

Or else beshrew our hostesse: (quoth he) neuer looking behind him to see who spake, till the Prince clapt him on the shoulder. But good Lord, how blank he was when he spied them, knowing not how to excuse the matter.

Well, the princes hauing ended their banket, *Garrat* comes and with one of his hands tooke the table of sixteene foote long quite from the ground ouer their heads, from before the princes, and set it on the other side of the hall, to the great admiration of all them that beheld it.

40 The princes being then ready to depart, the Clothiers moued them in pleasant maner, to be good to one of their company, that did neither sit, lie, nor stand.

Then he must needes hang (qd. the Princes).

And so he doth, most excellent princes (qd. they); and therewithall told them the whole matter.

When they heard the storie, downe to *Bosomes* Inne they go, where looking vp into the roofe, spied poore *Cutbert* pinned vp in a basket, and almost smoaked to death, who although he were greatly ashamed, yet most pitifully desired that they would get his release.

What is his trespasse (said the Prince)?

Nothing if it shall like your Grace (qd. he) but for looking for a cheese:

But he could not find it without my wife (said the goodman): the villaine had lately dined with mutton, and could not digest his meate without cheese, for which cause I haue made him to fast these twenty houres, to the end he may haue a better stomacke to eate his dinner, then to vse dalliance. 10

Let me intreate you (quoth the Prince) to release him: and if euer hereafter you catch him in the corne, clappe him in the pownd.

Your Grace shall request or command any thing at my hand (said the old man) and so *Cutbert* was let downe vnbound, but when he was loose, he vowed neuer to come within that house more.

And it is said, the old man *Bosome* ordained, that in remembrance of this deed, euery yeare once all such as came thither to aske for cheeses, should be so serued: which thing is to this day 20 kept.

How *Simons* wife of *South-hampton*, being wholy bent to pride and pleasure, requested her husband to see *London*, which being granted, how she got good wife *Sutton* of *Salisburie* to go with her, who tooke *Crab* to go along with them, and how he prophecied of many things. CHAP. 6.

THe Clothiers being all come from *London*, *Simons* wife of *South-hampton*, who was with her husband very mery and pleasant, brake her mind vnto him in this sort: 30

Good Lord husband, will you neuer be so kind as let me goe to *London* with you? shall I be pend vp in *South-hampton*, like a parret in a cage, or a Capon in a coope? I would request no more of you in lieu of all my paines, carke and care, but to haue one weeks time to see that faire Citie: what is this life, if it be not mixt with some delight? and what delight is more pleasing then to see the fashions and maners of vnknowne places? Therefore good husband, if thou louest me, deny not this simple request. You know I am no common gadder, nor haue oft troubled you with trauell. God knowes, this may be the last thing that euer 40 I shall request at your hands.

Woman (quoth he) I would willingly satisfie your desire, but you

1. his release] released *1623*   28. *Simons*] *Suttons 1623, 1632*

know it is not conuenient for both of vs to be abroad, our charge is so great, and therefore our care ought not to bee small. If you will goe your selfe, one of my men shall goe with you, and money enough you shall haue in your purse : but to go with you my selfe, you see my businesse will not permit me.

Husband (said she) I accept your gentle offer, and it may be I shal intreat my gossip *Sutton* to go along with me.

I shall be glad (qd. her husband) prepare your selfe when you will.

10 When she had obtained this license, she sent her man *Weasell* to *Salisbury*, to know of good wife *Sutton* if she would keepe her company to *London*. *Suttons* wife being as willing to go, as she was to request, neuer resting till shee had gotten leaue of her husband ; the which when she had obtained, casting in her minde their pleasure would be small, being but they twaine : thereupon the wily woman sent letters by collericke *Crabbe* her man, both to *Grayes* wife, and *Fitzallens* wife, that they would meet them at *Reading*, who liking well of the match, consented, and did so prouide, that they met according to promise at *Reading*, and from 20 thence with *Coles* wife they went altogether, with each of them a man to *London*, each one taking vp their lodging with a seuerall friend.

When the Merchants of *London* vnderstood they were in towne, they inuited them euery day home to their owne houses, where they had dilicate good cheere : and when they went abroade to see the commodities of the Cittie, the Merchants wiues euer bore them companie, being attired most daintie and fine : which when the Clothiers wiues did see, it grieued their hearts they had not the like.

30 Now when they were brought into *Cheap-side*, there with great wonder they beheld the shops of the Goldsmithes; and on the other side, the wealthy Mercers, whose shoppes shined with all sorts of coloured silkes: in *Watlingstreet* they viewed the great number of Drapers : in *Saint Martins* Shoomakers : at *Saint Nicholas Church*, the flesh shambles : at the end of the old *Change*, the fishmongers : in *Candleweeke streete* the Weauers : then came into the *Iewes street*, where all the Iewes did inhabite : then came they to *Blackwell hall*, where the country Clothiers did vse to meete.

40 Afterwards they proceeded, and came to *S. Pauls Church*, whose steeple was so hie, that it seemed to pierce the cloudes, on the top whereof, was a great and mightie Wether-cocke, of cleane siluer, the which notwithstanding seemed as small as a sparrow to mens eyes, it stood so exceeding high, the which goodly weather-cocke was afterwards stolen away, by a cunning cripple, who found meanes one night to clime vp to the top of the steeple, and tooke it downe : with the which, and a great summe of money which he

had got together by begging in his life time, he builded a gate on the North-side of the Citty, which to this day is called *Criple-gate*.

From thence they went to the Tower of *London*, which was builded by *Iulius Cæsar*, who was Emperour of *Rome*. And there they beheld salt and wine, which had lien there euer since the Romaines inuaded this land, which was many yeares before our Sauiour Christ was borne, the wine was growne so thicke, that it might haue beene cut like a ielly. And in that place also they saw the money that was made of leather, which in ancient time went currant amongst the people.   10

When they had to their great contentation beheld all this, they repaired to their lodgings, hauing also a sumptuous supper ordained for them, with all delight that might bee. And you shall vnderstand, that when the country weauers, which came vp with their dames, saw the weauers of *Candlewike-street*, they had great desire presently to haue some conference with them ; & thus one began to challenge the other for workemanship,

(Quoth *Weasell*) ile worke with any of you all for a crowne, take if you dare, and he that makes his yard of cloth soonest, shall haue it.   20

You shall be wrought withall (said the other) and if it were for ten crownes : but we will make this bargaine, that each of vs shall winde their owne quilles.

Content (quoth *Weasell*) : and so to worke they went, but *Weasell* lost.

Whereupon another of them tooke the matter in hand, who lost likewise : so that the *London* weauers triumphed against the country, casting forth diuers frumps.

Alas poore fellowes (quoth they) your hearts are good, but your hands are ill.   30

Tush, the fault was in their legges (quoth another) pray you friend, were you not borne at home ?

Why doe you aske (quoth *Weasell*)?

Because (said hee) the biggest place of your legge is next to your shooe.

Crab hearing this, beeing cholericke of nature, chafed like a man of law at the Bar, and he wagers with them four crownes to twaine : the others agreed, to worke they goe : but *Crab* conquered them all. Whereupon, the *London* weauers were nipt in the head like birds, and had not a word to say.   40

Now (saith *Crab*) as we haue lost nothing, so you haue wonne nothing, and because I know you cannot be right weauers, except you be good fellowes, therefore if you will go with vs, we will bestow the Ale vpon you.

That is spoken like a good-fellow and like a weauer (quoth the other).

So along they went as it were to the signe of the red Crosse.

36. *Crab*] *Cutbert 1623, 1632*   47. along *1632* : long *1623*

When they were set downe, & had drunke well, they began
merrily to prattle, and to extoll *Crab* to the skies. Whereupon
Crab protested, that he would come and dwell among them.

Nay, that must not be (said a *London* weauer) : the King hath
giuen vs priuiledge, that none should liue among vs, but such as
serue seuen yeeres in *London*.

With that *Crab*, according to his old maner of prophesying, said
thus :

> *The day is very neere at hand,*
> *When as the King of this faire land,*
> *Shal priuiledge you more then so :*
> *Then weauers shall in skarlet goe.*

> *And to one brotherhood be brought,*
> *The first is in* London *wrought,*
> *When other trades-men by your fame,*
> *Shall couet all to doe the same.*

> *Then shall you all liue wondrous well,*
> *But this one thing I shall you tell :*
> *The day will come before the doome,*
> *In* Candleweeke street *shall stand no loome.*

> *Nor any weauer dwelling there,*
> *But men that shall more credit beare :*
> *For Clothing shall be sore decayed,*
> *And men vndone that vse that trade.*

> *And yet the day some men shall see,*
> *This trade againe shall raised be.*
> *When as Bayliffe of* Sarum *towne ;*
> *Shall by and purchase* Bishops downe.

> *When there neuer man did sow,*
> *Great store of goodly corne shall grow ;*
> *And woad, that makes all colours sound,*
> *Shall spring vpon that barren ground.*

> *At that same day I tell you plaine,*
> *Who so aliue doth then remaine,*
> *A proper Maiden they shall see,*
> *Within the towne of* Salisburie.

> *Of fauour sweet, and nature kind,*
> *With goodly eies, and yet starke blind,*
> *This poore blind Maiden I do say,*
> *In age shall goe in rich array.*

> *And he that takes her to his wife,*
> *Shall lead a ioyfull happy life,*
> *The wealthiest Clothier shall he be,*
> *That euer was in that country.*

But clothing kept as it hath beene,
In London *neuer shall be seene :*
For weauers then the most shall win,
That worke for cloathing next the skin.

Till pride the Common-wealth doth peele,
And causeth huswiues leaue their wheele.
Then pouerty vpon each side,
Vnto those workemen shall betide.

At that time, from an Eagles neast,
That proudly builded in the West, 10
A sort shall come with cunning hand,
To bring strange weauing in this land,

And by their gaines that great will fall,
They shall maintaine the weauers Hall :
But long they shall not flourish so,
But folly will them ouerthrow.

And men shall count it mickle shame,
To beare that kind of Weauers name,
And this as sure shall come to passe,
As here is ale within this glasse. 20

When the silly soules that sate about him heard him speake in
this sort, they admired, and honoured *Crabbe* for the same.

Why my masters (said *Weasell*) doe you wonder at these words?
he will tell you twenty of these tales, for which cause we call him
our canuas Prophet : his attire fits his title, said they and we
neuer heard the like in our liues : and if this shold be true, it
would be strange.

Doubt not but it will be true (qd. *Weasel*) : for ile tell you what,
he did but once see our *Nicke* kisse *Nel*, and presently he powred
out this rime : 30

That kisse, O Nel, *God giue thee ioy,*
Will nine months hence breed thee a boy.

And ile tell you what, you shall heare : we kept reckoning, and
it fell out iust as *Iones* buttockes on a close stoole, for which
cause, our maids durst neuer kisse a man in his sight :

Vpon this they broke company, & went euery one about his
busines, the *London* weauers to their frames, and the countrey
fellowes to their dames, who after their great banquetting &
merriment, went euery one home to their owne houses, though
with lesse money than they brought out, yet with more pride. 40

Especially *Simons* wife of *South-hampton*, who told the rest of
her gossips, that she saw no reason, but that their husbands
should maintaine them, aswell as the Merchants did their wiues :
for I tell you what (quoth she) we are as proper women (in my

conceit,) as the proudest of them all, as handsome of body, as faire of face, our legs as well made, and our feet as fine: then what reason is there (seeing our husbands are of as good wealth,) but we should be as well maintained.

You say true gossip (said *Suttons* wife): trust me, it made me blush, to see them braue it out so gallantly, and wee to goe so homely:

But before God (said the other) I will haue my husband to buy me a *London* gowne, or in faith he shall haue little quiet:

10   So shall mine (said another):

And mine too (qd. the third): and all of them sung the same note: so that when they came home, their husbands had no little to doe: Especially *Simon*, whose wife dayly lay at him for *London* apparell, to whome he said, Good woman, be content, let vs goe according to our place and abilitie: what will the Bailiffes thinke, if I should pranke thee vp like a Peacocke, and thou in thy attire surpasse their wiues? they would either thinke I were madde, or else that I had more mony then I could well vse, consider, I pray thee good wife, that such as are in their youth masters, doe proue
20 in their age starke beggars.

Besides that, it is enough to raise me vp in the Kings booke, for many times, mens coffers are iudged by their garments: why, we are country folks, and must keepe our selues in good compasse: gray russet, and good hempe-spun cloath doth best become vs; I tell thee wife, it were as vndecent for vs to goe like Londoners as it is for Londoners to goe like courtiers.

What a coyle keepe you (quoth she)? are not we Gods creatures as well as Londoners? and the Kings subiects, aswell as they? then finding our wealth to be as good as theirs, why should we
30 not goe as gay as Londoners? No husband, no, here is the fault, wee are kept without it, onely because our husbands be not so kind as Londoners: why man, a Cobler there keepes his wife better then the best Clothier in this countrey: nay, I will affirme it, that the *London* Oyster-wiues, and the very kitchin-stuffe cryers, doe exceed vs in their Sundaies attire: nay, more then that, I did see the Water-bearers wife which belongs to one of our Merchants, come in with a Tankerd of water on her shoulder, and yet halfe a dozen gold rings on her fingers.

You may then thinke, wife (quoth he) she got them not with
40 idlenesse.

But wife you must consider what *London* is, the chiefe and capitall Cittie of all the land, a place on the which all strangers cast their eies, it is (wife) the Kings chamber and his Maiesties royall seate: to that Cittie repaires all nations vnder heauen. Therefore it is most meete and conuenient, that the Citizens of such a Citie should not goe in their apparell like Peasents, but for the credit of our countrey, weare such seemely habits, as do carrie grauity and comelinesse in the eyes of all beholders.

But if we of the countrey went so (quoth she) were it not as great credit for the land as the other?

Woman (qd. her husband) it is altogether needlesse, and in diuers respects it may not be.

Why then, I pray you (quoth she) let vs goe dwell at London.

A word soone spoken (said her husband) but not so easie to be performed : therefore wife, I pray thee hold thy prating, for thy talke is foolish :

Yea, yea husband, your old churlish conditions will neuer be left, you keepe me here like a drudge and a droile, and so you may keepe your money in your purse, you care not for your credit, but before I will goe so like a shepheardesse, I will first goe naked : and I tell you plain, I scorne it greatly, that you should clap a gray gowne on my backe, as if I had not brought you two pence : before I was married you swore I should haue any thing that I requested, but now all is forgotten.

And in saying this, she went in, and soone after she was so sicke, that needes she must go to bed : and when she was laid, she draue out that night with many grieuous groanes, sighing and sobbing, and no rest she could take God wot. And in the morning when she should rise, the good soule fell downe in a swowne, which put her maidens in a great flight, who running downe to their master, cryed out ; Alas, alas, our Dame is dead, our Dame is dead.

The goodman heareing this, ran vp in all hast and there fell to rubbing and chafing of her temples, sending for *aqua vitæ*, and saying, Ah my sweet heart, speake to me, good wife, alacke, alacke, call in the neighbours, you queanes (quoth he).

With that shee lift vp her head, fetching a great groane, and presently swouned againe, and much a doe ywis, he had to keepe life in her : but when she was come to her selfe, How dost thou wife (qd. he)?

What wilt thou haue? for Gods sake tel me if thou hast a mind to any thing, thou shalt haue it.

Away dissembler (qd. she) how can I beleeue thee? thou hast said to me as much a hundred times, and deceiued me, it is thy churlishnesse that hath killed my heart, neuer was woman matcht to so vnkind a man.

Nay good wife, blame me not without cause ; God knoweth how dearely I loue thee.

Loue me! no, no, thou didst neuer carry my loue but on the tip of thy tongue (quoth she) I dare sweare thou desirest nothing so much as my death, and for my part, I would to God thou hadst thy desire : but be content, I shall not trouble thee long : and with that fetching a sigh, she swouned and gaue a great groane.

The man seeing her in this case was wondrous woe : but so soone as they had recouered her, he said, O my deare wife, if any bad conceit hath ingendered this sicknesse, let me know it ; or if

thou knowst any thing that may procure thy health, let me vnderstand thereof, and I protest thou shalt haue it, if it cost me all
that euer I haue.

O husband (quoth she) how may I credite your wordes, when
for a paltrie sute of apparell you denied mee ?

Well wife (quoth he) thou shalt haue apparell or any thing else
thou wilt request, if God send thee once health.

O husband, if I may find you so kind, I shall thinke my selfe
the happiest woman in the world, thy words haue greatly com-
10 forted my heart, mee thinketh if I had it, I could drinke a good
draught of renish wine.

Well, wine was sent for: O Lord (said she) that I had a peece
of chicken, I feele my stomacke desirous of some meate :

Glad am I of that (said her husband) and so the woman within
a few daies after was very well.

But you shall vnderstand, that her husband was faine to dresse
her London-like, ere he could get her quiet, neither wold it please
her except the stuffe was bought in *Cheapeside* : for out of *Cheapside* nothing would content her, were it neuer so good : insomuch,
20 that if she thought a taylor of *Cheapside* made not her gowne, she
would sweare it were quite spoiled.

And hauing thus wonne her husband to her will, when the rest of
the Clothiers wiues heard thereof, they would be suted in the like
sort too ; so that euer since, the wiues of *South-hampton, Salisbury,*
of *Glocester, Worcester,* and *Reading,* went all as gallant and as
braue as any Londoners wiues.

How the Clothiers sent the King aide into *France,* and how he ouercame his brother *Robert,* and brought him into *England,* and how the Clothiers feasted his
30 Maiestie and his sonne at *Reading.*   CHAP. 7.

THe Kings Maiestie being at the warres in *Fraunce,* against
Lewis the French King, and Duke *Robert* of *Normandie,*
sending for diuers supplies of souldiers out of *England,* the
Clothiers at their owne proper cost set out a great number, and
sent them ouer to the King.

Which *Roger* Bishop of *Salisburie,* who gouerned the Realme
in the Kings absence, did certifie the King thereof, with his
letters written in their commendations.

And afterwards it came to passe, that God sent his Highnes
40 victory ouer his enemies, and hauing taken his brother prisoner,
brought him most ioyfully with him into *England,* and appointed
him to be kept in *Cardife* castle prisoner, yet with this fauour,
that he might hunt and hawke where he would, vp and downe

the countrey, and in this sorte hee liued a good while, of whom we will speake more at large hereafter.

The King being thus come home, after his winters rest, he made his summers progresse into the west countrey, to take a view of all the chiefe townes: whereof the Clothiers being aduertised, they made great preparation against his comming, because he had promised to visite them all.

And when his Grace came to *Reading*, he was entertained and receiued with great ioy and triumph: *Thomas Cole* being the chiefe man of regard in all the towne, the King honored his 10 house with his princely presence, where during the Kings abode, he, and his son, and Nobles were highly feasted.

There the King beheld the great number of people, that was by that one man maintained in worke, whose hearty affection and loue toward his Maiestie did well appeare, aswell by their outward countenances, as their gifts presented vnto him. But of *Cole* himselfe the King was so well perswaded, that he committed such trust in him, and put him in great authoritie in the towne. Furthermore the King said, That for the loue which those people bore him liuing, that he would lay his bones among them when 20 he was dead. For I know not (said he) where they may be better bestowed, till the blessed day of resurrection, then among these my friends which are like to be happy partakers of the same.

Whereupon his Maiestie caused there to be builded a most goodly and famous Abbey: in which he might shew his deuotion to God, by increasing his seruice, and leaue example to other his successors to doe the like. Likewise within the towne he after builded a faire and goodly castle, in the which he often kept his Court, which was a place of his chiefe residence during his life, saying to the Clothiers, that seeing he found them such faithfull 30 subiects, he would be their neighbor, and dwell among them.

After his Maiesties royal feasting at *Reading*, he proceeded in progresse, till he had visited the whole west countries, being wondrously delighted, to see those people so diligent to apply their busines: and comming to *Salisburie*, the Bishop receiued his Maiestie with great ioy, and with triumph attended on his Grace to his palace, where his Highnesse lodged.

There *Sutton* the Clothier presented his Highnesse with a broad cloth, of so fine a threed, and exceeding good workmanship, and therewithall of so faire a colour, as his Grace gaue 40 commendation thereof, and as it is said, he held it in such high estimation, that thereof he made his parliament robes, & the first parliament that was euer in *England*, was graced with the Kings person in those robes, in requitall whereof his Highnes afterward yeelded *Sutton* many princely fauours.

And it is to be remembred, that *Simon* of *South-hampton* (seeing the King had ouerpast the place where he dwelt) came with his wife and seruants to *Salisburie*, and against the K. going forth of that Citty, he caused a most pleasant arbour to be made vpon the toppe of the hill leading to *Salisburie*, beset all with red and white roses, in such sort, that not any part of the timber could be seene, within the which sat a maiden attired like a Queen, attended on by a faire traine of maidens, who at the Kings approach presented him with a Garland of sweet flouers, yeelding him such honour as the Ladies of *Rome* were wont to doe to their Princes after their victories : which the King tooke in gracious part, and for his farewell from that country, they bore 10 him company ouer part of the Plaine, with the sound of diuers sweet instruments of musicke. All which when his Grace vnderstood was done at the cost of a Clothier, he said hee was the most honoured by those men, aboue all the meane subiects in his land : & so his highnes past on to *Exceter*, hauing giuen great rewards to these Maidens.

Thomas Doue and the residue of the Clothiers, against his Graces comming thither, had ordained diuers sumptuous shewes ; first, there was one that presented the person of *Augustus Cæsar* the Emperour, who commanded after the Romone inuasion, that 20 their citie should be called *Augustus*, after his owne name, which before time was called *Isca*, and of later yeeres, *Exeter*.

There his Maiesty was royally feasted seauen daies together, at the onely cost of Clothiers, but the diuers delightes and sundry pastimes which they made there before the King, and his Nobles, is too long here to be rehearsed, and therefore I will ouerpasse them to auoid tediousnesse.

His Grace then coasting along the country, at last came to *Gloucester*, an ancient Citie, which was builded by *Gloue*, a Brittish King, who named it after his owne name, *Glocester*. 30 Here was his Maiestie entertained by *Gray* the Clothier, who profest himselfe to be of that auncient family of *Grayes*, whose first originall issued out of that auncient and Honorable Castle and Towne of *Rithin*.

Here was the King most bountifully feasted, hauing in his company his brother *Robert* (although his prisoner the same time.) And his Grace being desirous to see the Maidens card and spinne, they were of purpose set to their worke: among whom was faire *Margaret* with her white hand, whose excellent beauty hauing pierct the eyes of the amorous Duke, it made such 40 an impression in his heart, that afterward he could neuer forget her : and so vehemently was his affection kindled that he could take no rest, till by writing he had bewrayed his minde : but of this we will speake more in another place : and the King at his departure said, that to gratifie them, hee would make his sonne *Robert* their Earle, who was the first Earle that euer was in *Glocester*.

Now when his Grace was come from thence, hee went to *Worcester*, where *William Fitz-allen* made preparation in all

honourable sort to receiue him, which man being borne of great
parentage, was not to learne how to entertaine his Maiestie, being
desended of that famous family, whose patrimonie lay about the
Towne of *Oswestrie*, which Town his predecessors had inclosed
with stately walls of stone.

Although aduerse fortune had so grieuously frowned on some
of them, that their children were faine to become tradesmen, whose
handes were to them instead of landes, notwithstanding God
raised againe the fame of this man, both by his great wealth, and
also in his posteritie, whose eldest son *Henry*, the Kings god-son, 10
became afterward the Maior of *London*, who was the first Maior
that euer was in that Cittie, who gouerned the same 23 yeares:
and then his sonne *Roger Fitz-allen* was the second Maior.

The princely pleasures that in *Worcester* were shown the King,
were many and maruelous, and in no place had his Maiesty
receiued more delight then here: for the which at his departure
he did shew himselfe very thankfull. Now when his Grace had
thus taken view of all his good townes Westward and in that
progresse had visited these Clothiers, he returned to *London*, with
great ioy of his Commons. 20

How *Hodgekins* of *Hallifax* came to the Court, and complained to the King, that his priuiledge was nothing
worth, because when they found any offender, they
could not get a hangman to execute him: and how
by a Frier a gin was deuised to chop off mens heads
of it selfe. CHAP. 8.

AFter that *Hodgkins* had got the priuiledge for the towne of
Halifax, to hang vp such theeues as stole their cloath in the
night, presently without any further iudgement, all the Clothiers
of the towne were exceeding glad, and perswaded themselues, 30
that now their goods would be safe all night, without watching
them at al, so that whereas before, the town maintained certaine
watchmen to keepe their cloath by night, they were hereupon
dismissed as a thing needlesse to be done, supposing with themselues, that seeing they should be straight hanged that were
found faultie in this point, that no man would bee so desperate to
enterprise any such act. And indeed the matter being noysed
through the whole countrey, that they were straight to be hanged
that vse such theeuery, it made many lewd liuers to restraine
such theeuery. 40

Neuertheles, there was at that same time liuing, a notable
Theefe named *Wallis*, whom in the north they called *Mighty
Wallis*, in regard of his valour and manhood: This man being

most subtile in such kind of knauerie, hauing heard of this late
priuiledge, and therewithall of the Townes securitie, said that
once he would venture his necke for a packe of Northerne
cloth : and therefore comming to one or two of his companions,
he asked if they would be partners in his aduenture, and if (quoth
he) you will herein hazard your bodies, you shall be sharers in all
our booties.

At length by many perswasions the men consented : whereupon late in the night, they got them all into a Farriours shop,
10 and called vp the folkes of the house.

What the foule ill wald you haue (quoth they) at this time of
the night?

Wallis answered, saying good fellowes, we would haue you to
remoue the shooes of our horses feete, and set them on againe,
and for your paines you shall be well pleased.

The Smith at length was perswaded, and when he had pluckt
off al the shooes from their horses feete, they would needes haue
them all set on againe, quite contrary with the cakins forward,
that should stand backward.

20 How? fay, fay man (quoth the Smith) are ye sicke fules? what
the deele do you meane to breake your crags? gud faith I tro the
men be wood.

Not so Smith (qd they) do thou as we bid thee, & thou
shalt haue thy mony : for it is an old prouerbe,

> *Be it better, or be it worse,*
> *Please you the man that beares the purse.*

Gud faith and see I sall (qd. the Smith) and so did as hee
was willed.   When *Wallis* had thus caused their Horses to be
shod, to *Hallifax* they went, where they without any let laded
30 their Horses with cloth, and so departed contrary way.

In the morning, so soone as the Clothiers came to the field,
they found that they were robd, whereupon one ranne to another to
tell these things.   Now when *Hodgkings* heard thereof, rising vp
in hast, he wild his neighbors to mark and to see, if they could
not descry either the footesteppes of men or Horses.   Which
being done, they perceiued that horses had been there, and
seeking to pursue them by their footesteppes, they went a cleane
contrary way, by reason that the horses were shodde backward :
& when in vaine they had long pursude them, they returned, being
40 neuer the neere.

Now *Wallis* vsed his feate so long, that at length he was taken,
and two more with him : whereupon according to the priuilege
of the Towne, they put Halters about the theeues neckes presently to hang them vp.

When they were come to the place appointed, *Wallis* and
the rest being out of hope to escape death, prepared themselues
patiently to suffer the rigor of the law.   And therewith the rest

laying open the lewdnesse of his life, grieuously lamenting for his sinnes, at length commending their soules to God, they yeelded their bodies to the graue, with which sight the people were greatly mooued with pity, because they had neuer seene men come to hanging before : but when they shold haue beene tyed vp, *Hodgekins* willed one of his neighbors to play the Hangmans part, who would not by any meanes doe it, although he was a very poore man, who for his paines should haue beene possest of all their apparell. When he would not yeeld to the office, one of those which had his cloth stolen, was commanded 10 to doe the deed; but he in like manner would not, saying : When I haue the skill to make a man, I will hang a man, if it chance my workmanship do not like me.

And thus from one to another, the office of the hangman was posted off. At last a Rogue came by, whom they would haue compelled to haue done that deed.

Nay, my masters (qd. he) not so : but as you haue got a priuiledge for the Towne, so you were best to procure a Commission to make a hangman, or else you are like to be without for me.   20

Neighbor *Hodgkins* (quoth one) I pray you do this office your selfe, you haue had most losse, and therefore you should be the most readie to hang them your selfe.

No, not I (quoth *Hodgkings*) though my losse were ten times greater then it is, notwithstanding look which of these theeues will take vpon him to hang the other, shall haue his life saued, otherwise they shall all to prison till I can prouide a hangman.

When *Wallis* saw the matter brought to this passe, he began stoutly to reply, saying, My masters of the Town of *Halifax*, though your priuiledge stretch to hang men vp presently that 30 are found stealing of your goods, yet it giues you no warrant to imprison them till you prouide them a hangman, my selfe, with these my fellowes, haue here yeelded our selues to satisfie the Law, and if it be not performed, the fault is yours, and not ours, and therefore we humbly take our leaue : from the gallowes the xviii of August. And with that he leapt from the ladder, and hirld the halter at *Hodgkings* face.

When the Clothiers saw this, they knew not what to say, but taking them by the sleeues, entreated to haue their owne againe.

No so (qd. *Wallis*) you get not the value of a packe or 40 a bawby : we haue stolen your cloth, then why doe you not hang vs ? here we haue made our selues ready, and if you wil not hang vs, chuse. A plague vpon you (quoth he) you haue hindred me God knowes what, I made account to dine this day in heauen, and you keepe me here on earth where there is not a quarter of that good cheare. The foule euill take you all, I was fully prouided to giue the gallowes a boxe on the eare, and now God knowes when I shall be in so good a minde againe: and so he with the rest of his companions departed.

When *Hodgekings* saw, that notwithstanding their theeuery, how they flowted at their lenitie, he was much mooued in minde; and as he stood in his dumps chewing his cud, making his dinner with a dish of melancholy, a gray Frier reuerently saluted him in this sort: All haile, goodman *Hodgekins*, happinesse and health be euer with you, and to all suppressors of lewd liuers, God send euerlasting ioyes.

10 I am sory goodman *Hodgekings*, that the great priuiledge which our King gaue to this towne, comes to no greater purpose; better far had it bin that it had neuer beene graunted, then so lightly regarded; the towne hath suffered through their owne peeuishnesse, an euerlasting reproch this day, onely because foolish pitty hath hindred iustice.

Consider, that compassion is not to be had vpon theeues and robbers; pitty onely appertaineth to the vertuous sort, who are ouerwhelmed with the waues of miserie and mischaunce. What great cause of boldnesse haue you giuen to bad liuers, by letting 20 these fellowes thus to escape, & how shall you now keepe your goods in safetie, seeing you fulfill not the law which should be your defence? neuer thinke that theeues will make any conscience to carry away your goods, when they find them selues in no danger of death, who haue more cause to praise your pitty, then commend your wisedome: wherefore in time seeke to preuent the ensuing euill.

For my owne part, I haue that care of your good, that I would worke all good meanes for your benefit, and yet not so much in respect of your profit, as for the desire I haue to vphold iustice, and 30 seeing I find you and the rest so womanish, that you could not find in your hearts to hang a theefe, I haue deuised how to make a gin, that shall cut off their heads without mans helpe, and if the King will allow thereof.

When *Hodgekins* heard this, he was somewhat comforted in mind, and said to the Frier, that if by his cunning he would performe it, he would once againe make sute to the King to haue his grant for the same. The Frier willed him to haue no doubt in him: and so when he had deuised it, he got a Carpenter to frame it out of hand.

40 *Hodgekins* in the meane time posted it vp to the Court, and told his Maiestie that the priuiledge of *Hallifax* was not worth a pudding.

Why so (said the King)?

Because (quoth *Hodgekins*) we can get neuer a hangman to trusse our theeues: but if it shall like your good Grace (quoth he) there is a feate Frier, that will make vs a deuise, which shall without the hand of man cut off the cragges of all such Carles, if your Maiestie will please to allow thereof.

The King vnderstanding the full effect of the matter, at length granted his petition: whereupon till this day, it is obserued in *Halifax*, that such as are taken stealing of their cloth, haue their heads chopt off with the same gin.

How the Bailiffes of *London* could get no man to bee a Catch-pole, and how certaine Flemings tooke that office vpon them, whereof many of them were fledde into this Realme, by reason of certaine waters that had drowned a great part of their Countrey. CHAP. 9.

THe Citty of *London* being at that time gouerned by 10 Bailiffes, it came to passe, that in a certaine fray two of their Catch-poles were killed, for at that time they had not the name of Sergeants: and you shall vnderstand, that their office was then so much hated and detested of Englishmen, that none of them would take it vpon him: so that the Bailiffes were glad to get any man whatsoeuer, and to giue him certain wages to performe that office.

It came to passe, as I said before, that two of their Officers by arresting of a man, were at one instant slaine, by meanes whereof the Bailiffes were enforced to seeke others to put in 20 their roomes; but by no meanes could they get any, wherefore according to their wonted manner, they made proclamation, that if there were any man that would present himselfe before them, he should not onely be settled in that office during their liues, but also should haue such maintenance and allowance, as for such men was by the cittie prouided: and notwithstanding that it was an Office most necessary in the Commonwealth, yet did the poorest wretch despise it, that liued in any estimation among his neighbours.

At last a couple of Flemings, which were fled into this land, 30 by reason that their countrey was drowned with the sea, hearing the proclamation, offered themselues vnto the Bayliffes, to serue in this place, who were presently receiued and accepted, & according to their order had garments giuen them, which were of 2. colors, blue & red their coates, breeches & stockings, whereby they were knowne and discerned from other men.

Within halfe a yeare after, it came to passe, that *Thomas Doue* of *Exeter* came vp to *London*, who hauing by his iollity and good fellowship, brought himselfe greatly behind hand, was in danger to diuers men of the Citty, among the rest, one of his 40 Creditors feed an Officer to arrest him. The Dutch-man that had not bin long experienced in such matters, and hearing how

18. Officers *1632*: Offices *1623*

many of his fellowes had bin killed for attempting to arrest
men, stood quiuering and quaking in a corner of the street to
watch for *Thomas Doue*, and hauing long waited, at length he
spied him: whereupon he prepared his mace ready, and with
a pale countenance proceeded to his office; at what time
comming behind the man, suddenly with his mace he knockt
him on the pate, saying, I arrest you, giuing him such a blow,
that he fell him to the ground.

The Catchpole thinking he had killed the man, he left his
10 Mace behind him and ranne away: the creditor he ranne after
him, calling and crying that he should turne againe: But the
Fleming would not by any meanes turne backe, but got him quite
out of the Citty, and tooke Sanctuary at *Westminster*.

Doue being come to himselfe, arose and went to his Inne, no
man hindring his passage, being not a little glad he so escaped
the danger. Yet neuerthelesse, at his next comming to *London*,
another Catchpole met with him, and arrested him in the Kings
name.

Doue being dismaied at this mischieuous mischance, knew not
20 what to doe: at last he requested the Catchpole that hee would
not violently cast him in prison, but stay till such time as he could
send for a friend to be his surety; and although kindnesse in
a Catchpole be rare, yet was he won with faire words to doe him
this fauour: whereupon *Doue* desired one to goe to his Host
Iarrat, who immediately came vnto him, and offered himselfe to
be *Doues* surety.

The Officer, who neuer saw this man before, was much mazed
at his sight: for *Iarrat* was a great and mighty man of body, of
countenance grim, and exceeding high of stature, so that the
30 Catchpole was wonderfully afraid, asking if he could neuer find
a surety but the deuell, most fearefully intreating him to coniure
him away, and he would doe *Doue* any fauour.

What, will you not take my word (qd. *Iarrat*)?

Sir (qd. the Catchpole) if it were for any matter in hell, I would
take your word as soone as any diuels in that place, but seeing it
is for a matter on earth, I would gladly haue a surety.

Why thou whorson cricket (quoth *Iarret*) thou maggat-a-pie,
thou spinner, thou paultry spider, dost thou take me for a Diuell?
Sirra, take my word, I charge thee for this man, or else goodman
40 butterflie, ile make thee repent it.

The officer, while he was in the house, said, he was content, but
as soone as he came into the street, he cried, saying: Helpe,
helpe, good neighbors, or else the Diuill will carry away my
prisoner: notwithstanding, there was not one man would stirre to
be the Catchpoles aide. Which when he saw, he tooke fast hold
on *Thomas Doue*, and would not by any meanes let him goe.

Iarret seeing this, made no more to doe, but comming to the
Officer, gaue him such a fillop on the forehead with his finger,

that he fell the poore Fleming to the ground : and while he lay in the streete stretching his heeles, *Iarrat* tooke *Doue* vnder his arme and carried him home, where he thought himselfe as safe, as King *Charlemaine* in mount Albon.

The next morning *Iarret* conueyed *Doue* out of Towne, who afterward kept him in the countrey, and came no more in the Catchpoles clawes.

How Duke *Robert* came a wooing to *Margaret* with the white hand, and how he appointed to come and steale her away from her Masters. CHAP. 10.

THe beautifull *Margaret*, who had now dwelt with her Dame the space of foure yeares, was highly regarded and secretly beloued of many gallant and worthy Gentlemen of the countrey, but of two most especially, Duke *Robert*, and Sir *William Ferris*.

It chanced on a time, that faire *Margaret* with many others of her Masters folkes, went a hay-making attired in a red stammell peticoate, and a broad strawne hatte vpon her head, she had also a hay-forke, and in her lappe shee did carry her breake-fast. As she went along, Duke *Robert*, with one or two of his Keepers, met with her, whose amiable sight did now anew re-inkindle the secret fire of loue, which long lay smothering in his heart. Wherefore meeting her so happily, he saluted her thus friendly.

Faire maid, good morrow, are you walking so diligently to your labour? Needes must the weather be faire, when the Sun shines so cleare, and the hay holesome that is dried with such splendant rayes.

Renowned and most notable Duke (qd. she) poore haruest folkes pray for faire weather, and it is the laborers comfort to see his worke prosper, and the more happy may we count the day, that is blessed with your princely presence.

But more happy (said the Duke) are they which are conuersant in thy company. But let me intreat thee to turne backe to thy Masters with me, and commit thy forke to some that are fitter for such toyle : trust me, methinkes thy dame is too much ill aduised, in setting thee to such homely busines. I muse thou canst indure this vile beseeming seruitude, whose delicate lims were neuer framed to proue such painfull experiments.

Albeit (quoth she) it becommeth not me to controule your iudiciall thoughts, yet were you not the Duke, I would say, your opinion deceiued you : though your faire eyes seem cleare, yet I deemed them vnperfect, if they cast before your mind any shadow or sparke of beauty in me : But I rather thinke, because it hath beene an old saying, that women are proude to heare themselues praised, that you either speake this, to driue away the

time, or to wring me from my too apparant imperfections. But
I humbly intreate pardon, too longe haue I fore-slowed my
businesse, and shewen myselfe ouer bold in your presence; and
therewith, with a courtly grace, bending her knees to the courteous
Duke, shee went forward to the field, and the Duke to the Towne
of *Glocester*.

When he came thither, he made his Keepers great cheare,
intreating them they would giue him respite to be awhile with old
Gray; for we twaine must haue a game or two (quoth he): and for
10 my safe returne, I gage to you my princely word, that as I am
a true Knight and a Gentleman, I will returne safe to your charge
againe.

The Keepers being content, the Duke departed, and with old
Gray goes to the field, to peruse the Workefolkes, where while
Gray found himselfe busie in many matters, he took opportunity
to talke with *Margaret*; she who by his letters before was priuie
to his purpose; guest before hand the cause of his comming: to
whom he spake to this effect:

Faire Maide, I did long since manifest my loue to thee by my
20 letter; tell me therefore, were it not better to be a Dutches then
drudge? a Lady of high reputation, then a seruant of simple
degree? with me thou mightest liue in pleasure, where here thou
drawest thy daies forth in paine; by my loue thou shouldst be
made a Lady of great treasures: where now thou art poore and
beggarly: all manner of delights should then attend on thee, and
whatsoeuer thy heart desireth, thou shouldst haue: wherefore
seeing it lies in thy owne choice, make thy selfe happy, by consenting to my suite.

Sir (quoth she) I confesse your loue deserues a Ladies fauour,
30 your affection a faithfull friend, such a one as could make but one
heart and minde of two hearts and bodies; but farre vnfit it is that
the Turtle should match with the Eagle, though her loue be neuer
so pure, her wings are vnfit to mount so high. While *Thales*
gazed on the starres, he stumbled in a pit. And they that clime
vnaduisedly, catch a fall suddenly: what auaileth high dignitie in
time of aduersity? it neither helpeth the sorrow of the heart, nor
remoues the bodies miserie: as for wealth and treasure, what are
they, but fortunes baits to bring men in danger? good for nothing
but to make people forget themselues: and whereas you alleadge
40 pouerty to be a hinderer of the hearts comfort, I find it my selfe
contrary, knowing more surety to rest vnder a simple habite, then
a royall robe: and verily there is none in the world poore, but
they that think themselues poore: for such as are indued with
content, are rich, hauing nothing els, but he that is possessed with
riches, without content, is most wretched and miserable. Wherefore most Noble Duke, albeit I account my life vnworthy of your
least fauour, yet I would desire you to match your loue to your
like, and let me rest to my rake, and vse my forke for my liuing.

Consider, faire *Margaret* (quoth he) that it lies not in mans power to place his loue where he list, being the worke of an high deity. A bird was neuer seen in *Pontus*, nor true loue in a fleeting mind : neuer shall I remoue the affection of my heart which in nature resembleth the stone Abiston, whose fire can neuer be cooled : wherefore sweet Maiden giue not obstinate deniall, where gentle acceptance ought to be receiued.

Faire sir (quoth she) consider what high displeasure may rise by a rash match, what danger a Kings frownes may breed, my worthlesse matching with your Roialty, may perhaps regaine your 10 libertie, and hazard my life ; then call to mind how little you should enioy your loue, or I my wedded Lord.

The Duke at these words made this reply, that if she con sented, she should not dread any danger. The thunder (quoth he) is driuen away by ringing of belles, the Lions wrath qualified by a yeelding body : how much more a Brothers anger with a Brothers intreaty ? By me he hath receiued many fauors, and neuer yet did he requite any one of them : and who is ignorant that the Princely Crown which adorneth his head, is my right ? all which I am content he shall still enioy, so he requite my 20 kindnesse. But if he should not, then would I be like those men (that eating of the tree Lutes) forget the country where they were borne, and neuer more should this clime couer my head, but with thee would I liue in a strange land, being better content with an egge in thy company, then with all the delicates in England.

The Maiden hearing this, who with many other wordes was long wooed, at last consented ; where yeelding to him her heart with her hand, he departed, appointing to certifie her from *Cardiffe* Castle, what determination he would follow : so taking 30 his leaue of *Gray* he went to his keepers, and with them posted to *Cardiffe*.

Now it is to be remembred, that sir *William Ferrers* within a day or two after came vnto *Grayes* house, as it was his ordinary custome, but not so much ywis for *Grayes* company, as for the minde he had to *Margaret* his Maide, who although he were a married man, and had a faire Lady to his wife, yet he laid hard siege to the fort of this Maidens chastity, hauing with many faire words sought to allure her, and by the offer of sundry rich gifts to tempt her. But when she saw, that by a hundred denials she 40 could not be rid of him, she now chanced on a sudden to giue him such an answere, as droue him from a deceit into such a conceit, as neuer after that time he troubled her.

Sir *William Ferrers* being very importunate to haue her grant his desire, and when after sundry assaults she gaue him still the repulse, he would needes know the reason why she would not loue him (quoth he) if thou didst but consider who he is that

31. keepers] brothers *1632, 1635*

seeketh thy fauour, what pleasure he may doe thee by his purse,
& what credit by his countenance, thou wouldst neuer stand
on such nice points.   If I be thy friend, who dareth be thy foe?
and what is he that will once call thy name in question for any
thing? therefore sweet girle, be better aduised, and refuse not
my offer being so large.

Truly sir *William* (quoth she) though there be many reasons
to make me deny your suite, yet is there one aboue the rest that
causes me I cannot loue you.

10   Now I pray thee, my wench let me know that (quoth he) and I
will amend it whatsoeuer it be.

Pardon me sir (said *Margaret*) if I should speake my mind, it
would possibly offend you, and do me no pleasure because it is
a defect in nature, which no phisicke can cure.

Sir *William* hearing on her so, being abashed at her speech,
said, Faire *Margaret*, let me (if I may obtaine no more at thy
hands) yet intreat thee to know what this defect should be, I am
not wry-neckt, crook-legd, stub-footed, lame-handed, nor bleare-
eyed: what can make this dislike? I neuer knew any body that
20 tooke exceptions at my person before.

And the more sorry am I (quoth she) that I was so malapert to
speake it, but pardon my presumption, good sir *William*, I would
I had beene like the storke tonguelesse, then should I neuer haue
caused your disquiet.

Nay sweet *Margaret* (quoth he) tell me deare loue, I commend
thy singlenesse of heart, good *Margaret* speake.

Good sir *William* let it rest (quoth she) I know you will not
beleeue it when I haue reuealed it, neither is it a thing that you
can helpe: and yet such is my foolishnesse, had it not beene for
30 that, I thinke verily I had granted your suite ere now.   But
seeing you vrge me so much to know what it is, I will tell you:
it is sir, your ill-fauoured great nose, that hangs sagging so loth-
somely to your lips, that I cannot find in my heart so much
as to kisse you.

What, my nose (quoth he)? is my nose so great and I neuer
knew it? certainly I thought my nose to be as comely as any
mans: but this it is we are all apt to think well of our selues,
and a great deale better then we ought: but let me see? my
nose! by the masse tis true, I do now feele it my selfe: Good
40 Lord, how was I blinded before?

Hereupon it is certaine, that the Knight was driuen into such
a conceit, as none could perswade him but his nose was so great
indeed; his Lady, or any other that spake to the contrarie, he
would say they were flatterers, and that they lied, insomuch
that he would be ready to strike some of them that commended
and spake well of his nose.   If they were men of worship, or any
other that contraried him in his opinion, he would sweare they
flowted him, and be ready to challenge them the field.   He

became so ashamed of himselfe, that after that day he would neuer goe abroad, whereby *Margaret* was well rid of his company.

On a time, a wise and graue gentleman seeing him grounded in his conceit so strongly, gaue his Lady counsell, not to contrary him therein, but rather say that she would seeke out some cunning Phisitian to cure him : for (said he) as sir *William* hath taken this conceit of himselfe, so is he like neuer to heare other opinion, till his owne conceit doth remoue it, the which must be wisely wrought to bring it to passe. 10

Whereupon the Lady hauing conferred with a Phisitian that beare a great name in the countrey, hee vndertooke to remoue this fond conceit by his skill. The day being appointed when the Phisitian should come, and the Knight beeing told thereof, for very ioy he would goe forth to meete him, when a woman of the Towne saw the Knight, hauing heard what rumor went because of his nose, shee looked very stedfastly vpon him : the Knight casting his eye vpon her, seeing her to gaze so wistly in his face, with an angry countenance, said thus to her, Why how now good huswife, cannot you get you about your busines? 20

The woman being a shrewish queane, answered him cuttedly, No mary can I not (qd. she).

No, you drab ! What is the cause (said the Knight) ?

Because (quoth she) your nose stands in my way : wherewith the Knight being very angry, and abashed, went backe againe to his house.

The Phisitian being come, hee had filled a certaine bladder with sheepes blood, and conueyed it into his sleeue, where at the issue of the bladder he had put in a piece of swane quil, through the which the bloud should runne out of the 30 bladder so close by his hand, that he holding the Knight by the nose, it might not be perceiued, but that it issued thence. All things being prepared, he told the knight, that by a foule corrupt blood wherewith the veines of his nose were ouercharged, his impediment did grow, therefore (quoth he) to haue redresse for this disease, you must haue a veine opened in your nose, whence this foule corruption must be taken : whereupon it will follow, that your nose will fall againe to his naturall proportion, and neuer shall you be troubled with this griefe any more, and thereupon will I gage my life. 40

I pray you Master Doctor (said the Knight) is my nose so big as you make it ?

With reuerence I may speake it (said the Physitian) to tell the truth, and auoid flattery, I neuer saw a more misshapen nose so foule to sight.

Loe you now Madam (quoth the Knight) this is you that said my nose was as well, as hansome, and as comely a nose as any mans.

Alas sir (qd. she) I spake it (God wot) because you should
not grieue at it, nor take my words in ill part, neither did it
indeed become me to mislike of your nose.

All this we will quickly remedy, said the Phisitian, haue no
doubt: and with that, he very orderly prickt him in the nose,
but not in any veine whereby he might bleed: and presently
hauing a tricke finely to vnstop the quill, the blood ranne into
a bason in great abundance : and when the bladder was empty,
and the bason almost full, the Phisitian seemed to close the
10 veine, and asked him how he felt his nose, shewing the great
quantite of filthy blood which from thence he had taken.

The Knight beholding it with great wonder, said, he thought
that no man in the world had bin troubled with such abundance of corrupt bloud in his whole bodie, as lay in his mis-shapen
nose, and therewithall he began to touch and handle his nose,
saying that he felt it mightily asswaged. Immediately a glasse
was brought wherein he might behold himselfe.

Yea mary (qd. he) now I praise God, I see my nose is come into
some reasonable proportion, and I feele my selfe very well eased
20 of the burthen thereof; but if it continue thus, thats all.

I will warrant your worship (said the Phisitian) for euer being
troubled with the like againe.

Whereupon the Knight receiued great ioy, and the Doctor a
high reward.

How *Thomas* of *Reading* was murdered at his Hosts house of *Colebrooke*, who also had murdred many before him, and how their wickednesse was at length reuealed. CHAP. 11.

THomas of *Reading* hauing many occasions to come to
30 London, aswell about his own affaires, as also the Kings
businesse, being in a great office vnder his Maiestie, it chanced on
a time, that his Host and Hostesse of *Colebrooke*, who through
couetousnes had murdered many of the guests, and hauing every
time he came thither great store of his mony to lay vp, appointed
him to be the next fat pig that should be killed: For it is to
be vnderstood, that when they plotted the murder of any man,
this was alwaies their terme, the man to his wife, and the woman
to her husband : wife, there is now a fat pig to be had, if you
want one.

40 Whereupon she would answer thus, I pray you put him in the
hogstie till to-morrow.

This was, when any man came thither alone without others in
his company, and they saw he had great store of money.

This man should be then laid in the chamber right ouer the kitchin, which was a faire chamber, and better set out then any other in the house: the best bedstead therein, though it were little and low, yet was it most cunningly carued, and faire, to the eye, the feet whereof were fast naild to the chamber floore, in such sort, that it could not in any wise fall, the bed that lay therein was fast sowed to the sides of the bedstead: Moreouer, that part of the chamber whereupon this bed and bedsteed stood, was made in such sort, that by the pulling out of two yron pinnes below in the kitchin, it was to be let downe and taken vp by a draw bridge, or in manner of a trap doore: moreouer in the kitchin, directly vnder the place where this should fall, was a mighty great caldron, wherein they vsed to seethe their liquor when they went to brewing. Now, the men appointed for the slaughter, were laid into this bed, and in the dead time of the night, when they were sound a sleepe, by plucking out the foresaid yron pinnes, downe would the man fall out of his bed into the boyling caldron, and all the cloaths that were vpon him: where being suddenly scalded and drowned, he was neuer able to cry or speake one word.

Then had they a little ladder euer standing ready in the kitchin, by the which they presently mounted into the said chamber, and there closely take away the mans apparell, as also his money, in his male or capcase: and then lifting vp the said falling floore which hung by hinges, they made it fast as before.

The dead body would they take presently out of the caldron and throw it downe the riuer, which ran neere vnto their house, whereby they escaped all danger.

Now if in the morning any of the rest of the guests that had talkt with the murdered man ore eue, chanst to aske for him, as hauing occasion to ride the same way that he should haue done, the goodman would answere, that he tooke horse a good while before day, and that he himselfe did set him forward: the horse the goodman would also take out of the stable, & conuay him by a hay-barne of his, that stood from his house a mile or two, whereof himselfe did alwaies keepe the keies full charily, and when any hay was to be brought from thence, with his owne hands he would deliuer it; then before the horse should goe from thence, he would dismarke him: as if he ware a long taile, he would make him curtall; or else crop his eares, or cut his mane, or put out one of his eies; and by this meanes he kept himselfe vnknowne.

Now *Thomas* of *Reading,* as I said before, being markt, & kept for a fat pig, he was laid in the same chamber of death, but by reason *Gray* of *Gloucester* chanced also to come that night, he escaped scalding.

The next time he came, he was laid there againe, but before he fell aslepe, or was warme in his bed, one came riding thorow the

towne and cried piteously, that *London* was all on a fire, and that it
had burned downe *Thomas Beckets* house in *West cheape*, and
a great number more in the same street, and yet (quoth he) the
fire is not quencht.

Which tidings when *Thomas* of *Reading* heard, he was very
sorrowfull, for of the same *Becket* that day he had receiued a great
peece of money, and had left in his house many of his writings,
and some that appertained to the King also : therfore there was
no nay but he would ride backe againe to *London* presently, to see
10 how the matter stood ; thereupon making himselfe ready, departed
This crosse fortune caused his hoast to frowne, neuertheless the
next time (qd. he) will pay for all.

Notwithstanding God so wrought, that they were preuented the
likewise, by reason of a great fray that hapned in the house
betwixt a couple that fell out at dice, insomuch as the murderers
themselues were inforced to cal him vp, being a man in great
authority, that he might set the house in quietnes, out of the
which by meanes of this quarrell, they doubted to lose many
things.

20 Another time when he should haue beene laid in the same
place he fell so sicke, that he requested to haue some body to
watch with him, whereby also they could not bring their vile
purpose to passe. But hard it is to escape the ill fortunes wher-
vnto a man is allotted : for albeit that the next time that he came
to *London*, his horse stumbled and broke one of his legges as he
should ride homeward, yet hired he another to hasten his owne
death ; for there is no remedy but he should goe to *Colbrooke* that
night : but by the way he was heauy asleepe, that he could scant
keepe himselfe in the saddle ; and when he came neere vnto the
30 Towne, his nose burst out suddenly a bleeding.

Well, to his Inne he came, and so heauy was his heart that he
could eate no meat : his host and hostesse hearing he was so
melancholy, came vp to cheare him, saying, Iesus Master *Cole*,
what ayles you to night ? neuer did we see you thus sad before :
will it please you to haue a quart of burnt sacke ?

With a good will (quoth he) and would to God *Tom Doue* were
here, hee would surely make me merry, and we should lacke no
musicke : but I am sorry for the man with all my heart, that he is
come so farre behind hand : but alasse, so much can euery man
40 say, but what good doth it him ? No no, it is not words can
helpe a man in this case, the man had need of other reliefe then
so. Let me see : I haue but one child in the world and that is
my daughter, and halfe that I haue is hers, the other halfe my
wifes. What then ? shall I be good to no body but them ? In
conscience, my wealth is too much for a cupple to possesse, and
what is our Religion without charity ? And to whom is charity
more to be shewen, then to decayed housholders ?

Good my hoast lend me a pen and inke, and some paper, for

I will write a letter vnto the poore man straight; and something
I will giue him: That almes which a man bestowes with his
owne hands, he shal be sure to haue deliuered, and God knowes
how long I shall liue.

With that, his hostesse dissemblingly answered, saying: Doubt
not, Master *Cole*, you are like enough by the course of nature to
liue many yeares.

God knowes (quoth he) I neuer found my heart so heauy
before.

By this time pen, inke, and paper was brought, setting himselfe 10
in writing as followeth.

*IN the name of God, Amen, I bequeath my soule to God, and my
body to the ground, my goods equally betweene my wife* Elenor,
and Isabel, *my daughter. Item I giue to* Thomas Doue *of* Exeter
one hundred pounds, nay that is too little, I giue to Thomas Doue
*two hundred pounds in money, to be paid vnto him presently vpon his
demand thereof by my said wife and daughter.*

Ha, how say you hoast (qd. he) is not this well? I pray you
reade it.

His hoast looking thereon, said, why Master *Cole*, what haue 20
you written here? you said you would write a letter, but me thinks
you haue made a Will, what neede haue you to doe thus? thanks
be to God, you may liue many faire yeares.

Tis true (quoth *Cole*) if it please God, and I trust this writing
cannot shorten my daies, but let me see, haue I made a Will?
Now, I promise you, I did verily purpose to write a letter: notwithstanding, I haue written that that God put into my mind:
but looke once againe my host, is it not written there, that *Doue*
shall haue two hundred pounds, to be paid when he comes to
demand it?   30

Yes indeed (said his hoste).

Well then, all is well (said *Cole*) and it shall go as it is for me.
I will not bestow the new writing thereof any more.

Then folding it vp, he sealed it, desiring that his host would
send it to *Exceter*: he promised that he would, notwithstanding
Cole was not satisfied: but after some pause, he would needs hire
one to carry it. And so sitting downe sadly in his chaire againe,
vpon a sudden he burst forth a weeping; they demanding the
cause thereof, he spake as followeth:

No cause of these feares I know: but it comes now into my 40
minde (said *Cole*) when I set toward this my last iourney to
London, how my daughter tooke on, what a coyle she kept to
haue me stay: and I could not be rid of the little baggage a long
time, she did so hang about me, when her mother by violence
tooke her away, she cryed out most mainly, O my father, my
father, I shall neuer see him againe.

Alas, pretty soule (said his hoastesse) this was but meer kind-

nesse in the girle, and it seemeth she is very fond of you. But
alasse, why should you grieue at this? you must consider that it
was but childishnes.

I, it is indeed (said *Cole*) and with that he began to nod.

Then they asked him if he would go to bed.

No (said he) although I am heauy, I haue no mind to go to bed
at all.

With that certaine musitians of the towne came to the chamber,
and knowing Master *Cole* was there, drue out their instruments,
10 and very solemnly began to play.

This musicke comes very well (said *Cole*) and when he had
listned a while thereunto, he said, Methinks these instruments
sound like the ring of *S. Mary Oueries* belles, but the base
drownes all the rest: and in my eare it goes like a bell that rings
a forenoones knell, for Gods sake let them leaue off, and beare
them this simple reward.

The musitians being gone, his hoste asked if now it would
please him to go to bed; for (quoth he) it is welneare eleuen of
the clocke.

20 With that *Cole* beholding his host and hostesse earnestly, began
to start backe, saying, what aile you to looke so like pale death?
good Lord, what haue you done, that your hands are thus bloody?

What my hands (said his host)? Why, you may see they are
neither bloudy nor foule: either your eies doe greatly dazell, or
else fancies of a troubled minde do delude you.

Alas my hoste, you may see (said he) how weake my wits are,
I neuer had my head so idle before. Come, let me drinke once
more, and then I will to bed, and trouble you no longer.

With that he made himselfe vnready, and his hostesse was very
30 diligent to warme a kerchiffe, and put it about his head.

Good Lord (said he) I am not sicke, I praise God, but such an
alteration I find in my selfe as I neuer did before.

With that the scritch owle cried piteously, and anone after the
night rauen sate croking hard by his window.

Iesu haue mercy vpon me (quoth hee) what an ill fauoured cry
doe yonder carrion birds make, and therewithall he laid him
downe in his bed, from whence he neuer rose againe.

His host and hostesse, that all this while noted his troubled
mind, began to commune betwixt themselues thereof. And the
40 man said, he knew not what were best to be done. By my
consent (quoth he) the matter should passe, for I thinke it is
not best to meddle on him.

What man (quoth she) faint you now? haue you done so many
and doe you shrinke at this? Then shewing him a great deale of
gold which *Cole* had left with her, she said, Would it not grieue
a bodies heart to lose this? hang the old churle, what should he
doe liuing any longer? he hath too much, and we haue too little:
tut husband, let the thing be done, and then this is our owne.

Her wicked counsell was followed, and when they had listned at his chamber doore, they heard the man sound asleepe : All is safe (quoth they) and downe into the kitchin they goe, their seruants being all in bedde, and pulling out the yron pins, downe fell the bed, and the man dropt out into the boyling caldron. He being dead, they betwixt them cast his body into the riuer, his clothes they made away, and made all things as it should be : but when he came to the stable to conuey thence *Coles* horse, the stable doore being open, the horse had got loose, and with a part of the halter about his necke, and straw trusted vnder his 10 belly, as the ostlers had dressed him ore eue, he was gone out at the backe side, which led into a great field adioyning to the house, and so leaping diuers hedges, being a lustie stout horse, had got into a ground where a mare was grasing, with whom he kept such a coile, that they got into the high way, where one of the Towne meeting them, knew the mare, and brought her and the horse to the man that owd her.

In the meane space, the Musicians had beene at the Inne, and in requitall of their euenings gift, they intended to giue *Cole* some musicke in the morning. The goodman told them he 20 tooke horse before day : likewise there was a guest in the house that would haue bore him company to *Reading*, vnto whom the hoste also answered, that he himselfe set him vpon horsebacke, and that he went long agoe. Anone came the man that owed the mare, inquiring vp and downe, to know and if none of them missed a horse, who said no. At the last hee came to the signe of the Crane where *Cole* lay : and calling the hostlers he demanded of them if they lackt none, they said no :

Why then (said the man) I perceiue my mare is good for some-thing, for if I send her to field single, she will come home double : 30 thus it passed on all that day and the night following.

But the next day after, *Coles* wife musing that her husband came not home, sent one of her men on horse-backe, to see if he could meete him : and if (quoth she) you meet him not betwixt this and *Colebrooke*, aske for him at the Crane, but if you find him not there, then ride to *London* ; for I doubt he is either sicke, or else some mischance hath fallen vnto him.

The fellow did so, and asking for him at *Colebrooke*, they answered, he went homeward from thence such a day. The seruant musing what should be become of his Master, and 40 making much inquiry in the Towne for him : at length one told him of a horse that was found on the high way, and no man knew whence he came. He going to see the horse, knew him presently, and to the Crane he goes with him. The hoast of the house perceiuing this, was blancke, and that night fled secretly away. The fellow going vnto the Iustice desired his helpe : presently after word was brought that *Iarman* of the Crane was gone, then all the men said, he had sure made *Cole* away : and the musitians told what *Iarman* said to them, when they would haue giuen *Cole* musicke. Then the woman being apprehended & examined, confessed the truth. *Iarman* soone after was taken in *Windsor Forest.* He and his wife were both hangd, after they had laid open al these things before expressed. Also he confessed, that he being a Carpenter made that false falling floore, and how his wife deuised it. And how they had murdered by that means lx. persons. And yet notwithstanding all the money which they had gotten thereby, they prospered not, 10 but at their death were found in debt.

When the King heard of this murder, he was for the space of vii daies so sorrowfull and heauie, as he would not heare any sute, giuing also commandement, that the house should quite be consumed with fire, wherein *Cole* was murdred, and that no man should euer build vpon that cursed ground.

Coles substance at his death was exceeding great, hee had daily in his house an hundred men seruants and xl. Maids ; he maintained beside aboue two or three hundred people, spinners and carders, and a great many other housholders. His Wife 20 after neuer married, and at her death shee bestowed a mightie summe of money toward the maintaining of the new builded monastery. Her daughter was most richly married to a Gentleman of great worship, by whom she had many Children. And some say, that the riuer whereinto *Cole* was cast, did euer since carry the name of *Cole*, being called The riuer of *Cole*, and the Towne of *Colebrooke.*

How diuers of the Clothiers wiues went to the Churching of *Suttons* wife of *Salisbury*, and of their meriment. CHAP. 12.

30 SVttons wife of *Salisbury* which had lately bin deliuered of a sonne, against her going to Church, prepared great cheare : at what time *Simons* wife of *South-hampton* came thither, and so did diuers others of the Clothiers wiues, onely to make merry at this Churching feast : and whilest these Dames sat at the Table, *Crab, Weasell,* and *Wren,* waited on the boord, and as the old Prouerbe speaketh, Many women many words, so fell it out at that time : for there was such pratling that it passed : some talkt of their husbands frowardnes, some shewed their Maids sluttishnes, othersome deciphered the costlines of their gar-40 ments, some told many tales of their neighbors : and to be briefe, there was none of them but would haue talke for a whole day.

But when *Crab, Weasell,* and *Wren* saw this, they concluded betwixt themselues, that as oft as any of the women had a good bit of meate one their trenchers, they offering a cleane one, should catch that commodity, and so they did: but the women being busie in talke, marked it not, till at the last one found leisure to misse her meat: whereupon she said, that their boldnes exceeded their diligence.

Not so, forsooth (said *Weasell*) there is an hundred bolder than wee.

Name me one (said the woman) if you can.

A flea is bolder (quoth *Crabbe*).

How will you proue that (said the woman)?

Because (quoth he) they creepe vnder your coates, where we 10 dare not come, and now & then bite you by the buttocks as if they were brawne.

But what becomes of them (qd. the woman)? their sweet meat hath sowre sauce, and their lustines doth often cost them their liues, therefore take heed.

A good warning of a faire woman (said *Wren*) but I had not thought so fine a wit in a fat belly.

The women seeing their men so merry, said it was a signe there was good ale in the house.

Thats as fit for a Churching (quoth *Weasell*) as a cudgell for a 20 curst queane.

Thus with pleasant communication and merry quips they droue out the time, till the fruit and spice cakes were set on the boord: At what time one of them began to aske the other, if they heard not of the cruell murder of *Thomas* of *Reading*?

What (said the rest) is old *Cole* murdered? when, I pray you was the deede done?

The other answered, on Friday last.

O good Lord (said the women) how was it done, can you tell?

As report goes (said the other) he was rosted aliue. 30

O pitifull! was he roasted? Indeed I heard one say, a man was murdred at *London*, and that he was sodden at an Inholders house, and serued it to the guests in stead of porke.

No neighbor, it was not at *London* (said another); I heare say twas comming from *London*, at a place called *Colebrooke*, and it is reported for truth, that the Inholder made pies of him, and penny pasties, yea, and made his owne seruant eate a piece of him. But I pray you good neighbour, can you tell how it was knowne: some say, that a horse reuealed it.

Now by the masse (quoth *Grayes* wife) it was told one of 40 my neighbours, that a certaine horse did speake, and told great things.

That sounds like a lie (said one of them).

Why (said another) may not a horse speake, as well as *Balaams* asse?

It may be, but it is vnlikely (said the third). But where was the horse when he spake?

As some say (qd. she) he was in the field, and had broke out

of the stable, where he stood fast locked in mighty strong iron
fetters, which he burst in peeces, as they had beene strawes, and
broke downe the stable doore, and so got away.

The good man comming in at these speeches, asked what that
was they talkt of.

Marry (said his wife) wee heare that *Cole* of *Reading* is murdred :
I pray you is it true?

I (said *Sutton*) it is true, that vile villaine his hoast murdered
him, in whose house the man had spent many a pound.

10   But did they make pies of him (said his wife);

No, no (quoth her husband): he was scalded to death in a
boyling caldron, and afterward throwne into a running riuer that
is hard by.

But good husband, how was it knowne?

By his horse (quoth hee).

What, did he tell his Master was murthered? could the horse
speake English?

Iesus what a foolish woman are you (quoth he) to aske such
a question? But to end this, you are all heartily welcome, good
20 neighbors, and I am sorry you had no better cheere.

So with thanks the women departed.

Thus haue ye heard the diuers tales that will be spred abroad
of an euil deed.

How Duke *Robert* deceiued his keepers, and got from
    them: how he met faire *Margaret*, and in carrying
    her away was taken, for the which he had his eies
    put out. Chap. 13.

D
Vke *Robert*, hauing, as you heard, obtained the loue of faire
    Margaret, did now cast in his minde, how hee might delude
30 his Keepers, and carry her quite away. In the end he being
absolutely resolued what to doe, sent this letter vnto her, wherein
he requested, that she would be ready to meet him in the forrest,
betwixt *Cardiffe* and *Gloucester*.

The young Lady hauing secretly receiued his message, vnknown
to her Master or dame, in a morning betime made her ready
and got forth, walking to the appointed place, where her Loue
should meete her.

During her aboade there, and thinking long ere her loue came,
she entred into diuers passions, which indeed presayged some
40 disaster fortune to follow.

O my deare loue, said shee, how slacke art thou in performing
thy promise! why doe not thy deedes agree with thy inditing?
see these are thy wordes, Come, my deare *Margaret*, and with
Cupids swift wings flie to thy friend, be now as nimble in thy
footing, as the Camels of Bactria, that runne an hundred miles

a day, I will waite and stay for thee, so I stay not too long. There
is no Country like Austria for ambling horses, & to carry thee I
haue got one.

O my Loue (quoth she) here am I, but where art thou?
O why doest thou play the trewant with time, who like the wind
slides away vnseene? An ambling gennet of Spaine is too
slow to serue our turnes. A flying horse, for flying Louers
were most meete. And thus casting many lookes through the
Siluane shades, vp and downe to espie him, she thought euery
minute an houre, till she might see him, sometimes she would 10
wish her selfe a bird, that she might flie through the ayre to
meete him, or a pretty squirill to clime the highest tree to descry
his comming: but finding her wishes vaine, she began thus to
excuse him and perswaded herselfe, saying.

How much too blame am I, to finde fault with my friend?
Alasse, men that lacke their liberty, must come when they can,
not when they would, poore prisoners cannot doe what they
desire, and then why should I be so hastie? Therefore if
safely I may lay me down I will beguile vnquiet thoughts with
quiet sleepe: it is said that *Galino* breeds no Serpents, nor 20
doth *Englands* forrests nourish Beares or Lyons, therefore
without hurt I hope I may rest awile. Thus leauing faire
Margaret in a sweet slumber, we will returne to Duke *Robert*,
who had thus plotted his escape from his keepers.

Hauing liberty of the King to hawke and hunt, hee determined
on a day, as he should follow the chase, to leaue the hounds to
the Hart, and the hunters to their hornes, and being busie in their
sport, himselfe would flie, which he performed at that time when
he appointed *Margaret* to meete him, and so comming to the place,
his horse all on a water, and himself in a sweat, finding his loue 30
asleepe, he awaked her with a kisse, saying, Arise faire *Margaret*,
now comes the time wherein thou shalt be made a Queene: and
presently setting her on horsebacke he posted away.

Now when the keepers saw they had lost his company, and that
at the killing of the game, he was not present, they were among
themselues in such a mutinie, that they were ready one to stabbe
another.

It was thy fault (said one) that he thus escapt from vs, that
hadst more mind of thy pleasure, then of thy prisoner, and by this
meanes we are all vndone. 40

The other said as much to him, that he had thought he had
followed him in the chase: but leauing at last this contention, the
one posted vp to the King, while the others coasted vp and downe
the country to search for the Duke, who hauing kild his horse in
trauelling, was most vnhappily mette on foot with faire *Margaret*,
ere he could come to any towne, where he might for money haue
another. But when he spied his Keepers come to take him, he
desired *Margaret* to make shift for herselfe, and to seeke to

escape them.   But she being of a contrary mind, said, she would liue and die with him.

The Duke seeing himselfe ready to be surprised, drew out his sword, and said, he would buy his liberty with his life, before he would yeeld to be any more a prisoner; and thereupon began a great fight betwixt them, insomuch that the duke had killed two of them : but himselfe being sore wounded, and faint with ouer-much bleeding, at length fell downe, being not able any longer to stand : and by this means the good Duke was taken with his faire
10 loue, & both of them committed to prison.

But in the meane space, when *Grayes* wife had missed her Maide, and saw she was quite gone, she made great lamentation for her among her neighbors, for she loued her as dearly as any child that euer she bore of her owne body.   O *Margaret* (quoth she) what cause hadst thou thus to leaue me? if thou didst mis-like of any thing, why didst thou not tell me?   If thy wages were too little, I would haue mended it : If thy apparell had beene too simple, thou shouldst haue had better : If thy worke had bin too great, I would haue had helpe for thee.
20   Farewell my sweet *Meg*, the best seruant that euer came in any mans hause, many may I haue of thy name, but neuer any of thy nature, thy diligence is much, in thy hands I laid the whole gouernment of my house, and thereby eased my selfe of that care, which now will cumber me.

Heere she hath left me my keyes vnto my chests, but my comfort is gone with her presence, euery gentle word that she was wont to speake, comes now into my mind, her courteous behauiour shall I neuer forget : with how sweet and modest a countenance would she qualifie my ouer-hastie nature?   It repents
30 my heart that euer I spoke foule word vnto her.   O *Meg*, wert thou here againe, I would neuer chide thee more : but I was an vnworthy Dame for such a seruant : what will become of me now, if I should chance to be sicke, seeing shee is gone, that was wont to be both my Apoticary and Phisitian?

Well (quoth her neighbors) there is no remedy now, but to rest content, you shall one day heare of her doubt you not, and thinke this, that she was not so good, but you may get another as good, and therefore do not take it so heauily.

O neighbour, blame me not to grieue, seeing I haue lost so
40 great a iewell, and sure I am perswaded, that scant in a bodies life time, they shall meete with the like.   I protest, I would circuit *England* round about on my bare feete to meete with her againe.   O, my *Meg* was surely stole away from me, else would she not haue gone in such sort.

Her husband on the other side grieued as much, & rested not night nor day riding vp and downe to seeke her; but she, poore soule, is fast lockt vp in prison, and therefore cannot be met withall.

But when the King vnderstood of his brothers escape, hee was maruelous wroth, giuing great charge and commandement when he was taken, that both his eies should be put out and be kept in prison till his dying day; appointing also that the Maid should lose her life for presumption of louing him.

This matter being rumored ouer all *England*, it came to the eares of *Gray* and his wife, who hearing that *Margaret* also was there in prison appointed to die, the good aged woman neuer rested till she came to the Court, where kneeling before the King with many teares she besought his Maiestie to spare the Maidens 10 life, saying, Most royall King consider, I humbly beseech you, that the Duke your brother was able to intice any woman to his loue: much more a silly Maiden, especially promising her marriage, to make her a Lady, a Dutchesse, or a Queene, who would refuse such an offer, when at the instant they might get both a Princely husband and a high dignity? if death be a Louers guerdon, then what is due to hatred? I am in my heart perswaded, that had my poore *Margaret* thought it would haue bred your Highnes displeasure, she would neuer haue bought his loue so dear. Had your Grace made it knowen to your Commons, 20 that it was vnlawfull for any to marry the Duke your brother, who would haue attempted such an action? if she had wilfully disobeyed your Graces commandement, she might haue bin thought worthy of death; but seeing ignorantly she offended, I beseech your Grace to recall the sentence, and let me still enioy my seruant, for neuer will I rise, till your Maiestie haue granted my petition.

His Highnes, who was of nature mercifull, beholding the womans abundant teares, tooke pitie on her, and granted her suite: which being obtained, shee went home in all haste pos- 30 sible. And from thence, she with her husband taking their iourny to *Cardiffe* castle, they came at that very instant when the Maiden was led toward her death, who went in most ioyfull sort to the same, saying, that they were not worthie to be accounted true louers, that were not willing to die for loue: and so with a smiling countenance she passed on, as if she had eaten *Apium Risus*, which causeth a man to die laughing: but her dame *Gray* seeing her, fell about her necke, and with many kisses imbraced her, saying, Thou shalt not die my wench, but goe home with me; and for thy deliuery, behold here the Kings letters; and with that 40 she deliuered them vp to the gouernour of the Castle: who reading them found these words written: Wee pardon the maids life, and grant her libertie, but let her not passe, till she see her louers eies put out, which we wil haue you do in such sort, that not onely the sight may perish, but the eie continue faire, for which cause I haue sent downe Doctor *Piero*, that he may execute the same.

The gouernour of the Castle hauing read the Kings letter, said thus to the Maiden :   The Kings Maiesty hath pardoned thy life, and allowed thy libertie : but you must not passe before you see your louers eies put out.

O sir (said the Maiden) mistake not your selfe, they are my eies that must be put out, and not the Dukes : as his offence grew by my meanes, so I being guiltie, ought to receiue the punishment.

The Kings commandement must be fulfilled, said the gouernour : and therewithall D. *Robert* was brought forth, who hearing that he must lose his eies, said thus : the Noble mind is neuer 10 conquered by griefe, nor ouercome by mischance : but as the Hart reneweth his age by eating the serpent, so doth a man lengthen his life with deuouring sorrow : my eies haue offended the King, and they must be punished, my heart is in as great fault, why is not that killed ?

The Kings Maiesty (said the Gouernour) spares your life of mere loue, and onely is content to satisfie the Law with the losse of your eies, wherefore take in good part this punishment, and thinke you haue deserued greater then is granted.

With this *Margaret* cryed out, saying, O my deare loue, most 20 gentle Prince, well may you wish that I had neuer bin borne, who by seeing of me must lose your sight ; but happie should I count my selfe, if it so please the King, that I might redeeme thy eies with my life : or else, that being an equall offender, I might receiue equall punishment : hadst thou sustained this smart for some queene or princesse of high blood, it might with the more ease be borne, but to indure it for such a one as I, it must needs cause a treble griefe to be increased

Content thee faire *Margaret* (said the Duke) : for honor ought to be giuen to vertue, and not riches : for glory, honor, nobility, 30 and riches without vertue, are but clokes of maliciousnes. And now let me take my leaue of thy beauty, for neuer must I behold thy face : notwithstanding I account my eies well lost, in that, I do forgoe them for so peerelesse a paragon.   Now faire heauens farewell, the Sunne, Moone, and Starres shall I in this world neuer behold againe ; and farewell also the fruitfull earth ; well may I feele thee, but those poore windowes of my body are now denied to view thee any more : and though the world hath euer bin my foe, yet will I bid it farewell too, and farewell all my friends, whiles I live heare in this world, I must suppose to sleepe, 40 & wake when I come in heauen, where I hope to see you all againe.   Yet had it pleased the King, I had rather haue lost my life then my eies.   Life, why, what is it but a floure, a bubble in the water, a spanne long, and full of miserie : of such small account is life, that euery Souldier will sell it for sixe pence.   And trust me I doe now detest life, worse then a goat doth hate Basill.

With that the Doctor prepared his instrument, and being ready to set to the Dukes eies, he said, O stay, Master Doctor, till I haue conueyed my Loues countenance downe into my heart: Come hither my sweet, and let me giue thee my last kisse, while mine eies may direct me to thy cherry lips. Then imbracing her in his armes, he said, O that I might giue thee a kisse of xx yeares long, and to satisfie my greedie eies with thy faire sight: yet it doth somewhat content me, because thou art present at my punishment, that I may hold thee by the hand, to comfort my heart, at the sudden pricke of my eie.

This being said, the Doctor performed his duty, and so put out the christall sight: at what time D. *Robert* started vp and with a most manly courage said, I must thanke his Maiestie, that though hee depriueth me of my sight, yet he leaueth me eies to weepe for my sinnes.

But so soone as *Margaret* beheld the deed, she fell downe in a swoune, and much adoe her dame had to recouer her life: which when the Duke vnderstood, hee was wondrous woe, groaping for her with his bleeding eies, saying O where is my Loue? for Gods sake haue regard to her. And I pray you most heartily, good goodwife *Gray*, let her haue this fauour for my sake, that she may be vsed kindly. And with that the Keepers led him into the Castle, and *Margaret* was carried away wondrous sicke and ill: but her dame was most tender ouer her; and would suffer her to lacke nothing. When she was somewhat well recouered, her Dame *Gray* set her on horsebacke: and at her comming to *Gloucester*, there was no small ioy.

How *Thomas Doue* being fallen to decay, was forsaken of his friends, and despised of his seruants: and how in the end he was raised againe through the liberality of the Clothiers. CHAP. 14.

SVch as seeke the pleasure of the world, follow a shadow wherein is no substance: and as the adder *Aspis* tickleth a man to death, so doth vaine pleasure flatter vs, till it makes vs forget God, and consume our substance, as by *Tom Doue* it is apparant, who had through a free heart, and a liberall minde wasted his wealth; and looke how his goods consumed, so his friends fled from him: And albeit he had beene of great ability, and thereby done good vnto many, yet no man regarded him in his pouerty, but casting a scornefull countenance vpon him, they passed by him with slender salutation: neither wold any of his former acquaintance do him good, or pleasure him the value of a farthing; his former friendship done to them was quite forgot, and he made of as much account, as *Iob* when he sate on the dunghill.

Now, when his wicked seruants saw him in this disgrace with the world, they on the other side began to disdaine him. Notwithstanding that hee (to his great cost) had long time brought them vp, yet did they nothing regard it, but behind his backe in most scornefull sort derided him, and both in their words and actions greatly abuse him, reuerence they would do none vnto him, but when they spake, it was in such malapert sort, as would grieue an honest mind to heare it.

At last it came to passe, that breaking out into meere contempt, they said they would stay no longer with him, and that it was a great discredit for them, to serue a person so beggarly: 10 whereupon they thought it conuenient to seeke for their benefits elsewhere. When the distressed man found the matter so plaine being in great griefe, he spake thus vnto them:

Now do I find, to my sorrow, the smal trust that is in this false world. Why, my Masters (quoth he) haue you so much forgotten my former prosperity, that you nothing regard my present necessity? in your wants I forsooke you not, in your sicknesse I left you not, nor despised you in your great pouerty: it is not vnknowne, though you doe not consider it, that I tooke some of you vp in the high way, othersom from your needy 20 parents, and brought the rest from meere beggery to a house of bounty; where from paltrie boies, I brought you vp to mans state, and haue, to my great cost, taught you a trade, whereby you may liue like men. And in requitall of all my courtesie, cost & good will, will you now on a sudden forsake me? Is this the best recompence that you can find your hearts to yeeld me?

This is far from the minds of honest seruants. The fierce Lion is kind to those that doe him good: plucke but one thorne out of his foote, and for the same he will shew manifold fauors. The wilde Bull will not ouerthrow his Dam: and the very 30 Dragons are dutefull to their nourishers. Bee better aduised and call to mind, I beseech you, that I haue not pluckt a thorn out of your feete, but drawne your whole bodies out of perils, and when you had no meanes to helpe your selues, I only was your support, and he, that when all other forsooke you, did comfort you in all your extremities.

And what of all this (quoth one of them)? because you tooke vs vp poore, doth it therefore follow, that we must be your slaues? We are young men, and for our part, we are no further to regard your profit, then it may stand with our preferment: 40 Why should we lose our benefit to pleasure you? if you taught vs our trade, and brought vs vp from boies to men, you had our seruice for it, whereby you made no small benefit, if you had as well vsed it, as we got it. But if you be poore, you may thanke your selfe, being a iust scourge for your prodigalitie, and is my opinion plaine, that to stay with you, is the next way to make vs like you, neither able to helpe our selues, nor our friends: therfore in briefe; come pay me my wages, for I will not stay, let the rest doe as they will, for I am resolued.

Wel (said his Master) if needs thou wilt be gone, here is part of thy wages in hand, and the rest as soone as God sends it, thou shalt haue it : and with that, turning to the rest, he said, Let me yet intreat you to stay, and leaue me not altogether destitute of helpe : by your labours must I liue, and without you I know not what to doe. Consider therefore my need, and regard my great charge. And if for my sake you will do nothing, take compassion on my poore Children ; stay my sliding foote, and let me not vtterly fall, through your flying from me.

Tush (quoth they) what do you talke to vs? we can haue 10 better wages, and serue a man of credit, where our fare shal be far better, and our gaines greater : therfore the world might count vs right coxcomes, if we should forsake our profit, to pleasure you : therefore adieu, God send you more mony, for you are like to haue no more men : and thus they departed.

When they were gone, within a while after they met one with another, saying, What cheare? are you all come away :

In faith I, what should we doe else (quoth they) : but hear'st thou sirra, hast thou got thy wages?

Not yet (saith the other) but I shall haue it, and that is as good, 20 tis but x shillings.

Saist thou so (said he) now I see thou art one of God Almighties ideots :

Why so (said the other)?

Because (quoth he) thou wilt be fed with shales : but ile tell thee one thing, twere better for thee quickly to arrest him, lest some other doing it before, and there be nothing left to pay thy debt : hold thy peace, faire words make fooles faine, and it is an old saying, One bird in hand is worth two in bush : if thou dost not arrest him presently, I will not giue thee two pence for thy 30 x. shillings.

How shall I come by him, quoth the other?

Giue me but two pots of ale, and ile betray him (said he).

So they being agreed, this smooth-fac'd *Iudas* comes to his late Master, and told him that a friend of his at the doore would speake with him. The vnmistrusting man thinking no euill, went to the doore where presently an Officer arrested him at his mans suite.

The poore man seeing this, being strucken into a sudden sorrow, in the griefe of his heart spake to this effect : Ah thou 40 lewd fellow, art thou the first man that seekes to augment my miserie? Haue I thus long giuen thee bread, to breed my ouer-throw? and nourish thee in thy need, to worke my destruction? Full little did I thinke, when thou so often diddest dip thy false fingers in my dish, that I gaue food to my chiefest foe : but what booteth complaints in these extreames? go wife (quoth he) vnto my neighbours, and see if thou canst get any of them to be my baile.

But in vaine was her paines spent. Then he sent to his
kinsfolkes, and they denied him : to his brother, and he would
not come at him, so that there was no shift, but to prison he
must : but as he was going, a messenger met him with a letter
from Master *Cole*, wherein as you heard, he had promised him
two hundred pounds : which when the poore man read, he
greatly reioyced, and shewing the same to the officer, he was
content to take his owne worde. Whereupon *Tom Doue* went
presently to *Reading*, where at his comming, he found all the
10 rest of the Clothiers, lamenting *Coles* vntimely death ; where
the wofull widdow paid him the money, by which deed all the
rest of the Clothiers were induced to doe something for *Doue*.
And thereupon one gaue him ten pounds, another twenty,
another thirty pounds, to begin the world anew : and by this
meanes (together with the blessing of God) he grew into greater
credit then euer he was before. And riches being thus come
vpon him, his former friendes came fawning vnto him and when
he had no neede of them, then euery one was ready to proffer
him kindnesse. His wicked seruants also that disdained him in
20 his distresse, were after glad to come creeping vnto him, intreating with cappe and knee for his fauour and friendship. And
albeit he seemed to forgiue their trespasses done against him,
yet he would often say, he would neuer trust them for a straw.

And thus he euer after liued in great wealth and prosperitie,
doing much good to the poore, and at his death, left to his
children great lands.

How faire *Margaret* made her estate and high birth
knowne to her Master and Dame: and for the intire
loue she bore to Duke *Robert*, made a vowe neuer to
30   marry, but became a Nun in the Abbey at *Glocester*.
CHAP. 15.

A Fter faire *Margaret* was come againe to Glocester neuer did
she behold the cleare day, but with a weeping eie : and so
great was the sorrow which she conceiued, for the losse of Duke
Robert her faithfull Louer, that she vtterly despised all the
pleasures of this life, and at last bewrayed her selfe in this sort
vnto her Dame :

O my good Master and Dame, too long haue I dissembled my
parentage from you, whom the froward destinies do pursue to
40 deserued punishment. The wofull daughter am I of the vnhappy Earle of *Shrewsbury*, who euer since his banishment,
haue done nothing but drawne mischaunce after mee : wherefore let me intreat you (deare Master and Dame) to haue your
good wils, to spend the remnant of my life in some blessed
Monasterie.

When *Gray* and his wife heard this, they wondred greatly, as well at her birth, as at her strange demaund. Whereupon her Dame knew not how to call her, whether Maiden or Madam, but said, O good Lord, are you a Lady, and I know it not? I am sory that I knew it not before.

But when the folkes of the house heard that *Margaret* was a Lady, there was no small alteration : and moreouer her Dame said, that she had thought to haue had a match between her and her son : and by many perswasions did seeke to withdraw her from being a Nun, saying in this manner : What *Margaret*, thou 10 art young and faire, the world (no doubt) hath better fortune for thee, whereby thou maist leaue an honourable issue behind thee, in whom thou maist liue after death.

These and many other reasons did they alleadge vnto her, but all in vaine : she making this reply, Who knowes not that this world giueth the pleasure of an houre, but the sorrow of many daies? for it paieth euer that which it promiseth, which is nothing els but continuall trouble & vexation of the minde. Do you think, if I had the offer and choice of the mightiest princes of Christendom, that I could match my selfe better 20 then to my Lord Iesus? No, no, he is my husband, to whom I yeeld my selfe both body and soule, giuing to him my heart, my loue and my most firme affection : I haue ouerlong loued this vile world : therefore I beseech you farther disswade me not.

When her friendes by no meanes could alter her opinion, the matter was made knowne to his Maiestie, who against the time that she should be receiued into the Monasterie, came to *Gloucester* with most part of his Nobilitie, to honour her action with his princely presence.

All things being therefore prepared, the young Lady was in 30 most princely wise attired in a gowne of pure white sattin, her kirtle of the same, embrodered with gold about the skirts, in most curious sort, her head was garnished with gold, pearles, and precious stones, hauing her hair like thrids of burnisht gold, hanging downe behind in manner of a princely bride : about her yuory necke iewels of inestimable price were hung, and her handwreasts were compassed about with bracelets of bright-shining Diamonds.

The streets thorow the which she should passe, were pleasantly deckt with greene oaken boughs. Then came the yong Lady 40 most like an heauenly Angell out of her Masters house, at what time all the bels in *Gloucester* were solemnly rung : she being led betwixt the Kings Maiestie, hauing on his royall robes, and im-periall crown, and the chiefe Bishop wearing his Miter, in a Cope of cloth of gold, ouer her head a Canopy of white silke, fringed about in princely manner : before her went an hundred Priests singing, and after her all the chiefe Ladies of the Land : then all the wiues and Maidens of *Gloucester* followed, with an innumerable sort of people on euery side standing to behold her. In this sort she passed on to the Cathedrall Church, where she was brought to the Nunry gate.

The Lady Abbesse receiued her: where the beautiful Maiden kneeling downe, made her prayer in sight of all the people: then with her owne hands she vndid her virgins faire gowne, and tooke it off, and gaue it away to the poore: after that, her kirtle, then her iewels, bracelets and rings, saying, Farewell the pride & vanity of this world. The ornaments of her head 10 were the next she gaue away: and then was she ledde on one side, where she was stripped, and in stead of her smocke of soft silke, had a smocke of rough haire put vpon her.

Then came one with a paire of sheares, and cut off her golden-coloured lockes, and with dust and ashes all bestrewed her head and face. Which being done, she was brought againe into the peoples sight barefoot & bareleg'd, to whom she said: Now farewell the world, farewell the pleasures of this life, farewell my Lord the King, and to the Dukes sweet loue farewell, now shall my eies weepe for my former transgressions, and no more shall 20 my tongue talke of vanity; farewell my good Master and Dame, and farewell all good people.

With which words she was taken away, and neuer after seene abroad. When Duke *Robert* heard thereof, he desired that at his death, his body might be buried in *Glocester*: in that Towne (quoth he) where first my cleare eies beheld the heauenly beauty of my loue, and where for my sake shee forsooke the world: which was performed accordingly.

The King also at his death requested to be buried at *Reading*, for the great loue he bare to that place, among those Clothiers, 30 who liuing were his hearts comfort. *Gray* dying wondrous wealthy, gaue land to the Monasterie whereinto *Margaret* was taken. *William Fitzallen* also dyed a most rich man, hauing builded many houses for the poore, whose sonne *Henry* after was the first Maior that was euer in *London*.

Sutton of *Salisbury* did also at his death much good, and gaue an hundred li. to be yeerely lent to poore weauers of the Towne, to the worlds end. *Simon* of *South-hampton* gaue a most bounteous gift towards the building of a Monastery at *Winchester*. *Hodgkins* of *Hallifax* did also great good, and so did 40 *Cutbert* of *Kendall*, who had married xxiii. couples out of his owne house, giuing each of them x.li. to beginne the world withall. *Martin Briam* of *Manchester* gaue toward the building of a free-schoole in *Manchester*, a great masse of money.

And thus (gentle Reader) haue I finished my storie of these worthy men, desiring thee to take my paines in good part, which will incourage me to greater matters, perceiuing this curteously accepted.

FINIS.

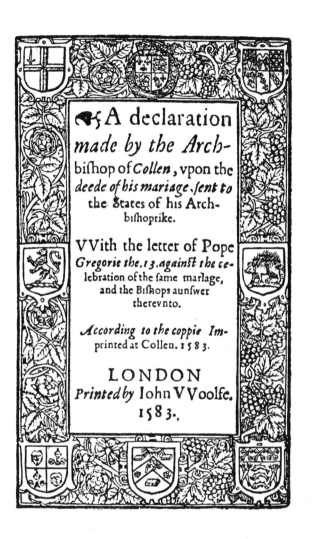

❧A declaration
made by the Arch-
biſhop of *Collen*, vpon the
deede of his mariage, ſent to
the States of his Arch-
biſhoprike.

VVith the letter of Pope
Gregorie the.13.against the ce-
lebration of the ſame marlage,
and the Biſhops aunſwer
therevnto.

According to the coppie Imprinted at Collen. 1 5 8 3.

LONDON
Printed by Iohn VVoolfe.
1 5 8 3.

¶ To the right reuerend Father in God

Iohn, *Bishoppe of London*, Thomas Delone,
wisheth increase of grace, and continuall happinesse, both of body and soulè.

IT is not vnknowne to the learned, nor of the wise forgotten,
(right reuerend Father) in what miserable seruitude, intollerable
tormentes, heauines of heart, and griefe of conscience, the godlie
hath from time to time continued vnder the tyranny of superstitious
Popes, and Prelates of *Rome*, whose intollerable pride is of the
Lord detested, and of all christian people abhorred, through whose 10
hipocrisie the world hath been so long deceaued, & many
thousand soules drawne from the truth, to the abhominable
seruice of idolatry, forsaking the lawes and commaundements of
God, to followe the vanities & traditions of men. Neuerthelesse,
they are not ashamed most impudently to challenge to themselues
the name and title of Catholiques and the seruants of Christ, &
yet treadeth his word vnder feete, despising his holy ordinances
and institutions, and as it were in despite of his glory, follow the
works of their owne imaginations. But after the world had of
long time beene blinded, by the notable dissimulation of this 20
deceauing church, the Lord of his mercy and loue, sending the
light of his holy worde, for the reliefe of his afflicted flocke,
plainly discouered their hipocrisie, and their filthines to all flesh.
Wherby it is come to passe that many worthy personages, lately
liuing in darknes and ignorance, is now turned to the trueth, with
most earnest repentance of their former life. And among the rest,
through the great mercy and grace of God, this worthy Prince, &
bishop of *Collen*, *Ghebbard*, whose hart being opened, and his
eyes cleared, hath most effectually showne the fruites of his
vnfained repentance, and hauing made declaration therof through- 30
out his dominions and iurisdictions, hath abolished the abhominable masse, and in steed thereof planted the euerlasting & glorious
Gospel of Christ, to the great comfort of many grieued and
wounded consciences. Which when the Pope perceiued & knew
with great flattery and adulation, he sought to withdraw him from
this most godly & christian enterprise, charging him with the othe
he made to the church Apostolique, & with his duty towards God,
which he both by scripture, but specially by their owne lawes,
counsell, & decrees, doth manifestly defend, & by the same
approue, that he hath done nothing against his othe or duty in 40
any respect : and the rather dooth he reproue them by their owne

aucthoritie, for as much as the same is the greatest confutation that maye be against them. And because the same was done by a worthy person of noble race and parentage, and a bishop by office & calling, I thought none more meete for the patron of such a specialty, then your Lordship, vnto whome I owe all duty & reuerence, who for the good will borne to your Lordshippe, hath dedicated vnto you this simple translation, faithfully & iustlie done according to the coppy. Trusting you will accept the same according to the worthines therof, and be a defence against all
10 that shall seeme to mislike of the matter : and in so doing, you shall binde me for euer at your commaund, vnto whome I wish continual prosperity in this present life, & in the world to come ioyes euerlasting.

Your Lordships most humble at commaund,

Thomas Deloney.

¶ *A Christian declaration touching the*
Religion which the *right reuerend Prince, the*
Lord Ghebbard, chosen, and confirmed Arch-
bishop of *Collen*, Elector of the Empire, and
Chancelor for the Prouince of *Italie*, Duke of
Westphalie and *Enghern*, and proclaimed
throughout his dominions, the 17.
daye of *Ianuarie*. 1583.

WE *Ghebbard*, by the grace of God elected, and confirmed
Archbishop of *Collen*, Chancellor for the prouince of *Italie*, 10
Elector of the Empire, Duke of *Westphalie, Enghern*, &c. to yᵉ
Estates, Earles, Gentlemen, Citizens, & subiects, of our Arch-
bishoprike in generall, and to euerie one particular, and to all
other vnder our obedience. Know you by this present, all aboue
named, and euerie of you, as we neuer had nothing more in
minde, since it pleased God to call vs to the estate & office of
this our Archbishoppe, by a lawfull election (which yet we also
haue) then the safegard and defence of this Archbishop sea and
electorshippe, committed vnto vs by God, and likewise of *Germanie*,
one part of vs, principally in that which concerneth the glorie of 20
God : and hauing had most humble supplications & requests,
made vnto vs by some of the Estates and Nobles of our dominions,
ioyned with earnest sute of the most noblest Estates of this great
and mightie Empire, to haue the Gospell publiquely preached,
and the Sacramentes administred in all places of our dominions :
as it is ordained and appointed by the word of God. Following
the articles, and confession of *Auspourg*, and the christian exposition thereof, according to the will of God, which is that Iesus
Christ his sonne, should of vs be hearkened vnto, and his commaundementes obserued and kept : that all Princes and Magistrates 30
of this world, might open their gates to the king of glory, that
thereby we may learne to knowe our duety in the charge to vs
committed, knowing there is no excuse for vs, at the last day,
when Christ shall come in iudgement : what time we must render
account of the charge and office wherein he hath placed vs. For
if by vs the way of saluation should be stopt toward our subiectes,
being nothing ignorant thereof, God which is a iust and feuere
Iudge, vnto whose will and commaundement we are all bound to
obey (& that without dissimulation) would not see it vnreuenged.
We for these causes, vnderstanding the humble peticions of 40
our sayd States and subiectes, are determined no longer to deferre

the graunt of their iust and rightfull request, hauing had the
aduise of our Lords and counsayle, and after great deliberation
we haue permitted, to our aforesayd subiects, vnder the dominion
of our Archbishop sea, of what state or condition soeuer, not
only the libertie of their conscience (always agreeing to the word
of GOD) but also assuraunce by this our present ordinaunce, and
by vertue therof, that they shall not be grieued, molested, or
troubled in their personnes, dignities, honors, or goods, by any
gouernors, Iustices, or other inferiour magistrates, whatsoeuer.
10 For the profession of their faith, conscience, & rule of Religion,
being according to Gods word & the confession of *Auspurg*.
Graunting freely to al prelats, Earles, Lords, Cities, & towns, w^t
all other our commons & subiects vnder our Archbishop sea, &
Electorship, ful libertie to vse publique preaching in all parts of
our dominion, & to exercise the administration of the holy Sacraments, as it is ordained by the writings of the Apostles & Prophets,
folowing ye Christian exposition of *Auspurg*, & notwithstanding
all impeachments of our Lieutenants and Magistrates, or other
persons whatsoeuer : assuring for the same (as it is the duty and
20 office of a christian Prince) of all and euerie vnder our dominion
and iurisdiction, to defende and maintaine them through the helpe
and grace of GOD, being certainly perswaded, that his almightie
power hath beene the onely direction of this our christian enterprise, and that he will defend his glory and holy worde, against
all the gates of hell.

Moreouer we protest before the maiestie of almightie God, which
is the searcher of the hearts and raines, that we haue not taken in
hand this godlie and christian enterprise, moued by ambition or
desire of honour, or any other thing to our particuler profit and
30 commoditie : but for the glorie of Christe Iesus our onely sauiour
and redeemer, and the aduancement of his holy word, and for the
eternall felicitie and saluation of our subiectes, which he hath
giuen vs in charge.   Neither haue we done it to rayse discord and
discention in the common wealth, but rather to set and establish
one christian order, in the Churches and Schooles of this countrey,
as it is thought conuenient, by the counsayle and aduise of the
principall of our Estates : minding to take delyberation and aduise
vpon the reformation of the Churches and Schooles of our sayd
Archbishop sea, & Electorship, at the first assembling of our
40 States & Lordes, as soone as oportunitie shall serue.   Admonishing the while all those vnder the obedience of our foresayd Elector,
which shall be moued to vnbrace and follow the religion established
at *Auspourg*, and the expositions of the same, agreeing to the worde
of God, behauing themselues in all modesty, as it becommeth all
such as are led by true christian zeale.   Forbidding them expresly,
that they shall doo no wrong nor iniury to any in deede, or in
wordes, to the ende that euerie one of them maye liue quietly
and peaceably one with an other.

And for the perticular safegarde of our person, if it come to passe by the will of God, that we should ioyne our selues in mariage, to the end that none might take occasion to blame vs, as doing the same against our duety, seeking thereby some perticular profite or commodity, or that our intent were, to leaue to our heires some aduantage, to the preiudice of our sayd Archbishop sea, or Electorship, and to gratifie the same against all reason or honestie. We protest by this our publique writing, and before the eternall & euerliuing God, that the same was neuer our purpose or intent : that is to say, to drawe vnto our heires, our sayd Archbishop sea, or to bring them to any right of the same succession, or for any other perticular profite to their commoditie.

And for this cause we will haue it openly declared, by the publication, of this our present ordinaunce, that whosoeuer shall hereafter come, the election ought to remaine at libertie, vnto the consent of ye rest of our most noble Electors (as heretofore it hath beene) and after our decease, to be resigned without force. And for this cause, all and euerie of our subiectes and other personnes vnder the obedience of our Archbishop and Electorship, shall vnderstand, that they are not held, or bound to owe any obedience, or in any respect to reuerence, any man whatsoeuer (as their true and rightfull Lord) tyll such time, as by the consent and councell of our Electors, the Prince which shall succeed, be lawfullie and rightfullie chosen. And that they shall not acknowledge, or take for their Prince, any that shall enterprise to take it in hand, without the ordinarie and lawfull election of our aforesayde Electors, and the expresse declaration of him which shall succeede, by their aucthoritie : as it hath beene obserued by long and auncient custome (notwithstanding any disposition heretofore made by vs, or any other preposed) against this our present ordinaunce : but without regard therof, we vtterly at this present, and for the time to come, declare them of no effect. Abrogated and abolished them in the straitest manner and forme that maye be, being ready at all times to conferre, and take more deliberation vpon the same, with our aforesayde Electors and States of our prouince, making them such confirmation and assuraunce of this our present promise, in such maner that no daunger, nor feare, or other damageable enterprise maye come or happen, for any such matter by vs, or by our heires. Therefore, we charge and commaund, all and euerie of our Lordes, gouernors, magistrates, Iudges, Treasurers, Receauers, Consulles, Citizens, commons, and all in generall, diligently, and straitly, to obserue this our present commaund, that euerie one may be maintained according therevnto. And that they may neither hurt, or doo iniurie to any, nor they of any, be iniuried or molested, for whosoeuer shall herein be found faultie, shall incurre our indignation and displeasure, and shall not escape most grieuous punishment : for this is the truth

of our last charge and commaundement.   In witnesse whereof, we
haue published, and imprinted, and sealed with our seale, this our
prefent declaration, causing it to be caried into all partes and
places of our dominions, vnto such, as shall make it known to all.
Giuen at our Citie of *Bonne* the .16. daye of *Ianuarie* in the yeere
of our Lord. 1583.

¶ Pope *Gregorie* the 13. to our right
reuerend and beloued brother, *Ghebbard*
Archbishop of *Collen*, Prince, and
Elector of the Empire.

Right reuerend & beloued brother, the great & woorthy personage, proceeding from the Noble house of *Truchces*, your
auncient & honorable progenitors, as well in auncient time, as of
fresher memorie, hath left vs sufficient witnes of the worthines
thereof, and nobilitie of their blood : whose affection and constancie, hath alwaies beene manifestlie declared towardes the
catholique faith, but principallie, by Cardinall *Augustus,* which
held the first seate hereof, vnder whose discipline you haue beene
most religiouslie and holilie brought vp, as it was conuenient for
ye holie Church of *Rome,* in such manner as there was no small
hope conceaued of you, trusting that you will shew your selfe a
person worthy so noble a race, by the like instruction : from
whence hath growne the fatherly good will, which hitherto we
haue borne vnto you : which we haue not onely since that time
entertained, but also in like manner augmented, by the meanes of
the good report of honorable personages : which promised vnto vs
all things with you most excellent & iust.   After it came to passe,
that you were elected by the charter of *Collen,* to the dignitie &
Archbishop sea of this church, and although that election was
disturbed by sundrie & manifold difficulties, in such sort that it
was not onlie stronglie withstoode, but in a maner vanquished &
made vaine.   Neuerthelesse, we vsed such benignitie towards you,
that all impeachmentes reiected, we approued and allowed the
iudgement and election, made by the same charter for you.
Increasing the force and vertue of our Apostolique confirmation :
by reason whereof we are persuaded, that there is none which
ought to beare greater reuerence to the holie seate of *Rome,* nor
that ought to be a greater obseruer of the ecclesiasticall discipline,
then you, hoping that we should haue had great helpe, through your
constancie & fidelitie.   But it doth greatly displease vs, and
merueilously grieue vs, that our hope therein is not only weakned
and made lesse, but also vtterly lost.   And further, we vnderstand

from day to day, by the letters of many, and the report of diuerse, such thinges of you, so vnworthy the dignitie & degree wherein you are, that without great shame, we are not able to expresse it. And although verilie we haue oftentimes refused to beleeue such vnworthy reportes, yet the daylie clamor hath constrained vs greatlie to doubte thereof, being afraid of your fall, which now we wil no longer dissemble, wherfore we doo admonishe you, that you would haue a regard and a foresight to your honour and saluation (while it is time) and if possible you haue gone any further, then reason required, speedilie withdraw your selfe, that those things 10 which heretofore hath been declared of you, may be proued false (which is our onlie desire) & that you will openly manifest your mind & ful intent, inwardlie conceiued in your hart: to ye end, that your good name, princelie parentage, & the ecclesiasticall order, be not by your means for euer stained, w^t ignominius reproch, by ye aduersaries of our honor.

Againe, consider your duty towards God, which hath raised you to the dignitie and degree of the sea Apostolique, which you should cherish with singuler affection and fauour, and for the same it is that you ought to spend your blood in all christian profession: 20 For by how much the more you are of hie calling, and honourable estate, by so much the more is your fault greater, then any others, when you fall from any parte of your duety. And by so much the more, wil your fault be greater, as you were of honour and dignitie, in the church of God, and in great aucthoritie with the Princes of the Empire. Consider then what troubles and daungers proceedeth from such now remoouings of thinges, and how heedfull the prudent and godlie man ought to be, from hazarding so lightly his honour, state, dignitie, and his soule, whereof there hath been so many straunge and wonderfull examples in our time, which 30 may make vs to be better aduised in our dealings, but if we haue possible suffered somewhat to much in former time, attribute the same to our affection towards you, and to the desire we haue had of your honor and dignitie. Neither doo we any thing doubt, but that this our fatherly kindnes, shall be receaued of you with that effect which it ought to be, for many good reasons and iust causes: and that you will not forgette to shew due reuerence towardes this holy seate, that we maye acknowledge you, for our deere and beloued sonne, as heretofore we haue done, which wil be an occasion to vs greatly to reioyce: and because we haue not thought 40 it sufficient to send our letters onely, we haue sent our reuerend Brother, the Archbishop of *Treues*, to take his iourney towardes you, to conferre more at large, of these our affaires, who shall more cleerelye discouer vnto you our will, counsayle, and intent, to whome we are assured that you will giue both faith and credite. Giuen at *Rome*, at saint *Peters* in the yeere of our Lord 1582. the 17. day of *December*, and in the 11. yeere of our Pontificalitie.

Io. Baptista Canobius.

To Pope *Gregorie* the .13. *Ghebbard*
Archbishop of Collen, *Prince, and*
Elector of the Empire, sendeth greeting.

I Haue vnderstood by your letter, your fatherlie affection, and
worthinesse of such a Prelate, but in this principally, that you
will not lightlie giue place, to vntrue tales, neither faith to the
euill reports spread abroad of my actions and deeds. For if it
were sufficient to accuse, who should be in these corrupted dayes
excused, wherein the most godliest men, are assailed with enuie :
10 and what is he that can, defend himselfe against the conspiracies
of euil willers : I acknowledge you as a good father, exhorting
me to perseuere in the faith, integrete good discipline, and
obedience vnto the Chatholique, Apostolique, and true beleeuing
Church. Giuing me aduertisement of the great and manifold
daungers, falling on those, which are desirous of nouelties, which
folowing their disordinate lustes and affections, are drawne from
the company of the Apostolique church. Wherefore my duty is
to accept of your charitable & holie admonitions, knowing that
which is said by *Salomon,* that he which refuseth discipline, hath
20 no regarde of his owne soule : but he that harkeneth to correction,
shall obtaine knowledge. I must needes confesse, that I haue
beene ouer slacke and negligent in thinges appertaining to the
saluation of my soule, the rest of my conscience, and the duetie
I owe to the glorie of God, and the dignitie of the Church.
But your letters hath serued me as a spurre, pricking me
forward, & greatly prouoking me, y^t all dissimulation laid aside,
& all superstition by me reiected, I am minded openly to declare
(euen as you haue admonished me) y^t which I haue conceaued in
my heart, & considering the faith I owe vnto GOD, that hath
30 called me to this hie degree, that which I owe to the church
Apostolique, to my countrey, & the publique wealth thereof and
also to my selfe, knowing the saying of that great and holie man
Augustine to be true, and worthy to be had in memory, that there
is none that doth more harme to the flocke of Christ then such as
counterfeiteth the lambe in the roome and office of the ministerie,
the same is cited 83. distinction, the second cannon. For as
much then I am come to the age, wherein I am able without the
aduice of others to gouern my selfe, and by the onely will of our
Lord Iesus Christe, which hath vouchsaued to call me to the
40 great charge of an Archbishop : and as it is a thing proper to the
nature of a christian man, to inquire and followe after the trueth,
I am setled in the furtheraunce of this good worke, without
musing at all, on any custome or humaine authority : finding by
the holie scriptures, and among the ecclesiasticall histories, y^t this

which we haue commaunded to be done, becommeth him which is the child of God : and which is also required in the office of a bishop, which thing I promised as wel in the holy baptisme, as afterward to the Church.

The sum wherof is, that we are bound to the holy and Apostolique lawes, hauing had this earnest care, it is almost not to be beleeued in what torment of minde I continued, my spirit being at debate within it selfe, could not tast or finde any true or assured comfort, insomuch that I could take no rest, till such time I was earnestly bent & resolued to follow the ordinance of 10 Iesus Christ, and example of the Apostolique church : being ashamed to be a bishop in name only, and not in deede, and ashamed to beare within my hart a continual fire, euill and vnsauery desires, couered from the beautie of chaste virginitie. But I was abashed that a seruant of Iesus Christ should seeme to be bound to the traditions of men, and it was a horror to my hart, that the honor and nobilitie of my race, should remaine stained or corrupted, by casting my selfe among yᵉ pleasures of voluptuous worldlings, wherein I was altogeather plunged. For there I did feele my selfe solisseted (or as our manner of speech is) 20 puld by the eare, by many worthy and excellent persons, in doctrine and holines of life, which hath in their time borne great reuerence to the church of God (& which hath not forgetten the honor due vnto them) found great fault against yᵉ decrees & examples of many Bishops & prelats of yᵉ Church, which hath passed these 700. yeeres. *Vlricus,* a most religious Bishop, saint *Augustine,* *Bernard,* the Abbot of *Clereuaux,* the Cardinal *Cusan* with many other of the same calling & degree : so that it is very easie for me to shew that I haue doon nothing against my oth, so long as I put my selfe & my deedes, according to the rule of the holy 30 Apostolique Church. And for the first point, it is a thing confirmed which cannot be altred or chaunged, and perpetuall established : pronounced by saint *Paule* and saint *Peter,* and by generall consent at all times it hath been approued by all men, confessing the doctrine of the Apostles, that no other foundation can be layd, then that which GOD himself hath already established, yᵗ is to say, Iesus Christ, which is yᵉ only way, the trueth, and the life, in whose name, as also with the Father and the holie Ghost we are baptised : to whome appertaineth yᵉ catholique church, hauing redeemed ye same by his precious blood. Vpon this 40 foundation is the church sustained, being also beautified and inriched with most excellent tytles, which he hath giuen by S. *Paule* in the first to *Timothy,* the third chapter : calling her the house of yᵉ liuing God, the fortitude & strength of the trueth. Then the Romane church which was in the time of S. *Paule,* and certaine yeeres after, was of great renoume and estimation, for the faith they had in Iesus Christ, and at that time taught through the whole world : the which faith was her onelie ornament, insomuch

that the Priests & Elders of the same Romane Church, plainly
confessed, writing to S. *Ciprian* in his 7. epistle of his 2. booke,
in these words, That letting the honor & praise decay, which
S. *Paule* gaue to the Romanes, was a great & grieuous crime, and
y^t it had beene lesse shame, neuer to haue had those prayses
spoke of, or preached abroade, then after the publishing therof,
to lose the honour of such high commendations.   Therfore as
often as it comes in question, to speake of the pure, true, Apostolique, and vniuersall church : reason requireth, and all wise men
10 giueth counsaile, that we ought to discerne betweene that, which is
grounded vpon the head corner stone, Christ, vpon the holy
Gospell (the honour and name wherof shal endure euerlastingly :)
and that which is ye bastard church, going against the trueth,
worshippeth God in vaine, following after the commaundements &
traditions of men.   And therfore ye golden rule of *Tertullian*,
hath euer pleased al good and vertuous men, saying, that the first
hath been alwayes the truth, & that which came afterward
corrupted, and that is it which bindeth mee to the othe which
I haue made, which othe dooth commaund, that I must acknow-
20 ledge the sayde Apostolique church, which holdes the ancient
beleefe of the Romane church, agreeing to the beleefe of *Nice*,
and of *Constantinople*, which dooth acknowledge and beleeue one
baptisme for remission of sinnes, by ye blood of our Lord Iesus
Christ : which is our onely purgatorie that cleanseth vs of all our
sinnes, which receaueth no other traditions then this only, that
are appointed by the Apostles, leauing & deliuering faithfully, that
which they receiued from our Lord Iesus Christ.   After whose
example I am bounde by my othe, to take the holy scriptures,
interpreting and vnderstanding the same, not after the sence or
30 interpretation of any Bishop or Councell, whatsoeuer, but after the
vnderstanding and exposition of the true, Apostolique, and holy
mother Church, that (I say) which hath followed the steps of the
holy Apostles.   Wherunto the auncient Fathers hath from time to
time consented, so that without any blemish to the othe which
I haue made, I am addressed after this rule, & bound to this
foundation, neither will I receyue or beleeue any thing, which is
not brought from the same, wheresoeuer it was written, whether
at *Rome*, or at *Trent*, being reasonable to prefer these auncient
things with new, the truth with falsehood, & the traditions of the
40 Apostles, with ye commaundements of men.   For our lawes as it
dooth euidently appeare in the 15. distinction of ye third canon :
doth not alowe these auncient and most renoumed Councelles the
like aucthority, as they do to the holie Scriptures & Apostles, which
sayth thus : *The holy church of* Rome, *after the writinges of the old
and new Testament, which we receiue for certaine rules, doth not
forbid but that we may receiue the Councell of* Nice, *of* Constantinople,
Ephesus, *and of* Chalcedona.   Thus haue I hytherto shewed,
what was the band and foundation of ye othe which I lent, vpon

the which I protest, that (by the grace of God) I will not starte
nor turne, from the true faith in Iesus Christe, nor seperate my
selfe from the holy and Apostolique church, to the which I do
owe all reuerence, as I wil doo all my life: in remembrance of
that which I did vowe in baptisme to God, and promised to the
Church.   For the rest, it is out of doubt betweene all good and
learned men, that whatsoeuer we haue promised or sworne, if it
be wrong & contrarie to our first faith, receyued in baptisme, that
it bindeth vs not at all, this (I saye) is to be seene by the rule of the
right cannon Lawe, that is to say, that an oth taken against good 10
and godlie workes, bindeth not: and following the right cannon,
the othes that are made against good deeds, drawes vs vnto sinne.
Whereupon the Maister of Sentences hath wiselie sayd, in the 39.
Distinction after Saint *Hierome*, that an othe hath three proper
companions, veritie, iudgement, and iustice, and if any of these
lacke, it is not a true othe, but a false othe : But *Gratian* giueth
these aduertisements vpon the deede of an oth, *Euil promises* (saith
he) *breakes faith, chaunge therfore the ordinaunce of euill and
dishonest thinges, and do not that, which thou hast vnwiselie
promised, for that promise is against God, which is accomplished* 20
with wickednesse.
   In the seuenth cannon of our lawe, we haue a rule giuen, which
we ought straitlie to obserue, not onely for the regard of othes,
but in all the actions of our life (that is to say) that if by the
sutteltie of our craftie enimie, we are falling into any faulte, we
must seeke to escape it, by that meanes which we see is least
hurtfull and daungerous : thus you see, that the olde and auncient
Fathers hath generally concluded, that all vndiscrete and vnlawfull
othes, ought not to be obserued and kept : and that it is more
tollerable for to breake an othe, then to perseuere in the sinne of 30
fornication.   The same is also learned by the aucthority of
S. *Augustine,* that if faith be not obserued, to the intent to returne
to the right waye, it cannot be called y⁰ violating of faith, for as
much that the same is not true faith, which is requisite to commit
sinne.   It is easie to shew by many learned men, and also by the
holie scriptures, and by the auncient Doctors, that partly the
slacknes and slouthfulnes : and partly by the couetousnes and
malice of many Popes, sundrie things hath crept in y⁰ Romane
church, as *Platinus* (though otherwise greatly affectionated to y⁰
Roman seat) certifieth that those things do not agree to the 40
Apostolique & catholique church, but they are notably iniurious
against Iesus Christ, which is established for to be the redeemer
of peace, by the faith in his blood, & also most idolatrous, which
whosoeuer should followe of a trueth, should sinne greeuouslie
against God : and yet as *Arnobius* sayeth in his seuenth booke
against the Gentiles, that we ought to forgiue liberally and freely,
though it were against the Church, and against our owne conscience.
For these thinges then, I am not drawne through any cause by

you, (as many other great & woorthy personages hath taken occasion, to withdraw themselues) not from the catholique church, but from the corruption & abuses, which turneth vpside downe the foundation thereof. I wil not for this time enter into long disputation, but I would rather come to the crime, wherein I feel my selfe by you most accused. I see, I see, or at the least, I feele a certaine smell, that cannot be lesse then a sinnefull thing, the peine whereof, craueth the losse of my life, or of my charge and dignitie : for the which I am accused among you,
10 which maketh me most odious, & maketh the world to thinke, that I reiect all discipline, all duety, and all honour, but the shame thereof (falselie accusing me) maketh your selues almoste to blush. Which is, because I am purposed to marie, which S. *Paule* neuerthelesse affirmeth, to be honourable among all men : and which is also sette in the Romane church, among the number of the Sacramentes. But whensoeuer I am minded to accomplishe this thing, what shall I doo, or enterprise against the examples of the holy Apostles, and their rules and decrees? What doo I against the aduise of *Clement, Alexandrian*? or
20 against our owne Lawes, in the .28. Distinction, the .11. and .12. Chapters, where mention is made of the wiues of Priests, and Deacons, being aboundantly contained in the .17. cannon, as it was decreed by the Councell of *Gangar*, that, *If any reiect a maried Priest, being of opinion that he ought not to offer, because he is maried, and for that cause will not come to his seruice, let him be accurst.*

Moreouer, those words spoken with great grauitie by *Paphuntius*, in the Councell of *Nice*, are commended in the second parte of their decree, which did not feare to call mariage the second
30 degree of chastitie. Wherefore is it then that the aucthoritie of *Siricius* or *Pelagious*, should be of greater waight among vs, then that of the Apostles? Of generall Counselles? Of auncient Fathers before mentioned? Or of GOD himselfe? Which plainly pronounced, that it was not good for man to be alone. What follie, or what madnesse I praye you is it then, to endure rather adulterers, fornicators, and Sodomiticall liuers, in the ministerie and church of Christ, then those which hath true & lawfull wiues, following the commaundements of God? From what spring, or from whose mouth came the same doctrine, which
40 forbiddeth and condemneth mariage? It appeareth by the eleuenth chapter of *Daniel*, vers. 36. 37. and the first of *Timothy*, the fowrth chapt. ver. 1. 2. 3. *Æneus Silueus*, in his discription of *Germany*, witnesseth that the holy bishoppe *Vldricus*, strongly withstoode the lawes of *Celebat*, against the Popes of his time, writing an Epistle vnto Pope *Nicholas*, wherin he greatly complained that the chiefest Prelates, and Priests (namelie of Italy,) were so much giuen to lust and lecherie, that they would not abstaine from deflowring, maid, wife, or any other, nor spare theyr

owne kindred, but commit sinne against nature, with ye masquelin
sort, & also with very brute beasts : and there he declareth an
historie worthy the noting, that Pope *Gregorie* the first, being he,
that did first forbid ecclesiastical persons to marie, sending afterwarde, certaine fishers to fishe in a mote, hard adioyning to
a Nunrie, they founde more then six thousand childrens heads
that had beene throwne therein, which when *Gregorie* sawe, and
perceyued the wicked fruit of his *Celebat,* sorowing to heare the
same, he brake that decree, alledging the sentence of S. *Paul,*
that, *It is better to marie then to burne* : Adding also, that it is 10
farre better to suffer mariage, then to be the cause of murder.
The Abbot *Vspergus* also in his Chronicle, maketh mention of an
epistle in the most renoumed councell of the ecclesiasticall states
at *Bresse Nore,* made against *Heldebrand,* wherin among other
things, was a complaint made, y^t he deuorsed spyrituall persons
from theyr wiues, & vnder this detestable Pope, the Churches
were in great daunger, & also he declared y^t they were not bound
in any promise to the Pope, for it is a greater thing to make
a vow to obey God, and the catholique church, then to submitte
our selues to the will and pleasure of any Pope, whatsoeuer, For 20
these reasons, I that knoweth my duetie towarde Iesus Christe,
and his Church, I am determined to take the lawfull way and
remedy, permitted to all manner of men (without exception)
against euill and disordinate lustes, as it becommeth a true bishop,
and a man of noble race to doo : to the ende, that I may keepe
my soule chaste, and arme the same against all allurements of the
flesh. Therefore am I determined to enter into mariage, not
being mooued by any light or disobedient minde : but after long
tryall made of my selfe, I haue knowne that it is not good for me
to liue vnmaried. Which gifte is not permitted to all, nor for 30
euer, (that is to say, to make so long a triall of themselues :)
I am resolued, following the lawes of the church aboue mentioned,
to leaue that vndiscrete vow of the *Celebat,* which is not in my
power to performe, esteeming that this is lawful for me, for the
auoiding of a greater euill, and for the better obseruing & accomplishing the vowe of chastitie, which I made vnto Iesus Christ :
and in so dooing I haue framed my selfe according to the commaundement of God, submitting to his prouidence, and staying to
his protection, not caring what euill men may iudge, nor for y^e
threatnings, daungers, or any other thing whatsoeuer, hauing in 40
memorie that which *Theodorus* hath written in his fourth booke,
the tenth chapter, of the auncient Christians. Whiche dyd
knowe no greater griefe then the renouncing of pietie : and
although the tyrants went about raging and running vpon men,
as stormes, or tempestes, yet could they not be shaken or put
backe from pietie and godlines. Therefore, in all extremities,
I haue recourse to the iudgement of those which hath right
intelligence and knowledge. Vnto whome I doo appeale and

submit my selfe, after the example of *Iustinus Martyr*, in his
Apolligie for the Christians. In this submission most rightfull
and iust, that by those which religiously feareth God the trueth
alone is reuerenced, and to the same, all and euerie thing must be
agreeing.

Nowe I addresse my selfe to you Pope *Gregorie*, to the ende
I may obtaine of you this my purpose, (being most chaste and
according to the discipline of the true and auncient Catholique
Church) some protection and defence. Therefore I doo earnestlie
10 pray and beseech you, that of the same affection which it hath
pleased you to admonish me, that you will take my part in my
most iust enterprise, remembring that those which smothlie
flatters you, (a sort of bribe takers, which dooth but lightlie and
softlie touch the moste daungerous woundes) bee not those that
dooth most honour, and reuerence vnto you and the Church : but
well are they, which *Plutarch* speakes of, in his Treates of the
difference betweene the flatterer and the friend : which boldlie
and lyberallie speaketh, admonishing, and rebuking, not according
to theyr owne appetite and desire. What am I then that should
20 speake or brall against the Popes? if they take all that they say
out of the word, lawes and commaundementes of God, and out
of the writings of the Apostles and Prophetes, vppon which
doctrine, the Church and the Popes, ought to be founded and
builded, by GOD which hath the sufferaintie ouer kinges and
Popes. Oh that it were the good will and pleasure of him, that
I might see the daye, that you would not take the care to oppresse
me, and all other men, louers and followers of the doctrine and
life of the Apostles ; but rather that you should earnestlie vnder-
take to cast farre away from you, so many vanities, so many
30 idolatries, simonies, and sacrileges, and cut off these effeminates,
fornicators, and adulterers, drunkardes, and idle personnes, which
our owne lawes dooth excommunicate, to the ende that the
Romane church, might recouer her auncient dignitie, and that
peace and tranquilitie might come againe, among all Christians,
that many grieued and wounded consciences might finde rest and
consolation. Nowe as it is commonlie sayde, that of a poore
gardener, or a simple man, something may be heard of reasonable
sence : so I hope that you will not take this my small admonition,
otherwise, then with a fatherlie, religious, and equitable hart :
40   which is made vnto you by one of your Brothers in Iesus
Christ, and an *Almayn*, which could neuer
dissemble, whereuppon, I praye God
to keepe you in his protection.

F I N I S.

The Proclama-

tion and Edict of the

Archbyſhop, and Prince Elector
of CVLLEYN.

Declarynge his occaſion and earneſt
intention, to bring in the free exerciſe of
the preaching of the Goſpel, and peace and
lybertie to true Chꝛiſtian Religion.

¶ Proclaymed at B O N, in the yeare
of our Lorde, 1 5 8 3.

¶ Impꝛinted at Antwerp, in Tanners ſtrete,
at the Signe of the Gylden Bible, by
PAVLE BRAECKVELT, 1583.

With the conſent and Priuiledge of the
the Lordes of the Cittie of Antwerp.

¶ Impꝛinted at London, by Richard Iones
and I.C. the. 18. of March. 1 5 8 3.

¶ Aucthoriſed and allowed.

The Copie out of
the high Dutche

The Christian Edict & Proclamation, of the Archbishop and Prince Elector of Culleyne : concernyng his Princely intention to bring in the holy Gospell. Geuen at Bon, the XVI. of Ianuarie 1583.

WE GEBHART by the grace of God elected, and accepted Archbyshoppe of *Culleyn*, and chauncellour of the holye Empire through all *Italie*, and Elector : Duke of *Westphalen* and *Ingrene*. &c : do let and giue to witte and vnderstande vnto all and singuler Archdeacons of our Iurisdiction, Countrey States, Earles, Knights, States and other Persons, subiectes vnto vs : and to all others that shall haue occasion to vse our grace and fauour and to euery of them, ioyntly and seuerallie. That since we receyued the state & place of our Archbishopricke and Prince Electours Gouernment, wherin the Almightie God, by free and lawfull election hath placed vs, wee haue alwayes acknowledged and at this present doe acknowledge that we are bounde to doe our duety and endeuours, to maintayne and defende all such as by God are commytted to our Princely Election and Archbyshop-ricke, and lykewise our common natiue Countrey of the Dutch Nation : & most speciallye and aboue all other respectes to aduance and set before our eyes the honour of God before all other matters, whereunto with al diligence and hartie affection wee are inclined.

For asmuch as most earnest, obedient & hartie petition & request hath been lately made vnto vs by our Nobilitie & knights, & other Prouinces & countreies in no smal number, & also by the letters of some great personages of high estate & calling, within the sacred & holy Empyre, to suffer, admit & allow vnto them in al places of our Iurisdiction & auctorytie, the publike & open exercise of ye preaching of ye holy Gospell, and vse & administra-tion of the holy Sacraments, accordyng to the sacred words and Scriptures of God, and the Confession of *Auspurghe*, grounded vppon the same holy Scriptures. And theruppon, consideryng the euerlastyng & vnchangeable wyll of God, that it is our duties to heare his Sonne, and earnestlye to do his wyll. And that all Princes and Gouernours of the worlde, ought too cause the Gates to bee sette wide open, for the kyng of Glory, and to let all people to enter in vnto him. Whereunto wee haue speciall Commaundement from God in our vocation, and do feele in our conscience, how greeuously in the day of iudgment, we shall yeeld accompt and make answer before God for all our actions, and shuttyng vp the waye of saluation to our leage people.

And acknowledging and confessyng our selues to bee bounde to

feare God, from the bottom of our heartes, and obedientlie to follow his Commaundements, and that hee is a mightie and iuste Iudge, and consuming fire, whose feare wee oughte continuallie to set before our eyes. And for that wee being Christian superior, thought it our duetie before God, no longer to refuse to accomplishe the earneste and humble petition and suite, of our Nobilitie and Subiectes. Wee therefore by the aduise of our Lordes and frendes, and after mature consultation thereupon had and taken, doe graunte and permit vnto all persons, of what estate, degree, or
10 callinge soeuer they bee, eyther subiecte vnto our Aucthority or frends, and bearing good wil to our Archbishopprick, the Christian lybertie of their consciences, by Gods worde allowed. And do wyll, consent, graunt and confirme vnto them by vertue of these Presentes, that if any of the Subiectes or Inhabitauntes of any Cytie, Towne or place of our Iurisdiction, shall by any of our Officers, Commissioners, Maiestrates or ministers, whatsouer, in or about maters of faith, religion or conscience, be imprisoned, damnified, mollested or troubled either in Honour, dignitie, Fame, Reputation, bodie or goodds, for Gods woorde, or following the confession of
20 *Auspurghe.* That then euerie of them shall bee freely cleared, set at liberty, and discharged from all imprisonment, losse and molestation & trouble whatsoeuer, growinge for anie such respect.

Also we doe license, graunte and confirme herewithall vnto our Prelates, Earles, Lordes, Inhabitantes, Estates, Commons, Townes, and other Congregations of people, of our princely Election and Archbyshopricke, that they maye and shall, by warrante hereof, haue full power and Authoritie, to exercise and put in vse, the free and open Exercise of the preachynge of the Gospell, and the Administratyon and vse of the holye Sacramentes, accordynge to
30 the holye Scryptures of the Prophetes and Apostles, and agreeable to the Contentes and vse of the confession of *Auspurghe*, there-vppon grounded, without molestation of our Commissioners, Iustyces and Offycers, or anye other either of our Iurisdiction, whome wee doe meane to defende & assist with the helpe of the Almightie God : trusting also vpon the mighty power of God, that he will mercifullie assist and fauour vs in our so godly an enterprise and meaning, and be our defence agaynst all the Gates of Hell, to the maintenance of his glorie and holie worde.

More ouer, wee doe hereby declare and proteste before the
40 Almightie God, who is the chiefe truth, and a knower of the secrets of all mens heartes, that wee are not mooued and ledde to this our christian intention, through worldly wisedome, desire of Honour, or anie other worldly respect : neyther herein do seeke the profit, honour, dignitie, or estimation of our selfe, but onelye doe seeke to aduance the honour and glorie of our Redeemer, and to set foorth his holye woorde. And our intent and meaning herein, is chiefly to seeke the prosperitye and Saluation of our Subiectes whome God hath committed to our charge.

Let no man therefore imagine or thinke, that wee are inclined to nouelties or troubles. For oure intente and desyre is, to see good Christian orders maynteined and Kepte with peace and quyetnes, in Churches and Schooles of mens heartes.

And so wee are minded by the aduyse & counsayle of the States of our Countreys, and other our Lordes and frendes, to publishe & set foorthe Christyan Orders to bee obserued and followed in all Churches and Schooles of oure Archbishopricke.

In the meane tyme wee are aduysed, to giue warnynge to all suche as intende to lyue after the woorde of GOD, and the Confession of *Auspurghe*, to vse and behaue themselues with all reason and affectyon, as good Christians oughte to doe. And wee requyre and praye them most hartilye, that no man mollest, trouble, defy, blaspheme or vexe one an other by woorde or deede. But that euerye of them behaue themselues one towards an other peaceably and quyetlye in their conuersation and dealynges. And to lyue and continue accordynge to the Contentes of this oure presente Edict.

And as touchynge oure owne Person in this case. Whereas accordynge to the Counsayle and appoyntmente of Almighty God, wee haue entered into the Holye State of Marryage, and that publiquelye, wherein no man is able iustlie to accuse vs to haue doone the same agaynste the accustomed Order, or that we haue anye meanynge to seeke our pryuate aduantage, or anye other thynge preiudyciall to oure Archbyshopricke, and Prince Elector-shyppe, or to appropryate the same in Successyon and Inherytaunce to our Heyres: Wee therefore, doe make oppen and playne Testimonie and Declaration by these presents, by the highest trueth : (which is God Almightie him selfe) and hereby do protest that we haue no meaning or will, nor are in aniewyse inclyned or bent, to bringe our Byshoppricke, to the propryetie or possessyon of our Heyres, neyther to bringe in anie Noueltie or Alteration, tendynge to oure pryuate profytte or aduancement. But doe here-by openlye publishe and declare, that after our Decease, our Honourable Chapyter of oure Cathedrall Churche of *Culleyn*, shall haue their free Libertye and Election lefte vnto them, and shall remaine in all respects, as in their auncient former estate.

Also we are content, and giue our Commaundement touchinge the premisses to all and singuler Inhabitantes and Subiectes of our Archbysshopryke and Prince Electorship : that an orderly choice and free election may be made of a future supreme head, to gouerne them after our decease or free resignation : yet neuerthe-lesse, our meanynge is, that, whosoeuer shall be in election to come to that succession by an orderly choice & free election, shall be no other but such a one as is bounde vnto our saide Chapiter of our saide Cathedrall Church, and a Lorde capable, by th' ordinaunces of the same to come to that degree, and a man of our iurisdiction, both obedient and fytte, and worthye in all respectes for the place when it shal fall vnto him : and otherwise, not to bee elected to such preferment by any meanes. And whatsoeuer, such person as shall be by suche orderly proceedinge choice and free election of our worthye Chapiter of our said Cathedrall Church, chosen and elected to succeede after our sayd decease or resignation. They shall acknowledge him for their future Lorde, any Lawe, Statute, Act, Ordinaunce, Edict or Proclamation, made, ordained, or prouided, either by vs, or any other what soeuer he be, to the contrary of this our publike declaration, in any wise notwithstandyng : for we, all such do now, & alwayes wyl cancel, adnihilate and make of none effect.

All the same premises, we wish to be done in the cheefest and best manner and forme that may bee, to thende the same may continue of the better force and effect : wherunto, we will be obedient and lay to our helping hande, and therein wyll agree and consent with our said Chapiter & inhabitants and confyrme the aforesaid conditions with assurance therof, in such sort that no man shall haue iust cause to mistrust or conceaue any feare of vs, or of our Heyres or Successours.

Wherefore, wee wyll and commaunde all our Baylyffes, Iustices, Offycers, Lieutennauntes, Gouernours, Customers, Burrough maisters, Cytizens, Common people, Ministers and Subiectes and whatsoeuer, vpon this our publique Edict and Proclamation, with all their endeuour, to obserue and performe the same : and to cause the same Edict and Proclamation to bee obeyed and maintayned from point to point :

And also contrarye to the true meanynge thereof, not to encomber or trouble, or suffer to bee encumbred or troubled, any person or persons of any degree, vocation, or calling whatsoeuer, vppon paine of our high displeasure and indignation, & greeuous punishment to be inflicted withall vppon the offenders, breakers or repugners of this our present Edict and Proclamation : for such is our earnest and finall intent and wyll.

In witnesse wherof, we haue caused this our Proclamation to be openly printed and confirmed with our Seale, and that through al our Archbishoprick and Prince Electorship, to thend, that euery man should haue knowledge thereof.

GIVEN IN OUR CITIE
of Bon, the XVI Day of Ianuarie, in the
yeare of the Computation of the byrth
of our Lorde Iesus Christ 1583

PRINTED AT LONDON
by Richard Jones: at the Signe
of the *Rose* and the *Crowne*,
neere *Holburne* Bridge,
19. March, 1583

THE
GARLAND
OF
Good Will.
Diuided into three parts:Containing
many pleasant Songs,and prety
poems,to sundry new
Notes.

With a Table to finde the names of all the Songs.

Written by T.D.

Imprinted at London for *Robert Bird,* at the Bible
in Saint Lawrence Lane 1 6 3 1.

The Table.

1. Part.

In the second Part.

In the third Part.

FINIS.

A Mournfull Dittie, on the

death of *Rosamond*, King *Henry*
the seconds Concubine.

To the Tune of When flying Fame.

WHenas King *Henry* rul'd this land,
    the second of that name,
Besides the Queene, he deerely lou'd
    a faire and Princely Dame.
Most peerelesse was her beauty found,
    her fauour and her face :
A sweeter creature in this world,
    did neuer Prince embrace.

Her crisped locks like threds of Gold
    appeared to each mans sight :   10
Her comely eyes like Orient pearles,
    did cast a heauenly light.
The bloud within her Christall cheekes,
    did such a colour driue :
As though the Lilly and the Rose
    for maistership did striue.

Yea *Rosamond*, faire *Rosamond*,
    her name was called so :
To whom Dame *Elinor* the Queene,
    was knowne a cruell foe.   20
The King therefore, for her defence,
    against the furious Queene,
At *Woodstocke* builded such a bower,
    the like was neuer seene.

Most curiously this Bower was built
    of stone and timber strong,
An hundred and fifty doores
    did to that bower belong.

15 the rose *B C D E* : and rose *A*   17 yea *B C D E* : yet *A*

And they so cunningly contriu'd
   with turnings round about,   30
That none but with a clew of threed,
   could enter in or out.

And for his loue and Ladies sake,
   that was so faire and bright:
The keeping of that bower he gaue
   vnto a valiant Knight.
But fortune that doth often frowne,
   where she before did smile:
The Kings delight, the Ladies ioy,
   full soone she did beguile.   40

For why, the Kings vngracious sonne,
   whom he did high aduance:
Against his Father raised warre,
   within the Realme of France.
But yet before our comely King,
   the English land forsooke:
Of *Rosamond* his Lady faire,
   his farewell thus he tooke.

My *Rosamond*, the onely Rose
   that pleaseth best mine eye: 50
The fairest Rose in all the world
   to feed my fantasie.
The flower of mine afflicted heart,
   whose sweetnesse doth excell:
My royall Rose a thousand times,
   I bid thee now farwel.

For I must leaue my fairest flower,
   my sweetest Rose a space.
And crosse the seas to famous *France*,
   proud Rebels to abase.   60
But yet, my Rose be sure thou shalt
   my coming shortly see:
And in my heart while hence I am
   Ile beare my Rose with me.

41 for why *C D*: for while *A*   45 before *B C D E*: *A omits*

When *Rosamond*, the Lady bright,
   did heare the King say so :
The sorrow of her grieued heart,
   her outward lookes did show ;
And from her cleare and cristall eyes,
   the teares gusht out apace :   70
Which, like a siluer pearled dew,
   ran downe her comly face.

Her lips, like to a Corall red,
   did wax both wan and pale,
And for the sorrow she conceiu'd,
   her vitall spirits did faile.
So falling downe all in a swoond
   before King *Henries* face :
Full oft betweene his Princely armes
   her corpes he did embrace.   80

And twenty times, with watry eyes,
   he kist her tender cheeke :
Vntill she had receiu'd againe
   her senses mild and meeke.
Why grieues my Rose, my sweetest Rose
   the King did euer say ;
Because (quoth she) to bloudy warres,
   my Lord must part away.

But sith your grace, in forren coast,
   among your foes vnkind,   90
Must go to hazard life and limbe,
   why should I stay behind ;
Nay rather let me, like a Page,
   your shield and Target beare,
That on my brest the blow may light,
   that should annoy you there.

O let me in your Royall Tent
   prepare your bed at night :
And with sweet baths refresh your Grace
   at your returne from fight.   100

     91 go to hazard *C D E* : go hazard *A*

So I your presence may enioy,
    no toyle I must refuse:
But wanting you my life is death,
    which doth true loue abuse.

Content thy selfe my dearest loue,
    thy rest at home shall be:
In *Englands* sweet and pleasant soile,
    for trauel fits not thee.
Faire Ladies brooke not bloudy warrs,
    sweet peace their pleasure breede: 110
The nourisher of hearts content,
    which fancy first doth feed.

My Rose shall rest in *Woodstocke* Bower,
    with Musickes sweet delight:
While I among the piercing pikes
    against my foes do fight.
My Rose, in robes and pearles of Gold,
    with Diamonds richly dite:
Shall dance the Galliard of my loue,
    while I my foes do smite.   120

And you, Sir *Thomas*, whom I trust
    to be my loues defence:
Be carefull of my gallant Rose,
    when I am parted hence.
And therewithall he fetcht a sigh,
    as though his heart would breake:
And *Rosamond*, for inward griefe,
    not one plaine word could speake.

For at his parting, well they might
    in heart be grieued sore: 130
After that day, faire *Rosamond*
    the King did see no more.
For when his grace had past the seas,
    and into France was gone:
Queene *Elinor*, with enuious heart,
    to *Woodstocke* came anon.

117 pearles of Gold *A B* : pearles and Gold *C D E*

And forth she cal'd this trusty Knight,
   which kept this curious Bower :
Who, with his clew of twined thred,
   came from that famous flower.   140
And when that they had wounded him
   the Queene his thred did get :
And came where Lady *Rosamond*
   was like an Angell set.

But when the Queene with stedfast eyes
   beheld her heauenly face :
She was amazed in her mind,
   at her exceeding grace.
Cast off thy Robes from thee, she said,
   that rich and costly be :   150
And drink thee vp this deadly draught
   which I haue brought for thee.

But presently vpon her knee,
   sweet *Rosamond* did fall :
And pardon of the Queene she crau'd
   for her offences all.
Take pitty on my youthfull yeares,
   faire *Rosamond* did cry :
And let me not with poyson strong,
   enforced be to dye.   160

I will renounce this sinfull life,
   and in a cloister bide :
Or else be banisht, if you please,
   to range the world so wide.
And for the fault that I haue done,
   though I were forct thereto :
Preserue my life, and punish me,
   as you thinke best to do.

And with these words her Lilly hands
   she wrung full often there :   170
And downe along her louely cheekes,
   proceeded many a teare.
But nothing could this furious Queene
   therewith appeased be :
The cup of deadly poyson fil'd,
   as she sat on her knee.

She gaue this comely Dame to drinke,
  who tooke it from her hand :
And from her bended knee arose,
  and on her feet did stand ;   180
And casting vp her eyes to Heauen,
  she did for mercy call :
And drinking vp the poyson then,
  her life she lost with all.

And when that death through euery limbe,
  had done his greatest spight :
  er chiefest foes did plaine confesse
  she was a glorious wight.
Her body then they did intomb,
  when life was fled away :   190
At Godstow, neere to *Oxford* Towne
  as may be seene this day.

FINIS.

2.

A New Sonnet, conteining the Lamentation of *Shores*
wife, who was sometime Concubine to King *Edward*
the fourth, setting forth her great fall, and withall
her most miserable and wretched end.

To the tune of, the hunt is vp.

Listen, faire Ladies,
  Vnto my misery :
That liued late in pompous state,
  most delightfully.
And now by Fortune's faire dissimulation,
Brought to cruell and vncouth plagues,
  most spightfully.

Shores wife I am,
So knowne by name :
And at the *Flower-de-luce* in *Cheapside*   10
  was my dwelling :
The only daughter of a wealthy merchant man,
Against whose counsel euermore,
  I was rebelling.

Young was I loued;
No affection moued
My heart or mind to giue or yeeld
   to their consenting.
My Parents thinking richly for to wed me,
Forcing me to that which caused   20
   my repenting.

Then being wedded,
I was quickly tempted,
My beauty caused many Gallants
   to salute me.
The King commanding, I straight obayed :
For his chiefest iewel then,
   he did repute me.

Brave was I trained,
Like a Queene I raigned,   30
And many poore mens suits
   by me was obtained.
In al the Court to none was such resort,
As vnto me, though now in scorn,
   I be disdained.

When the King dyed,
My griefe I tryed :
From the Court I was expelled,
   with despight.
The Duke of *Gloster* being Lord Protector,   40
Tooke away my goods, against
   all law and right.

In a Procession,
For my transgression,
Bare foot he made me go,
   for to shame me.
A Crosse before me there was carried plainly,
As a pennance for my former life,
   so to tame me.

Then through London,   50
Being thus vndone,
The Lord Protector published,
   a Proclamation :

On paine of death I should not be harbord,
Which furthermore encreast my sorrow
   and vexation.

I that had plenty,
And dishes dainty :
Most sumptuously brought to my boord
   at my pleasure :   60
Being full poore, from doore to doore,
I begd my bread with clacke and dish,
   at my leasure.

My rich attire,
By fortunes yre,
To rotten rags and nakednesse
   they are beaten.
My body soft, which the King embraced oft,
With vermine vile annoyd
   and eaten.   70

On stalls and stones,
Did lye my bones,
That wonted was in beds of downe
   to be placed.
And you see my finest pillowes be,
Of stinking straw, with dirt and dung
   thus disgraced.

Wherefore, Fair Ladies,
With your sweet babies,
My grieuous fall beare in your mind,   80
   and behold me :
How strange a thing, that the loue of a King
Should come to dye vnder a stall,
   as I told yee.

FINIS.

76 with dirt *C D E* : both dirt, *A B*

3.

A New Song of King *Edgar*, King of *England*, how he was depriued of a Lady, which he loued, by a Knight of his Court.

To be sung in the old ancient sort, or else to the Tune of Labandalashot.

WHenas King *Edgar* did gouerne this land,
 adowne, adowne, downe, down, down,
And in the strength of his yeeres did stand,
 call him downe a:
Such praise was spread of a gallant Dame,
Which did through *England* carry great fame,
And she a Lady of noble degree,
The Earle of Deuonshires daughter was she.
The King which lately had buried his Queene,
And not long time had a Widdower beene,   10
Hearing this praise of this gallant Maid,
Vpon her beauty his loue he laide,
And in his sighes he wold often say,
I will go send for that Lady gay:
Yea, I will go send for that Lady bright,
Which is my treasure and delight:
Whose beauty, like to *Phœbus* beames,
Doth glister through all Christian Realmes.
Then to himselfe he would reply,
Saying, How fond a Prince am I,   20
To cast my loue so base and low,
Vpon a Gyrle I do not know:
King *Edgar* will his fancy frame,
To loue some peerelesse Princely Dame,
The daughter of a royall King,
That may a worthy dowry bring:
Whose matchlesse beauty brought in place,
May *Estrilds* colour cleane disgrace.
But senseless man, what do I meane,
Vpon a broken reede to lean: 30
Or what fond fury doth me moue
Thus to abase my dearest loue?
Whose visage, grac't with heauenly hue
Doth *Helens* honour quite subdue:

32 A B: abuse C D E

The glory of her beauties pride,
Sweet *Estrilds* fauor doth deride.
Then pardon my vnseemely speech,
Deare loue and Lady, I beseech :
For I my thoughts will henceforth frame,
To spread the honour of thy name.40
Then vnto him he cal'd a Knight,
Which was most trusty in his sight,
And vnto him thus did he say :
To earle *Orgarus*, go thy way,
Where ask for *Estrild*, comely Dame,
Whose beauty went so farre by Fame.
And if thou find her comely grace,
As Fame hath spred in euery place :
Then tell her Father she shall be
My crowned Queene, if she agree.50
The Knight in message did proceed,
And into *Deuonshire* with speed :
But when he saw the Lady bright,
He was so rauisht at her sight,
That nothing could his passion moue,
Except he might obtaine her loue :
For day and night while there he staid,
He courted still this peerelesse Maid :
And in his suit he shewed such skill,
That at the length won her good-will,60
Forgetting quite the duty tho
Which he vnto the King did owe.
Then comming home vnto his Grace,
He told him with dissembling face,
That those reporters were to blame,
That so aduanc't the Maidens name.
For I assure your Grace (quoth he)
She is as other women bee :
Her beauty of such great report,
No better than the common sort,70
And farre vnmeet in euery thing,
To match with such a Noble King.
But though her face be nothing faire,
Yet sith she is her Fathers heire,

Perhaps some Lord of high degree,
Would very faine her husband be:
Then if your Grace would giue consent,
I would my selfe be well content,
The Damsell for my wife to take,
For her great Lands and Liuings sake.　　　80
The King whom thus he did deceiue,
Incontinent did giue him leaue:
For on that point he did not stand,
For why, he had no need of Land.
Then being glad he went his way,
And wedded straight that Lady gay:
The fairest creature bearing life,
Had this false Knight vnto his wife:
And by that match of high degree,
An Earle soone after that was he.　　　90
Ere he long time had married beene,
That many had her beauty seene:
Her praise was spred both farre and neere;
The King againe thereof did heare:
Who then in heart did plainely proue,
He was betrayed of his loue.
Though thereat, he was vexed sore,
Yet seem'd he not to grieue therefore,
But kept his countenance good and kinde,
As though he bare no grudge in minde.　　　100
But on a day it came to passe,
When as the King full merry was,
To *Ethelwood* in sport he said,
I muse what cheere there would be made,
If to thy house I should resort
A night or two for Princely sport:
Hereat the earl shewd countenance glad,
Though in his heart he was sore sad:
Saying, Your Grace should welcome be,
If so your Grace would honour me.　　　110
When as the day appointed was,
Before the King did thither passe,
The Earle beforehand did prepare,
The Kings comming to declare:
And with a countenance passing grim,
He cal'd his Lady vnto him.

Saying with sad and heauy cheare,
I pray you when the King comes here,
Sweet Lady as you tender me,
Let your attire but homely be: 120
Nor wash not thou thy Angels face,
But doe thy beauty quite disgrace.
Thereto thy gesture so apply,
It may seeme lothsome to the eye.
For if the King should there behold
Thy glorious beauty so extold:
Then should my life soone shortned be,
For my deserts and trechery.
When to thy Father first I came,
Though I did not declare the same,   130
Yet was I put in trust to bring
The ioyfull tyding from the King,
Who for thy glorious beauty seene,
Did thinke of thee to make his Queene:
But when I had thy person found,
Thy beauty gaue me such a wound,
No rest nor comfort could I take,
Till you, sweet loue, my griefe did slake:
And thus, though duty charged me,
Most faithfull to my Lord to be: 140
Yet loue vpon the other side,
Bade for my self I should prouide:
Then for my suit and seruice showne,
At length I won you for my owne,
And for your loue and wedlocke spent,
Your choise you need no whit repent.
Then sith my griefe I haue exprest,
Sweet Lady, grant me my request.
Good words she gaue with smiling cheere,
Musing at that which she did heare;   150
And casting many things in mind,
Great fault herewith she seem'd to find:
But in her selfe she thought it shame,
To make that foule which God did frame:
Most costly robes and rich therefore,
In brauest sort that day she wore:

Doing all things that ere she might,
To set her beauty forth to sight.
And her best skill in euery thing
She shewed to entertaine the King.　　　　160
Whereby the King so snared was,
That reason quite from him did passe:
His heart by her was set on fire,
He had to her a great desire,
And for the lookes he gaue her then,
For euery looke she lent him ten:
Wherefore the King perceiued plaine,
His loue and lookes were not in vaine.
Vpon a time it chanced so,
The King he would a hunting goe,　　　　170
And as they through a wood did ride,
The Earle on horseback by his side:
For so the story telleth plaine,
That with a shaft the Earle was slaine.
So when that he had lost his life,
He tooke the Damsell vnto wife,
Who married her, all shame to shunne,
By whom he did beget a sonne.
Thus he that did the King deceiue,
Did by desert this death receiue.　　　　180
Then to conclude and make an end,
Be true and faithful to thy friend.

FINIS.

4.

How *Couentry* was made free by *Godina,* Countesse of *Chester.*

To the Tune of Prince Arthur died at Ludlow.

L Eofricus, that Noble Earle
　Of *Chester,* as I reade,
Did for the City of *Couentry,*
Many a noble deed.
Great priuiledges for the towne,
This Nobleman did get,

And of all things did make it so,
That they tole-free did sit:
Saue onley that for horses still,
They did some custome pay,   10
Which was great charges to the towne,
Full long and many a day.
Wherefore his wife, *Godina* faire,
Did of the Earl request,
That therefore he would make it free,
As well as all the rest.
So when the Lady long had sued,
Her purpose to obtaine:
Her Noble Lord at length she tooke,
Within a pleasant vaine,   20
And vnto him with smiling cheare,
She did forthwith proceed,
Entreating greatly that he would
Performe that goodly deed.
You moue me much, faire Dame (quoth he)
Your suit I faine would shunne:
But what would you performe and do,
To haue this matter done?
Why any thing, my Lord (quoth she)
You will with reason craue,   30
I will performe it with good will,
If I my wish may haue.
If thou wilt grant one thing (said he)
Which I shall now require,
So soone as it is finished,
Thou shalt haue thy desire.
Command what you thinke good, my Lord,
I will thereto agree:
On this condition that this Towne
For euer may be free.   40
If thou wilt thy cloaths strip off,
And here wilt lay them downe,
And at noone day on horsebacke ride
Starke naked thorow the Towne,
They shall be free for euermore:
If thou wilt not do so,

41 *B C D*: If thou wilt strip thy clothes off *A E*

More liberty than now they haue,
I neuer will bestow.
The lady at this strange demand,
Was much abasht in mind :50
And yet for to fulfil this thing,
She neuer a whit repinde.
Wherefore to all the Officers
Of all the Towne she sent :
That they perceiuing her good will,
Which for the weale was bent,
That on the day that she should ride,
All persons thorow the Towne,
Should keepe their houses and shut their doores,
And clap their windowes downe,60
So that no creature, yong or old
Should in the street be seene :
Till she had ridden all about,
Throughout the City cleane.
And when the day of riding came,
No person did her see,
Sauing her Lord : after which time,
The towne was euer free.

FINIS.

5.

How the Dukes daughter of *Cornwall* being married vnto King *Locrine*, was by him put away, and a strange Lady whom he better loued, hee married, and made her his Queene, and how his wife was auengéd.

To the tune of, in Creete.

WHen *Humber* in his wrathfull rage,
King *Albanacke* in field had slaine,
Thóse bloody broiles for to asswage,
King *Locrine* then applyed his paine,
And with a hoast of Brittaines stout,
At length he found King *Humber* out.

At vantage great he met him then,
And with his hoast beset him so,

That he destroy'd his warlike men,
And *Humbers* power did ouerthrow: 10
And *Humber*, which for feare did flie,
Leapt into a Riuer desperately.

And being drowned in the deepe,
He left a Lady there aliue,
Which sadly did lament and weepe,
For feare they should her life depriue.
But for her face that was so faire,
The King was caught in *Cupids* snare.

He tooke this Lady to his loue,
Who secretly did keepe her still: 20
So that the Queene did quickly proue,
The King did beare her small good will:
Which though in wedlocke late begun,
He had by her a gallant sonne.

Queene *Guendoline* was grieu'd in minde,
To see the King was altered so:
At length the cause she chanc'd to finde,
Which brought her to most bitter woe:
For *Estrild* was his ioy (God wot)
By whom a Daughter he begot.   30

The Duke of *Cornwall* being dead,
The Father of that Gallant Queene:
The King with lust being ouerled,
His lawfull wife he cast off cleane:
Who with her deare and tender sonne,
For succour did to *Cornewall* runne.

Then *Locrine* crowned *Estrild* bright,
And made of her his lawfull wife,
With her, which was his hearts delight,
He thought to lead a pleasant life: 40
Thus *Guendoline*, as one forlorne,
Was of her husband held in scorne.

But when the Cornish men did know
The great abuse she did endure:
With her a number great did goe,
Which she by prayers did procure:
In battell then they marcht along,
For to redresse this grieuous wrong.

And neere a riuer called *Store*,
The King with all his hoast she met: 50
Where both the armies fought full sore,
But the Queene the field did get:
Yet ere they did the conquest gaine,
The King was with an arrow slaine.

Then *Guendoline* did take in hand,
Vntill her sonne was come to age,
The gouernment of all the Land:
But first her fury to asswage,
She did command her souldiers wild,
To drowne both *Estrild* and her child.   60

Incontinent then did they bring
Faire *Estrild* to the Riuers side,
And *Sabrine* daughter to a King,
Whom *Guendoline* could not abide:
Who being bound together fast,
Into the riuer there were cast.

And euer since, that running stream,
Wherein the Ladies drowned were,
Is called *Seuerne* through the Realme,
Because that *Sabrine* dyed there.   70
Thus they that did to lewdnesse bend,
Were brought vnto a wofull end.

FINIS.

6.

A song of Queene *Isabel*, wife to King *Edward* the
second, how by the *Spencers* she was constrained
secretly to goe out of *England* with her elder sonne
Prince *Edward*, to seeke for succour in *France*, and
what hapned vnto her in her iourney.

PRoud were the *Spencers*, and of condition ill,
    All *England* and the King likewise,
    they ruled at their will:
And many Lords and Nobles of this Land,
Through their occasions lost their liues,
    and none durst them withstand.

And at the last they did encrease their grief,
Betweene the King and *Isabel*,
   his queen and faithfull wife.
So that her life she dreaded wondrous sore,   10
And cast within her secret thoughts,
   some present help therefore.

Thus she requests with countenance graue and sage,
That she to *Thomas Beckets* tombe,
   might go on Pilgrimage.
Then being ioyfull to haue that happy chance,
Her sonne and she tooke ship with speed,
   and sailed into France.
And royally she was receiued then,
By the King and all the rest   20
   of Peeres and Noblemen.
And vnto him at length she did expresse
The cause of her arriuall there,
   her griefe and heauinesse.

When as her brother her griefe did vnderstand,
He gaue her leaue to gather men,
   throughout his famous Land:
And made his promise to aid her euermore,
As oft as she could stand in need,
   of Gold and Siluer store.   30
But when indeed he should performe the same,
He was as farre from doing it,
   as when she thither came,
And did proclaime while matters yet were greene,
That none on paine of death should go
   to aide the English Queene.

This alteration did greatly grieue the Queene,
That downe along her comely face,
   the bitter teares were seene.
When she perceiu'd her friends forsooke her so,   40
She knew not for her safety
   which way to turne or go:
But through good hap at last she then decreed,
To looke in fruitfull *Germanie*,
   some succour in this need.

29 As oft] Often *B C D E* : As ough *A*

And to Sir *Iohn Henault* then went she,
Who entertain'd this wofull Queene,
   with great solemnitie.

And with great sorrow to him she then complaind,
Of all her griefes and iniuries   50
   which she of late sustaind :
So that with weeping she dimd her Princely sight,
The summe whereof did greatly grieue
   that Noble courteous Knight :
Who made an oath he would her Champion be,
And in her quarrell spend his bloud :
   from wrong to set her free ;
And all my friends with whom I may preuaile,
Shall helpe for to aduance your state,
   whose truth no time shall faile.   60

And in this promise most faithful he was found,
And many Lords of great account
   were in this voyage bound.
So setting foward with a goodly traine,
At length, through Gods especiall grace,
   into *England* they came.
At *Harwich* then when they were come ashore,
Of English Lords and Barons bold,
   there came to her great store,
Which did reioyce the Queenes afflicted heart,   70
That English Nobles in such sort,
   did come to take her part.

When as King *Edward* hereof did vnderstand,
How that the Queene with such a power,
   was entred on his Land,
And how his Nobles were gone to take her part,
He fled from *London* presently,
   euen with a heauy heart :
And with the *Spencers* did vnto *Bristoll* goe,
To fortifie that Gallant Towne   8c
   great cost he did bestow :
Leauing behind to gouern *London* Towne,
The stout Bishop of *Exceter*,
   whose pride was soone pul'd downe.

The Mayor of *London* with citizens great store
The Bishop and the *Spencers* both,
  in heart they did abhorre:
Therefore they tooke him without feare & dread,
And at the *Standard* in *Cheapside*,
  they soone smote off his head.   90
Vnto the Queene this message then they sent,
The City of *London* was
  at her commandement:
Wherefore the Queene with all her companie,
Did straight to *Bristow* march amaine,
  whereas the King did lye.

Then she besieg'd the City round about,
Threatning sharpe and cruell death
  to those that were so stout:
Wherefore the townsmen their children & their wiues,
Did yeeld the City to the Queene,   101
  for safegard of their liues.
Where was tooke, the story plaine doth tell,
Sir *Hugh Spencer*, and with him
  the Earle of *Arundel*.
This iudgement iust the Nobles did set downe,
They should be drawne and hanged both,
  in sight of *Bristow* Towne,

Then was King *Edward* in the Castle there;
And young *Hugh Spencer* still with him,   110
  in dread and deadly feare.
And being prepar'd from thence to sail away,
The winds were found so contrary,
  they were enforc't to stay:
But at the last Sir *Henry Beaumond* Knight,
Did bring their sailing ship to shore,
  and so did stay their flight:
And so these men were taken speedily,
And brought as prisoners to the Queene,
  which did in *Bristow* lye.   120

The Queene by counsell of the Lords & Barons bold
To *Barkeley* Castle sent the King,
  there to be kept in hold.

87 heart *B C D E* : hearts *A*   118 taken speedily *B C D E* :
full speedily *A*

And young *Hugh Spencer*, that did much ill procure,
Was to the Marshal of the Hoast
   sent vnto keeping sure.
And then the Queene to *Hereford* tooke her way,
With al her warlike company,
   which late in *Bristow* lay :
And here behold how *Spencer* vsed was,   130
From towne to towne, euen as the Queene
   to *Hereford* did passe

Vpon a Iade which they by chance had found,
Young *Spencer* mounted was,
   with legs and hands fast bound :
A written paper along as he did go,
Vpon his head he had to weare,
   which did his treason show.
And to deride this Traytor lewd and ill,
Certaine men with Reeden Pipes,   140
   did blow before him still :
Thus was he led along in euery place,
While many people did reioyce,
   to see his great disgrace.

When vnto *Hereford* our noble Queene was come,
She did assemble all the Lords
   and Knights, both all and some :
And in their presence yong *Spencer* iudgment had
To be both hang'd and quartered,
   his treasons were so bad.   150
Then was the King deposed of his Crowne,
From rule and Princely dignitie,
   the Lords did cast him downe.
And in his life his son both wise and sage,
Was crowned King of faire *England*,
   at fifteene yeares of age.

FINIS.

7.

A Song of the banishment of two Dukes, *Hereford* and *Norfolke*.

TWo Noble Dukes of great renowne,
  that long had liu'd in fame,
Through hatefull enuie were cast downe,
  and brought to sudden shame.
The Duke of *Hereford* was the one,
  a prudent Prince and wise:
Gainst whom such malice there was showne,
  which soone in fight did rise.

The Duke of *Norfolk*, most vntrue,
  declared to the King: 10
The Duke of *Hereford* greatly grew
  in hatred of each thing,
Which by his grace was acted still,
  against both high and low:
And how he had a trayterous will,
  his state to ouerthrow.

The Duke of *Hereford*, then in hast,
  was sent for to the King:
And by his Lords in order plac't,
  examined of each thing.   20
Which being guiltlesse of this crime,
  which was against him laid:
The Duke of *Norfolk* at that time,
  these words vnto him said.

How canst thou with a shamelesse face,
  deny a truth so stout:
And here before his Royall Grace,
  so falsly face it out:
Did not these treasons from thee passe,
  when we together were,   30
How that the King vnworthy was,
  the Royall Crown to beare:

Wherefore, my gracious lord (quoth he)
    and you his noble Peeres:
To whom I wish long life to be,
    with many happy yeares.
I doe pronounce before you all,
    the Duke of *Hereford* here,
A traitor to our noble King,
    as time shall shew it cleare.   40

The Duke of *Hereford* hearing that
    in mind was grieued much:
And did returne this answer flat,
    which did Duke *Norfolke* touch.
The terme of traitor trothlesse Duke,
    in scorne and deepe disdaine:
With flat defiance to thy face
    I do returne againe.

And therefore if it please your Grace,
    to grant me leaue (quoth he)   50
To combate with my knowen foe,
    that here accuseth me;
I doe not doubt but plainly proue:
    that like a periured Knight,
He hath most falsly sought my shame,
    against all truth and right.

The King did grant this iust request,
    and did therewith agree:
At *Couentry* in August next,
    this combate fought should be.   60
The Dukes on backed steeds full stout,
    in coats of steel most bright:
With spears in rests did enter lists,
    this combate fierce to fight.

The King then cast his warder downe,
    commanding them to stay:
And with his Lords he counsell tooke,
    to stint that mortall fray.
At length vnto these noble Dukes,
    the King of Heralds came,   70
And vnto them with lofty speech,
    this sentence did proclaime.

Sir *Henry Bullingbrooke* this day,
   the Duke of *Hereford* here,
And *Thomas Moubray, Norfolkes* Duke,
   so valiant did appeare :
And hauing in honourable sort,
   repaired to this place :
Our noble King, for speciall cause,
   hath altred thus the case.   80

First *Henry* Duke of *Hereford*,
   ere fifteene dayes be past :
Shall part this Realme on paine of death,
   while ten yeares space doth last.
And *Thomas* Duke of *Norfolk*, thou,
   that hast begun this strife,
And thereof no good proofe canst bring,
   I say for term of life.

By iudgement of our Soueraigne Lord,
   which now in place doth stand :   90
For euermore I banish thee,
   out of thy natiue Land :
Charging thee on paine of death,
   when fifteene dayes are past :
Thou neuer tread on *English* ground,
   so long as life doth last.

Thus they were sworne before the King
   ere they did further passe :
The one should neuer come in place,
   where as the other was.   100
Then both the Dukes, with heauy hearts,
   were parted presently :
Their vncooth streams of froward chance,
   in forraigne Lands to try.

The Duke of *Norfolke* comming then,
   where hee should shipping take :
The bitter tears fell downe his cheeks,
   and thus his mone did make.
Now let me sob and sigh my fill,
   ere I from hence depart :   110
That inward pangs with speed may burst
   my sore afflicted heart.

Ah cursed man whose loathed life
  is held so much in scorne:
Whose company is cleane despis'd,
  and left as one forlorn.
Now take thy leaue and last adue,
  of this thy countrey deare.
Which neuer more thou must behold
  nor yet approach it neare.   120

How happy should I count my self,
  if death my heart had torne:
That I might haue my bones entomb'd
  where I was bred and borne.
Or that by *Neptunes* wrathfull rage,
  I might be prest to dye;
Whilst that sweet *Englands* pleasant banks,
  did stand before mine eye.

How sweet a sent hath *English* ground,
  within my senses now: 130
How faire vnto my outward sight,
  seemes euery branch and bow.
The fields and flowers, the trees and stones,
  seeme such vnto my mind:
That in all other Countries sure,
  the like I shall not find.

Oh that the Sun, with shining face,
  would stay his Steeds by strength:
That this same day might stretched be
  to twenty yeares of length.   140
And that the true performed tides,
  their hasty course would stay;
That *Eolus* would neuer yeeld,
  to beare me hence away.

That by the Fountaine of mine eye,
  the fields might watred be:
That I might graue my grieuous plaints,
  vpon each springing tree.

116 left *B C D E*: life *A*   142 would stay *B C D E*: to stay *A*

But time I see, with Eagles wings,
   so swift doth flye away: 150
And dusky clouds begin to dim
   the brightnes of the day.

The fatall houre draweth on,
   the winds and tides agree:
And now sweet *England* ouer soone,
   I must depart from thee.
The mariners haue hoisted sailes,
   and call to catch me in:
And now in wofull heart I feele,
   my torments to begin.   160

Wherefore farwel for euermore,
   sweet *England* vnto thee:
And farwel, all my freinds which I
   againe shall neuer see.
And *England* here I kisse thy ground
   vpon my bended knee:
Whereby to shew to all the world,
   how deare I loued thee.

This being said, away he went,
   as fortune did him guide: 170
And at the length with griefe of hart,
   in *Venice* there he died.
The Duke in dolefull sort,
   did leade his life in *France*:
And at the last the mighty Lord,
   did him full high aduance.

The Lords of *England* afterward,
   did send for him againe:
While that King *Richard* at the wars,
   in Ireland did remaine.   180
Who through the vile and great abuse,
   which through his deeds did spring,
Deposed was, and then the Duke
   was truly crowned King.

8.

The Noble Acts of *Arthur* of the round Table.

To the Tune of, Flying Fame.

WHen *Arthur* first in court began,
    and was approued King:
By force of armes great victories wan,
    and conquest home did bring.
Then into *Britaine* straight he came,
    where fiftie good and able
Knights then repaired vnto him,
    which were of the round Table.
And many Iusts and Turnaments,
    before them there were drest: 10
Where valiant Knights did then excell
    and farre surmount the rest.
But one Sir *Lancelot du Lake*,
    who was approued well,
He in his fights and deeds of arms,
    all other did excell:
When he had rested him a while,
    to play to game and sport,
He thought he would go proue himselfe,
    in some aduenturous sort.   20
He armed rode in forrest wide,
    and met a Damosell faire:
Who told him of aduentures great,
    whereunto he gaue good eare.
Why should I not (quoth *Lancelot*) tho,
    for that cause came I hither:
Thou seemst (quoth she) a Knight right good,
    and I will bring thee thither:
Where as the mightiest Knight doth dwell
    that now is of great fame: 30
Wherefore tell me what Knight thou art,
    and then what is your name,
My name is *Lancelot du Lake*;
    (quoth she) it likes me than:
Here dwels a Knight that neuer was
    orematcht with any man.

11 valiant *C D E*: both *A B*   15 fights *B C D E*: fight *A*

Who hath in prison threescore Knights,
  and foure that he hath won :
Knights of King *Arthurs* court they be,
  and of his Table round.   40
She brought him to a Riuers side,
  and also to a tree :
Whereas a copper Bason hung,
  his fellowes shields to see.
He stroke so hard the Bason broke,
  when *Tarquin* heard the sound,
He droue a horse before him straight,
  whereon a Knight lay bound.
Sir Knight then said Sir *Lancelot* tho,
  bring me that horse load hither :   50
And lay him downe and let him rest,
  weele trie our force together.
And as I vnderstand thou hast,
  so farre as thou art able,
Done great despight and shame vnto
  the Knights of the round Table.
If thou be of the Table round,
  (quoth *Tarquin*, speedily)
Both thee and all thy fellowship,
  I vtterly defie.   60
That's ouermuch (quoth *Lancelot* tho),
  defend thee by and by.
They put their spurs vnto their Steeds
  and each at other flie.
They coucht their speares and horses ran,
  as though there had been thunder.
And each stroake then amidst the shield,
  wherewith they brake in sunder.
Their horses backes brake vnder them,
  the Knights were both astound,   70
To void their horse they made great hast
  to light vpon the ground.
They tooke them to their shields full fast,
  their swords they drew out than :
With mighty strokes most egerly,
  each one to other ran.
They wounded were, and blew full sore,
  for breath they both did stand,

And leaning on their swords a while,
  (quoth *Tarquin*) hold thy hand.   80
And tell to me what I shall aske.
  say on (quoth *Lancelot* tho) :
Thou art (quoth *Tarquin*) the best Knight,
  that euer I did know :
And like a Knight that I did hate,
  so that thou be not he,
I will deliuer all the rest,
  and eke accord with thee.
That is well said (quoth *Lancelot* tho) :
  but sith it must be so,   90
What is the Knight thou hatest so,
  I pray thee to me show,
His name is Sir *Lancelot du Lake*,
  he slew my brother deare ;
Him I suspect of all the rest,
  I would I had him here.
Thy wish thou hast but now vnknowne,
  I am *Lancelot du Lake*,
Now Knight of *Arthurs* Table round,
  kind *Haunds* sonne of Benwake :   100
And I defie thee, do thy worst.
  Ha, ha (quoth *Tarquin* tho) :
One of vs two shall end our liues,
  before that we do go.
If thou be *Lancelot du Lake*,
  then welcome shalt thou be :
Wherefore see thou thy selfe defend,
  for now I thee defie.
They buckled then together so,
  like two wilde Boares, so rushing :   110
And with their swords and shields they ran
  at one another lashing,
The ground besprinkled was with bloud,
  Tarquin began to faint :
For he gaue backe, and bore his shield
  so low, he did repent.
That soone espied Sir *Lancelot* tho,
  he leapt vnto him then :
He pul'd him downe vpon his knees,
  and rushing off his helme.   120

And he stroke his necke in two
and when he had done so,
From prison threescore Knights and foure,
Lancelot deliuered though.

FINIS.

9.

A Song in praise of Women.

To a pleasant new Tune, called, My Valentine.

AMong all other things
that God hath made beneath the skie,
Most gloriously to satisfie the curious eye
of Mortall man withall :
The sight of *Eue*,
Did soonest fit his fancy :
Whose curtesie and amitie, most speedily,
had caught his heart in thrall :
Whom he did loue so deare,
as plainely did appeare :   10
He made her Queene of all the world
and Mistresse of his heart :
Though afterwards she wrought his woe,
his death and deadly smart,

What need I speake
Of matters passed long agoe :
Which all men know I need not show, to hie or low
the case it is so plaine,
Although that *Eue* committed then so great offence,
Ere she went hence,   20
A recompence in our defence,
she made mankind againe :
For by her blessed seed
we are redeemd indeede :

124 Lancelot *B C D E* : Tarquin *A*

Why should not then all mortall men,
  esteeme of women well :
And loue their wiues euen as their liues,
  as nature doth compell.

A vertuous wife.
The Scripture doth commend and say :   30
That night and day, shee is a stay from all decay,
  to keep her houshold still.
She vseth not
To giue her self to wandering,
Or flattering, or pratling, or any thing
  to do her neighbour ill :
But all her mind is bent,
  his pleasures to content.
Her faithfull loue doth not remoue,
  for any storme or griefe,   40
Then is not he well blest thinke ye,
  that meets with such a wife :

But now me thinkes,
I heare some men do say to me,
Few such there be in each degree and qualitie,
  at this day to be found :
And now adayes,
Some wiues do set their whole delight,
Both day and night, with all despight to brawle and fight,
  their rage doth so abound.   50
But sure I think and say,
  here comes none such to day.
Nor do I know of any she,
  that is within this place,
And yet for feare I dare not sweare,
  it is so hard a case.

But to conclude,
For maides, and wiues and virgins all,
Both great and small, in bowre or hall, to pray I shall
  so long as life doth last.   60
That they may liue,
With hearts content and perfect peace,
That ioyes increase may neuer cease, till death release
  the care that crept so fast :
        32 houshold *A* : husband *B C D E*

For duty doth me binde,
To haue them all in mind:
Euen for her sake, that doth vs make
  so merry to be seene:
The glory of the femall kind,
I meane our Noble Queene.   70

FINIS.

10.

A Song in praise of a single life.

To the Tune of the Ghosts hearse.

SOme do write of bloudy warres,
  Some shew the sundry iarres,
    twixt men, through enuy raised:
Some in praise of Princes write,
Some set their whole delight
    to heare faire beauty blazed.
Some other persons are moued,
    for to praise where they are loued:
And let louers praise beauty as they will;
Otherwayes I am intended: 10
True loue is little regarded,
And oftentymes goes vnrewarded,
    then to auoid all strife,
I'll resolue to lead a single life,
Whereby the heart is not offended.

O what suit and seruice too,
Is vsed by them that woo:
    and all to purchase fauor,
O what griefe in heart and mind,
What sorrow we do find,   20
    through womans fond behauiour:
Subiect to suffer each lowre,
    and speeches both sharpe and sowre,
And labour, loue & cost,
Perchance its but all lost,

14 *C D E: A and B omit*

and no way to be amended :
And so to purchase pleasure,
And after repent at leysure,
Then to auoid all strife, &c.

To a man in wedded state 30
Doth happen much debate,
   except Gods speciall fauour :
If his wife be proudly bent,
Or secretly consent,
   to any lewd behauiour :
If she be slothful or idle,
Or such as her tongue cannot bridle,
Oh then well were he,
If death his bane would be,
No sorrow else can be amended : 40
For looke how long he were liuing,
Euermore would he be grieuing.
Then to auoid all strife, &c.

Married folke we often heare,
Euen through their children deare :
   haue many causes of sorrowes,
If disobedient they be found,
Or false in any ground,
   by their vnlawfull borrowes,
To see such wicked fellows, 50
   shamefully come to the Gallowes.
Whom Parents with great care,
Nourished with dainty fare,
   from their cradle truly tended,
When as the mother before them,
   doth curse the day that ere she bore them.
Then to auoid all strife, &c.

Do we then behold and see,
When men and wiues agree,
   and liue and loue together : 60
Where the Lord hath sent them eke :
Faire children mild and meeke,
   like flowers in Summers weather

36 her *B C D E* : his *A*

How greatly are they grieued,
And will not by ioy be relieued,
  if that death doth call,
Either wife or children small,
  whom their vertues do commend,
Their losses whom they thus loued,
  from their hearts cannot be moued   70
Then to auoid all strife, &c.

Who being in that happy state,
Would work himself such hate,
  his fancy for to follow:
Or, liuing here deuoid of strife,
Would take to him a wife:
  for to procure his sorrow:
With carking and with caring,
Euermore must be sparing:
Were he not worse then mad,   80
  being merry wold be sad:
Were he to be commended,
That ere would seeke such pleasure,
  where griefe is all his treasure.
Then to auoid all strife, &c.

II.

The widdowes solace.

To the tune of Robinsons Almaine.

M Ourne no more faire widdow,
  teares are all in vaine:
Tis neither griefe nor sorrow,
  can call the dead againe.
Man's well enough compared
  vnto the Summers flower:
Which now is faire and pleasant,
  yet withered in an houre.
And mourne no more in vaine,
  as one whose faith is small: 10
Be patient in affliction,
  and giue god thanks for all

All men are borne to dye,
   the Scripture telleth plaine,
Of earth we are created,
   to earth we must againe.
Twas neither *Cressus* treasure,
   nor *Alexanders* fame,
Nor *Solomon* by wisdome,
   that could deaths fury tame.   20
No Physicke might preserue them
   when nature did decay :
What man can hold for euer,
   the thing that will away ?
     Then mourn no more, &c.

Though you haue lost your husband,
   your comfort in distresse :
Consider God regardeth
   the widdowes heauinesse.
And hath straightly charged,   30
   such as his children be,
The fatherlesse and widdow,
   to shield from iniury.
     Then mourn no more, &c.

If he were true and faithfull,
   and louing vnto thee,
Doubt not but ther's in *England*,
   enough as good as he.
But if that such affection,
   within his heart was none :   40
Then giue God praise and glory,
   that he is dead and gone.
     And mourn no more, &c.

Receiue such sutors friendly,
   as do resort to thee :
Respect not the outward person,
   but the inward grauity :
And with aduised iudgment,
   chuse him aboue the rest :
Whom thou by proofe hast tried,   50
   in heart to loue thee best.
     Then mourn no more, &c.

Then shalt thou leade a life,
   exempt from all annoy:
And whensoeuer it chanceth,
   I pray God giue thee ioy.
And thus I make an end,
   with true humilitie,
In hope my simple solace,
   shall well accepted be.   60
   Then mourn no more in vaine, &c.

FINIS.

12.

A Gentlewomans complaint, in that she found her
freind faithlesse, which should haue continued constant.

FAith is a figure standing now for nought:
   faith is a fancy which ought to rest in thought.
Faith now adaies, as all the world may see,
   resteth in few, and Faith is fled from thee.

Is there any Faith in strangers to be found:
   is there any Faith lies hidden in the ground:
Is there any Faith in men that buried be:
   no there is none, and Faith is fled from thee.

Fled is the Faith that might remaine in any,
   fled is the Faith that should remaine in many; 10
Fled is the Faith that should in any be.
   then farwell hope, for Faith is fled from thee.

From Faith I see, that euery one is flying:
   from Faith I see, that all things are a dying:
They flye from Faith that most in Faith should be,
   and Faithlesse thou, that brake thy Faith to me.

Thee haue I sought, but thee I could not find,
   thou of all other, was most within my mind;
Thee haue I left, and I alone will be,
   because I finde that Faith is fled from thee. 20

13.

Of a prince of *England*, who wooed the Kings daughter
of *France*, and how he was slaine, and she after
marred to a Forrester.

To the tune of Crimson velvet.

IN the dayes of old,
 when faire *France* did flourish ;
Stories plainly told,
 louers felt annoy.
The King a Daughter had,
Beautious, bright, and louely,
Which made her Father glad,
 she was his only ioy.
A Prince of *England* came,
Whose deeds did merit fame :   10
 he wooed her long, and loe at last,
Looke what he did require,
She granted his desire,
 their hearts in one were linked fast.
Which when her Father proued,
Lord how he was moued,
 and tormented in his mind :
He sought for to preuent them,
And to discontent them :
 fortune crosses Louers kind.   20
When the Princes twaine,
Were thus bard of pleasure,
Through the Kings disdaine,
 which their ioyes withstood,
The Lady got vp close,
Her iewels and her treasure,
Hauing no remorse,
 of state or royall Bloud.
In homely poore array,
She went from Court away,   30
 to meet her ioy and hearts delight :
Who in a Forrest great,
Had taken vp his seat,
 to wait her comming in the night.

3 told *Crawford* : tell *A*   30 went *Crawford* : got *A*

But see what sudden danger,
To this Princely stranger,
   chanced as he sate alone,
By out-lawes was he robbed,
And with ponyards stabbed,
   vttering many a dying groane.   40
The Princesse arm'd by him,
And by true desire:
Wandring all the night,
   without dread at all.
Still vnknowne she passed,
In her strange attire,
Comming at the last,
   in the echoes call.
You faire woods (quoth she)
Honoured may you be,   50
   harbouring my hearts delight,
Which doth compasse here,
My ioy and only deere,
   my trusty friend and Knight.
Sweet I come vnto thee,
Sweet I come to woe thee,
   that thou maist not angry be;
For my long delaying,
And thy courteous staying,
   amends for all Ile make to thee.   60
Passing thus alone,
Through the silent Forrest
Many a grieuous groan,
   sounded in her eares:
Where she heard a man,
To lament the sorest,
Chance that euer came,
   forced by deadly strife:
Farewell my deare (quoth he)
Whom I shall neuer see: 70
   for why my life is at an end,
Through villaines cruelty,
Lo here for thee I dye,
   to shew I am a faithfull friend,

61 alone *Crawford*: along *A*   63 *Crawford*: Many grieuous groanes, *A*
67 *Crawford*: That was euer seene, *A*   68 strife *Crawford*: feare *A*

Here I ly a bleeding,
While my thoughts are feeding,
  on thy dearest beauty found;
O hard hap that may be,
Litle knowes my Lady,
  my heart bloud lyes on the ground.   80
With that he gaue a groane,
Which did burst in sunder,
All the tender strings
  of his bleeding heart.
She which knew his voice,
At his tale did wonder:
All her former ioys
  did to griefe conuert.
Straight she ran to see,
Who this man should be,   90
  that so like her loue did speake:
And found when as she came,
Her louely Lord lay slaine,
  all smear'd in bloud, which life did breake.
When this deed she spied,
Lord how sore she cryed:
Her sorrow cannot counted be,
Her eyes like fountaines running,
Whiles she cryed out my darling,
Would God that I had dyed for thee.   100
His pale lips alas,
Twenty times she kissed,
And his face did wash,
  with her trickling teares;
Euery bleeding wound,
Her faire eyes bedewed,
Wiping off the bloud
  with her golden haire.
Speak my Lord (quoth she)
Speake faire Prince, to me,   110
One sweet word of comfort giue:
Lift vp thy faire eyes,
Listen to my cryes,
  think in what great griefe I liue.

87 ioys *Crawford*: ioy *A*   100 Would God *Crawford*: O would *A*
109 *Crawford*: *A omits*

All in vaine she sued,
All in vaine she wooed,
   the Princes life was dead and gone,
There stood she still mourning,
Till the Sunnes returning,
   and bright day was comming on.   120
In this great distresse,
(Quoth the royall Lady)
Who can now expresse,
   what will become of me?
To my Fathers Court,
Will I neuer wander,
But some seruice take,
   where I might placed be:
Whilst thus she made her mone,
Weeping all alone,   130
   all in dread and dreadfull feare.
A Forrester all in greene,
Most comely to be seene,
   ranging the woods did find her there,
Round beset with sorrow,
Maid (quoth he) good morrow,
   what hard hap hath brought you here:
Harder hap did neuer,
Chance to a maiden euer,
   here lies slaine my brother deare.   140
Where might I be placed,
Gentle Forrester, tell me:
Where should I procure
   a seruice in my need.
Paines I will not spare,
But will do my duty,
Ease me of my care,
   help my extreme need.
The Forrester all amazed,
On her beauty gazed,   150
   till his heart was set on fire.
If faire Maide (quoth he)
You will go with me,
You shall haue your hearts desire.

116 wooed *Crawford*: viewed *A*   119 returning] approaching *A B C D E*
29 Whilst *Crawford*: And *A*   144 need *Crawford*: care *A*

He brought her to his mother,
And aboue all other,
   he sets forth this maidens praise:
Long was his heart enflamed,
At last her loue he gained:
   thus did he his glory raise.   160
Thus vnknowne he matched,
With the Kings faire Daughter:
Children seuen he had,
   ere she to him was knowne:
But when he vnderstood,
She was a royall Princesse,
By this meanes at last,
   he shewed forth her fame:
He cloath'd his Children then,
Not like other men,   170
   in party colours strange to see:
The left side cloth of Gold,
The right side to behold,
   of woollen cloth still framed he.
Men hereat did wonder,
Golden fame did thunder
   this strange deed in euery place.
The King of *France* came thither,
Being pleasant weather,
   in the woods the Hart to chase.   180
The children then did stand,
As their Father willed,
Where the Royall King,
   must of force come by.
Their Mother richly clad
In faire Crimson veluet:
Their Father all in gray,
   comely to the eye.
Then the famous King,
Noted euery thing,   190
   asking how he durst be so bold,
To let his wife to weare,
And decke his children there,
   in costly robes, in cloth of gold.

164 *Crawford*: ere he knew the same *A*   173 to *Crawford*: now *A*

The forrester bold replyed,
And the cause descried,
   to the King thus did he say:
Well may they by their Mother,
Weare rich gold like other,
   being by birth a Princesse gay.   200
The King vpon these words,
More heedfully beheld them:
Till a Crimson blush,
   his conceit did crosse.
The more I looke, he said,
On thy wife and children,
The more I call to mind,
   my Daughter whom I lost.
I am that Child (quoth she)
Falling on her knee,   210
   pardon me my Soueraigne Liege.
The King perceiuing this,
His daughter deare did kisse
   and ioyfull teares did stop his speech:
With his traine he turned,
And with her soiourned;
   straight way he dub'd her husband knight,
Then made him Earle of *Flanders,*
One of his chiefe Commanders:
   thus was their sorrow put to flight.   220

FINIS.

14.

Of the faithfull friendship that lasted betweene two faithfull friends.

To the Tune of Flying Fame.

IN stately *Rome* sometimes did dwell
  a man of noble Fame:
Who had a sonne of seemely shape,
Alphonso was his name:

195 bold *Crawford*: both *A*

When he was growne and come to age,
  his father thought it best
To send his sonne to *Athens* faire,
  where wisdomes Schoole did rest.

And when he was to *Athens* come,
  good Lectures for to learne.   10
A place to board him with delight,
  his friends did well discerne,
A noble Knight of *Athens* Towne,
  of him did take the charge,
Who had a sonne *Ganselo* cald,
  iust of his pitch and age.

In stature and in person both,
  in fauour, speech and face,
In qualitie and condition eke
  they greed in euery place.   20
So like they were in all respects,
  the one vnto the other;
They were not knowne but by their name,
  of father or of mother.

And as in fauour they were found
  alike in all respects :
Euen so they did most dearly loue,
  as prou'd by good effects.
Ganselo loued a Lady faire,
  which did in *Athens* dwell,   30
Who was in beauty peerlesse found,
  so farre she did excell.

Vpon a time it chanced so,
  as fancy did him moue :
That he would visit for delight,
  his Lady and his loue :
And to his true and faithfull friend,
  he did declare the same :
Asking of him if he would see,
  that faire and comely Dame.   40

28 effects *B C D E* : respect *A*

Alphonso did thereto agree,
  and with *Ganselo* went :
To see the Ladie whom he lou'd
  which bred his discontent.
But when he cast his Christall eyes
  vpon her angels hue :
The beauty of that Ladie bright,
  did straight his heart subdue,

His gentle heart so wounded was,
  with that faire Ladies face,   50
That afterward he daily liu'd
  in sad and wofull case.
And of his griefe he knew not how
  thereof to make an end :
For that he knew the Ladies loue,
  was yeelded to his friend.

Thus being sore perplext in mind,
  vpon his bed he lay :
Like one which death and deepe despaire,
  had almost worne away.   60
His friend *Ganselo* that did see,
  his griefe and great distresse :
At length requested for to know
  his cause of heauinesse.

With much adoe at length he told
  the truth vnto his friend :
Who did release his inward woe,
  with comfort in the end.
Take courage then deare friend (quoth he)
  though she through loue be mine :   70
My right I will resigne to thee,
  the Lady shall be thine.

You know our fauours are alike,
  our speech alike likewise :
This day in mine apparell then,
  you shall your selfe disguise.
And vnto Church then shall you goe,
  directly in my sted :
So though my friends suppose tis I,
  you shall the Lady wed.   80

Alphonso was so well appaid,
  and as they had decreed :
He went next day and wedded plaine,
  the Lady there indeed.
But when the Nuptiall Feast was done,
  and *Phœbus* quite was fled,
The Lady for *Ganselo* tooke
  Alphonso to her bed.

That night they spent in pleasant sport,
  and when the day was come,   90
A Post for faire *Alphonso* came,
  to fetch him home to *Rome.*
Then was the matter plainley prou'd,
  Alphonso wedded was,
And not *Ganselo* to that Dame,
  which wrought great wo alas.

Alphonso being come to *Rome,*
  with his Lady gay,
Ganseloes friends and kindred all,
  in such a rage did stay,   100
That they depriu'd him of his wealth,
  his lands and rich attyre,
And banishd him their Country quite,
  in rage and wrathfull yre.

With sad and pensiue thoughts alas
  Ganselo wandred then,
Who was constrain'd, through want to beg
  reliefe of many men.
In this distresse oft would he say,
  to *Rome* I meane to go: 110
To seeke *Alphonso* my deare friend,
  who will relieue my woe.

To *Rome* when poore *Ganselo* came
  and found *Alphonsoes* place,
Which was so famous huge & faire,
  himselfe in such poore case.
He was asham'd to shew himselfe,
  in that his poore array :
Saying *Alphonso* knowes me well,
  if he should come this way.   120

Wherfore he staid within the street
   Alphonso then came by :
But heeding not *Ganselo* poore
   his friend that stood so nie.
Which grieu'd *Ganselo* to the hart :
   (quoth he) and is it so?
Doth proud *Alphonso* now disdaine
   his friend indeed to know?

In desperate sort away he went,
   into a Barne hard by :   130
And presently he drew his knife,
   thinking thereby to die.
And bitterly in sorrow there
   did he lament and weepe :
And being ouer swayed with grief,
   he there fell fast asleepe.

Where soundly there he sweetly slept,
   came in a murthering thiefe,
And saw a naked knife, lie by
   this man so full of griefe   140
The knife so bright he tooke vp straight
   and went away amaine :
And thrust it in a murthered man,
   which he before had slaine.

And afterward he went with speed,
   and put this bloudie knife
Into his hand that sleeping lay,
   to saue himself from strife.
Which done, in hast away he ran,
   and when that search was made,   150
Ganselo with his bloudie knife,
   was for the murther staid.

And brought before the Magistrates,
   who did confesse most plaine,
That he indeed with that same knife,
   the murthered man had slaine.

   139 *C D E* : And with a naked knife, lay by *A B*

Alphonso sitting there as Iudge,
  and knowing *Ganseloes* face :
To saue his friend, did say himselfe
  was guiltie in that case.   160

None (quoth *Alphonso*) kil'd the man,
  my Lord but onely I :
And therefore set this poore man free,
  and let me iustly die.
Thus while for death these faithfull friends
  in striuing did proceed :
The man before the Senate came,
  which did the fact indeed.

Who being moued with remorse,
  their friendly hearts to see,   170
Did proue before the Iudges plaine,
  none did the fact but he.
Thus when the truth was plainly told,
  of all sides ioy was seene :
Alphonso did embrace his friend,
  which had so wofull beene.

In rich array he clothed him,
  as fitted his degree :
And helpt him to his lands againe,
  and former dignity.   180
The murtherer he for telling truth,
  had pardon at that time :
Who afterwards lamented much,
  his foul and grieuous crime.

FINIS.

The second part of the Garland of good Will.

I.

A pastorall Song.

To the Tune of Heigh ho, Holiday.

VPon a Downe where shepheards keepe,
  piping pleasant Layes :
Two Country maids were tending sheepe,
  and sweetly chanted Roundelayes.
Three shepheards each an Oaten Reed,
  blaming *Cupids* cruell wrong,
Vnto these rurall Nimphs agreed,
  to keepe a tunefull vnder-song.

And for they were in number fiue,
  musicks number sweet :   10
And we the like let vs contriue,
  to sing their song in order meet.
Faire *Phillis* part Ile take to me,
  she gainst louing Hinds complaines :
And *Amarillis* thou shalt be,
  she defends the shepheard swaines.

Ph. Fie on the sleights that men deuise.
Sh.   Heigh ho, silly sleights.
Ph. When simple maids they would entice.
Sh.   Maids are young mens chiefe delights.   20
Am. Nay, women they witch with their eyes.
Sh.   Eyes like beames of burning Sun.
Am. And men once caught, they soone despise
Sh.   So are Shepheards oft vndone.

Ph. If any young man win a maid.
Sh.   Happy man is he.
Ph. By trusting him she is betrai'd.
Sh.   Fie vpon such trechery.

16 shepheard *D* : shepherds *A B C E*

Am. If maids win yong men with their guiles.
Sh.   Heigh ho, heigh ho, guilefull griefe.   30
Am. They deale like weeping Crocodiles.
Sh.   That murther man without reliefe.

Ph. I know a silly Country Hind.
Sh.   Heigh ho, heigh ho, silly Swaine.
Ph. To whom faire *Daphne* proued kind.
Sh.   Was not he kind to her againe?
Ph. He vowed to *Pan* with many an oath.
Sh.   Heigh ho, shepheards God is he.
Am. Yet since hath chang'd and broke his troth.
Sh.   Troth-plight broke will plagued be.   40

Am. She had deceiued many a Swaine
Sh.   Fie vpon such false deceit.
Am. And plighted troth to them in vaine.
Sh.   There can be no griefe more great.
Am. Her measure was with measure paid.
Sh.   Heigh ho, heigh ho, equall meed.
Am. She was beguiled that had betrai'd.
Sh.   So shall all deceiuers speed.

Ph. If euery maid were like to me.
Sh.   Heigh ho, heigh ho, hard of heart.   50
Ph. Both loue and louers scorn'd should be.
Sh.   Scorners should be sure of smart.
Am. If euery maid were of my mind,
Sh.   Heigh ho, heigh ho, louely sweet.
Am. They to their louers shold proue kind.
Sh.   Kindnes is for maidens meet.

Ph. Me thinkes loue is an idle toy.
Sh.   Heigh ho, heigh ho, busie paine.
Ph. Both wit and sence it doth annoy.
Sh.   Both wit and sence thereby we gaine.   60
Am. Tush *Phillis*, cease, be not so coy.
Sh.   Heigh ho, heigh ho, coy disdaine.
Am. I know you loue a Shepheards boy,
Sh.   Fie that woman so can faine.

47 had] was *A B C D E*

Ph. Well, *Amaryllis*, now I yeeld.
Sh.   Shepheards sweetly pipe aloud.
Ph. Loue conquers both in towne and field.
Sh.   Like a tyrant fierce and proud.
Am. The Euening Starre is vp wee see.
Sh.   Vesper shines wee must away.   70
Ph. Would euery louer would agree.
Sh.   So we end our Roundelay.

2.

Of patient *Grissel* and a Noble Marquesse.

To the Tune of, The Brides good morrow.

A Noble Marquesse, as he did ride a hunting
    hard by a riuers side :
A proper Maiden, as she did sit a spinning,
    his gentle eyes had spide.
Most faire & louely, & of comely grace was she,
    although in simple attire :
She sang full sweet, with pleasant voyce melodiously,
    which set the Lords heart on fire.
The more he lookt, the more he might,
Beautie bred, his hearts delight.   10
    and to this daintie Damsel then he went,
God speed (quoth he) thou famous Flower,
Fair Mistresse of this homely bower,
    where loue & vertue liues with sweet content.

With comely gesture, & modest fine behauiour,
    she bade him welcome then :
She entertain'd him in faithful friendly maner,
    and all his Gentlemen.
The noble Marques in his hart felt such a flame
    which set his senses at strife :   20
(Quoth he) faire Maiden shew me soone what is thy name,
    I mean to make thee my wife.
Grissel is my name (quoth she)
Farre vnfit for your degree,
    a silly Maiden and of parents poore.
Nay *Grissel*, thou art rich, he said,
A vertuous, faire, and comely maid,
    grant me thy loue, and I will aske no more.

At length she consented, & being both contented,
    they married with speed :   30
Her country russet was chang'd to silke & veluet
    as to her state agreed.
And when that she was trimly tired in the same
    her beauty shined most bright :
Far staining euery other braue & comely Dame
    that did appeare in her sight,
Many enuied her therefore,
Because she was of parents poore,
    and twixt her Lord & she great strife did raise :
Some saide this and some said that,   40
Some did call her beggars brat,
    and to her Lord they would her oft dispraise.

O, noble Marques (qd. they) why do you wrong vs
    thus basely for to wed :
That might haue gotten an honourable Lady
    into your Princely bed :
Who will not now your noble issue still deride
    which shall be hereafter borne,
That are of bloud so base by their mothers side,
    the which will bring them to scorn :   50
Put her therfore, quite away,
Take to you a Lady gay,
    whereby your Linage may renowned be.
Thus euery day they seeme to prate,
At malic'd *Grissels* good estate,
    who tooke all this most mild and patiently.

When that the Marques did see that they were bent thus
    against his faithfull wife,
Whom most dearley, tenderly, and entirely,
    he loued as his life :   60
Minding in secret for to proue her patient heart
    therby her foes to disgrace :
Thinking to play a hard discourteous part,
    that men might pitty her case,
Great with child this Lady was,
And at length it came to passe,

two goodly children at one birth she had.
A sonne and daughter God had sent,
Which did their Father well content,
   and which did make their mothers heart full glad.   70

Great royall Feastings was at the Childrens christning,
   and Princely triumph made:
Six weekes together, all Nobles that came thither
   were entertaind and staid.
And when that al these pleasant sportings quite were done,
   the Marquesse a messenger sent
For his yong daughter, & his prety smiling son
   declaring his full intent:
How that the babes must murthered be,
For so the Marquesse did decree: 80
   come, let me haue the children, then he said,
With that faire *Grissel* wept full sore,
She wrung her hands, and said no more,
   my gracious Lord must haue his will obayd.

She tooke the Babies from the nursing Ladies,
   betweene her tender armes:
She often wishes, with many sorrowfull kisses,
   that she might helpe their harmes.
Farwel farwel (quoth she) my children deere,
   neuer shall I see you againe: 90
Tis long of me your sad & wofull mother here,
   for whose sake ye must be slaine:
Had I beene borne of Royall race,
You might haue liu'd in happy case:
   but you must die for my vnworthinesse,
Come messenger of death (said she)
Take my despised Babes to thee,
   and to their father my complaints expresse.

He tooke the children, and to his Noble Master
   he brought them forth with speed.   100
Who secret sent them vnto a noble Lady,
   to be nurst vp indeed.
Then to faire *Grissel* with a heauy heart he goes
   where she sate mildly all alone:
A pleasant gesture and a louely looke she shows,
   as if griefe she had neuer knowne.

(Quoth he) my children now are slaine,
What thinkes faire *Grissel* of the same,
   sweet *Grissel* now declare thy mind to mee.
Sith you my Lord, are pleased with it,   110
Poor *Grissel* thinks the action fit,
   both I and mine at your command will be.

The Nobles murmure fair *Grissel*, at thy honor,
   and I no ioy can haue :
Till thou be banisht both from my Court & presence,
   as they vniustly craue :
Thou must be stript out of thy stately garments,
   and as thou camst vnto me,
In homely gray, instead of Bisse and purest Pal,
   now all thy clothing must be.   120
My Lady thou shalt be no more,
Nor I thy Lord which grieues me sore,
   the poorest life must now content thy mind.
A groat to thee I may not giue,
Thee to maintaine while I do liue ;
   against my *Grissel* such great foes I find.

When gentle *Grissel* heard these wofull tidings,
   the teares stood in her eyes :
She nothing saide, no words of discontentment
   did from her lips arise :   130
Her veluet gowne most patiently she slipt off,
   her kirtle of silke with the same :
Her russet gowne was brought again with many a scoffe,
   to heare them all her selfe she did frame.
When she was drest in this array :
And ready was to part away :
   God send long life vnto my Lord (quoth she)
Let no offence be found in this,
To giue my Lord a parting kis :
   with watered eyes, farewel my deere (qd. he).   140

From stately Palace vnto her Fathers cottage,
   poore *Grissel* now is gone :
Full fifteen winters, she liued there contented,
   no wrong she thought vpon ;

And at that time through all the land the speeches went,
  the Marquess should married be,
Vnto a Lady great of high discent,
  and to the same all parties did agree.
The Marquesse sent for *Grissel* faire,
The Brides bed chamber to prepare,   150
  that nothing should therein be found awry.
The Bride was with her Brother come,
Which was great ioy to all and some,
  and *Grissel* tooke all this most patiently.

And in the morning when that they should be wedded
  her patience now was tried:
Grissel was charged her selfe in princely manner,
  for to attire the Bride.
Most willingly she gaue consent vnto the same,
  the Bride in her brauery was drest: 160
And presently the noble Marques thither came,
  with all his Lords at his request.
Oh *Grissel*, I would ask of thee,
If thou to this match would agree,
  me thinks thy looks are waxen wondrous coy:
With that they all began to smile,
And *Grissel* she replies the while:
  God send Lord Marques many yeeres of ioy.

The Marques was moued to see his best beloued
  thus patient in distresse: 170
He stept vnto her, and by the hand he tooke her,
  these words he did expresse.
Thou art the Bride, & all the Brides I mean to haue,
  these two thine own children be:
The youthfull Lady on her knees did blessing craue
  her brother as willing as she
And you that enuy her estate,
Whom I haue made my louing mate,
  now blush for shame, and honour vertuous life,
The Chronicles of lasting fame,   180
Shall euermore extoll the name
  of patient *Grissel*, my most constant wife.

FINIS.

166 all began *B C D E*: began all *A*

3.

A pleasant Dialogue betweene plaine *Truth,* and blind *Ignorance.*

Truth.

GOd speed you, aged Father,
 and giue you a good day :
What is the cause I pray you,
 so sadly here to stay :
And that you keepe such gazing
 on this decaied place :
The which for superstition
 good Princes downe did race.

Ignorance.

Chill tell thee by my vazonne
 that sometime che haue knowne   10
A vaire and goodly Abbey,
 stand here of brick and stone :
And many holy Friers,
 as ich may zay to thee :
Within these goodly Cloysters
 che did full often zee.

Truth.

Then I must tell thee Father,
 in truth and veritie :
A sort of greater hypocrites,
 thou couldst not likely see.   20
Deceiuing of the simple,
 with false and feigned lyes :
But such an order, truly,
 Christ neuer did deuise.

Ignorance.

Ah, ah, che zmell thee now, man,
 che know well what thou art :
A vellow of new learning,
 che wis not worth a vart :
Vor when we had the old Law
 a mery world was then :   30
And euery thing was plenty,
 among all zorts of men.

Truth.

Thou giuest me an answer,
   as did the Iewes sometime
Vnto the Prophet *Ieremy*,
   when he accusd their crime.
Twas merry (said the people)
   and ioyful in our Realme,
Which did offer spice cakes
   vnto the Queene of heauen.   40

Ignorance.

Chill tell thee what, good vellow;
   beuore the Vriers went hence,
A bushell of the best wheat
   was zold for vorteene pence:
And vorty Eggs a penny,
   that were both good and new:
And this che zay my selfe haue zeene
   and yet ich am no Iewe.

Truth.

Within the sacred Bible,
   we find it written plaine: 50
The latter dayes should troublesome
   and dangerous be certaine:
That we should be selfe louers,
   and charitie waxen cold:
Then tis not true Religion,
   that makes this griefe to hold.

Ignorance.

Chill tell thee my opinion plaine,
   and chould that well ye knew,
Ich care not for this Bible Booke,
   tis too big to be true.   60
Our blessed Ladies Psalter,
   zhall for my mony go:
Such pretty prayers as there be,
   the Bible cannot zhew.

Truth.

Now hast thou spoken truly,
　for in that Booke indeed :
No mention of our Lady,
　or Romish Saints we read.
For by the blessed Spirit,
　that Booke indited was :　　　　　70
And not by simple persons,
　as is your foolish Masse.

Ignorance.

Cham zure they are not voolish
　that made the Masse che trow :
Why man, 'tis all in Latine,
　and vooles no Latine knowe.
Were not our Vathers wisemen,
　and they did like it well :
Who very much reioyced
　to hear the zacring bell.　　　　　80

Truth.

But many Kings and Prophets,
　as I may say to thee :
Haue wisht the light that you haue,
　and neuer could it see.
For what art thou the better
　a Latine song to heare :
And vnderstandest nothing,
　that they sing in the Quire :

Ignorance.

O hold thy peace che pray thee,
　the noise was passing trim :　　　　90
To heare the Friers zinging,
　as we did enter in.
And then to zee the Roodloft,
　zo brauely zet with Zaints :
And now to zee them wanting,
　my heart with zorrow faints.

Truth.

The Lord did giue commandement,
    no Image thou shouldst make,
Nor that vnto Idolatry
    you should your selfe betake.
The golden Calfe of *Israell*,
    Moses did therefore spoile:
And *Baal* his Priests and Temple,
    he brought to vtter foyle.

100

Ignorance.

But our Lady of *Walsingham*
    was zure an holy Zaint:
And many men in pilgrimage,
    did shew to her complaint.
Yea zweet Zaint *Thomas Becket*,
    and many others moe:
The Holy Maid of *Kent*, likewise
    did many wonders zhow,

110

Truth.

Such Saints are well agreeing,
    to your profession sure:
And to the men that made them
    so precious and so pure.
The one was found a Traitor,
    and iudged worthy death,
The other eke for Treason
    did end his hatefull breath.

120

Ignorance.

Yea yea it is no matter,
    dispraise them how you wille:
But zure they did much goodnesse,
    when they were with vs still.
We had our holy water,
    and holy bread likewise:
And many holy Reliques
    we zaw before our eyes.

Truth.

And all this while they feed you,
   with vaine and sundry showes,   130
Which neuer Christ commanded,
   as learned Doctors knowes.
Search then the holy Scriptures,
   and thou shalt plainly see :
That headlong to damnation,
   they alwayes trained thee.

Ignorance.

If it be true good vellow :
   as thou dost zay to me :
Then to my Zauiour Iesus
   alone then will I flie.   140
Beleeuing in the Gospell,
   and passion of his Zonne :
And with these subtill Papists
   ich haue for euer done.

FINIS.

4.

The ouerthrow of proud *Holofornes,* and the triumph of vertuous Queene *Iudith.*

W Hen King *Nebuchadonezar,*
   was puffed vp with pride :
Hee sent for many men of warre,
   by *Holofornes* guide
To plague and spoile the world throughout,
   by fierce *Bellonaes* rod :
That would not feare and honor him,
   and knowledge him their God.

Which when the holy *Israelites*
   did truly vnderstand :   10
For to preuent his tyrannie,
   they fortified their Land.

Their Towns and stately Cities strong
   they did with victuals store:
Their warlike weapons they prepar'd,
   their furious foe to gore.

When stately *Holofornes* then
   had knowledge of that thing:
That they had thus prepar'd themselues
   for to withstand the King   20
(Quoth he) what God is able now,
   to keep those men from me:
Is there a greater than our King,
   whom all men feare to see.

Come march with mee therefore (he said)
   my Captaines euery one:
And first vnto *Bethulia*,
   with speed let vs be gone.
I will destroy each mothers sonne
   that is within the Land: 30
Their God shall not deliuer them
   out of my furious hand.

Wherefore about *Bethulia*,
   that little City then:
On foot he planted vp and downe,
   an hundred thousand men.
Twelue thousand more on horses braue,
   about the Towne had he,
He stopt their springs and water pipes
   to worke their misery.   40

When foure and thirty days they had
   with warres besieged beene:
The poore *Bethulians* at that time
   so thirsty then was seene,
That they were like to starue and die,
   they were both weake and faint:
The people gainst the Rulers cry,
   and thus was their complaint:

Better it is for vs (quoth they)
   to yeeld vnto our foe :   50
Then by this great and grieuous thirst,
   to be destroyed so.
O render vp the Towne therefore,
   God hath forsaken quite :
There is no meanes to scape their hands,
   who can escape their might?

When as their grieued Rulers heard
   the clamors which they made.
Good people be content (they said)
   and be no whit dismaid.   60
Yet fiue dayes stay in hope of helpe,
   God will regard our woe :
But if by then no succour come,
   weele yeeld vnto our foe.

When *Iudith* (prudent princely Dame)
   had tidings of this thing :
Which was *Manesses* vertuous wife,
   that sometime was their king.
Why tempt ye God so sore (she said)
   before all men this day :   70
Whom mortall men in conscience ought
   to feare and eke obay.

If you will grant me leaue (quoth she)
   to passe abroad this night :
To *Holofornes* I will go,
   for all his furious might.
But what I there intend to do,
   enquire not now of me :
Go then in peace, faire Dame (they said)
   and God be still with thee.   80

When she from them was gotten home,
   within her Palace gate :
She called to her chiefest maid,
   that on her then did waite.
Bring me my best attire (quoth she)
   and Iewels of finest gold :
And wash me with the finest balmes
   that are for siluer sold.

The fairest and the richest robes,
    that then they did possesse: 90
Vpon her dainty corps she put,
    and eke her head did dresse.
With costly pearles and precious stones,
    and Earings of fine gold:
That like an Angell she did seeme,
    most sweet for to behold.

A pot of sweet and pleasant oyle,
    she tooke with her that time:
A bag of Figs, and fine white flower,
    a bottle of fine Wine: 100
Because she should not eat with them
    that worship gods of stone:
And from the City thus she went,
    with one poore maid alone.

Much ground alas she had not gone
    out of her owne City:
But that the Centinels espide
    her comming presently.
From whence come you faire Maid (qd. they)
    and where walke you so late? 110
From yonder Towne, good Sir (quoth she)
    to your Lord of high estate.

When they did marke and view her well,
    and saw her faire beauty:
And there with all her rich array,
    so gorgeous to the eye:
They were amazed in their minds,
    so faire a Dame to see:
They set her in a Chariot then,
    in place of high degree. 120

An hundred proper chosen men
    they did appoint likewise,
To waite on Princely *Iudith* there,
    whose beauty bleard their eyes,

112 estate CDE : state AB

And all the souldiers running came,
  to view her as she went :
And thus with her they past along
  vnto the Generals Tent.

Then came his stately Guard in hast,
  fair *Iudith* for to meet :   130
And to their high renowned Lord,
  they brought this Lady sweet.
And then before his honour high,
  vpon her knees she fell :
Her beauty bright made him to muse,
  so farre she did excell.

Rise vp renowned Dame (quoth he)
  the glory of thy kind :
And be no whit abasht at all,
  to shew to me thy mind.   140
When she had vttered her intent,
  her wit amaz'd them all,
And *Holofernes* heart therewith
  by loue was brought in thrall.

And bearing in his lofty breast,
  the flames of hot desire :
He granted euery thing to her,
  she did of him require.
Each night therfore, he gaue her leaue,
  to walke abroad to pray,   150
According to her owne request,
  which she did make that day.

When she in Camp had three days beene,
  neare *Holofernes* Tent :
His chiefest friend, Lord Treasurer,
  vnto her then he sent.
Faire Dame (quoth he) my Lord commands,
  this night your company :
(Quoth she) I will not my good Lord
  in any thing deny.   160

A great and sumptuous Feast,
    did *Holofernes* make:
Amongst the chiefest Lords and Knights,
    and all for *Iudiths* sake:
But of their dainties in no case,
    would pleasant *Iudith* taste,
Yet *Holofernes* merry was,
    so near him she was plac't.

And being very pleasantly
    disposed at that time: 170
He drunk with them abundantly
    of strong delicious Wine.
So that his strength and memory,
    so far from him was fled:
There lay him down, and *Iudith* then
    was brought vnto his bed.

When all the doores about were shut,
    and euery one was gone,
Hard by the Pillar of his bed
    his sword shee spide anon,   180
Then down she took it presently,
    to God for strength she pray'd,
She cut his head from shoulders quite,
    and gaue it to her maid.

The rich and golden Canopy,
    that hung ouer his bed:
She took the same with her likewise,
    with *Holofornes* head.
And thus through all the Court of guard
    she scaped clean away.   190
None did her stay, thinking that shee
    had gone forth for to pray.

When shee had past, scaped quite
    the danger of them all,
And that shee was come near vnto
    the sieged Cities wall:

163 *Here severa₁ pages are missing in A, and the text is supplied from B,*
till l. 110 *in the Winning of Cales*   166 pleasant *C D E* : present *B*
taste *D E* : take *B C*

Come ope the gates (quoth shee)
  our foe the Lord hath slain;
See here his head within my hand,
  that bore so great a fame. 200

Vpon a Pole they pitcht his head,
  that all men might it spie:
And ore the City walls forthwith,
  they set it presently.
Then all the Souldiers in the Town,
  marcht forth in rich array:
But sure their foes spide their approach
  for twas at break of day.

Then running hastily to call
  their Generall out of bed: 210
They found his liuelesse body there,
  but clean without his head.
When this was known, all in a maze
  they fled away each man:
They left their tents full rich behind,
  and so away they ran.

Lo here behold how God prouides
  for them that in him trust:
When earthly hope is all in vain,
  he takes vs from the dust. 220
How often hath our *Iudith* sau'd,
  and kept vs from decay:
Gainst *Holofernes*, Deuill and Pope,
  as may be seen this day.

FINIS.

5.

A Princely Ditty, in praise of the English Rose.

Translated out of French.

A Mong the Princely Paragons,
    bedect with dainty Diamonds,
Within mine eye, none doth come nie,
    the sweet red Rose of *England*,
The Lillies passe in brauery,
    in *Flanders*, *Spain*, and *Italy* :
But yet the famous flower of *France*
    doth honour the Rose of *England*.

As I abroad was walking,
    I heard the small birds talking :   10
And euery one did frame her Song
    in praise of the Rose of *England*,
The Lillies, &c.

Cæsar may vant of Victories,
    and *Crœsus* of his happinesse :
But he were blest, that might bear in his brest
    the sweet red Rose of *England*,
The Lillies, &c.

The brauest Lute bring hither,
    and let vs sing together :   20
While I do ring on euery string,
    the praise of the Rose of *England*,
The Lillies, &c.

The sweet Perfumes and Spices,
    the wise men brought to Iesus :
Did neuer smell a quarter so well
    as doth the Rose of *England*,
The Lillies, &c.

Then faire and princely flower,
    that ouer my heart doth tower,   30
None may be compared to thee,
    which art the fair Rose of *England*.
The Lillies, &c.

9 was *C D E* : am *B*   14 Victories *D E* : Histories *B C*

The third part of the Garland of good Will.

Song. 1.

A Maidens choice twixt Age and Youth.

CRabbid Age and Youth
 cannot liue together:
Youth is full of pleasure,
 Age is full of care.
Youth like Summers morn,
 Age like Winters weather:
Youth is full of sport,
Ages breath is short:
 Youth is nimble, Age is lame;
Youth is hot and bold,   10
Age is weak and cold:
 Youth is wild, and Age is tame:
Age I do abhor thee;
Youth I do adore thee,
 O my loue, my loue is young,
Age I do defie thee:
O sweet Shepherd hie thee,
 for me thinks thou stay'st too long,

Here I do attend,
 arm'd by loue and pleasure,   20
With my youthfull friend,
 ioyfully to meet,
Here I do wait
 for my only treasure,
Venus sugred bait,
 fancies dainty sweet;
Like a louing wife,
 so lead I my life,

9 lame *C D E*: tame *B*   26 fancies dainties sweet *B*: fancy dainty
sweet *C D E*

thirsting for my hearts desire,
Come sweet youth, I pray,   30
Away old man a way,
    thou canst not giue that I require.
For old age I care not,
Come my loue and spare not,
    Age is feeble, Youth is strong,
Age I do defie thee,
O sweet Shephard, hie thee,
    for me thinks thou stayest too long.

Phœbus stay thy Steeds
    ouer swiftly running: 40
Driue not on so fast,
    bright resplendent Sun.
For fair *Daphnes* sake
    now expresse thy cunning:
Pittie on me take,
    else I am vndone,
Your hours swift of flight,
That waste with Titans sight,
    and so consume the cheerfull day,
O stay a while with me,   50
Till I my loue may see,
    O Youth thou dost too long delay,
Time will ouer slip vs,
And in pleasures trip vs,
    come away therefore with speed,
I would not lose an houre,
For faire *London* Tower,
    Venus therefore, help my need.

Floras banks are spread,
    in her rich attire,   60
With the dainty Violet,
    and the Primrose sweet,
Dazes white and red,
    fitting youths desire:
Where the Daffadilly,
    and the Cowslip meet,
All for youths behooue,
Their fresh colours moue,

in the Medowes green and gay,
The Birds with sweetest notes,　　　　　70
Do strain their pritty throates,
　　to entertain my loue this way.
I with twenty wishes,
And an hundred kisses,
　　would receiue him by the hand,
If he gaue not a fall,
I would him Coward call,
　　and all vnto my word would stand.

Loe where he appears
　　like to young *Adonis*,　　　　　80
Ready to set on fire,
　　the chastest heart aliue.
Iewell of my life,
　　welcome where thine own is,
Pleasant are thy looks,
　　sorrowes to depriue.
Embrace thy darling dear,
Without all doubtfull fear :
　　at thy command I wholy rest,
do what thou wilt to me,　　　　　90
Therein I agree,
　　and be not strange to my request :
To youth I only yeeld,
age fits not *Venus* field,
　　though I be conquer'd, what care I,
In such a pleasant warre,
Come meet me if you dare,
　　who first mislikes, first let him cry

FINIS.

2.

A S you came from the holy land
　　of *Walsingham*,
Met you not with my true loue,
　　by the way as you came ?

79 he *C D E* : she *B*

How should I know your true loue,
    that haue met many a one,
As I came from the holy Land,
    that haue come, that haue gone?

She is neither white nor brown,
    but as the heauens fair: 10
There is none hath her form so diuine
    on the earth, in the ayr.
Such an one did I meet (good Sir)
    with Angell-like face:
Who like a Nimph, like a Queen did appear
    in her gate, in her grace.

She hath left me here alone,
    all alone vnknown:
Who sometime loued me as her life,
    and called me her own.   20
What is the cause shee hath left thee alone,
    and a new way doth take,
That sometime did thee loue as her self,
    and her Ioy did thee make?

I haue loued her all my youth,
    but now am old as you see:
Loue liketh not the falling fruit,
    nor the withered tree.
For loue is a carelesse child,
    and forgets promise past,   30
He is blind, he is deaf, when he list,
    and in faith neuer fast.

His desire is fickle, fond,
    and a trustlesse ioy:
He is won with a world of despair,
    and is lost with a toy.
Such is the loue of Women kind,
    or the word (Loue) abused:
Vnder which many childish desires,
    and conceits are excused.   40

But Loue it is a durable fire,
    in the mind euer burning:
Neuer sick, neuer dead, neuer cold,
    from it self neuer turning.

33 fickle, ford, *Percy Folio* : fickle found, *B C D E*

3.

The Winning of Cales.

L Ong the proud Spaniard
   aduanced to conquer vs,
Threatning our Country
  with fire and sword,
Often preparing
  their Nauy most sumptuous,
With all the prouision
  that *Spain* could afford,
Dub, a dub, dub,
  thus strikes their Drummes,   10
Tan ta ra ra, tan ta ra ra,
  English men comes.

To the Seas presently,
  went our Lord admirall,
With Knights couragious,
  and Captains full good,
The Earl of *Essex*,
  a prosperous Generall,
With him prepared,
  to passe the salt flood :   20
Dub a dub, &c.

At Plimouth speedily,
  take they ships valliantly :
Brauer ships neuer
  were seen vnder sails :
With their fair coulers spred,
  and streamers ore their head :
Now bragging Spaniards
  take heed of your taile :
Dub a dub, dub, &c.   30

Vnto *Cales* cunningly
  came we most happily
Where the Kings Nauie
  securely did ride,
Being vpon their backs,
  peircing their Buts of Sacks,

32 came C D E : come B

Ere that the Spaniard
  our comming descrid
Tan ta ra ra ra, English-men comes
  bounce abounce, bounce abounce   40
Off went our Guns.

Great was the crying,
  running and riding,
Which at that season
  was made in that place ;
Then Beacons were fired,
  as need then required :
To hide their great treasure,
  they had little space :
Alas they cryed,   50
  English men comès.

There might you see the Ships,
  how they were fired fast :
And how the men drowned
  themselues in the Sea,
There might you hear them cry,
  wail and weep piteously :
When as they saw no shift
  to escape thence away,
Dub a dub, &c.   60

The great *Saint Philip*,
  The pride of the Spaniards,
Was burnt to the bottom
  and sunk in the sea,
But the *Saint Andrew*,
  and eke the *Saint Matthew*,
We took in fight manly,
  and brought them away.
Dub a dub, &c.

The Earl of *Essex*,   70
  Most valiant and hardy,
With horsemen and footmen,
  marcht towards the Town.
The enemies which saw them,
  full greatly affrighted,
Did fly for their safegard,
  and durst not come down.
Dub a dub, &c.

Now quoth the noble Earl,
    courage my Soldiers all,   80
Fight and be valiant,
    and spoyl you shall haue,
And well rewarded all,
    from the great to the small:
But look that Women
    and Children you saue,
Dub a dub, &c.

The Spaniard at that sight,
    saw 'twas in vain to fight:
Hung vp their flags of truce,   90
    yeelding the Town:
We marcht in presently,
    decking the walls on hie,
With our English coulors,
    which purchast renown:
Dub a dub, &c.

Entring the houses then
    of the richest men,
For Gold and Treasure
    we searched each day: 100
In some places we did finde
    pies baking in the Ouens,
Meat at the fire roasting,
    and men ran away.
Dub a dub, &c.

Full of rich marchandize
    euery shop we did see,
Damask and Sattins
    and veluet full faire:
Which souldiers measured out   110
    by the length of their swords
Of all commodities,
    each one had share.
Dub a dub, &c.

Thus Cales was taken,
   and our braue Generall
Marcht to the Market place,
   there he did stand :
There many prisoners
   of good account were tooke :   120
Many crau'd mercy,
   and mercy they found.
Dub a dub, &c.

When our braue Generall
   saw they delayed time,
And would not ransom
   the Towne as they said :
With their faire Wainscots,
   their Presses and Bedsteds,
Their Ioynt-stooles and Tables,   130
   a fire we made :
And when the town burnt in a flame,
With tan ta ra, tan ta ra ra,
From thence we came.

4.

Of King *Edward* the third, and the faire Countesse of
Salisbury, setting forth her constancy and endlesse
glory.

WHen as King *Edward* the third did liue,
   that valiant King :
Dauid of *Scotland* to rebell,
   did then begin.
The towne of *Barwicke* suddenly
   from vs he wonne :
And burnt *New-castle* to the ground,
   thus strife begun.
To *Rosbury* Castle marcht he then,
   and by the force of warlike men,   10
Besieg'd therein a gallant faire Lady,
   while that her husband was in France,
His countries honour to aduance,
   the noble and famous Earle of *Salisbury*.

Braue Sir *William Mountague*,
  rode then in post :
Who declard vnto the King,
  the Scottish mens hoast.
Who like a Lyon in his rage,
  did straight way prepare   20
For to deliuer that faire Lady,
  from wofull care :
But when the Scottishmen did heare say,
Edward our King was come that day :
They raised their siege, and ran away with speed,
So when that he did thither come
With warlike Trumpet, Fife and Drum,
  none but a gallant Lady did him meet.

Whom when he did with greedy eyes
  behold and see :   30
Her peerlesse beauty straight inthrald
  his Maiestie.
And euer the longer that he look't
  the more he might :
For in her onely beauty was,
  his hearts delight.
And humbly then vpon her knee,
  she thankt his royall Maiestie,
That he had driuen danger from her Gate.
Lady (quoth he) stand vp in peace,   40
Although my warre doth now increase,
Lord keepe (quoth she) all hurt from your estate.

Now is the King full sad in soule,
  and wot not why ?
All for the loue of the faire Countesse
  of *Salisbury*.
She little knowing his cause of Griefe,
  did come to see :
Wherfore his Highnesse sate alone
  so heauily,   50
I haue beene wrong'd, fair Dame (quoth he)
  since I came hither vnto thee.

No, God forbid my Soueraigne (she said)
　if I were worthy for to know
The cause and ground of this your woe,
　you should be helpt if it did lye in me.

Sweare to performe thy words to me
　thou Lady gay:
To thee the sorrow of my heart,
　I will bewray.　　　　　　　　　　　　　60
I sweare by all the Saints in heauen,
　I will (quoth she):
And let my Lord haue no mistrust
　at all in me.
Then take thy selfe aside (he said)
　for why thy beauty hath betraid,
Wounding a King with thy bright shining eye,
If thou do then some mercy show:
Thou shalt expell a Princes woe:
　so shall I liue, or else in sorrow die.　　70

You haue your wish, my Soueraigne Lord,
　effectually:
Take all the loue that I can giue
　your Maiestie.
But in thy beauty all my ioys
　haue their abode:
Take then my beauty from my face
　my gracious Lord.
Didst thou not swear to grant my will:
　all that I may I will fulfill.　　　　　　80
Then for my loue let thy true loue be seene:
My Lord, your speech I might reproue,
You cannot giue to me your loue,
　for that belongs vnto your Queene.

But I suppose your Grace did this,
　only to try
Whether a wanton tale might tempt
　Dame *Salisbury*.
Nor from your selfe therfore my Liege,
　my steps do stray:　　　　　　　　　　90
But from your tempting wanton tale,
　I go my way.

O turne againe thou Lady bright,
   come vnto me my harts delight.
Gone is the comfort of my pensiue heart :
Here comes the Earle of *Warwicke* he,
The Father of this faire Lady :
   my mind to him I meane for to impart.

Why is my Lord and Soueraigne King
   so grieu'd in mind :   100
Because that I haue lost the thing
   I cannot find.
What thing is that, my gracious Lord
   which you haue lost ?
It is my heart which is neare dead,
   betwixt fire and frost.
Curst be that fire and frost too,
   that causeth this your highnesse woo,
O *Warwick*, thou dost wrong me very sore,
   it is thy daughter noble Earle :   110
That heauen bright lampe that peereles pearle
   which kils my heart, yet do I her adore.

If that be all (my gracious King :)
   that workes your griefe,
I will perswade that scornefull Dame
   to yeeld reliefe :
Neuer shall she my daughter be,
   if she refuse.
The loue and fauour of a King
   may her excuse.   120
Thus wise *Warwicke* went his way,
   and quite contrary he did say :
When as he did the beauteous Countesse meet,
   well met my daughter deare (quoth he)
A message I must do to thee :
Our royall King most kindly doth thee greet

The King will die, lest thou to him
   do grant thy loue :
To loue the King my husbands loue
   I should remoue,   130

It is right charitie to loue,
   my daughter deare:
But not true loue so charitable
   for to appeare.
His greatnesse may beare out the shame,
But his kingdome cannot buy out the blame,
   he craues thy loue that may bereaue thy life.
It is my dutie to moue this,
But not my honestie to yeeld, I wis:
   I meane to die a true vnspotted wife.   140

Now hast thou spoken my daughter deare,
   as I would haue:
Chastitie beares a golden name
   vnto her graue.
And when vnto thy wedded Lord
   thou prouest vntrue:
Then let my bitter curses still
   thy soule pursue.
Then with a smiling cheare go thou
   as right and reason doth allow.   150
Yet shew the King thou bearest no strumpets mind
I go deare father with a trice
   and by a slight of fine deuice:
Ile cause the King confesse that I am kind.

Here comes the Lady of my life
   the King did say:
My father bids me, Soueraigne Lord
   your will obay:
And I consent, if you will grant
   one boone to me.   160
I grant it thee, my Lady faire,
   whatere it be.
My husband is aliue you know,
   first let me kill him, ere I go.
And at your command I wil for euer be.
Thy husband now in *France* doth rest:
No, no he lyes within my brest,
   and being so nie, he will my falsehood see.

139 my *A* : thy *B C D E*   140 wife *B C D E* : life *A*

With that she started from the King,
  and tooke hir knife :   170
And desperately she sought to rid
  her selfe of life.
The King vpstarted from his chaire,
  her hand to stay,
O noble King you haue broke your word
  with me this day.
Thou shalt not do this deed (quoth he)
  then neuer will I ly with thee.
No, liue thou still, and let me beare the blame,
Liue in honour and high estate   180
With thy true Lord and wedded mate :
  I neuer will attempt this suit againe.

5.

The Spanish Ladies Loue to an English Gentleman.

WIll you heare a Spanish Lady
  how she wooed an Englishman :
Garments gay as rich as may be,
  deckt with Iewels had she on,
Of a comely countenance,
  and grace was she :
And by birth and parentage
  of high degree.

As his prisoner there he kept her,
  in his hands her life did lye :   10
Cupids bands did tie her faster,
  by the liking of her eye.
In his courteous company,
  was all her ioy ;
To fauour him in any thing,
  she was not coy.

At the last there came commandment,
  for to set the Ladies free :
With their Iewels still adorning,
  none to do them iniury.   20

Alas, then said the Lady gay,
  full woe is me:
O let me still sustaine this kind
  captiuity.

Gallant captaine take some pittie
  of a Lady in distresse:
Leaue me not within the Citie,
  for to dye in heauinesse.
Thou hast set this present day,
  my body free: 30
But my heart in prison strong,
  remaines with thee.

How should you, faire Lady loue me
  whom thou knowest thy Countries foe:
Thy faire words make me suspect thee,
  serpents lie where flowers grow.
All the euill I thinke to thee,
  most courteous Knight:
God grant vnto my selfe the same,
  may fully light.   40

Blessed be the time and season,
  that you came on Spanish ground,
If you may our foe be termed,
  gentle foes we haue you found.
With our Cities, you haue won,
  our hearts each one:
Then to your Country beare away,
  that is your owne.

Rest you still most gallant Lady,
  rest you still and weepe no more: 50
Of faire louers there are plenty,
  Spaine doth yeeld a wondrous store.
Spaniards fraught with iealousie,
  we often find:
But English men through all the world
  are counted kind.

Leaue me not vnto a Spaniard,
  you alone enioy my heart:
I am louely, yong and tender,
  loue is likewise my desert.   60

Stil to serue thee day and night,
 my mind is prest:
The wife of euery Englishman
 is counted blest.

It would be a shame, faire Lady,
 for to beare a woman hence:
English souldiers neuer carry
 any such without offence.
I will quickly change my selfe,
 if it be so: 70
And like a Page Ile follow thee,
 wherere thou go.

I haue neither gold nor siluer,
 to maintaine thee in this case:
And to trauell is great charges,
 as you know in euery place,
My chaines and Iewels euery one
 shall be thine owne:
And eke fiue hundred pound in gold,
 that lyes vnknowne.   80

On the Seas are many dangers,
 many storms do there arise:
Which will be to Ladies dreadfull,
 and force tears from watry eyes,
Well, in worth I should endure
 extremity:
For I could find in heart to lose
 my life for thee.

Courteous Lady be contented,
 here comes all that breeds the strife,   90
I in *England* haue already
 a sweet woman to my wife.
I will not falsifie my vow
 for gold nor gaine:
Nor yet for all the fairest Dames
 that liue in *Spaine*.

O how happy is that woman
 that enioyes so true a friend:
Many dayes of ioy God send you,
 of my suit Ile make an end.   100

Vpon my knees I pardon craue
  for this offence:
Which loue and true affection
  did first commence.

Commend me to thy louing Lady
  beare to her this chaine of gold,
And these bracelets for a token,
  grieuing that I was so bold.
All my Iewels in like sort
  beare thou with thee: 110
For these are fitting for thy wife,
  and not for me.

I will spend my dayes in prayer,
  loue and all her lawes defie:
In a Nunnery will I shrowd me,
  farre from other company,
But ere my prayers haue end,
  be sure of this:
To pray for thee and for thy loue,
  I will not misse.   120

Thus farewell most gentle Captaine,
  and farewell my hearts content:
Count not Spanish Ladies wanton,
  though to thee my loue was bent.
Ioy and true prosperitie
  go still with thee:
The like fall euer to thy share,
  most faire Lady.

6.

A farewell to Loue.

FArewell false Loue the Oracle of lyes,
  A mortall foe, an enemy to rest;
An enuious boy from whence great cares arise:
A Bastard vile, a beast with rage possest.
A way for error, tempest, full of treason;
In all respect contrary vnto reason.

A poyson'd Serpent couered all with flowers,
Mother of sighs, and murtherer of repose;
A sea of sorrow, whence run all such showres
As moysture giues to euery griefe that growes: 10
A schoole of guile, a nest of deepe deceit,
A golden hooke that holds a poysoned bait.

A fortlesse field, whom reason did defend:
A Syrens song, a feruour of the mind:
A maze wherein afflection finds no end:
A raining cloud, that runs before the wind,
A substance like the shadow of the Sunne:
A gole of griefe for which the wisest runne.

A quenchlesse fire, a nest of trembling feare:
A path that leads to perill and mishap: 20
A true retreat of sorrow and despaire,
An idle boy that sleepes in pleasures lap:
A deepe mistrust of that which certaine seemes,
A hope of that which reason doubtfull deemes.

Then sith thy reigne my yonger yeeres betraid:
And for my faith ingratitude I find:
And sith repentance hath the wrong bewraid,
Whose crooked course hath not beene after kind,
False loue go backe, and beauty fraile adew,
Dead is the root from whence such fancies grew.   30

FINIS.

7.

The Louer by his gifts thinkes to conquer chastitie,
And with his gifts sends these verses to the Lady.

WHat face so faire that is not crackt with gold?
What wit so worth but hath gold in his wonder?
What learning but with golden lines will hold?
What state so hie, but gold could bring it vnder?
What thought so sweet but gold doth better season?
And what rule better than the Golden reason?

8 murtherer *B C D E*: murtherers *A*   9 sea *B C D E*: season *A*   run *B C D E*: ran *A*   19 nest] rest *A B C D E*   25 thy *B C D E*: my *A*   28 course] cause *A B C D E*
5 better *C D E*: bitter *A B*

The ground is fat that yeelds the golden fruit :
The study high, that fits the golden state :
The labour sweete that gets the golden suit :
The reckning rich, that scornes the golden rate :   10
The loue is sure, that golden hope doth hold :
And rich again that serues the god of Gold.

FINIS.

8.

The womans answer.

FOule is the face, whose beauty gold can race :
  Worthless the wit that hath gold in her wonder :
Vnlearned lines puts gold in honours place :
Wicked the state that will to coine come vnder :
Base the conceit that seasoned is with gold :
And beggars rule that such a reason hold.

Earth giues the gold but Heauen giues greater grace,
Men study wealth, but Angels wisdomes state,
Labour seekes peace, loue hath an higher place :
Death makes the reckning, life is all my rate :   10
Thy hope is hell, my hope of heauen doth hold,
God giue me grace, let *Diues* die with gold.

FINIS.

2 Worthless *C D E* : Worthy *A B*   6 rule *A B C D E* : rude ?

STRANGE

HISTORIES,

Of Kings, Princes, Dukes

Earles, Lords, Ladies, Knights, and Gentlemen.

With the great troubles and miseries of the Dutches of Suffolke.

Veric pleasant either to bee read or sunge, and a most excellent warning for all estates.

LONDON

Printed by William Barley, the asigne of I. M. and are to be sold at his shop in Gracious streete,
1 6 0 2.

Cum Priuslegio.

THE TABLE.

Henry] *Edward 1602*

The valiant courage and policie of the Kentishmen
with long tayles, whereby they kept their ancient
Lawes and Customes, which *William* the Conquerer
sought to take from them.

Cant. I.

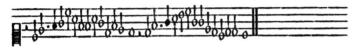

Or to the tune of Rogero.

WHen as the Duke of *Normandie*,
 with glistering speare and shield :
Had entred into faire *England*,
 and foild his foes in fielde.
On Christmas day in solemne sort,
 then was he crowned heere,
By *Albert* Archbishop of *Yorke*,
 with many a noble Peere.

Which being done he changed quite,
 the customes of this land :   10
And punisht such as daily sought,
 his statutes to withstand.
And many Citties he subdude,
 faire *London* with the rest :
But *Kent* did still withstand his force,
 which did his lawes detest.

To *Douer* then he tooke his way,
 the Castle downe to fling :
Which *Aruiragus* builded there,
 the noble Brutaine king :   20
Which when the braue Arch-Bishop bolde,
 of *Canterburie* knew :
The Abbot of S. *Austines* eke,
 with all their gallant crue.

They set themselues in armour bright
 these mischiefes to preuent :
With all the yeomen braue and bold,
 that wer in fruitfull Kent.

At Canterburie did they meete,
 vpon a certaine day: 30
With sword and speare with bill and bowe,
 and stopt the conquerers way.

Let vs not liue like bondmen poore,
 to Frenchmen in their pride
But keepe our ancient liberties,
 what chance so ear betide.
And rather die in bloudie field
 in manlike courage prest:
Then to endure the seruile yoake,
 which we so much detest.   40

Thus did the Kentish Commons crie,
 vnto their leaders still:
And so march foorth in warlike sort,
 and stand at *Swanscombe* hill.
Where in the woods they hid themselues,
 vnder the shadie greene,
Thereby to get them vantage good,
 of all their foes vnseene.

And for the Conquerours comming there,
 they priuily laid waite: 50
And thereby suddainely appald,
 his loftie high conceipt.
For when they spied his approch,
 in place as they did stand:
Then marched they to hem him in,
 each on a bow in hand.

So that vnto the conquerers sight,
 amazed as he stood
They seemd to be a walking groue,
 or els a mouing wood.   60
The shape of men he could not see,
 the bowes did hide them so:
And now his hart with feare did quake,
 to see a forrest goe.

Before, behind, and on each side,
 as he did cast his eye:
He spide these woods with sober pace,
 approch to him full nye.

But when the kentishmen had thus,
  inclos'd the conquerer round :   70
Most suddenly they drew their swords,
   and threw the bowes to ground.

There banners they displaid in sight,
  there Trumpets sound a charge.
There ratling Drummes strickes vp a larme,
  there troopes stretch out at large.
The Conquerour with all his traine
  were ·hereat sore agast :
And most in perill when he thought,
  all perill had beene past.   80

Vnto the kentish men he sent,
  the cause to vnderstand :
For what intent and for what cause,
  they tooke this warre in hand.
To whom they made this short replye,
  for libertie we fight :
And to enioy S. *Edwards* lawes,
  the which we hold our right.

Then said the dreadfull conquerer,
  you shall haue what you will :   90
Your ancient customes and your lawes,
  so that you will be still :
And each thing els that you will craue,
  with reason at my hand,
So you will but acknowledge me,
  chiefe King of faire *England*.

The kentishmen agreed here on,
  and laid their armes aside :
And by this meanes King *Edwards* lawes,
  in Kent do still abide,   100
And in no place in *England* else,
  those customes do remaine :
Which they by manly pollicie,
  did of Duke *William* gaine.

FINIS.

¶ How King *Henry* the first had his children drowned in the sea, as they came out of *france.*

Cant. II.

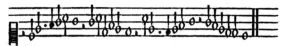

Or to the tune of the Ladies daughter.

Fter our royall King,
    had foild his foes in *France*:
And spent the pleasant spring,
    his honor to aduance.
Into faire *England* he returnde,
    with fame and victorie:
What time the subiects of his land,
    receiued him ioyfully.

But at his home returne,
    his children left he still: 10
In *France* for to soiourne
    to purchase learned skill.
Duke *William* with his brother deare,
    Lord *Richard* was his name:
Which was the Earle of *Chester* then,
    who thirsted after fame.

The Kings faire daughter eke,
    the Ladie *Marie* bright:
With diuers noble Peeres,
    and manie a hardie Knight.   20
All those were left together there,
    in pleasure and delight:
When that our King to *England* came,
    after the bloodie fight.

But when faire *Flora* had,
    drawne forth her treasure drie:
That winter colde and sad,
    with hoarie head drewe nie.
Those Princes all with one consent,
    prepared all things meete: 30
To passe the seas for faire *England,*
    whose sight to them was sweet.

To *England* let vs hie,
    thus euerie one did say,
For Christmas draweth nie,
    no longer let vs stay.
But spend the merrie Christmas time,
    within our Fathers court:
Where Ladie pleasure doth attend,
    with manie a Princely sport.   40

To sea these Princes went,
    fulfilled with mirth and ioye,
But this their meriment,
    did turne to deare annoy.
The Saylers and the shipmen all,
    through foule excesse of wine,
Were so disguisde that at the sea,
    they shewd themselues like swine.

The sterne no man could guide,
    the master sleeping lay,   50
The saylers all beside,
    went reelling euerie way.
So that the Ship at randome roode,
    vpon the foaming flood,
Whereby in perill of their liues,
    the Princes alwayes stood.

Which made distilling teares,
    from their faire eyes to fall:
Their heartes were fild with feares,
    no helpe they had at all.   60
They wisht themselues vpon the land,
    a thousand times and more.
And at the last they came in sight,
    of *Englands* pleasant shore.

Then euery one began,
    to turne their sighes to smiles:
There coulours pale and wan,
    a cheerefull looke exciles.
The princely Lordes most louingly,
    their Ladies do imbrace: 70
For now in *England* shall we be,
    (quoth they) in little space.

Take comfort now they said,
  behold the land at last :
Then be no more dismaid,
  the worst is gone and past,
But while they did this ioyfull hope,
  with comfort entertaine :
The goodly ship vpon a rocke,
  on suddaine burst in twaine.   80

With that a grieuous screeke,
  among them there was made,
And euery one did seeke,
  on something to be staid.
But all in vaine such helpe they sought,
  the ship so soone did sinke :
That in the sea they were constraind,
  to take their latest drinke.

There might you see the Lords,
  and Ladies for to lie :   90
Amidst the salt sea foame,
  with manie a grieuous crie :
Still labouring for their liues defence,
  with stretched armes abroad :
And lifting vp their Lillie handes,
  for helpe with one accorde.

But as good fortune would,
  the sweet yong Duke did get,
Into the Cock-boat then,
  where safely he did sit.   100
But when he heard his sister crie,
  the Kings faire daughter deere.
He turnd his boat to take her in,
  whose death did draw so neere.

But while he stroue to take,
  his sweet yong sister in :
The rest such shift did make.
  in Sea as they did swimme.
That to the boate a number got.
  so many that at last :   110
The boate and all that were therein,
  was drownd and ouercast.

95 Lillie] little *1607*

Of Lords and Gentlemen,
  and Ladies faire of face:
Not one escaped then,
  which was a heauie case.
Threescore and ten were drownd in all,
  and none escaped death,
But one poore Butcher which had swome,
  himselfe quite out of breath.   120

This was most heauie newes,
  vnto our comly King:
Who did all mirth refuse,
  this word when they did bring
For by this meanes no child he had,
  his kingdome to succeede:
Whereby his Sisters Sonne was King,
  as you shall plainely reede.

The Dutchesse of *Suffolkes* Calamitie.

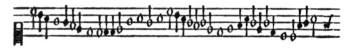

Or to the tune of Queene Dido.

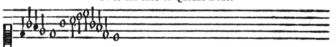

WHen God had taken for our sinne,
  that prudent Prince K. *Edward* away:
Then bloudie *Bonner* did begin
  his raging mallice to bewray:
Al those that did the Gospell professe,
  he persecuted more or lesse.

Thus when the Lord on vs did lower,
  many in prison did he throwe:
Tormenting them in *Lollards* tower,
  whereby they might the truth forgoe: 10
Then *Cranmer, Ridlie,* and the rest,
  were burnt in fire, that Christ profest.

Smithfield was then with Faggots fyld,
    and many places more beside:
At *Couentry* was *Sanders* kild,
    at *Gloster* eke good *Hooper* dyed:
And to escape this bloudie day,
    beyond seas many fled away.

Among the rest that sought reliefe.
    and for their faith in danger stood: 20
Lady *Elizabeth* was cheefe.
    King *Henries* daughter of royall bloud:
Which in the tower prisoner did lye,
    looking each day when she should die.

The Dutches of *Suffolke* seeing this,
    whose life likewise the Tyrant sought:
Who in the hope of heauenly blisse,
    which in Gods word her comfort wrought:
For feare of death was faine to flye,
    and leaue her house most secretly.   30

That for the loue of Christ alone,
    her landes and goodes she left behinde:
Seeking still for that pretious stone,
    the word of truth so rare to finde.
She with her nurse, her Husband and childe,
    in poore aray their sights beguild.

Thus through *London* they past along,
    each one did take a seuerall streete:
Thus all vnknowne, escaping wrong,
    at *Billinsgate* they all did meete   40
Like people poore in *Grauesend* Barge,
    they simply went with all their charge.

And all along from *Grauesend* Towne,
    with easie iourneis on foote they went:
Vnto the sea coast they came downe,
    to passe the seas was their intent:
And God prouided so that day,
    that they tooke Ship and saild away.

And with a prosperous gale of wind,
    in *Flaunders* safe they did ariue.   50

This was to their great ease of mind
   which from their harts much woe did driue,
And so with thankes to God on hie,
   they tooke their way to *Germanie.*

Thus as they traueld thus disguisde,
   vpon the hie waie sudainely:
By cruell theeues they were supprisde,
   assailing their small company:
And all their treasure and their store
   they tooke away, and beat them sore.   60

The Nurse in middest of their fight,
   laide downe the childe vpon the ground:
She ran away out of their sight,
   and neuer after that was found:
Then did the Dutches make great mone,
   with her good husband all alone.

The theeues had there their horses kilde,
   and all their money quite had tooke:
The prettie babie almost spild,
   was by their Nurse likewise forsooke: 70
And they farre from friends did stand,
   all succourlesse in a strange land.

The skies likewise began to scowle,
   it hailde and rainde in pittious sort:
The way was long and wonderous foule,
   then may I now full well report
Their griefe and sorrow was not small,
   when this vnhappy chance did fall.

Sometime the Dutchesse bore the child,
   as wet as euer she could be,   80
And when the Ladie kinde and milde
   was wearie, then the childe bore he:
And thus they one another easde,
   and with their fortunes were well pleasde.

And after many wearied steppes,
   all wet-shod both in dyrt and myre:
After much griefe their heart it leapes,
   for labour doth some rest require,

58 assailing] assaulting *1607*   76 I now full *1607* : I full *1602*   87 it]
yet *1607*

A towne before them they did see,
  but lodgd therein they could not be.   90

From house to house they both did goe,
  seeking where they that night might lie,
But want of money was their woe,
  and still the babe with colde did crie.
With cap and knee they courtsey make,
  but none on them would pitie take.

Loe here a Princesse of great blood
  doth pray a Peasant for reliefe :
With teares bedewed as she stood,
  yet few or none regards her grief :   100
Her speech they could not vnderstand,
  but gaue her a penny in her hand.

When all in vaine the paines was spent,
  and that they could not house-roome get :
Into a Church-porch then they went,
  to stand out of the raine and wet :
Then said the Dutchesse to her deare,
  O that we had some fier heere.

Then did her husband so prouide,
  that fire and coales he got with speede :   110
Shee sate downe by the fires side,
  to dresse her daughter that had neede :
And while she drest it in her lap,
  her husband made the Infant pap.

Anon the Sexten thither came,
  and finding them there by the fire :
The drunken knaue all voyde of shame,
  to driue them out was his desire :
And spurning forth this noble Dame,
  her husbands wrath it did inflame.   120

And all in furie as he stood,
  he wroung the Church keyes out of his hand :
And strooke him so that all of bloud,
  his head ran downe where he did stand.
Wherefore the Sexten presently,
  for helpe and aide aloud did crye,

Then came the Officers in hast,
  and tooke the Duchesse and her child,
And with her husband thus they past,
  like Lambs beset with Tigers wilde: 130
And to the Gouernour were they brought,
  who vnderstood them not in ought.

Then Master *Bartue* braue and bolde,
  in Latine made a gallant speech,
Which all their miserie did vnfolde,
  and their high fauour did beseech:
With that a Doctor sitting by,
  did know the Dutchesse presently.

And thereupon arising straight,
  with minde abashed at this sight   140
Vnto them all that there did waight,
  he thus brake forth in words aright:
Beholde within your sight (quoth he)
  a Princesse of most high degree.

With that the Gouernour and the rest,
  were all amazde the same to heare,
And welcomed these new come guests,
  with reuerence great and princely cheare:
And afterwarde conueyde they were,
  vnto their friend Prince *Cassemere*.   150

A sonne she had in *Germanie*,
  Peregrine Bartue cald by name:
Surnamde the good Lord *Willobie*:
  of courage great and worthie fame.
Her Daughter young which with her went,
  was afterward Countesse of *Kent*.

For when Queene *Marie* was deceast,
  the Dutchesse home returnd againe:
Who was of sorrow quite releast,
  by Queene *Elizabethes* happie raigne   160
For whose life and prosperitie,
  we may all pray continually.

FINIS.

162 we may prayse God continually *1607*

How King *Henry* the second crowning his Sonne king
of *England,* in his owne lifetime, was by him most
grieuously vexed with warres : whereby he went about
to take his Fathers Crowne quite from him. And
how at his death he repented him thereof, and asked
his Father hartily forgiuenesse.

Cant. III.

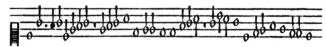

Or to the tune of Wygmors Galliard.

YOu parents whose affection fond,
    vnto your children doth appeare :
Marke well the storie nowe in hand.
    wherin you shall great matters here.
And learne by this which shalbe tolde,
    to holde your children still in awe :
Least otherwise they prooue too bolde,
    and set not by your state a strawe.

King *Henrie* second of that name,
    for verie loue that he did beare :   10
Vnto his sonne, whose courteous fame,
    did through the land his credite reare.
Did call the Prince vpon a day.
    vnto the court in royall sort :
Attyred in most rich aray,
    and there he made him Princely sport.

And afterward he tooke in hand,
    for feare he should deceiued be :
To crowne him king of faire *England,*
    while life possest his Maiestie.   20
What time the king in humble sort,
    like to a subiect waited then :
Vpon his Sonne, and by report
    swore vnto him his Noble-men.

And by this meanes in *England* now,
    two kings at once together liue.
But lordly rule will not allow
    in partnership their daies to driue.

The Sonne therefore ambitiously,
   doth seeke to pull his Father downe,   30
By bloudie warre and subtiltie,
   to take from him his princely crowne.

Sith I am king thus did he say,
   why should I not both rule and raigne :
My heart disdaines for to obay.
   yea all or nothing will I gaine.
Hereon he raiseth armies great,
   and drawes a number to his part :
His Fathers force downe right to beat.
   and by his speare to pearce his hart.   40

In seuen set battles doth he fight,
   against his louing Father deere :
To ouerthrow him in despight,
   to win himselfe a kingdom cleere.
But naught at all could he preuaile,
   his armie alwaies had the worst :
Such griefe did then his hart asaile,
   he thought himselfe of God accurst.

And therefore falling wondrous sicke,
   he humbly to his Father sent :   50
The worme of conscience did him pricke.
   and his vile deedes he did lament :
Requiring that his noble grace,
   would now forgiue all that was past :
And come to him in heauie case,
   being at poynt to breath his last.

When this word came vnto our king,
   the newes did make him wondrous woe :
And vnto him he sent his Ring,
   where he in person would not goe :   60
Commend me to my Sonne he said,
   so sicke in bed as he doth lye :
And tell him I am well apaide,
   to heare he doth for mercie crie :

The Lord forgiue his foule offence,
   and I forgiue them all quoth he :
His euill with good Ile recompence,
   beare him this message now from me,

When that the Prince did see this ring,
　　he kissed it in ioyfull wise　　　　　　　　70
And for his faults his hands did wring,
　　while bitter teares gusht from his eys.

Then to his Lords that stood him nye,
　　with feeble voyce then did he call:
Desiring them immediately,
　　to strip him from his garments all.
Take off from me these roabes so rich,
　　and lay me in a cloth of haire:
(Quoth he) my grieuous sinnes are such,
　　hell fires flame I greatly feare.　　　　　　80

A hempen halter then he tooke,
　　about his neck he put the same:
And with a grieuous pittious looke,
　　this speech vnto them did he frame,
You reuerend Bishops more and lesse,
　　pray for my soule to God on hye:
For like a theefe I do confesse,
　　I haue deserued for to dye.

And therefore by this halter heere,
　　I yeeld my selfe vnto you all:　　　　　　90
A wretch vnworthie to appeere,
　　before my God celestiall.
Therefore within your hempton bed,
　　all strewd with ashes as it is:
Let me be laid when I am dead,
　　and draw me thereunto by this.

Yea by this halter strong and tough,
　　dragge foorth my carcasse to the same:
Yet is that couch not bad inough.
　　for my vile bodie wrapt in shame.　　　　　100
And when you see me lye along,
　　bepowdered in ashes there:
Say there is he that did such wrong,
　　vnto his Father euerie where.

And with that word he breath'd his last,
　　wherefore according to his mind:
They drew him by the necke full fast
　　vnto the place to him assignd.

And afterward in solemne sort,
    at *Roan* in *Fraunce* buried was he :   110
Where many Princes did resort.
    to his most royall obsequie.

¶ The Imprisonment of Queene *Elenor*, wife to King *Henrie* the second.

The Argument.

¶ The imprisonment of Queene *Elenor*, wife to King *Henrie* the second, by whose meanes the Kings sonnes so vnnaturally rebelled against their father. And her lamentation, being sixteene yeares in prison, whom her sonne Richard when he came to be King, relesed, and how at her deliuerance, she caused many prisoners to be set at libertie.

Cant. IIII.

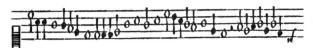

Or come liue with me and be my loue.

THrice woe is me vnhappy Queene,
    thus to offend my princely Lord :
My foule offence too plaine is seene,
    and of good people most abhord :
I doe confesse my fault it was,
    these bloudie warres cam this to passe.

My iealous mind hath wrought my woe,
    let all good Ladies shun mistrust :
My enuie wrought my ouerthrow,
    and by my mallice most vniust,   10
My Sonnes did seeke their fathers life,
    by bloudie warres and cruell strife,

What more vnkindnesse could be showne
   to any Prince of high renoune :
Then by his Queene and loue alone,
   to stand in danger of his Crowne.
For this offence most worthily
   in dolefull prison doe I lye.

But that which most torments my mind,
   and makes my grieuous heart complaine   20
Is for to thinke that most vnkind,
   I brought my selfe in such disdaine :
That now the king cannot abide
   I should be lodged by his side.

In dolefull prison I am cast,
   debard of princely company :
The Kings good will quite haue I lost,
   and purchast nought but infamy :
And neuer must I see him more,
   whose absence griues my hart full sore.   30

Full sixteene winters haue I beene
   imprisoned in the dungeon deepe :
Whereby my ioyes are wasted cleane,
   where my poore eys haue learnd to weepe.
And neuer since I could attaine,
   his kingly loue to me againe.

Too much indeed I must confesse.
   I did abuse his royall grace :
And by my great malitiousnesse,
   his wrong I wrought in euerie place.   40
And thus his loue I turnde to hate,
   which I repent but all too late.

Sweete *Rosamond* that was so faire,
   out of her curious bower I brought,
A poysoned cup I gaue her there,
   whereby her death was quickly wrought.
The which I did with all despight,
   because she was the Kings delight.

Thus often did the Queene lament,
   as she in prison long did lie.   50
Her former deedes she did repent :
   with many a watrie weeping eye :

But at the last this newes was spred.
the King was on a suddaine dead :

But when she heard this tydings tolde,
most bitterly she mourned then :
Her wofull heart she did vnfolde,
in sight of many Noble men.
And her sonne *Richard* being King,
from dolefull prison did her bring. 60

Who set her for to rule the land,
while to *Ierusalem* he went :
And while she had this charge in hand,
her care was great in gouernment.
And many a prisoner then in holde,
she set at large from yrons colde.

¶ The lamentable death of King *Iohn*, how he was
poysoned in the Abbey at *Swinsted*, by a false Fryer.

Cant. V.

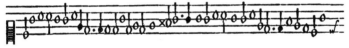

Or to the tune of Fortune.

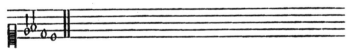

A Trecherous deede forthwith I shall you tell,
Which on King *Iohn* vpon a sudden fell :
To Lincolneshire proceeding on his way,
At *Swinestead* Abby, one whole night he lay.

There did the King oppose his welcome good,
But much deceit lyes vnder an Abbots hood.
There did the King himselfe in safetie thinke,
But there the King receiued his latest drinke.

60 her *1607* : he *1602*

Great cheare they made vnto his royall grace,
While he remaind a guest within that place.   10
But while they smilde and laughed in his sight,
They wrought great treason, shadowed with delight.

A flat faced Monke comes with a glosing tale,
To giue the King a cup of spiced Ale :
A deadliar draught was neuer offered man,
Yet this false Monke vnto the King began.

Which when the king without mistrust did see,
He tooke the Cup of him most courteously :
But while he held the poisoned Cup in hand,
Our noble king amazed much did stand.   20

For casting downe by chance his princely eye,
On pretious iewels which he had full nye :
He saw the colour of each pretious stone,
Most strangely turne and alter one by one.

Their Orient brightnesse to a pale dead hue,
Were changed quite, the cause no person knew
And such a sweat did ouerspread them all,
As stood like dew which on faire flowers fall,

And hereby was their pretious natures tride,
For precious stones foule poyson cannot bide   30
But though our king beheld their colour pale,
Mistrusted not the poyson in the Ale.

For why the Monke the taste before him tooke,
Nor knew the king how ill he did it brooke.
And therefore he a hartie draught did take,
Which of his life a quicke dispatch did make.

Th'infectious drinke fumd vp into his head :
And through the veines into the heart it spred,
Distempering the pure vnspotted braine,
That doth in man his memorie maintaine.   40

Then felt the King an extreame grief to grow,
Through all his intrels being infected so :
Whereby he knew through anguish which he felt
The Monks with him most traiterously had delt.

18 courteously] couragiously *1607*

The grones he gaue did mak al men to wonder,
He cast as if his heart would split in sunder,
And still he cald while he thereon did thinke,
For that false Monke which brought the deadly drinke.

And then his Lords went searching round about
In euerie place to find this Traytor out :   50
At length they found him dead as any stone,
Within a corner lying all alone.

For hauing tasted of that poysoned Cup,
Whereof our King the residue drunke vp,
The enuious Monk himself to death did bring
That he thereby might kill our royall king.

But when the king with wonder hard them tel,
The Monks dead body did with poyson swel :
Why then my Lords ful quickly now (quoth he)
A breathlesse King you shall among you see.   60

Behold (he said) my vaines in peeces cracke,
A grieuous torment feele I in my backe :
And by this poyson deadly and accurst,
I feele my heart strings ready for to burst.

With that his eyes did turne within his head :
A pale dead colour through his face did spread,
And lying gasping with a cold faint breath,
The royall King was ouercome by death.

His mournful Lords which stood about him then
With al their force and troopes of warlike men :   70
To Worcester the corpes they did conueye,
With Drumbe & trumpet marching al the waye.

And in the faire Cathedrall Church I find,
They buried him according to their mind :
Most pompiously best fitting for a king,
Who wer aplauded greatly for this thing.

F I N I S.

Of the Imprisonment of King *Edward* the second.

The Argument.

¶ The cruell imprisonment of King *Edward* the second, at the Castle of *Barkley*, the 22. of September. 1327.

Cant. VI.

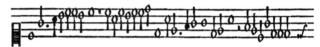

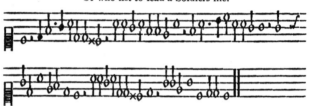

Or who list to lead a Soldiers life.

W Hen *Isabell* faire *Englands* Queene,
  In wofull warres had victorious beene:
Our comely King her husband deere,
  Subdued by strength as did appeare,
By her was sent to prison stronge,
  for hauing done his countrie wrong.
In *Barkly* Castle cast was he,
  denied of royall dignitie:
Where he was kept in wofull wise,
  his Queene did him so much dispise.   10

There did he liue in wofull state,
  such is a womans deadly hate:
When fickle fancie followes change,
  and lustfull thoughts delight to range.
Lord *Mortimer* was so in minde
  the Kings sweete loue was cast behinde:
And none was knowne a greater foe,
  vnto King *Edward* in his woe:
Then *Isabell* his crowned Queene,
  as by the sequell shall be seene.   20

While he in prison poorely lay,
  a Parliament was helde straight way,
What time his foes apace did bring,
  billes of complaint against the King :
So that the Nobles of the land,
  when they the matter throughly scand,
Pronounced then these speeches plaine,
  he was vnworthie for to raigne :
Therefore they made a flat decree,
  he should forthwith deposed be. 30

And his Sonne *Edward* young of yeares,
  was iudged by the Noble Peares,
Most meete to weare the princely Crowne,
  his Father being thus pulde downe.
Which wordes when as the Queene did heare :
  dissemblingly as did appeare :
She wept, shee waild, and wrong her handes,
  before the Lordes whereas she stands :
Which when the Prince her Sonne did see,
  he spoke these words most courteously. 40

My sweete Queene mother weepe not so,
  thinke not your Sonne will seeke your woe :
Though English Lords chuse me their king,
  my owne deere Father yet liuing :
Think not I will thereto consent,
  except my Father be content :
And with good will his Crowne resigne,
  and grant it freely to be mine.
Therefore Queene mother thinke no ill,
  in me or them for their good will. 50

Then diuers Lords without delay,
  went to the King whereas he lay :
Declaring how the matter stood.
  and how the Peeres did think it good :
To chuse his Sonne there King to bee,
  if that he would thereto agree :
For to resigne the princely crowne,
  and all his title of renowne :
If otherwise they told him plaine,
  a stranger should the same attaine. 60

This dolefull tidings most vnkind,
　did sore afflict king *Edwards* mind :
But when he saw no remedie,
　he did vnto their wils agree :
And bitterly he did lament
　saying the Lord this plague had sent :
For his offence and vanitie,
　which he would suffer patiently.
Beseeching all the Lords at last,
　for to forgiue him all was past.　　　　70

When thus he was deposed quite,
　of that which was his lawfull right :
In prison was he kept full close,
　without all pittie or remorce.
And those that shewd him fauour still,
　were taken from him with ill will :
Which when the Earle of *Kent* did here,
　who was in bloud to him full neere.
He did intreate most earnestly,
　for his release and libertie.　　　　80

His words did much the Queene displease,
　who said he liu'd too much at ease :
Vnto the Bishop did shee goe,
　of *Hereford* his deadly foe :
And cruell letters made him wright,
　vnto his keepers with dispight :
You are to kind to him (quoth shee)
　henceforth more straighter looke you bee :
And in their writing subtillie,
　they sent them word that he should die.　　　　90

The Lord *Matreuers* all dismaid,
　vnto Sir *Thomas Gourney* said :
The Queene is much displeas'd (quoth he)
　for *Edwards* too much libertie,
And by her letters doth bewray,
　that soone he shall be made away :
Tis best, Sir *Thomas* then replide,
　the Queenes wish should not be denide :
Thereby we shall haue her good-will,
　and keepe our selues in credite still.　　　　100

66 had] hath *1607*

Of King *Edward* the second, being poysoned.

The Argument.

¶ How the King was poisoned, and yet escaped and afterward,
how when they saw that thereby he was not dispatched of life,
they locked him in a most noysome filthie place : that with the
stinke thereof he might be choaked, and when that preuailed
not, how they thrust a hot burning spit into his fundament, till
they had burnt his bowels within his bodie, whereof he dyed.

Cant. VII.

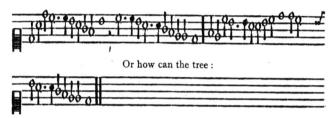

Or how can the tree :

THe Kings curst keepers ayming at reward,
　hoping for fauour of the furious Queene :
On wretched *Edward* had they no regard,
　far from their hearts is mercie mooued cleene
Wherefore they mingle poyson with his meate,
　which made the man most fearefull for to eate.

For by the taste he oftentimes suspected,
　the venome couched in a daintie dishe :
Yet his faire bodie was full sore infected,
　so ill they spiced both his fleshe and fishe :　　10
But his strong nature all their craft beguiles,
　the poyson breaking foorth in blaines and byles.

An vgly scabbe ore spreds his Lyllie skinne,
　foule botches breake vpon his manly face,
Thus sore without and sorrowfull within :
　the dispisde man doth liue in loathsome case :
Like to a Lazer did he then abide,
　that shewes his sores along the hiewaies side :

15 Thus] This *1602*

But when this practise prooued not to their minde,
    and that they saw he liu'd in their dispight :   20
Another dam'd deuice then they finde,
    by stinking sauours for to choake him quight.
In an od corner did they locke him fast,
    hard by the which their carrion they did cast.

The stinch whereof might be compared well nie,
    to that foule lake where cursed *Sodome* stood :
That poysoned birdes which ouer it did flie,
    euen by the sauour of that filthie mud :
Euen so the smell of that corrupted den,
    was able for to choake ten thousand men.   30

But all in vaine, it would not doe God wot,
    his good complexion still droue out the same :
Like to the boyling of a seething pot.
    that castes the scumme into the fierce flame :
Thus still he liu'd, and liuing still they sought,
    his death, whose downefall was alreadie wrought.

Loathing his life at last his keepers came,
    into his chamber in the dead of night :
And without noise they entred soone the same,
    with weapons drawne & torches burning bright,   40
Where the poore prisoner fast asleepe in bed
    lay on his belly, nothing vnder his head.

The which aduantage when the murderers saw
    a heauie table on him they did throw :
Wherewith awakt, his breath he scant could drawe,
    with waight thereof they kept him vnder so,
Then turning vp the cloathes aboue his hips.
    to hold his legges, a couple quickly skips.

Then came the murtherers, one a horne had got,
    which far into his fundament downe he thrust :   50
Another with a spit all burning hot,
    the same quite through yᵉ horne he strongly pusht.
Among his intrels in most cruell wise,
    forcing hereby most lamentable cries.

And while within his body they did keepe,
    the burning spit still rolling vp and downe :
Most mournefully the murthered man did weepe,
    whose wailefull noise wakt many in the towne,

Who gessing by his cries his death drew neere,
  tooke great compassion on that noble Peere.   60

And at each bitter skreeke which he did make,
  they praide to God for to receiue his soule:
His gastly grones inforst their harts to ake,
  yet none durst goe to cause the bell to towle:
Ha me poore man alacke, alacke he cried,
  and long it was before the time he dyed.

Strong was his heart, & long it was God knowes
  ear it would stoope vnto the stroke of death:
First was it wounded with a thousand woes,
  before he did resigne his vitall breath: 70
And being murdered thus as you doe heare,
  no outward hurt vpon him did appeare.

This cruell murder being brought to passe,
  the Lord *Matreuers* to the Court doth hie
To shew the Queene her will performed was,
  great recompence he thought to get thereby.
But when the Queene the sequell vnderstands,
  dissemblingly shee weepes and wrings her hands.

Ah cursed traytor hast thou slaine (quoth shee)
  my noble weded Lord in such a sort: 80
Shame and confusion euer light on thee,
  O how I griefe to heare this vile report:
Hence cursed catiue from my sight (shee said)
  that hath of me a wofull widdow made.

Then all abasht *Matreuers* goes his way,
  the saddest man that euer life did beare:
And to Sir *Thomas Gurney* did bewray,
  what bitter speech the Queene did giue him there:
Then did the Queene out-law them both together,
  and banisht them faire *Englands* bounds for euer.   90

Thus the dissembling Queene did seeke to hide,
  the heinous act by her owne meanes effected:
The knowledge of the deed shee still denied,
  that shee of murder might not be suspected:
But yet for all the subtiltie shee wrought,
  the truth vnto the world was after brought.

74 doth] did *1607*

Of the Lord *Matreuers* and Sir *Thomas Gurney,* being banished.

The Argument.

¶ The dolefull lamentation of the lord *Matreuers* and Sir *Thomas Gurney*, being banished the Realme.

Cant. VIII.

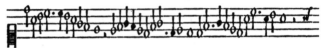

Or to the tune of light of loue.

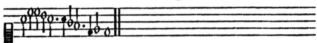

ALas that euer that day we did see,
    that false smiling fortune so fickle should bee:
Our miseries are many our woes without end,
    to purchase vs fauour we both did offend.
Our deedes haue deserued both sorrow and shame,
    but woe worth the persons procured the same:
Alacke, and alacke, with griefe we may crie,
    that euer we forced king *Edward* to die.

The Bishop of *Hereford* ill may he fare,
    he wrote vs a letter for subtiltie rare: 10
To kill princely *Edward*, feare not it is good,
    thus much by his letter we then vnderstood.
But curst be the time that we tooke it in hand,
    to follow such counsell and wicked command:
Alacke, and alacke, with griefe we may crie,
    that euer we forced King *Edward* to die.

Forgiue vs sweet Sauiour that damnable deed,
    which causeth with sorrow our harts for to bleed:
And taking compassion vpon our distresse,
    put far from thy presence our great wickednesse.   20
With teares all be dewed for mercie we crie,
    and doe not the penitent mercie denie.
Alacke, and alacke, with griefe we may say,
    that euer we made king *Edward* away.

For this haue we lost both our goods and our lands,
    our Castles and towers, so stately that stands :
Our Ladies and babies are turnd out of doore,
    like comfortlesse catiues both naked and poore.
Both friendlesse and fatherlesse do they complaine,
    for gon are their comforts y^t should them maintaine : 30
Alacke, and alacke, and alas may we crie,
    that euer we forced king *Edward* to die.

And while they go wringing their hands vp & down :
    in seeking for succour from towne vnto towne :
All wrapped in wretchednesse doe we remaine,
    tormented, perplexed in dolour and paine.
Despised, disdained and banished quite,
    the coasts of our countrie so sweete to our sight.
Alacke, and alacke, and alas may we crie,
    that euer we forced king *Edward* to die.   40

Then farwel faire *England* wherin we were borne,
    our friends & our kindred which holds vs in scorn :
Our honours and dignities quite haue we lost,
    both profitt and pleasure our fortune haue crost.
Our Parkes and our Chases, our mansions so faire,
    our Iems and our Iewels most precious & rare :
Alacke, and alacke, and alas may we crie,
    that euer we forced king *Edward* to die.

Then farwell deare Ladies and most louing wiues,
    might we mend your miseries w^t losse of our liues, 50
Then our silly children which begs on your hand,
    in griefe and calamitie long should not stand,
Nor yet in their Countrie dispised should bee,
    that lately was honoured of euerie degree :
Alacke, and alacke, and alas we may crie,
    that euer we forced king *Edward* to die.

In Countries vnknowne we range too and fro,
    cloying mens eares with report of our woe :
Our food is wild beries, greene bankes is our bed,
    the trees serue for houses to couer our head.   60
Browne bread to our taste is most daintie & sweete,
    our drinke is cold water tooke vp at our feete :
Alacke and alacke and alas may we crie,
    that euer we forced king *Edward* to die.

30 their] our *1607*

Thus hauing long wandred in hunger and cold,
   dispising liues safetie most desperate bold :
Sir *T. Gurney* toward *England* doth goe,
   for loue of his Ladie distressed with woe.
Saying how happie and blessed were I,
   to see my sweete children and wife ear I die.   70
Alacke, and alacke, and alas may we say,
   that euer we made king *Edward* away.

But three yeares after his wofull excile,
   behold how false fortune his thoghts doth begile :
Comming toward *England* was tooke by the way,
   & least that he should the chief murderers bewray,
Commandement was sent by one called *Lea*,
   he should be beheaded forthwith on the sea :
Alacke, and alacke, and alas did he crie,
   that euer we forced king *Edward* to die.   80

Thus was Sir *Thomas* dispatched of life,
   in comming to visite his sorrowfull wife :
Who was cut off from his wished desire,
   which he in his heart so much did require.
And neuer his Lady againe did he see,
   nor his poore children in their miserie :
Alacke, and alacke, and alas did he crie,
   that euer we forced king *Edward* to die.

The Lord *Matreuers* the storie doth tell,
   in *Germanie* after long time he did dwell :   90
In secret manner for feare to be seene,
   by any persons that fauoured the Queene :
And there at last in great miserie,
   he ended his life most penitently.
Alacke, and alacke, and alas did they say,
   that euer we made king *Edward* away.

71-2 *1607 reads same as lines 63-4*

Of the winning of the Ile of *Man*, by the
Earle of *Salisburie*.

The Argument.

¶ The winning of the Yle of *Man*, by the noble
Earle of *Salisburie*.

Cant. IX.

Or the Queenes goeing to the Parliament.

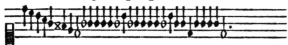

THe noble Earle of *Salsburie*,
  with many a hardie Knight:
Most valiantly preparde himselfe,
  against the Scots to fight.
With his speare and his shield,
  making his proud foes to yeeld:
Fiercely on them all he ran,
  to driue them from the Ile of *Man*:
Drummes stricking on a row
    Trumpets sounding as they goe.   10
      Tan ta ra ra ra tan.

There silken Ensignes in the field,
  most gloriously were spred:
The Horsemen on their prauncing steeds,
  strucke many a Scotchman dead:
The browne bils on their Corslets ring,
  the bowmen with the gray Goose wing:
The lustie Launce the pearcing speare,
  the soft flesh of their foes doe teare.
Drummes stricking on a rowe,   20
  trumpets sounding as they goe.
    Tan ta ra ra ra tan.

(*under music*) Queenes] Kings *1607*

The batell was so fearce and hot,
　the Scots for feare did flie:
And many a famous Knight and Squire,
　in gorie bloud did lie:
Some thinking to escape away,
　did drowne themselues within the sea:
Some with many a bloudy wound,
　lay gasping on the clayey ground.　　　　30
Drummes stricking on a row,
　trumpets sounding as they goe.
　　　Tan ta ra ra ra tan.

Thus after many a braue exployt,
　that day performd and donne:
The noble Earle of *Salsburie*,
　the Ile of *Man* had wonne.
Returning then most gallantlie,
　with honour fame and victorie:
Like a conquerer of fame,　　　　40
　to Court this warlike champion came,
Drummes stricking on a row,
　trumpets sounding as they goe.
　　　Tan ta ra ra ra tan.

Our King reioycing at this act,
　incontenent decred
To giue the Earle this pleasant Ile,
　for his most valiant deed:
And forthwith did cause him than,
　for to be Crowned king of *Man*,　　　　50
Earle of famous *Salsburie*,
　and King of *Man* by dignitie:
Drummes stricking on a row,
　trumpets sounding as they goe.
　　　Tan ta ra ra ra tan.

Thus was the first King of *Man*,
　that euer bore that name:
Knight of the princely Garter blew,
　an order of great fame:
Which braue king *Edward* did deuise,　　　　60
　and with his person royallise:

Knights of the Garter are they cald,
    and eke at *Winsor* so instald.
With princely royaltie,
    great fame and dignitie.
    This knight-hood still is held.

How *Wat Tiler* and *Iacke Straw*, rebelled against king *Richard* the second.

The Argument.

¶ The rebellion of *Wat Tiler* and *Iacke Straw*, with others, against King *Richard* the second.

Cant. X.

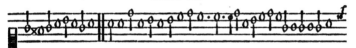

Or the Miller would a woing ride.

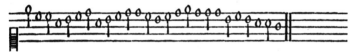

*W*At *Tilor* is from *Darford* gon,
    and with him many a proper man :
And he a Captaine is become,
    marching in field with Phife and Drumme,
Iacke Straw an other in like case,
    from *Essex* flockes a mightie pace.
Hob Carter with his stragling traine,
    Iacke Shepperd comes with him a maine :
So doth *Tom Miller* in like sort,
    as if he ment to take some Fort :   10
With bowes and bils, with speare and shield,
    on *Blacke-heath* haue they pitcht their field,
An hundred thousand men in all,
    whose force is not accounted small.
And for king *Richard* did they·send,
    much euill to him they did intend :
For the taxe the which our king,
    vpon his Commons then did bring :

And now because his royall grace,
    denied to come within their Chace,   20
They spoyled *Southwarke* round about,
    and tooke the Marshals prisoners out :
All those that in the Kings bench lay,
    at libertie they set that day,
And then they marcht with one consent,
    through *London* with a lewd intent :
And for to fit their lewd desire,
    they set the *Sauoy* all on fire,
For the hate which they did beare,
    vnto the Duke of *Lancastere*,   30
Therefore his house they burned quite,
    through enuie, malice, and dispighte.
Then to the Temple did they turne,
    the Lawyers bookes there did they burne :
And spoyld their Lodgings one by one,
    and all they could lay hand vpon.
Then vnto *Smithfield* did they hie,
    to Saint *Iohns* place that stands thereby,
And set the same on fire flat,
    which burned seuen dayes after that.   40
Vnto the Tower of *London* then,
    fast troped these rebellious men,
And hauing entered soone the same,
    with hidious cries and mickle shame :
The graue Lord Chauncelor thence they tooke,
    amas'd with fearefull pittious looke :
The Lord high Treasurer likewise they,
    tooke from that place that present day :
And with their hooting lowd and shrill,
    strucke off their heads on *Tower hill* :   50
Into the Cittie came they then,
    like rude disordered franticke men :
They robd the Churches euerie where,
    and put the Priests in deadly feare.
Into the Counters then they get,
    where men imprisoned lay for debt :
They broke the doores and let them out,
    and threw the Counter bookes about,
Tearing and spoyling them each one,
    and Recordes all they light vpon.   60

The doores of *Newgate* broke they downe,
   that prisoners ran about the towne :
Forcing all the Smithes they meete,
   to knocke the yrons from their feete :
And then like villaines voide of awe,
   followed *Wat Tylor* and *Iacke Straw.*
And though this outrage was not small,
   the King gaue pardon to them all,
So they would part home quietly,
   but they his pardon did defie :   70
And being all in *Smithfield* then,
   euen threescore thousand fighting men,
Which there *Wat Tylor* then did bring
   of purpose for to meete our king.
And there withall his royall grace,
   sent Sir *Iohn Newton* to that place :
Vnto *Wat Tylor* willing him,
   to come and speake with our young king.
But the proud Rebell in dispight,
   did picke a quarrell with the knight.   80
The Mayor of *London* being by,
   when he beheld this villanie :
Vnto *Wat Tylor* rode he then,
   being in midst of all his men :
Saying Traytor yeelde tis best.
   in the Kings name I thee arrest :
And therewith to his Dagger start,
   and thrust the Rebbell to the heart.
Who falling dead vnto the ground,
   the same did all the hoast confound :   90
And downe they threwe their weapons all
   and humbly they for pardon call.
Thus did that proud Rebellion cease,
   and after followed a ioyfull peace.

FINIS.

A speeche betweene Ladies, being shepheards on *Salisburie* plaine.

Ruely (said the Ladies) this was a most hardie & couragious Mayor, that durst in the midst of so mightie a multitude of his enemies arrest so impudent and bold a Traytor, and kill him in the face of all his friendes, which was a deed worthie to be had in euerlasting memory and highly to be rewarded :

Nor did his Maiestie forget (said the Lady *Oxenbridge*) to dignifie that braue man for his hardie deed, for in remembrance of that admired exploit, his maiestie made him Knighte, and fyue 10 Aldermen more of the Cittie, ordayning also, that in rememberance of Sir *Wil. Walworthes* deede, against *Watte Tyler*, that all the Mayors that were to succeede in his place should be Knighted : and further he granted, that there shoulde be a Dagger added to the Armes of the Citie of *London*, in the right quarter of the shielde for an augmentation of the armes.

You haue tolde vs (quoth the Ladies) the end of *Wat Tylor*, but I pray you what became of *Iacke Strawe*, & the rest of the rebellious rout.

I will shew you (quoth she) *Iacke Straw* with the rest of that 20 rude rabble, being in the ende apprehended (as Rebels neuer florish long) was at last broght to be executed at *London*, where he confest that there intent was, if they could haue brought their vile purpose to passe, to haue murdered the King and his Nobles, and to haue destroyed so neere as they coulde : all the gentilitie of the land, hauing especially vowed the death of all the Bishops, Abbots & Monks, and then to haue inriched themselues, they determined to set *London* on fire, and to haue taken the spoyle of that honourable Cittie, but the gallowes standing betwixt them & home, they were there trust vppe before they could effect any 30 thing.

And such ends (said the ladies) send all Rebels, and especially the desperate Traytors, which at this present vexeth the whole state.

With that word, one of their seruants came running, saying : Madam, the Rebels are now marched out of *Wiltshire* & *Hampshire*, making hastie steppes towards *London*, therefore now you need not feare to come home, and commit the flockes to there former keepers.

The Ladies beeing ioyfull thereof, appointed shortly after a 40 banquet to bee prepared, where they all met together againe, by which time the Kings power hauing incountered the Rebels on *Blacke-heath*, ouerthrew their whole power where the lorde *Awdly* was taken and committed to *Newgate*, from whence hee was drawne to the *Tower hill* in a cote of his owne Armes painted vpon paper, reuersed and all to torne, and ther was beheaded the 24. of Iune. And shortly after *Thomas Flamocke*, and *Michaell Ioseph* the blacke Smith were drawne, hanged & quartered after the manner of Traytors, but when the husbands to these faire ladies came home & heard how their wiues had dealt to saue 50 themselues in this daungerous time, they coulde not chuse but heartily laugh at the matter, saying, that such shepheards neuer kept sheepe on *Salisburie* plaine before.

CANAANS
CALAMITIE

Ierusalems Misery,

OR

The dolefull deſtruction of faire Ie-
ruſalem by *TYTVS,* the Sonne of *Vaſpaſian*
Emperour of Rome, *in the yeare of* Chriſts
Incarnation 74.

Wherein is ſhewed the woonderfull miſeries which
God brought vpon that Citty for ſinne, being vtterly
ouer-throwne and deſtroyed by Swo:d,
peſtilence and famine.

AT LONDON,
¶ Printed for *Thomas Bayly,* and are to be ſould at
the corner-ſhop in the middle rowe in Holborne,
neere adioyning vnto *Staple Inne.*
1618.

TO THE RIGHT WORSHIPFVLL

M. Richard Kingsmill Esquier, Iustice of peace
and Quorum in the Countie of Southampton, and
Surveyer of her Maiesties Courtes of Wardes
and Liveries. All prosperitie and happines.

Hauing (Right worshipfull) often heard of your extraordinary
fauour, shewed in the depth of extremitie, to some poore
freindes of mine, remayning in your pleasant Lordship of *Highcleere*: by meanes whereof, they haue had no small comfort for
the recouerie of their wished desire: I haue been studious how
I might in some measure declare both their thankfulnesse and
mine owne for so great a good. But such is our weake abillity
that we cannot requite the least poynt of that life prolonging
kindnes, which the riches of your courtesie did yeeld: neuerthelesse to make apparent, that our poore estates shall not obscure,
or clowd with ingratitude, the well intending thoughts of our
hearts: I haue presumed to present to your worship this little
booke, an vnfaigned token of our good affection, hoping that like
the Princely *Pertian* you will more respect the good will then
the gift, which I confesse farre vnworthy so worthy a Patron in
respect of the simple handling of so excellent a matter: But
a playne stile doth best become plaine truth, for a trifling fable
hath most neede of a pleasant pen. Wherefore if it shall please
your Worship to esteeme of my simple labour, and to let
this passe vnder your fauorable protection, I shall
haue the end of my desire. And resting thus
in hope of your worships courtesie I cease,
wishing you all hearts content in this
life, and in the world to come
eternall felicitie.

Your worships most humblie affectionate:

T. D.

To the Gentlemen Readers health.

*G*Entlemen, *I present you heere with the mourning song of* Ierusalems *sorrow: whose destruction was Prophesied by our Lord Iesus Christ, while he liued among them: notwithstanding they neither regarded, nor beleeued his words.* And after they had *in the mallice of their hearts compact his death, and that the Iudge sought to cleare himselfe of so foule a crime: The curssed Iewes cryed with one consent saying:* his blood be on vs, and one our children. *Which wicked wish of theirs the Lord brought to passe within a short time after, as in this following Historie you shall perceiue. At what time both Cittie and Temple was brought to vtter confusion: the misery whereof was so extreame as the like was neuer before, nor since: And you shall perceiue that this destruction came vpon them in the time of their greatest prosperitie, when their gould and Treasure most abounded, when pride excelled, and that the people were bent to all wantonnes. Such was their daintinesse and delicasie, that they could not deuise, with what meate they might best please their nice stomacks, wishing for better bread then could be made of Wheate: abusing in such sort, the blessings of God (which was in great abundance bestowed vpon them) that being glutted with to much wealth and plentie, they loathed euery thing that bore not an high price: casting scornefull eyes vpon Gods great blessings: but in reading this Historie, you shall see how soone their state was changed, and the great plagues that followed their peuish and hatefull pride: by whose wofull fall, God graunt vs and all Christians to take example, least following them in the like sinne, we feele the like smart.* Vale.

Yours in all courtesie. T. D.

A description of Ierusalem *and the Riches thereof.*

L Ike to a Mourner clad in dolefull black,
That sadly sits to heare a heauie tale:
So must my pen proceed to shew the wrack,
That did with terror *Syon* hill assaile.
What time *Ierusalem* that Cittie faire,
Was sieg'd and sackt by great *Vespatians* heire.

A noble Iew *Iosephus* writes the storie.
Of all the stories euer yet recited,
Neuer could any make the mind more sorie,
Than that which he so dolefully indighted:　　　　10
Which sets in sight how for abhomination.
That goodly City came to desolation.

In all the world the like might not be seene.
To this faire Citty famous to behold,
A thousand Towers stood there the streetes between,
Whose carued stones great cunning did vnfold:
The buildings all, so stately fine and rare,
That with *Ierusalem* no place might compare.

In mid'st whereof the glorious Temple stood,
Which *Nehemia* had so faire erected,　　　　20
Whose Timber worke was all of precious wood,
By Gods appointment wounderously effected:
Where all the People came with one accord,
And offered sacrifice, vnto the Lord.

Three stately walles begirt this Citty round,
Strongly raild vp of gallant squared stone,
Vnpossible in fight foes should them confound,
By warlike Engines seized therevpon.
The spacious gates most glorious to behold,
Were all gilt ouer, with rich burnisht gould.　　　　30

And round about *Ierusalem* likewise,
Were pleasant walkes prepard for recreation,
Sweet daintie gardens feeding gazers eyes,
With workes of wonder and high admiration,
Where in the midst of sweetest smelling flowers,
They built for pleasure, many pleasant bowers.

In treasures store this Citty did excell,
For pompe and pride it was the onely place,
In her alone did richest Marchants dwell,
And famous Princes sprung of Royall race :   40
   And fairer Dames did nature neuer frame,
   Then in that Citty dwelt and thither came.

Christs Prophesie of the destruction

of this Cittie and how it came to passe accordingly
within Forty yeares after, shewing the cause that
mooued the Emperour to come against it.

OVr Sauiour Christ tracing the bordring hilles,
   When he on this faire Cittie cast his eye
The teares along his rosiall cheekes distilles :
Mourning for their destruction drawing nie.
   O *Ierusalem Ierusalem* (quoth hee)
   My heart bewailes thy great calamitie.

The time shall come and neere it is at hand,
When furious foes shall trench thee round about,   50
And batter downe thy Towers that stately stand,
All thy strong holds within thee and without :
   Thy golden buildings shall they quite confound,
   And make thee equall with the lowly ground.

O woe to them that then giues sucke (he sayes)
And lulles their Infants on their tender knees,
More woe to them that be with child those dayes,
Wherein shalbe such extreame miseryes :
   Thou mightst haue shund these plagues, hadst thou bin wise,
   Which now for sinne is hidden from thy eyes.   60

This dreadfull Prophesie spoken by our Lord,
The stubborne people naught at all regarded,
Whose Adamantine heartes did still accord,
To follow sinne, which was with shame rewarded :
   They flouted him for telling of this storie,
   And crucifide in spite the Lord of glorie.

Reprochfully they fleered in his face,
That wept for them in tender true compassion,
They wrought his death and did him all disgrace,
That sought their life, and waild their desolation: 70
   Their hardened heartes beleeu'd not what was said,
   Vntill they saw the siege about them layd.

Full fortie yeares after Christes passion,
Did these proud people liue in peace and rest,
Whose wanton eyes seeing no alteration,
Christs words of truth, they turned to a iest:
   But when they thought themselues the surest of all,
   Lo then began their neuer raised fall.

Their mounting minds that towred past their strength
Scorning subiection to the Romaine state, 80
In boyling hatred loath'd their Lords at length,
Dispis'd the Emperour with a deadly hate:
   Reiecting his authoritie each howre,
   Sought to expell the pride of forraine power.

Which foule contempt the Emperours wrath inflam'd,
Mightie *Vespatian* hot reueng did threat,
But all in vaine they would not be reclaim'd;
Relying on their strength and courage great:
   And hereupon began the deadly iarre,
   And after followed bloody wofull warre. 90

The signes and tokens shewed be-
fore the destruction, alluring the Iewes to repentance, and their little regard thereof, interpreting all things to be for the best, flattering
themselues in their sinnes.

YEt marke the mercy of our gracious God,
  Before the grieuous scourge to them was sent,
That they might shun his heauie smarting rod,
And hartely their filthy faultes repent:
   Strange signes and wonders did he shew them still,
   Fore-runners of their ruine, woe, and ill.

For one whole yeare as well by day as night,
A blazing starre appeared in the skie,
Whose bushie tayle was so excelling bright,
It dim'd the glory of the sunns faire eye, 100
    And euery one that on this obiect gazed,
    At sight thereof stood wonderous sore amazed.

In right proportion it resembled well,
A sharp two edged sword of mighty strength,
The percing poynt a needle did excell,
And sure it seem'd a miracle for length:
    So strange a starre before was neuer seene,
    And since that time the like hath neuer been.

And ouer right that goodly famous Cittie,
Hung still this dreadfull apparition, 110
Which might haue mou'd had they bin gracious witty,
For outward follies, inward hearts contrition:
    And neuer did that wonder change his place,
    But still *Ierusalem* with woe menace.

The wondring people neuer lookt thereon,
But their mistrusting heart suspected much,
Saying great plagues would follow thereupon,
Such priuie motions did their conscience touch:
    But other-some would say it was not so,
    But signe that they their foes would ouerthrow. 120

Thinke not (quoth they) that *Iacobs* God will leaue
The blessed seed of *Abraham* in distresse,
First shall his Sword the heathens liues bereaue,
As by this token he doth plaine expresse,
    His fierie sword shall shield this holy towne,
    And heaw in heapes the proudest Romains downe.

Thus flattered they themselues in sinfull sort,
Their harts were hard, their deepest iudgments blinded
What godly teachers did to them report,
They soone forgot, such things they neuer minded: 130
    Their chiefest study was delight and pleasure,
    And how they might by all meanes gather treasure.

Men would haue thought this warning had bin faire,
When God his standard gainst them did aduance,
His flagge of Iustice waued in the ayre,
And yet they count it, but a thing of chance:

This bad them yeild, and from their sinnes conuart,
But they would not till sorrow made them smart.

Then in the ayre God shewed another wonder,
When azurd skies were brightest faire and cleere,   140
An hoast of armed men, like dreadfull thunder,
With hidious clamours, fighting did appeare:
   And at each other eagerly they ran,
   With burnisht Falchions murdering many a man.

And marching fiercely in their proud aray,
Their wrathfull eyes did sparkle like the fier,
Or like inraged Lyons for their pray,
So did they striue, in nature and desire:
   That all the plaine wherein they fighting stood,
   Seem'd to mens sight all staind with purple blood. 150

This dreadfull token many men amazed,
When they beheld the vncouth sight so strange,
On one another doubtfully they gazed,
With fearefull lookes their coulour quite did change:
   Yet all, they did interpret to the best,
   Thinking themselues aboue all other blest.

The conquering sort that did with warlike hand,
Suppresse the other in the bloudy field,
Declares (quoth they) that *Iudaes* sacred band,
Shall make vnhallowed Romaines die or yeeld: 160
   And ouer them we shall haue honour great,
   That proudly now vsurpes King *Dauids* seat.

See how the Diuell doth sinfull soules beguile,
Filling the same with vaine imagination,
Thinking themselues cock-sure, when al the while,
They stand vpon the brink of desolation:
   All faithfull Christians warning take by this,
   Interpret not Gods fearfull signes amisse.

Yet loe the Lord would not giue ouer so,
But to conuert them, if that it might bee,   170
Hee doth proceed more wonders yet to show,
All to reclayme them from iniquitie:
   That so he might remoue his plagues away,
   Which threatned their destruction euery day.

The Temple gates all made of shining brasse,
Whose massie substance was exceeding great,
Which they with yron barres each night did crosse,
And lockt with brazen bolts, which made them sweat,
    Did of themselues start open and vndoe,
    Which twenty men of might could scant put to.   180

Vpon a day most high and festiuall,
The high Priest went after a sacred manner,
Into the glorious Temple most maiesticall,
To offer sacrifice their God to honour:
    What time the Lord a wonder did declare,
    To all mens sight, prodigious, strange, and rare.

A goodly *Calfe* prepar'd for sacrifice,
And layd vpon the holy Alter there,
Brought forth a *Lambe* most plaine before their eyes,
Which filled some mens hearts with sodaine feare: 190
    And sore perplext the passions of their mind,
    To see a thing so farre against all kind.

Soone after this they heard a wailefull voice,
Which in the Temple shreeking thus did say,
Let vs go hence, and no man heere reioyce,
Thus figuring foorth their ruine and decay,
    All men did heare these speeches very plaine,
    But saw nothing, nor knew from whence it came.

And foure yeares space before the bloody fight,
One *Ananias* had a youthfull sonne,   200
Which like a Prophet cried day and night
About the streets as he did go and runne:
    Shewing the people without dread at all,
    Most wofull plagues should on the Cittie fall.

And in this sort began his dolefull cry:
A fearefull voyce proceedeth from the East,
And from the West, as great a voyce did fly,
A voyce likewise from blustering winds addrest:
    A voyce vpon *Ierusalem* shall goe,
    A voyce vpon the Temple full of woe.   210

A mournefull voyce on wretched man and wife,
A voyce of sorrow on the people all,
Woe and destruction, mortall war and strife,
Bitter pinching famine, misery and thrall:

In euery place these threatnings still he had,
Running about like one distraught and mad.

With lofty voyce thus ran he through the towne,
Nor day and night did he his clamours cease,
No man could make him lay these threatnings downe,
By no intreaty would he hould his peace: 220
   Although he was in Dungeon deeply layd,
   Yet there his cryes did make them more afraid.

The Maiestrates that most forbad his crie:
And saw his bouldnesse more and more arise,
With grieuous scourges whipt him bitterly,
Yet came no teares out of his pleasant eyes:
   The more his stripes, the higher went his voyce,
   In sorest torment did he most reioyce.

But when the Iewes perceau'd how he was bent,
And that their eares were cloyed with his cries,   230
They counted it but sportfull merriment,
A nine dayes wonder that in short time dyes:
   So that a fresh their follies they begin,
   And for his speech they passed not a pin.

But as the holy Scriptures doe bewray,
To dainty cheere they iocondly sat downe,
And well refresht, they rose againe to play,
In smiling sort when God did fircely frowne:
   And neuer more to mirth were they disposed,
   Then when the Lord his wrath to them disclosed.   240

¶ *The tydings brought of the enimies approach, and the feare
of the citizens: their prouision of victuals for twenty yeares
burnt in one night, by one of their owne captaines, of meere
malice, which caused a sodaine dearth to follow: their sedition
and diuision betweene themselues while the cittie was besieged.*

BVt whilst that they their sugred Iunkets tasted,
  Vnto the City came a tyred post,
Full weake and wearie, and with trauell wasted,
Who brought them word their foes were on their coast:
   Which when they knew, their merriments were dashed,
   These dolefull newes made them full sore abashed.

Their Cipres Tables then to ground they throw,
Their siluer dishes, and their cups of gould,
For haste to meet the proud inuading foe,
Feare makes them mad, but courage makes them bould :
 And to defend the brunt of future harmes,   251
 They leaue their Ladies and imbrace their Armes.

Instead of Lutes and sweete resounding Vials,
They sound the Trumpet and the ratling drum,
Their barbed Steeds they put to diuers tryals,
How they can manage, stop, carrie, and run :
 Their cunning harpers now must harnesse beare,
 Their nimble dauncers war-like weapons weare,

But ere their wrathfull foes approached neere,
The store-houses the Gouerners did fill,   260
With wholsome victuals which for twenty yeare
Would serue two hundred thousand cast by bill,
 But all the same by one seditious Squire
 Was in one night consum'd with flaming fire.

For why the Cittizens to discord fell,
So giddy headed were they alwaies found,
And in their rage like furious fiends of hell,
In murdering sort they did each other wound :
 And when they entred in this diuellish strife,
 They spared neither Infant, man, nor wife.   270

Into three parts the people were deuided,
And one against an other hatred bore,
The chiefest sort sediciously were guided,
Whereby vnciuell mutines vext them sore :
 So that the sorrow of the forreine warre,
 Was nothing to their bloody ciuill iarre.

And so malicious did their rancor rise,
That they the holy Temple did defile,
All such as came to offer sacrifice,
They murdered straight, remorce they did exile :   280
 The Sacrificer with the sacrifice,
 Both bath'd in blood, men saw before their eyes.

Thus did they make the sacred Temple there,
The slaughter house of many a humane soule,
So that the marble pauement euery where,
Was blacke with blood like to a butchers bowle :

247 Their] Three *1618, 1677*

And with the fat of men so slippery made,
That there for falling, none could goe vnstayd.

And by this wicked meanes it came to passe,
The streets and temple full of dead-men lay,   290
With wounds putrified, where no buriall was,
Which rais'd a grieuous pestilence that day:
　　So hot, and fell, that thereof dyed a number,
　　Whose foule infection all the towne did cumber.

And that which was more heauie to behold,
As men and women past along the street:
Their weeping eyes did to their hearts vnfold,
A mappe of Murder at their trembling feete:
　　Some saw their Fathers fetching deadly groanes,
　　Some their Husbands braines scattered on the stones.

Here lay a woman stabbed to the heart,   301
There a tender Infant one a souldiers speare,
Strugling with death, and sprawling with each part:
The channels ran with purple blood each wheare:
　　A thousand persons might you daily see,
　　Some gasping, groaning, bleeding fresh to bee.

Lo, all this mischiefe was within the towne
Wrought twixt themselues in wonderous hatefull sort,
While noble *Tytus* beat their bulwarkes downe,
And at their walles did shew them warlike sport: 310
　　But by distresse to bring them vnto thrall,
　　He brake their pipes, and stopt their cundits all.

¶ A description of the horrible Famine within
the Cittie of Ierusalem.

FOr true report rung in his royall eares,
　　That bitter Famine did afflict them sore,
Which was the cause of many bitter teares,
And he to make their miserie the more,
　　Depriu'd them quit of all their water cleere,
　　Which in their want they did esteeme so deere.

291 where buriall, *1618, 1677*

Alack, what pen is able to expresse?
The extreame miserie of this people then? 320
Which were with Famine brought to great distresse,
For cruell hunger vext the welthiest men :
 When night approacht, well might they lye & winke,
 But cold not sleepe for want of meat and drinke.

For by this time full Fourteene monthes and more,
Had warlike *Titus* sieg'd that famous towne,
What time the Iewes had quite consum'd their store,
And being staru'd, like Ghosts went vp and downe :
 For in the markets were no victuals found,
 Though for a *Lambe,* they might haue twenty pound. 330

When bread was gone, then was he counted blest,
That in his hand had either cat or dogge,
To fill his emptie maw : and thus distrest,
A dozen men would fight for one poore frogge,
 The fairest Lady lighting one a mouce,
 Would keepe it from her best friend in the house.

A weazell was accounted daynty meate,
A hissing snake esteem'd a Princes dish,
A Queene vpon a moule might seeme to eate,
A veanom neawt was thought a wholesome fish : 340
 Wormes from the earth were dig'd vp great & small,
 And poysoned spiders eaten from the wall.

A hundred men vnder this grieuous crosse,
With hunger-starued bodies wanting food,
Haue for a morsell of a stinking horse,
In deadly strife, shed one an others blood :
 Like famisht Rauens, that in a shole doe pitch,
 To seaze a caryon in a noysome ditch.

But when these things were all consumed quite,
(For famines greedy mawe destroyeth all,) 350
Then did they bend their study day and night,
To see what next vnto their share might fall :
 Necessitie doth seeke an hundred wayes,
 Famines fell torment from the heart to rayse.

Then did they take their horses leather raignes,
And broyling them suppos'd them wonderous sweete,
A hungry stomack naught at all refraines,
Nor did they spare their shooes vpon their feete :

But shooes, and bootes, and buskins, all they eate,
And would not spare one morsell of their meate.   360

But out alas my heart doth shake to show,
When these things fail'd, what shift these wretches made,
Without salt teares how should I write their woe,
Sith sorrowes ground-worke in the same is layd:
    All English hearts which Christ in armes doe hem,
    Marke well the woes of fayre *Ierusalem*.

When all was spent, and nothing left to eate,
Whereby they might maintaine their feeble life,
Then doth the wife her husband deere intreat,
To end her misery by his wounding knife: 370
    Maides weepe for foode, & children make their moane,
    Their parents sigh when they can giue them none.

Some men with hunger falleth raging mad,
Gnawing the stones and timber where they walke,
Some other staggering, weake and wonderous sad,
Dyes in the streetes, as with their friends they talke?
    And other some licks vp the vomit fast,
    Which their sick neighbours in their houses cast.

Nay more then this, though this be all to much,
Iosephus writes, that men and maidens young   380
The which of late did scorne brown-bread to touch,
Sustain'd themselues with one an others doong.
    Remember this you that so dainty bee,
    And praise Gods name for all things sent to thee.

All things were brought by famine out of frame,
For modest Chastitie to it gaue place,
High honoured Virgins that for very shame,
Would hardly looke on men with open face,
    One bit of bread neuer so course and browne,
    Would winne them to the foulest knaue in towne.   390

¶ The seditious Captaines *Schimion* & *Iehocanan* search
all the houses in the Citty for Victuals, they take from a noble
Lady all her prouision, leauing her and her Sonne comfort-
lesse, shewing the great moane she made.

THe curst seditious Captaines and their crue,
   When they perceiu'd the famine grow so great,
In all mens houses would they search, and view,
In euery corner both for bread and meat:
   If any did their bould request denie,
   On murdering swords they were right sure to dye.

Among the rest where they a searching went,
Vnto a gallant Ladyes house they came,
And there before her victuals quite was spent,
With hardened hearts, and faces void of shame: 400
   They tooke her store with many a bitter threat,
   And left her not one bit of bread to eate.

The noble Lady on her tender knees,
With floods of teares distilling from her eyes,
Their crueltie when she so plainely sees,
In mournefull sort vnto them thus she cries:
   Vpon a wofull Lady take some pittie,
   And let not famine slay me in this Cittie.

Of all the store which you haue tooke away,
Leaue one browne loafe, for my poore child and me: 410
That we may eat but one bit in a day,
To saue our liues from extreame misery.
   Thus holding vp her lillie hands she cried,
   The more she crau'd the more she was denied.

If you (quoth she) cannot afford me bread,
One dried stock-fish doe one me bestow,
For my poore Infants life I greatly dread,
If thus distrest you leaue me when you goe:
   Braue men of might, shew pittie for his sake,
   And I thereof a thousand meales will make.   420

O call to minde my childe is nobly borne,
Of honorable blood and high degree,
Then leaue vs not braue Captaines thus forlorne,
Your countries friend one day this child may bee:

O let me not this gentle fauour misse,
I may one day requite far more then this.

Then answered they in harsh and churlish sort,
Tut tell not vs of honourable state,
And if thou wilt we'l cut thy Infants throat,
So shall he neede no meate, then cease to prate :   430
   Men must haue meate, let children dye and starue,
   Yf we want foode, in warres how can we serue.

With bended browes they stroue to get away
But she vpon her knees did follow fast,
And taking hould on their confus'd aray,
This sad complaint from her hearts pallace past :
   Renouned Lords, our Citties sure defence,
   O let me speake once more, ere you goe hence.

Yf you lack money, see I haue good store,
Wherein great *Cesars* Image is portrayde,   440
Therefore of gift, I will demaund no more,
To buy me foode, let me not be denayd.
   For fiue red herrings, ten Crownes shall you haue,
   Ile pay it downe, with vantage if you craue.

That damned coyne (quoth they) wee doe detest,
And therewithall thy selfe, which all this while,
Hast kept our foes foule picture in thy chest,
Which seekes this holy Citty to defile :
   Thou getst no foode, and therefore hold thy toungue
   Hang, starue, & dye, thou canst not dye more young.   450

O pardon yet (quoth she) my earnest speech,
Do not my words to poyson so conuert,
Take heere my chaine, I humbly doe beseech,
Of pearle and Diamonds for one silly sprat :
   One sprat (sweete men) cast but vpon the ground,
   For this faire chaine, which cost a thousand pound.

Talke not to vs (quoth they) of Iems and chaines,
Of Diamonds, Pearls or precious rings of Gould,
One sprat to vs is sweeter gotten gaines,
Then so much siluer, as this house can hold :   460
   Gould is but drosse, where hunger is so great,
   Hard hap hath hee, that hath but gould to eate.

442 foode *1677* : some foode *1618*   455 cast but vpon *1677* : cast
vpon *1618*

With that the testie Souldiers get them out,
Proud of the purchast pray which they had got,
The woefull Ladye did they mocke and flout,
Her plaints and teares regarding not a iott:
   Shee sighes, they smile, she mournes, and they reioyce,
   And of their pray they make an equall choyce,

But Megar famine couetous of all,
Enuying those that should thereof haue part,   470
In sharing out there purchasse bread a brawle,
Wherein one stabd the other to the heart:
   This fellow said the other did deceiue him,
   He swore againe enough they did not leaue him.

Lo thus about the victuals they did fight,
Looke who was strongest bore away the prize,
And for a crust of bread, in dead of night,
They cut their Fathers throats in wofull wise:
   The mother would her childrens victuals snatch,
   And from his wife, the husband he did catch.   480

¶ How the noble Lady and her young Sonne went
out the dung of beasts to eate, being ready to dye with
hunger, and could finde none: shewing what moane
they made comming home without,

BVt now of *Miriams* sorrow will I speake,
  Whom the seditious Souldiers so distrest,
Her noble heart with griefe was like to breake,
With gnawing hunger was she sore opprest,
   No kind of foode had she, then to reliue her,
   Nor for her child: which most of all did grieue her.

Alas (quoth shee) that euer I was borne,
To see these gloomie daies of griefe and care,
Whome this false world hath made an open scorne,
Fraught full of miserie passing all compare: 490
   Blest had I been if in the painefull birth,
   I had receiu'd sweete sentence of my death.

Why hath the partiall heauens prolong'd my life,
Aboue a number of my deerest friends,
Whose blessed soules did neuer see the strife,
How happy were they in their happy ends :
    Great God of *Abraham* heare my mournefull crie,
    Soone rid my life or end this miserie.

With that her little sonne with eager looke,
Vnto his wofull mother crying came,   500
His pretty hands fast hold vpon her tooke,
Whose presence brought her praying out of frame :
    And to his Mother thus the child did say,
    Giue mee some meate, that eat nothing to day.

I am (deere Mother) hungry at the heart,
And scalding thirst makes me I cannot speake,
I feele my strength decay in euery part,
One bit of bread for me good Mother breake,
    My lesson I haue learnd, where you did lay it,
    Then giue me some-what : you shall heere me say it. 510

The sighing Ladie looking quite a-side,
With many sobs sent from her wofull soule,
Wroung both her hands, but not one word replide,
Sighes stopt her toung, teares did her tongue controul,
    Sweete Lady mother, mother speake (quoth he)
    O let me not with hunger murdered bee.

Deere child (she said) what wouldst thou haue of me :
Art thou a thirst, then come and drinke my teares,
For other succour haue I none for thee,
The time hath been, I could haue giuen thee peares: 520
    Rose coulered apples, cherries for my child,
    But now alas, of all wee are beguild.

But come (quoth she) giue me thy little finger,
And thou and I will to the back-yard goe,
And there seeke out a Cow-cake for thy dinner,
How saist thou sonne art thou contented so?
    The ioyfull child did hereat giue a smile,
    When both his eyes with water ran the while.

Then vp and downe with warie searching eye,
In euery place for beasts dung doth she seeke,   530
As if a long lost Iewell there did lye,
Close hidden in some narrow chink or creeke :

When she lookt and nought at all had found,
Then downe she coucheth on the sluttish ground.

And with her faire white fingers fine and small,
She scrapes away the dust and draffe togeather,
And so doth search through out the Oxes stall,
For dung or hoofes, or some old peece of leather :
　But when in vaine her paines she did bestow,
　She paid her heart the interest of her woe.　540

And lifting vp with sorow her bright eyes,
She cald her little Sonne to come away,
Who sought as fast for spiders, wormes and flies,
As she for Ordure mongst the mouldy hay,
　O stay a while good mother did he cry,
　For heere euen now I did a maggot spie.

At which sweete sight my teeth did water yet,
Euen as you cald, she fell her in the dust,
An hower were well spent, this prize to get,
To let her slip, I thinke I was accurst :　550
　My hungry stomacke well it would haue stayd,
　And I haue lost her I am sore affraid.

I, I, my Sonne, it may be so (quoth shee)
Then come away : let vs togeather dye,
Our lucklesse starres alots it so to be,
Peace my sweete boy, alack why dost thou cry,
　Had I found any thing, thou shouldst haue seen,
　That therewithall we would haue merry been,

Then be thou still (my sonne) and weepe no more,
For with my teares, thou kilst my wounded heart,　560
Thy neede is great, my hunger is as sore,
Which grieues my soule, and pinches euery part :
　Yet hope of helpe alack I know not any,
　Without, within, our foes they are so many.

Deare mother heare me one word and no moe,
See heere my foote so slender in your sight,
Giue me but leaue to eate my little toe,
No better supper will I aske to night :
　Or else my thumbe : a morsell small you see,
　And these two ioynts, me thinks may spared be.　570

My sonne (quoth she) great are thy cares God wot,
To haue thy hungry stomack fil'd with food,
Yet all be it we haue so hard a lot,
Dismember not thy selfe for any good:
    No brutish beast, will doe so foule a deede,
    Then doe not thou gainst nature so proceed,

But O my sonne, what shall I doe (quoth she)
My griefe of hunger is as great as thine,
And sure no hope of comfort doe I see,
But we must yeild our selues to starue and pine: 580
    The wrath of God doth siege the Citty round,
    And we within fell famine doth confound.

The sword without intends our desolation,
Consuming pestilence destroyeth heere within,
Ciuell dissention breedes our hearts vexation,
The angry heauens the same hath sent for sinne,
    Murders, and ruine through our streetes doe run,
    Then how can I feede thee, my louing sonne?

Yf pale fac't famine take away my life,
Why then, with whome should I trust thee my sonne 590
For heer's no loue, but hate and deadly strife,
Woe is that child, whose parents dayes are done:
    One thee sweete boy no person would take pitty,
    For milde compassion hath forsooke the citty.

Once I retaynd this ioyfull hope of thee,
When ripened yeares brought thee to mans estate,
That thou shouldst be a comfort vnto me,
Feeding my age, when youthfull strength did bate:
    And haue my meate my drinke and cloth of thee,
    Fit for a Lady of so high degree.   600

And when the span length of my life was done,
That God and nature claim'd of me their due,
My hope was then, that thou my louing Sonne,
In Marble stone my memorie should renew:
    And bring my corpes, with honour to the graue,
    The latest dutie men of children craue,

But now I see (my sweete and bonny boy)
This hope is fruitlesse, and these thoughts are vaine,
I see grim death hath seaz'd my earthly ioy,
For famines dart hath thee already slaine: 610

Thy hollow eyes and wrinckled cheekes declare,
Thou art not markt to be thy Fathers heire.

Looke on thy legges, see all thy flesh is gone,
Thy iollie thighes are fallen quite away,
Thy armes and handes, nothing but skin and bone
How weake thy heart is, thou thy selfe canst say:
   I haue no foode to strengthen thee (my child)
   And heere thy buriall would be too too vilde.

Wherefore my Sonne least vgly Rauens and Crowes
Should eate thy carcasse in the stincking streetes,   620
Thereby to be a scorne vnto our foes,
And gaule to me, that gaue thee many sweets:
   I haue prepaird this my vnspotted wombe,
   To be for thee an honourable Tombe.

Then sith thou canst not liue to be a man,
What time thou mightst haue fed thy aged mother,
Therefore my child it lyes thee now vpon,
To be my foode, because I haue no other:
   With my one blood, long time I nourisht thee,
   Then with thy flesh, thou oughtst to cherish mee.   630

Within this wombe thou first receiuedst breath,
Then giue thy mother, that which she gaue thee,
Here hadst thou life, then lye here after death,
Sith thou hadst beene so welbeloude of me:
   In spight of foes, be thou my dayly food,
   And saue my life, that can doe thee no good,

In blessed *Eden* shall thy soule remaine,
While that my belly is thy bodyes graue,
There is no taste of famine woe or paine
But ioyes eternall, more then heart can craue: 640
   Then who would wish, in sorrow to perseuer,
   That by his death might liue in heauen for euer.

The Lady with hunger is constrayned to kill her best
beloued and onely Sonne, and eate him:
whose body she Roasted.

WHen this was said, her feeble child she tooke,
   And with a sword which she had lying by,
She thrust him through turning away her looke,
That her wet eyes might not behold him die:
   And when sweete life was from his body fled,
   A thousand times she kist him being dead.

His milke white body staind with purple blood,
She clensd and washt with siluer dropping teares,   650
Which being done, she wipte it as she stood,
With nothing else, but her faire golden haires:
   And when she saw his litle lims were cold,
   She cut him vp, for hunger made her bold.

In many peeces did she then deuide him,
Some part she sod, some other part she rosted,
From neighbours sight she made great shift to hide him,
And of her cheere, in heart she greatly bosted:
   Ere it was ready, she began to eate,
   And from the spit, pluckt many bits of meate.   660

The smell of the meate is felt round about: the sediti-
ous Captaine thereupon came to the Lady, and threatens to
kill her for meate.   Whereupon the Lady, sets
part before them.

THe sent thereof was straight smelt round about,
   The neighbours then out of their houses ran,
Saying, we smell roast-meat out of all doubt,
Which was great wonder vnto euery man:
   And euery one like to a longing wife,
   In that good cheer did wish his sharpest knife.

This newes so swift in each mans mouth did flie,
The proud seditious heard thereof at last,
Who with all speed vnto the house did hye,
And at the doores and windowes knocked fast: 670
   And with vilde words & speeches rough and great,
   They askt the Lady, where she had that meat.

Thou wicked woman how comes this (quoth they)
That thou alone hast roast-meat in the towne?
While we with griping famine dye each day,
Which are your Lords, and leaders of renowne:
> For this contempt, we thinke it right and reason,
> Thou shouldst be punisht as in case of treason.

The louely Lady trembling at their speech,
Fearing their bloody hands and cruell actions,   680
With many gentle words, did them beseech,
They would not enter into further factions:
> But listen to her words and she would tell,
> The certaine truth, how euery thing befell.

Be not (she said) at your poore hand-maid grieued,
I haue not eaten all in this hard case,
But that your selues might something be relieued,
I haue kept part to giue you in this place:
> Then sit you downe, right welcome shall you be,
> And what I haue, your selues shall tast and see.   690

With diligence the Table then she layde,
And siluer trenchers on the boord she set,
A golden salt, that many ounces wayde,
And Damask napkins, dainty, fine, and neate:
> Her guests were glad to see this preparation,
> And at the boord they sat with contentation,

In massie siluer platters brought she forth
Her owne Sonnes flesh, whom she did loue so deere,
Saying my maisters take this well in worth,
I pray be merry: looke for no other cheere: 700
> See here my childs white hand, most finely drest,
> And here his foote, eate where it likes you best.

And doe not say this child was any others,
But my owne Sonne: whome you so well did know,
Which may seeme strange vnto all tender Mothers,
My owne childes flesh, I should deuoure so:
> Him did I beare, and carefully did feed,
> And now his flesh sustaines me in my need

Yet allbeit this sweet relieuing feast,
Hath dearest beene to me that ere I made,   710
Yet niggardize I doe so much detest,
I thought it shame, but there should some be layde

In store for you: although the store be small,
For they are gluttons which consumeth all.

Herewith she burst into a flood of teares,
Which downe her thin pale cheekes distilled fast,
Her bleeding heart, no sobs nor sighes forbeares,
Till her weake voyce breath'd out these words at last:
    O my deere Sonne, my pretty boy (quoth she)
    While thou didst liue, how sweet wast thou to me? 720

Yet sweeter farre, a thousand times thou art,
To thy poore mother, at this instant howre,
My hungry stomake hast thou eas'd of smart,
And kept me from the bloody Tyrants power,
    And they like friends doe at my table eat,
    That would haue kild me for a bit of meate.

When this was said, wiping her watery eyes,
Vnto her self fresh courage then she tooke,
And all her guests she welcom'd in this wise,
Casting on them a courteous pleasant looke: 730
    Be mery friends, I pray you doe not spare.
    In all this towne, is not such noble fare.

The Captaines and their company were so amazed
at sight of the childs limbes being by his mother set vpon
the table in platters, that wondring thereat, they
would not eat a bite, for the which the Lady
reproues them.

THe men amazed at this vncouth sight,
    One to another cast a steadfast eye,
Their hard remorcelesse hearts full fraught with spight
Were herewithall appalled sodenly,
    And though their extreame hunger was full great,
    Like sencelesse men they sat and would not eate.

O why (quoth she) doe you refraine this food,
I brought it forth vnto you for good will,   740
Then scorne it not (deere friends) for it is good:
And I euen now did thereof eate my fill:
    Tast it therefore and I dare sweare you'l say,
    You eate no meate, more sweete this many a day.

Hard hearted woman, cruell and vnkind
Canst thou (quoth they) so frankly feed of this?
A thing more hatefull did wee neuer finde,
Then keepe it for thy tooth, loe there it is.
   Most vild and odious is it in our eye,
   Then feed on mans flesh, rather would wee dye.   750

Alack (quoth she) doth foolish pitty mooue ye,
Weaker then womans, is your hearts become,
I pray fall too, and if that you doe loue me,
Eate where you will, and ile with you eat some:
   What greater shame to Captaines can befall,
   Then I in courage should surpasse you all,

Why, wast not you, that did with many a threat,
Charge me with eager lookes to lay the cloth:
And as I lou'd my life to bring you meate,
And now to eate it doe you seeme so loath?   760
   More fit I should, then you, heerewith be moued,
   Since twas his flesh whom I so deerly loued.

It was my sonne and not yours that is slaine.
Whose roasted limbes lies here within the platter,
Then more then you I ought his flesh refraine,
And ten times more be greeued at this matter,
   How chance you are more mercifull then I,
   To spare his flesh, while you for hunger dye.

Yet blame not me for this outragious deed,
For wast not you that first did spoyle my house?   770
And rob me of my food in my great need,
Leauing not behind a ratt or silly mouse:
   Then you alone are authors of this feast,
   What need you then this action so detest?

The starued Iewes hearing this dolefull tale,
Were at the matter smitten in such sadnesse,
That man by man with visage wan and pale,
Dropt out of dores, accusing her of madnesse,
   And noting well, their famine, warre and strife,
   Wisht rather death, than length of mortall life.   780

752 womans *1677*: a womans *1618*

And hereupon, much people of the Citty
Fled to the Romaines secret in the night,
Vpon their knees desiring them for pitty
To saue their liues, that were in wofull plight,
   And finding mercie, tolde when that was done,
   How famine forc't a Lady eate her Sonne.

Tytus the Romaine Generall wept at the report of
the famine in Ierusalem, *especially when he heard
of the Mother that did eate her Childe.*

THe Romaine Generall hearing of the same,
   Tytus I meane, *Vespasians* famous Sonne,
So grieu'd thereat, that griefe did teares constraine,
Which downe his manly cheekes did streaming runne, 790
   And holding vp to heauen his hands and eyes
   To this effect, vnto the Lord he cries.

Thou mighty God, which guides this mortall round,
That all hearts secrets sees, and knowes my heart,
Witnesse thou canst, I came not to confound
This goodly Cittie : or to worke their smart :
   I was not author of their bloudie iarrs,
   But offred peace, when they imbraced wars.

These eighteene moneths, that I with warlike force
Besieged their Cittiy : (Lord thou knowest it well,)   800
My heart was full of mercy and remorce,
And they alwayes did stubbornely rebell :
   Therfore good Lord, with their most hatefull rage,
   And wondrous deeds do not my conscience charge.

My eyes doe see, my heart doth likewise pity
The great calamitie that they are in,
Yet Lord, except thou wilt yeeld me the Cittie,
I'le raise my power, and not behold more sinne :
   For they with famine are become so wilde,
   That hunger made a woman eate her childe.   810

When Noble *Titus* thus had made his moane,
All those, that from *Ierusalem* did fly,
He did receaue to mercy euery one,
And nourisht famisht men at poynt to dye :

But cruell *Schimion* that seditious Iewe,
And Proud *Iehocanan,* more mischiefe still did brew.

For albeit braue *Tytus* by his power,
And warlike Engines, brought vnto that place,
Had layde their strong walles flat vpon the flower,
And done their Citty wonderfull disgrace.   820
  Yet stubbornly they did resist him still,
  Such place they gaue to their seditious will.

Tytus ouerthrowing the walls of *Ierusalem* enters the
Cyty and *Temple with his power burning downe the siluer
gate thereof, which led the way to the* Sanctum Sanctorum
and setteth Souldiers to keepe it from further hurt.

ABout that time with wonderous dilligence,
They rais'd a wall, in secret of the night,
Which then was found their Citties best defence,
For to withstand the conquering Romaines might :
  Which once rac't the Citty needs must yeeld,
  And Iewes giue place to Romaines sword and shield,

Renowned *Tytus* well perceiuing this,
To his best proued Captaines gaue a charge,   830
That new rais'd wall, the Iewes supposed blis,
Should scattered be, with breaches wide and large :
  And herupon, the troopes togither met,
  And to the walles their battering Engines set.

The feare of this made many a Iewish Lord,
That ioynde themselues with the seditious traine,
To steale away, and all with one accord,
At *Tytus* feete, sought mercie to obtaine :
  Whose milde submission he accepted then,
  And gaue them honour mong'st his noble men.   840

By this, the mellow wall was broke and scaled,
With fierce allarms the holy towne was entred,
Romaines tooke courage, but the Iewes harts failed,
Thousands lost their liues, which for honour ventred :
  Schimion, Iehocanan, all did flie for feare,
  Iewes mournd, and Romaines triumpht euery where.

The faire Temple, Gods holy habitation,
The worlds *non parallel*, the heathens wonder,
Their Citties glory, their ioyes preseruation,
To the Romaine power must now come vnder :   850
    There many Isralites for liues defence,
    Had lockt themselues, & would not come from thence.

The famous Citty being thus subdued,
The Romaines heads with glad-some baies wer crowned
For blesfull victory on their side ensued,
While on the Iewes the worlds Creator frowned :
    The Captaines of the foule seditious rout,
    To hide their heades did seeke odd corners out,

The Romaines resting in triumphant state,
Vnto the holy Temple turned their course,   860
And finding shut the siluer shining gate,
They fir'd it, retayning no remorce :
    And when the fiers flame did sore abound,
    The melting siluer streamd along the ground.

Their timber worke into pale ashes turning,
Downe dropt the goodly gate vpon the flower,
What time the wrathfull Romaines went in running,
Shouting and crying with a mighty power :
    The glory of which place, their bright sight drew,
    To take thereof a wondring greedy view.   870

Yet did that place but onely lead the way,
Vnto the holyest place, where once a yeare,
The high Priest went, vnto the Lord to pray,
The figure of whose glory did there appeare :
    Sanctum Sanctorum so that place was called,
    Which *Tytus* wondring mind the most appalled.

Which holy holyest place, when *Tytus* sawe,
Hauing a view but of the outward part,
So glorious was it that the sight did draw
A wounderous reuerence in his soule and heart :   880
    And with all meeknesse on his Princely knees,
    He honours there the Maiestie he sees.

This place was closed in with goulden gates,
So beautifull and super excellent,
That Princely *Tytus* and the Romaine states
Said sure this is Gods house omnipotent :

And therefore *Tytus* who did loue and feare it,
Commanded straightly, no man should come nere it.

And through his Camp he made a proclamation,
That whosoeuer did come neere the same,   890
He should be hanged vp, without compassion,
Without respect of birth, desert, or fame :
    And more, a band of men he there ordained,
    To keepe the Temple not to be prophaned.

The seditious set vpon the Romaine guard that kept
the Temple, and sodenly slew them: whereupon the
Romaine souldiers set fire on the golden gate of Sanctum
Sanctorum, *and spoyled the holy place with fire.* Titus
sought to quench it but could not, for which he made
great lamentation.

WHile quiet thus the Romaine prince did ly,
    Without mistrust of any bloudy broyle,
Proclaiming pardon, life and liberty,
To euery yeelding soule, in that faire soyle :
    A crew of trayterous Iewes, of base condition,
    Assayled the Romaine guard, without suspition.   900

All *Tytus* gallant Souldiers which he set,
So carefully, the Temple gates to keepe,
Vpon a sodaine, they against them get,
In dead of night, when most were falne a-sleepe :
    And there without all stay, or further wordes,
    Each man they murdered on their drawn swordes.

Not one escap'd their bloody butchering hands,
Which noble *Tytus* hearing, grieued sore,
And thereon rais'd his best prepared bandes,
Slaying those Iewes, and many hundreds more.   910
    And with such fury, he pursu'd them still,
    That who escapt, fled vp to *Syon* hill,

But yet the Romaines full of hot reuenge,
For this vilde deede, by wicked Iewes committed,
Troopt to the Temple, with a mighty swinge :
And hauing all things for their purpose fitted :

Did in their rage, set on the fiers flame,
Those goodly goulden gates, of greatest fame,

And as the flaming fier gather'd strength,
Great spoyle was practisd by the Romaine rout,   920
The melting gould that streamed downe at length,
Did gild the marble pauement round about:
    The gates thus burned with a hidious din,
    Sanctum Sanctorum Romaines entred in.

Who hauing hereby won their hearts desier,
With mighty shootes they shewed signes of ioy,
While the holy place ⟨was⟩ burnt with flaming fier,
Which did earthes heauenly paradice destroy:
    This woefull sight when *Tytus* once did see,
    He sought to quench it: but it would not be.   930

For many wicked hands had busie beene,
To worke that holy house all foule disgraces,
Which *Tytus* would haue sau'd as well was seene,
But it was fier'd in so many places:
    That by no meanes the spoyle he could preuent,
    Which thing he did most grieuously lament.

He ran about and cri'd with might and maine,
O stay your hands, and saue this house I charge yee,
Fetch water vp, and quench this fire againe,
Or you shall smart, before I doe enlarge yee,   940
    Thus some he threatned, many he intreated:
    Till he was hoarse, with that he had repeated.

But when his voyce was gone with crying out,
He drew his sword, and slew the disobedient,
Till faint and weary, running round about,
He sat him downe, as it was expedient:
    And there twixt wrath and sorrow he bewayled,
    With froward Souldiers, he no more preuayled.

The Priests & Iewes that earst themselues had hidden
Within the compasse of that holy ground,   950
Against the Romaines fought: and had abidden,
For to defend it many a bleeding wound:
    But when they saw, there was no way to fly,
    They lept into the fier, and there did die.

917 on the fiers *1677*: on fiers *1618*   927 was burnt] place burnt
1618, 1677

So long they fought, vntill the parching fier,
Did burne the clothes, from off their sweating backes,
The more they fought, the more was their desier,
For to reuenge the Temples wofull wrackes:
 They layd about, as long as they could stand;
 Or moue a legge, or lift a feeble hand.   960

And all this while did noble *Tytus* mourne,
To see *Sanctorum* spoyled in such sort,
Layde on the ground, there did he tosse and turne:
And smote at such as did to him report,
 The woefull ruine of that holy place,
 And from his sight, with frownes he did them chace.

Titus with great reverence, entred into the *Sanctum*
Sanctorum, *and greatly wondred at the beautie
thereof, affirming it to be the house
of the God of heauen.*

THe cruell fire hauing wrought her worst,
 When that at length the fury thereof ceast,
Titus arose, all open and vntrust,
Of many teares vnburdned and releast: 970
 With head vncouered, mild and reuerently,
 Into *Sanctorum* humbly entred he.

And seeing the glorie and magnificence,
The wondrous beautie of that sacred place,
Which there appeared, for all the vehemence
The flaming fier made, so long a space:
 Tytus did stand amazed at the sight,
 When he considered euery thing a right.

And thereupon into this speech he broke,
How came I in this Paradice of pleasure?   980
This Place Celestiall may all soules Prouoke,
To scorne the world, and seeke no other treasure:
 Doe I from earth ascend by eleuation?
 Or see I heauen by diuine reuelation?

956 from off their *1677*: from their *1618*

Vndoubtedly the mightie God dwelt here,
This was no mortall creatures habitation,
For earthly Monarkes, it was all to deere,
Fit for none, but him who is our soules saluation :
   O earthly heauen or heauenly Saintes receauer,
   Thy sweete remembrance shall I keepe for euer.   990

Now well I wot, no maruell t'was indeed,
The Iewes so stoutly stood in fence of this :
O who could blame them, when they did proceed,
By all deuices to preserue their blis :
   Since first I saw the Sunne, I neuer knew,
   What heauens ioy ment, till I this place did view.

Nor did the Gentiles, without speciall cause,
From fardest partes both of the East and West,
Send heapes of gold by straight commaund of lawes,
This sacred place with glory to inuest :   1000
   For rich and wounderous is this holy seat,
   And in mans eye the Maiesty is great.

Far doth it passe the Romaine Temples all,
Yea all the Temples of the world likewise,
They seeme to this like to an Asses stall,
Or like a stie where swine still grunting lies :
   Great God of heauen, God of this glorious place,
   Plague thou their soules that did thy house deface.

Tytus, thus wearied, gazing vp and downe,
Yet not satisfied, with the Temples sight,   1010
Departed thence, to lodge within the towne :
Things out of frame, to set in order right,
   Where while he stayd the stubborne harted Iewes,
   Did there most wicked actions dayly vse.

For when they saw that fier had so spoyled,
Sanctum Sanctorum in such pitious sort,
Their diuillish harts that still with mischiefe broyled,
The treasure houses all, they burnt in sport,
   And precious Iewells wheresoeuer they stood.
   With all things else that should doe Romaines good.   1020

The rest of the Temple, likewise did they burne,
In desperat manner, without all regard :
Which being wrought, away they did returne,
But many scapt not without iust reward :

The Romaine Souldiers, quickly quencht the fier,
And in the Temple wrought their heartes desire.

Where they set vp their heathen Idolls all,
Their sence-lesse Images, of wood and stone,
And at their feete, all prostrate did they fall,
Their offering sacrifice to them alone :   1030
  In plaine derision of the conquered sort,
  Of whom the Romaines made a mocking sport.

A false Prophet arose among the Iewes, telling them
that the Temple should againe be builded by it selfe, with
out the helpe of mans hand, willing therefore to destroy
the Romaines: which they going about to doe, brought
further sorrow vpon themselues.

A False and lying Prophet then arose,
  Among the Iewes, at faire *Ierusalem,*
Which then an absurd fancie did disclose,
Among them all, who thus incourag'd them :
  Most valiant Iewes play you the men and fight,
  And God will shew a wonder in your sight.

Against the cursed Romaines turne againe,
And beate the boasting heathen to the ground,   1040
For God will shew vnto your sights most plaine,
His mightie power : if you doe them confound,
  The Temple by it selfe shall builded be,
  Without mans hand or helpe, most gloriously.

That *Iacobs* God thereby may shew his power,
To those proude Romaines : which doe glory so,
In there one strength : tryumphing euery hower,
In this our spoyle, and wofull ouerthrow :
  Then fight O Iewes, the Temple sanz delay,
  Shall by it selfe be builded vp this day.   1050

The wilde seditious, beleeuing this lye,
Did set a fresh vpon the Romaine band,
In such fierce sort, that many men did dye,
But yet the Romaines got the vpper hand :
  Who in new wakened wrath, that late did sleepe,
  Slew downe the Iewes like to a sort of sheepe.

Schimion and *Iehocanan* come to seeke peace with
Tytus, *but refuse to be in subiection to the Romaines: whereupon* Tytus *will shew them no fauour, but presently assayled
them with his power, whereupon* Schimion *and* Iehocanans
*followers, by some and some, forsake them, leauing them in
distresse: who there-upon hid them-selues in Caues.*

THen came false *Schimion* and *Iehocanan*,
 Chiefe Captaines to the seditious trayne,
With many followers, weapned euery man,
Requiring peace, if peace they could obtaine: 1060
 To whome Prince *Tytus* with his chiefest state,
 Did thus reply you seeke this thing to late.

How comes it now that yee intreate for life,
After so many mischeiefes by you wrought,
When you haue slaine and murthered man and wife,
And thousand thousands to destruction brought:
 Who then as faint as euer he could stand,
 Came to submit himselfe, to *Tytus* hand.

How oft haue I intreated you to peace,
And offered mercie, without all desert, 1070
When you refusing it, did still increase
Your trayterous dealings, your chiefest smart:
 It pittied me to see your woefull case,
 With your innumerable men dead in each place.

How can I pardon these outragious acts,
Your many murders and false sedition,
With diuers other abhominable facts,
For which I see in you no hearts contrition:
 You seeke for peace, yet armed do you stand,
 You craue for pardon, with your swords in hand. 1080

First lay a side your swords and weapons all,
And in submissiue manner ask for grace,
So shall you see what fauour may befall,
Perhaps I may take pitty on your case:
 And graciously withall your faults suspence,
 And giue you pardon, ere you goe from hence.

With bended browes proud *Schimion* then did looke
On gentle *Tytus*: *Iehocanan* likewise
In scornfull manner all his speeches tooke,
And both of them disdainefully replies :　　　　1090
　　By heauens great God, we both haue sworne (quoth they)
　　To make no seruile peace with thee this day.

For neuer shall earths misery prouoke
Our vndaunted heartes to stoope vnto thy will,
Or bend our neckes vnto the Romaine yoake,
While vital breath our inward parts doth fill :
　　Then vnto vs this fauour doe expresse,
　　To let vs part and liue in wildernesse.

At this contempt was *Tytus* greatly moued,
And doth your pride continue yet (quoth he)?　　1100
Will not your impudence be yet reproued?
Nor yet your stubborne heartes yet humbeld be?
　　And dare you say that you will sweare and vow,
　　That to the Romaine yoke you will not bow?

At this his wrath was wounderous sore inflamed,
Who hereupon gaue straight commandement,
By strength of sword to haue those rebels tamed,
On whom the Romaines set incontinent :
　　Who chac'd the Iewes and scattered them so sore,
　　That they were found to gather head no more.　　1110

For secretly the Iewes from *Schimion* fled,
By some and some they all forsooke him quite,
With false *Iehocanan* which so misled,
And forct them gainst them selues to murderous fight :
　　Who leauing them, to noble *Tytus* came,
　　Desiring grace, who graunted them the same.

Iehocanan and *Schimion* seeing this,
They were forsaken, and left post alone,
In their distresse lamented their amisse,
Closse hid in caues, they lay and made their mone : 1120
　　Where they remained perplext with famine great,
　　Till they were ready, their owne flesh to eate.

Iehocanan inforced by hunger comes out of his caue &
submits him-selfe to Tytus, *who caused
him to be hanged.*

A T length out of a deepe darke hollow caue,
    With bitter hunger *Iehocanan* was driuen,
Like to a Ghost new risen from his graue,
Or like Anatomy of all flesh beryuen:
    Who then as faint as euer he could stand,
    Came to submit himselfe, to *Tytus* hand.

Into this Princely presence when he came,
With all submission fell he at his feete,   1130
Saying, O King of most renouned fame,
Here am I come as it is right and meete:
    To yeeld my selfe into thy Princely hand,
    Whose life doth rest, vpon thy great command,

My disobedience doe I sore repent,
That euer I refus'd thy offered grace,
Bewayling my lewd life, so badly bent,
And my foule actions, gainst this holy place:
    Yet with thy mercy shadow my amisse,
    And let me tast what thy compassion is: 1140

Not from my selfe, did all my sinne proceede,
Though I confesse my faults were too too many,
But was prouokt to many a bloody deede,
By him that yet was neuer good to any:
    Blood-thirsty *Schimeon* led me to all euill,
    Who doth in malice far exceed the Diuell.

Too long alasse, he ouer-ruld my will,
And made me actor of a thousand woes,
What I refus'd his outrage did fulfill,
And his deuise did make my friends my foes: 1150
    Then worthy Victor mittigate my blame,
    And let thy glory ouer-spread my shame.

No more (quoth *Tytus*) stay thy traiterous tounge,
Infect vs not with thy impoysoned breath,
Ile doe thee right that hast done many wrong,
Thy end of sorrow shall begin thy death:
    And by thy death shall life arise to such,
    To whom thou thoughtst a minutes life too much.

With that he wild his Captaines take him thence,
When he with yron chaines was fettered fast,   1160
And afterward (meete meed for his offence)
Through all the Campe they led him at the last,
   That he of them might mockt and scorned be,
   And then in chaines they hangd him one a tree.

This was the end of proud *Iehocanan,*
That in *Ierusalem* did such harme,
And this likewise was that accursed man,
That in his malice with a fierce alarme
   Burnd all the Victuals laide in by the Peeres,
   That was inough to serue them twenty yeeres.   1170

Which was the cause, that in so short a space,
So great a famine fell within the towne:
Yea this was he burnt King *Agrippaes* place,
And in the Temple slew so many downe:
   But not long after he was gone and dead,
   Out of his den did *Schimion* shew his head.

Schimion in like sort being driuen with hunger out
of his den, apparelling himselfe in princely attire, desired
to be brought before Titus, *supposing he would haue saued*
his life: but he commanded his head to be stricken off,
and his body to be cut in peces and cast to the dogges.

WHo staring vp and down with feareful lookes,
   Least any one were nigh to apprehend him,
Like to a Panther doubting hidden hookes,
That any way might lye for to offend him: 1180
   Driuen out with famine, hungry at the hart,
   He sought for succour of his earned smart.

And hauing drest himselfe in Kingly tire,
In richest manner that he could deuise,
That men at him might wonder: and desire
To know what Monarke did from earth arise,
   Farre off he walked as it were in boast,
   And shewd himselfe vnto the Romaine hoast.

For his great heart could not abide to yeeld,
Though gnawing hunger vext his very soule :   1190
Thus faintly walkt he vp and downe the field
With lofty thoughts, which famine did controule,
　　Supposing firmely, though he liu'd in hate,
　　He should finde fauour, for his high estate :

For though (quoth he) I did the Romaines wrong,
Yet in my deeds, I shewed Princely courage,
Bearing a heart, that did to honour throng,
And thereupon their Campe so oft did forage,
　　To haughty acts all Princes honour owes,
　　For they must thinke that war hath made vs foes. 1200

Considering this, Prince *Tytus* may be proude,
To such an enemie he may fauour shew,
And herein may his action be allowd,
That magnanimitie he will nourish so :
　　And by his mercie make a friend of him,
　　That in his warres so great a foe hath beene.

While in this humour, hee him selfe did flatter,
Of him the Romaines had a perfect sight,
And round about him they themselues did scatter,
Yet were afraid to come within his might :   1210
　　And that they fear'd this was the onely reason,
　　They knew his craft, and doubted hidden treason.

But *Schimion* seeing that they shund him so,
He cald vnto them in couragious wise,
Maiestically walking to and fro,
And in this sort, his speech to them applies :
　　If any gallant Captaine with you be,
　　Let him approch, and talke one word with me.

With that stept out a braue couragious Knight,
With weapons well prouided euery way,   1220
A noble Romaine of great strength and might,
Who with his weapon drawne these words did say
　　Tell me, who art thou that in such attire,
　　Walkes in this place, and what is thy desire ?

1192 which famine *1677*: with famine *1618*　　　1207 While in this
humour *1677* : Which in this honour *1618*

I am (quoth he) vndaunted *Schimeon,*
The wrathfull Captaine of seditious Iewes,
That slew the Romaines, in their greatest throng,
The deed whereof I come not to excuse :
    Nor doe I passe what you can say thereto,
    I am the man made you so much a doe.   1230

Yet let me thus much fauour craue of thee,
As to conduct me to great *Tytus* sight,
Thy noble friend, but enemie to me :
Yet doubt I not, but he will doe me right :
    Bring me to him, what chaunce so ere I finde,
    That he may heare, and I may shew my mind.

The Romaine Captaine his request fulfild,
To *Tytus* royall presence was he brought,
Whose hatefull person, when the Prince beheld,
He did refuse to heare him speake in ought,   1240
    Away with him (he sayd) let him be bound,
    For of all woe this villaine was the ground.

And like a Captiue first let him be led,
About the Camp to suffer scoffes and scornes,
And after that strike of his hatefull head,
The mansion house of mischiefes pricking thornes :
    And let his carcase be in peeces torne,
    And euery gobbet vnto dogges be throwne.

What *Titus* charg'd was put in execution,
And in this sort was *Schimions* hatefull end,   1250
Who went to death with wonderous resolution,
Not like a man, but like an hellish fiend :
    Thus *Titus* conquer'd that most pretious Iem,
    The beautious Citie faire *Ierusalem.*

The number of those that had bin slaine at the siege
of Ierusalem, *and the number of the Prisoners that*
Titus *caried with him to* Rome.

THe perfect number of the people there,
 The which with hunger & with sword was slaine
A leauen hundred thousand did appeare,
As bookes of records did declare it plaine:
 Beside all such as did vnburied lye,
 And diuers moe that did in fier dye.   1260

And when to *Rome* the Conqueror went his way,
The number of his prisoners were full great,
Full sixteene thousand men that instant day,
Were carried captiue to the Romaine seat:
 Among the rest the man that wrote this story,
 Who by his wisedome purchast endless glory.

Thus Christs prophesie truely came to passe,
Which Forty yeares before he had expressed,
But with the Iewes of small account it was,
Till they did finde themselues so sore distressed: 1270
 He soght their life, his death they wrought with spite,
 Wishing his blood on them and theirs to light.

The which according to their owne request,
The Lord in wrath did perfectly fulfil,
There channels ran with blood and did not rest,
Their blood was spilt, that *Iesus* blood did spill:
 God grant we may our hatefull sins forsake,
 And by the Iewes a Christian warning take.

FINIS.

1261-6 *1618 defective, page torn ; emended from 1677 edition*

MISCELLANEOVS BALLADS

A proper newe sonet
declaring the lamentation of *Beckles* (a market towne in *Suffolke*),
which was in the great winde vpon S. *Andrewes* eue
last past most pittifully burned with fire, to the
losse by estimation of twentie thousande
pound and vpwarde, and to the
number of foure score
dwelling houses,
1586.

To Wilsons Tune.

WITH sobbing sighes, and trickling teares,
　　My state I doe lament,
Perceiuing how Gods heauie wrath
　　Against my sinnes is bent;
Let all men viewe my woefull fall,
　　And rue my woefull case,
And learne hereby in speedy sort
　　Repentaunce to embrace.

For late in *Suffolcke* was I seen
　　To be a stately towne,　　　　　　　　　10
Replenished with riches store,
　　And had in great renowne;
Yea, planted on a pleasant soyle,
　　So faire as heart could wish,
And had my markets, once a weeke,
　　Well storde with flesh and fish.

A faire fresh riuer running by,
　　To profite me withall,
Who with a cristall cleered streame
　　About my bankes did fall;　　　　　　　20
My fayres in somer welthely
　　For to increase my store;
My medowes greene and commons great,—
　　What could I wish for more?

But now beholde my great decay,
    Which on a sodaine came;
My sumptuous buildings burned be
    By force of fires flame:
A careless wretch, most rude in life,
    His chymney set on fire,   30
The instrument, I must confesse,
    Of Gods most heauie ire.

The flame whereof increasing stil
    The blustering windes did blowe,
And into diuers buildings by
    Disperst it to and fro;
So, kindling in most grieuous sort,
    It waxed huge and hie;
The riuer then was frozen, so
    No water they could come by.   40

Great was the crye that then was made
    Among both great and small;
The wemen wept, and wrong their handes,
    Whose goods consumed all;
No helpe was founde to slacke the fyre,
    Theyr paines was spent in vaine;
To beare theyr goods into the fieldes
    For safegarde they were fayne.

And yet, amid this great distresse,
    A number set theyr minde,   50
To filtch, and steale, and beare away
    So much as they could finde;
Theyr neighbors wealth, which wasted lay
    About the streetes that time,
They secretly convayde away,—
    O most accursed crime!

Thus, from the morning nyne a clocke
    Till four aclocke at night,
Fourescore houses in *Beckles* towne
    Was burnd to ashes quite;   60
And that which most laments my heart,
    The house of God, I say,
The church and temple by this fyre
    Is cleane consumde away.

The market-place and houses fayre,
    That stood about the same,
Hath felt the force and violence
    Of this most fearefull flame;
So that there is no Christian man
    But in his heart would grieue,   70
To see the smart I did sustaine
    Upon saint *Andrewes* eue.

Wherefore, good Christian people, now
    Take warning by my fall,—
Liue not in strife and enuious hate
    To breed each other thrall;
Seeke not your neighbors lasting spoyle
    By greedy sute in lawe;
Liue not in discord and debate,
    Which doth destruction draw.   80

And flatter not yourselues in sinne,
    Holde not Gods worde in scorne,
Repine not at his ministers,
    Nor be not false forsworne;
For, where such vices doth remaine,
    Gods grace will neuer be;
And, in your health and happie state,
    Haue yet some minde on me,—

Whose songes is changd to sorrowes sore,
    My ioyes to wayling woe,   90
My mirth to mourning sighes and grones,
    The which from griefe doth growe;
My wealth to want and scarsetie,
    My pleasure into payne,
All for the sinne and wickednesse
    Which did in me remaine.

If then you wish prosperitie,
    Be louing meeke and kinde,—
Lay rage and rancour cleane aside,
    Set malice from your minde;   100
And liue in loue and charitie,
    All hatefull pride detest,
And so you shall with happie dayes
    For euermore be blest.

And thus I ende my wofull song.
  Beseeching God I may
Remaine a mirrour to all such
  That doe in pleasure stay ;
And that amongest their greatest mirth
  And chiefest ioye of all,   110
They yet may haue a heart to thinke
  Of *Beckles* sodaine fall.

FINIS. T. D.

At London :
Imprinted by Robert Robinson, for Nicholas
Colma[n], of Norwich, dwelling in S.
Andrewes church yard.

A most ioyfull Songe,

made in the behalfe of all her Maiesties faithfull and louing Subiects:
of the great ioy, which was made in London at the taking of the
late trayterous Conspirators, which sought opportunity to kyll
her Maiesty, to spoyle the Cittie, and by forraigne inuasion
to ouerrun the Realme: for the which haynous Treasons,
fourteen of them haue suffered death on the 20 & 21
of Sept. Also a detestation against those Conspirators and all their confederates, giuing
God the prayse for the safe preseruation
of her maiesty, and their subuersion.
Anno Domini. 1586.

To the tune of : O man in desperation.

The names of
vij traitors
whiche wer
executed on
the xx of Sep-
tember beynge
Tuesday 1586
_____

OH Englishmen with Romish harts, what Deuil doth bewitch
  you,
To seeke the spoyle of Prince and Realme, like Traytors most
  vntrue ?
Why is your duetie so forgot, vnto your Royall Queene,
That you your faith and promise breake, O viperous broode
  vncleene ?

Blessed be God who knew your thought, and brought your treason out :

And your destruction now hath wrought that made vs so in doubt.

For if you might haue had your willes to make your bloudie day,

Many a widowe and fatherlesse childe, had then cryed well away.

Many a Citie had beene sackt, whose houses had beene firde,

Yea, many a Peere had lost his life, these fruits you all desirde, 10

But now fourteene of you haue felt, that death you haue deserued,

And God (in mercie) from your hands, our prince and vs preserued.

And would you seeke your Countries spoyle, your Mother and your Nurse,

That fostred you and brought you vp, what treason may be wurse?

Why is your false and poysoned harts, surprised with such hate,

That you must needes by forraigne power, suppresse your happy state?

Why do you beare such foolish loue vnto the Ragges of *Rome*,

That you would seeke sweete *Englands* spoyle, and Princes deadly doome?

Will nothing serue your deuillish turne in this your deadly strife,

But euen the blood of your good Queene, and her to reaue of life?　20

Doo you not know there is a God, that guides her night and day,

Who doth reueale her foes attempts, and brings them to decay?

O wicked men with Tygers harts, nay Monsters I should say,

That seekes to spoyle so good a Queene, as none the like this day.

Her tender loue procures your hate, her mercie makes you bolde,

Her gentle sufferaunce of your pride, presumptuous vncontrolde,

Doth make you to forget your God, your selues and dueties all,

Whereby you bend your busie braines to mischiefe and to thrall.

Know you not who her highnes is? King *Henries* daughter deere,

The mightiest Monarche in his dayes, or hath beene many a yeere :　30

She is our Prince and soueraigne Queene, annointed by Gods grace,

To set forth his most sacred word, his enimies to deface,

Iohn Ballard semenary Priest,

Anthonye Babyngton Esquier.

Iohn Sauage gent.

Robert Barnwell gent.

Chediorck Tichburne Esquier.

Charles Tylney Esquier.

Edward Abington Esquier.

The next day following these 7,

Thomas Salisbury Esquier.

Henry Dun gent.

EdwardIhones Esquier

Iohn Trauis gent.

Iohn Charnocke gent.

Robert Gage gent.

Ieremie Bellamy gent.

Haue you not holy scriptures read, how byrds with fluttering
  winges,
A Traytours thought they will betray against annoynted Kinges,
God will no secret treason hide, against a wicked Prince,
Much more, for safety of the good, their foes he will conuince.

Therefore you cruell cankred crue, why seeke you mischiefe
  still,
For to attempt with violent handes, Gods chosen for to kill.
How dare you once in hollow hart, thinke ill of such a Queene,
Whom God himselfe doth fauour so, as like was neuer seene.   40

Haue you such wicked hatefull hartes, in thirsting after blood,
That with false *Iudas* you can beare two faces in one hoode?
Too often hath her Maiesty behelde without mistrust,
The outwarde smiles of Crokadiles, whose harts were most
  vniust.

O liuing Lord who would suppose that vnder veluets fine,
Such cankred poyson should be hid, as hath beene found this
  time.
Is this the precious faithfull fruite, which doth from Papists
  spring?
Are these the workes whereby they thinke Gods Kingdome for to
  win?

Is not their greedie thirsting throates yet satisfied with blood?
When as it streamde doune *Paris* streets, much like to *Nylus*
  flood.   50
Or are they not yet drunke enough, in quaffing bloody bowles,
But looke they for a second draught among vs English soules?

O *England, England,* yet reioice, thy God beholdeth all,
And he hath giuen for euermore thy foes a shamefull fall.
By him all kinges and Princes raigne, he giues them life and
  breath,
He hath set vp and will maintaine our Queene *Elizabeth.*

The secret drift and ill intent of her late hatefull foes,
Vnto all faithfull Subiects ioyes, the Lord did well disclose,
Yea many Traytors false of faith, through his most mighty
  power,
Are taken in most happy time, and sent vnto the Towre.   60

Which happy sight for all to see, did glad eche Subiect true,
And many thousands ranne apace, those Caytiues vile to viewe,
Whom when the people did espie, they cryed lowde and shryll,
There goe the Traytors false of faith, which sought our Queene to
    kill.

There goe the wretched wicked ones, her Citie meant to spoyle,
And murther all her Citizens, but now they haue the foyle.
There go the enimies of the Realme, did thinke to ouerrunne
All *England*: to let in the Pope, but now Gods will is doone.

God sent them now their due deserts, as they in hart conspyrde,
To take away our gracious Queene, and Citie to haue fyrde.   70
God graunt we neuer liue to see, that dismall day to haue,
Who blesse our noble Queene and Realme, and eke her Citie
    saue.

And thus the people still did cry, both men and women all,
And children yong did shout alowde, and Traytors Traytors call.
Yea thousands trudging to and fro, to meete them still did runne,
And some stoode fasting all the day, till that daylight was doone,

To see these Traytors taken so, their harts for ioy did spring,
And to declare this perfect ioy, some ranne the Belles to ring.
The Belles I say did brauely ring, that day and all the night,
And throughout stately *London* streetes reioyced euery wight.   80

And when the day was past and gone, and that the night drewe
    neere,
The worthy Citizens many a one, prepared their good cheare.
And Bondfyres did they merely make, through all the streetes
    that time,
And in the streetes their Tables stoode, prepared braue and fine.

They came together gladly all, and there did mery make,
And gaue God thankes with cheerefull hartes, for Queene
    Elizabeths sake.
In solempne Psalmes they sung full sweete the prayse of God on
    hie,
Who now and euer keepes our Queene from Traytors tyranny.

But when our noble gratious Queene did vnderstand this thing,
She writ a letter presently, and seald it with her Ring.   90
A Letter such of royall loue, vnto her Subiectes cares,
That mooued them from watry eyes, to shed forth ioyfull teares.

O noble Queene without compare, our harts doth bleed for woe,
To thinke that Englishmen should seeke, thy life to ouerthroe.
But here wee humbly do protest, oh gracious Queene to thee,
That Londoners will be loyall still, whilst life in them shall be.

And all that would not gladly so, spend forth their dearest
    bloode,
God giue to them a shamefull ende, and neuer other good.
And Lord with hart to thee we pray, preserue our noble Queene,
And still confound her hatefull foes, as they haue alwayes
    beene.   100

FINIS. T.D.

Printed at London by Richard Iones

A proper new Ballad
breefely declaring the Death and Execution of fourteen
most wicked Traitors, who suffered death in
Lincolnes Inne feelde neere *London*:
the 20 and 21 of September,
1586.

To the tune of Weep, weep.

R Eioyce in hart, goood people all
    sing praise to God on hye,
Which hath preserued vs by his power
    from traitors tiranny;
Which now haue had their due desarts,
    in *London* lately seen;
And *Ballard* was the first that died
    for treason to our Queene.

O praise the Lord with hart and minde,
sing praise with voices cleere,   10
Sith traiterous crue haue had their due,
to quaile their parteners cheere.

Next *Babington*, that caitife vilde,
  was hanged for his hier :
His carcasse likewise quartered,
  and hart cast in the fier.
Was euer seene such wicked troopes
  of traytors in this land,
Against the pretious woord of truthe,
  and their goood Queene to stand?   20
     O praise, &c.

But heer beholde the rage of *Rome*,
  the fruits of Popish plants ;
Beholde and see their wicked woorks,
  which all good meaning wants ;
For *Sauage* also did receaue
  like death for his desert ;
Which in that wicked enterprise
  should then haue doon his part
     O praise, &c.   30

O cursed catifes, void of grace !
  will nothing serue your turne,
But to beholde your cuntries wrack,
  in malice while you burne ?
And *Barnwell* thou which went to view
  her grace in each degree,
And how her life might be dispatcht,
  thy death we all did see.
     O praise, &c.

Confounding shame fall to their share,   40
  and hellish torments sting,
That to the Lords anointed shall
  deuise so vile a thing !
O *Techburne* ! what bewitched thee,
  to haue such hate in store,
Against our good and gratious Queene,
  that thou must dye therefore ?
     O praise, &c.

What gaine for traitors can returne,
  if they their wish did win ;   50
Or what preferment should they get
  by this their trecherous sinne ?

Though forraine power loue treason well,
  the traitors they despise,
And they the first that should sustaine
  the smart of their deuise.
    O praise, &c.

What cause had *Tilney*, traitor stout,
  or *Abbington* likewise,
Against the Lords anointed thus   60
  such mischeef to deuise :
But that the Deuill inticed them
  such wicked woorkes to render ;
For which these seuen did suffer death
  the twentith of September.
    O praise, &c.

Seauen more the next day following
  were drawen from the *Tower*,
Which were of their confederates,
  to dye that instant hower :   70
The first of them was *Salsburie*,
  and next to him was *Dun*,
Who did complaine most earnestly
  of proud yong *Babington*.
    O praise, &c.

Both Lords and Knights of hye renowne
  he ment for to displace ;
And likewise all our towers and townes,
  and cities for to race.
So likewise *Iones* did much complaine   80
  of his detested pride,
And shewed how lewdly he did liue
  before the time he died.
    O praise, &c.

Then *Charnock* was the next in place
  to taste of bitter death,
And praying vnto holy Saints,
  he left his vitall breath.
And in like maner *Trauers* then
  did suffer in that place,   90

And fearfully he left his life
　　with cursing breast and face.
　　　O praise, &c.

Then *Gage* was stripped in his shirt,
　　who vp the lather went,
And sought for to excuse him selfe
　　of treasons falce intent.
And *Bellamie* the last of all
　　did suffer death that daye ;
Vnto which end God bring all such　　　　　100
　　as wish our Queenes decay !
　　　O praise, &c.

O faulce and foule disloyall men !
　　what person would suppose,
That clothes of veluet and of silke
　　should hide such mortall foes ?
Or who would think such hidden hate
　　in men so faire in sight,
But that the Deuill can turne him selfe
　　into an angell bright ?　　　　　　110
　　　O praise, &c.

But, Soueraigne Queene, haue thou no care,
　　for God which knoweth all,
Will still maintaine thy royall state,
　　and giue thy foes a fall :
And for thy Grace thy subiects all
　　will make their praiers still,
That neuer traitor in the land
　　may haue his wicked will.
　　　O praise, &c.　　　　　　　120

Whose glorious daies in *England* heere
　　the mighty God maintaine,
That long vnto thy subiectes ioye
　　thy Grace may rule and raigne.
And, Lord ! we pray for Christes sake,
　　that all thy secret foes
May come to naught which seeke thy life,
　　and *Englands* lasting woes.
　　　O praise the Lord with hart and minde, &c.

The names of the 7 Traitors who were executed on Tuesday being the xx of September. 1586	The names of the other vij which were executed on the next day after
Iohn Ballard Preest.	Thomas Salsbury.
Anthony Babington.	Henry Dun.
Iohn Sauage.	Edward Ihones.
Robert Barnwell.	Iohn Trauers.
Chodicus Techburne.	Iohn Charnock.
Charles Tilney.	Robert Gage.
Edward Abbington.	Harman Bellamy.

FINIS. T. D.

Imprinted at London at the Long Shop
adioyning vnto Saint Mildreds
Churche in the Pultrie by
Edward Allde.

A ioyful new Ballad,

Declaring the happie obtaining of the great Galleazzo, wherein
Don *Pedro de Valdez* was the chiefe, through the mightie
power and prouidence of God, being a speciall token
of his gracious and fatherly goodnes towards vs,
to the great encouragement of all those that
willingly fight in the defence of his
gospel and our good Queene
of *England*.

To the Tune of Monseurs Almaigne.

O Noble *England*,
    fall downe vpon thy knee :
And praise thy God with thankfull hart,
    which still maintaineth thee.
The forraine forces,
    that seekes thy vtter spoile :
Shall then through his especiall grace
    be brought to shamefull foile.
With mightie power
    they come vnto our coast :   10
To ouer runne our countrie quite,
    they make their brags and boast.

In strength of men
  they set their onely stay :
But we, vpon the Lord our God,
  will put our trust alway.

Great is their number,
  of ships vpon the sea :
And their prouision wonderfull,
  but Lord thou art our stay.   20
Their armed souldiers
  are many by account :
Their aiders eke in this attempt,
  doe sundrie waies, surmount.
The Pope of *Rome*
  with many blessed graines :
To sanctify their bad pretense
  bestowed both cost and paines.
But little land,
  is not dismaide at all :   30
The Lord no doubt is on our side,
  which soone will worke their fall.

In happy houre,
  our foes we did descry :
And vnder saile with gallant winde
  as they cam passing by.
Which suddaine tidings,
  to *Plymmouth* being brought :
Full soone oure Lord high Admirall,
  for to pursue them sought.   40
And to his traine,
  coragiously he said :
Now, for the Lord and our good Queene,
  to fight be not afraide.
Regard our cause,
  and play your partes like men :
The Lord no doubt will prosper vs,
  in all our actions then.

This great Galleazzo,
  which was so huge and hye :   50
That like a bulwarke on the sea,
  did seeme to each mans eye.

There was it taken,
   vnto our great reliefe :
And diuers Nobles, in which traine
   Don *Pietro* was the chiefe.
Stronge was she stuft,
   with Cannons great and small :
And other instruments of warre,
   Which we obtained all.   60
A certaine signe,
   of good successe we trust :
That God will ouerthrow the rest,
   as he hath done the first.

Then did our Nauie
   pursue the rest amaine :
With roaring noise of Cannons great ;
   till they neere *Callice* came :
With manly courage,
   they followed them so fast :   70
Another mightie Gallion
   did seeme to yeeld at last.
And in distresse,
   for sauegard of their liues :
A flag of truce they did hand out,
   with many mournfull cries :
Which when our men,
   did perfectly espie :
Some little Barkes they sent to her,
   to board her quietly.   80

But these false Spaniards,
   esteeming them but weake :
When they within their danger came,
   their malice forth did breake.
With charged Cannons,
   they laide about them then :
For to destroy those proper Barkes,
   and all their valiant men.
Which when our men
   perceiued so to be :   90
Like Lions fierce they forward went,
   to quite this iniurie.

And bourding them,
    with strong and mightie hand :
They kild the men vntill their Arke,
    did sinke in *Callice* sand.

The chiefest Captaine,
    of this Gallion so hie :
Don *Hugo de Moncaldo* he
    within this fight did die.   100
Who was the Generall
    of all the Gallions great :
But through his braines, with pouders force,
    a Bullet strong did beat.
And manie more,
    by sword did loose their breath :
And manie more within the sea,
    did swimme and tooke their death.
There might you see
    the salt and foming flood :   110
Died and staind like scarlet red,
    with store of Spanish blood.

This mightie vessell,
    was threescore yards in length :
Most wonderfull to each mans eie,
    for making and for strength.
In her was placed,
    an hundreth Cannons great :
And mightily prouided eke,
    with bread-corne wine and meat.   120
There were of Oares,
    two hundreth I weene :
Threescore foote and twelue in length,
    well measured to be seene.
And yet subdued,
    with manie others more :
And not a Ship of ours lost,
    the Lord be thankt therefore.

Our pleasant countrie,
    so fruitfull and so faire :   130
They doe intend by deadly warre.
    to make both poore and bare.

Our townes and cities,
   to rack and sacke likewise :
To kill and murder man and wife,
   as malice doth arise.
And to deflower
   our virgins in our sight :
And in the cradle cruelly
   the tender babe to smite.   140
Gods holy truth,
   they meane for to cast downe :
And to depriue our noble Queene,
   both of her life and crowne.

Our wealth and riches,
   which we enioyed long :
They doe appoint their pray and spoile,
   by crueltie and wrong.
To set our houses
   a fier on our heades :   150
And cursedly to cut our throates,
   As we lye in our beds.
Our childrens braines,
   to dash against the ground :
And from the earth our memorie,
   for euer to confound.
To change our ioy,
   to grief and mourning sad :
And neuer more to see the dayes,
   of pleasure we haue had.   160

But God almightie
   be blessed euermore :
Who doth encourage Englishmen,
   to beate them from our shoare.
With roaring Cannons,
   their hastie steps to stay :
And with the force of thundering shot
   to make them flye away.
Who made account,
   before this time or day :   170
Against the walles of faire *London,*
   their banners to display.

But their intent,
   the Lord will bring to nought :
If faithfully we call and cry,
   for succour as we ought.

And you deare bretheren,
   which beareth Arms this day :
For safegarde of your natiue soile,
   marke well what I shall say.   180
Regarde your dueties,
   thinke on your countries good :
And feare not in defense thereof,
   to spend your dearest bloud.
Our gracious Queene
   doth greete you euery one :
And saith, she will among you be,
   in euery bitter storme.
Desiring you,
   true English harts to beare :   190
To God, and her, and to the land,
   wherein you nursed were.

Lord God almightie,
   which hath the harts in hand :
Of euerie person to dispose
   defend this English land.
Bless thou our Soueraigne
   with long and happie life :
Indue her Councel with thy grace,
   and end this mortall strife.   200
Give to the rest,
   of Commons more and lesse :
Louing harts, obedient minds,
   and perfect faithfulnesse.
That they and we,
   and all with one accord :
On *Sion* hill may sing the praise,
   of our most mightie Lord.   T. D.

F I N I S.

LONDON.
Printed by Iohn Wolfe,
for Edward White
1 5 8 8.

The Queenes visiting of the Campe at *Tilsburie* with her entertainment there.

To the Tune of Wilsons wilde.

WIthin the yeare of Christ our Lord
 a thousand and five hundreth full :
And eightie eight by iust record
 the which no man may disannull.
And in the thirtieth yeare remaining,
 of good Queene *Elizabeths* raigning,
A mightie power there was prepared
 by *Philip*, then the king of *Spaine* :
Against the maiden Queene of *England*,
 which in peace before did raigne.   10

Her Royall ships to sea she sent,
 to garde the coast on euerie side :
And seeing how her foes were bent,
 her realme full well she did prouide.
With many thousands so prepared :
 as like was neuer erst declared,
Of horsemen and of footemen plentie,
 whose good harts full well is seene :
In the safegarde of their countrie,
 and the seruice of our Queene.   20

In *Essex* faire that fertill soile,
 vpon the hill of *Tilsbury* :
To giue our Spanish foes the foile,
 in gallant campe they now do lye.
Where good orders is ordained,
 and true iustice eke maintained,
For the punishment of persons,
 that are lewde or badly bent.
To see a sight so straunge in *England*,
 t'was our gracious Queenes intent. 30

And on the eight of August she,
 from faire *St. Iamess* tooke her way :
With many Lords of high degree,
 in princely robes and rich aray.

And to bardge vpon the water,
  being King *Henryes* royall daughter,
She did goe with trumpets sounding,
  and with dubbing drums apace:
Along the Thames that famous riuer,
  for to view the campe a space.   40

When she as farre as *Grauesend* came,
  right ouer against that prettie towne:
Her royall grace with all her traine,
  was landed there with great renowne.
The Lords and Captaines of her forces,
  mounted on their gallant horses,
Readie stood to entertaine her,
  like martiall men of courage bold:
Welcome to the campe dread soueraigne,
  thus they said both yong and old.   50

The Bulworkes strong that stood thereby,
  well garded with sufficient men:
Their flags were spred couragiously,
  their cannons were discharged then.
Each Gunner did declare his cunning,
  for ioy conceiued of her coming.
All the way her Grace was riding,
  on each side stood armed men:
With Muskets, Pikes, and good Caleeuers,
  for her Graces safegarde then.   60

The Lord generall of the field,
  had there his bloudie auncient borne:
The Lord marshals coulors eke,
  were carried there all rent and torne.
The which with bullets was so burned,
  when in Flaunders he soiourned.
Thus in warlike wise they martched
  euen as soft as foote could fall:
Because her Grace was fully minded,
  perfectly to view them all.   70

Her faithfull souldiers great and small,
  as each one stood within his place:
Vpon their knees began to fall,
  desiring God to saue her Grace.

For ioy whereof her eyes was filled,
   that the water downe distilled.
Lord blesse you all my friendes (she said)
   but doe not kneele so much to me :
Then sent she warning to the rest,
   they should not let such reuerence be.   80

Then casting vp her Princely eyes,
   vnto the hill with perfect sight :
The ground all couered, she espyes,
   with feet of armed souldiers bright.
Whereat her royall hart so leaped,
   on her feet vpright she stepped.
Tossing vp her plume of feathers,
   to them all as they did stand :
Chearfully her body bending,
   wauing of her royall hand.   90

Thus through the campe she passed quite,
   in manner as I haue declared :
At maister *Riches* for that night,
   her Graces lodging was preparde.
The morrow after her abiding,
   on a princely paulfrey riding.
To the camp she cam to dinner,
   with her Lordes and Ladies all :
The Lord generall went to meete her,
   with his Guarde of yeomen tall.   100

The Sargeant trumpet with his mace,
   And nyne with trumpets after him :
Bare headed went before her grace,
   in coats of scarlet colour trim.
The king of Heralds tall and comely,
   was the next in order duely.
With the famous Armes of *England*,
   wrought with rich embroidered gold :
On finest veluet blew and crimson,
   that for siluer can be sold.   110

With Maces of cleane beaten gold,
   the Queenes two Sargeants then did ride,
Most comely men for to behold,
   in veluet coates and chaines beside.

The Lord generall then came riding,
  and Lord marshall hard beside him.
Richly were they both atired,
  in princelie garments of great price:
Bearing still their hats and fethers
  in their handes in comely wise.   120

Then came the Queene on pranceing steede
  atired like an Angell bright:
And eight braue footemen at her feete,
  whose Ierkins were most rich in sight.
Her Ladies, likewise of great honor,
  most sumpteuously did waite vpon her.
With pearles and diamonds braue adorned,
  and in costly cales of gold:
Her Guarde in scarlet then ride after,
  with bowes and arrowes stoute and bold.   130

The valiant Captaines of the field,
  meane space them selues in order set:
And each of them with speare and sheelde,
  to ioyne in battaile did not let.
With such a warlike skill extended,
  as the same was much commended.
Such a battaile pitcht in *England*,
  many a day hath not beene seene:
Thus they stood in order waiting,
  for the presence of our Queene.   140

At length her grace most royally
  receiued was and brought againe:
Where she might see most loyally
  this noble hoast and warlike traine.
How they cam martching all together,
  like a wood in winters weather.
With the strokes of drummers sounding,
  and with trampling horses than:
The earth and aire did sound like thunder,
  to the eares of euerie man.   150

The warlike Armie then stood still,
  and drummers left their dubbing sound:
Because it was our Princes will,
  to ride about the Armie round.

Her Ladies she did leaue behind her,
  and her Guarde which still did minde her.
The Lord generall and Lord marshall,
  did conduct her to each place:
The pikes, the colours, and the lances,
  at her approch fell downe apace.   160

And then bespake our noble Queene,
  my louing friends and countriemen:
I hope this day the worst is seen,
  that in our wars ye shall sustain.
But if our enimies do assaile you,
  neuer let your stomackes faile you.
For in the midst of all your troupe,
  we our selues will be in place:
To be your ioy, your guide and comfort,
  euen before your enimies face.   170

This done the souldiers all at once,
  a mightie shout or crye did giue:
Which forced from the Assure skyes,
  an Eccoo loud from thence to driue.
Which filled her grace with ioy and pleasure,
  and riding then from them by leasure,
With trumpets sound most loyally,
  along the Court of guard she went:
Who did conduct her Maiestie,
  vnto the Lord chiefe generals tent.   180

Where she was feasted royally,
  with dainties of most costly price:
And when that night aproched nye,
  Her Maiestie with sage aduice,
In gracious manner then returned,
  from the Campe where she soiourned.
And when that she was safely set,
  within her Barge, and past away:
Her farewell then the trumpets sounded,
  and the cannons fast did play,   190

                    T. D.

FINIS.

Imprinted at London by Iohn Wolfe
for Edward White. 1588.

A new Ballet

of the straunge and most cruell Whippes which the Spanyards
had prepared to whippe and torment English men
and women : *which were found and taken
at the ouerthrow of certaine of the
Spanish Shippes*, in Iuly
last past, 1588.

To the tune of the valiant Soldiour.

AL you that list to looke and see
   what profite comes from *Spayne*
And what the Pope and Spanyards both,
   prepared for our gayne.
Then turne your eyes and bend your eares,
   and you shall heare and see,
What courteous minds, what gentle harts,
   they beare to thee and mee.

They say they seek for *Englands* good,
   and wish the people well :   10
They say they are such holie men,
   all others they excell.
They bragge that they are Catholikes,
   and Christes only Spouse :
And what so ere they take in hand,
   the holie Pope allowes.

These holie men, these sacred Saints,
   and these that thinke no ill :
See how they sought, against all right,
   to murder, spoyle, and kill.   20
Our noble Queene and Countrie first,
   they did prepare to spoyle :
To ruinate our liues and lands,
   with trouble and turmoyle.

And not content by fire and sword
   to take our right away :
But to torment most cruelly
   our bodies night and day.
Although they ment with murdring hands
   our guiltlesse bloud to spill :   30
Before our deathes they did deuise
   to whip vs first their fill.

And for that purpose had preparde
  of whips such wondrouse store,
So straungely made, that sure the like
  was neuer seene before.
For neuer was there Horse, nor Mule,
  nor dogge of currish kinde,
That euer had such whips deuisde
  by any sauadge minde.   40

One sorte of whips they had for men,
  so smarting fierce and fell :
As like could neuer be deuisde
  by any deuill in hell.
The strings whereof with wyerie knots,
  like rowels they did frame,
That euery stroke might teare the flesh
  they layd on with the same,

And pluck the spreading sinewes from
  the hardned bloudie bone,   50
To prick and pearce each tender veine,
  within the bodie knowne.
And not to leaue one crooked ribbe,
  on any side vnseene :
Nor yet to leaue a lumpe of flesh
  the head and foote betweene.

And for our seelie women eke,
  their hearts with griefe to clogge,
They made such whips wherewith no man
  would seeme to strike a dogge :   60
So strengthned eke with brasen tagges,
  and filde so rough and thin,
That they would force at euery lash
  the bloud abroad to spinne.

Although their bodies sweet and fayre
  their spoyle they ment to make :
And on them first their filthie lust
  and pleasure for to take.
Yet afterward such sower sauce
  they should be sure to finde   70
That they shoulde curse each springing braunch
  that cometh of their kinde.

49. pluck] pluckt

O Ladies fayre what spite were this,
  your gentle hearts to kill :
To see these deuilish tyrants thus
  your childrens bloud to spill.
What griefe vnto the husband deere,
  his louing wife to see
Tormented so before his face
  with extreame villainie.   80

And thinke you not that they which had
  such dogged mindes to make
Such instruments of tyrannie,
  had not like hearts to take
The greatest vengeance that they might
  vpon vs euery one :
Yes, yes, be sure, for godlie feare
  and mercie they haue none.

Even as in *India* once they did
  against those people there,   90
With cruel Curres, in shamefull sorte
  the men both rent and teare :
And set the Ladies great with childe
  vpright against a tree,
And shoot them through with pearcing darts,
  such would their practise bee.

Did not the Romans in this land,
  sometime like practise vse,
Against the Brittains bolde in heart,
  and wonderously abuse   100
The valiant King whom they had caught
  before his Queene and wife,
And with most extreame tyrannie
  despatcht him of his life ?

The good Queene *Voadicia,*
  and eke her daughters three :
Did they not first abuse them all
  by lust and lecherie :
And after stript them naked all,
  and whipt them in such sorte :   110
That it would grieue each Christian heart
  to heare that iust reporte.

And if these ruffling mates of *Rome*
　did Princes thus torment :
Think you the Romish Spanyards now
　would not shewe their desent.
How did they late in *Rome* reioyce,
　in *Italie* and *Spayne* :
What ringing and what Bonfires,
　what Masses sung amaine.　　　　　　120

What printed Bookes were sent about,
　as filled their desire :
How *England* was, by Spanyards wonne,
　and *London* set on fire.
Be these the men that are so milde,
　whom some so holie call :
The Lord defend our noble Queene
　and Countrie from them all.

FINIS. T. D.

Imprinted at London, by Thomas Orwin and
Thomas Gubbin, and are to be solde
in Paternoster-row, ouer against
the blacke Rauen
1588.

The Lamentation of Mr. Pages Wife

Of Plimouth, who, being forc'd to wed him, consented to his
Murder, for the loue of G. Strangwidge : for
which they suffered at Barnstable
in Deuonshire.

The Tune is Fortune my Foe, &c.

VNhappy she whom Fortune hath forlorne,
　Despis'd of grace that proffered grace did scorne,
My lawlesse loue hath lucklesse wrought my woe,
My discontent content did ouerthrowe.

My lothed life to late I doe lament,
My wofull deedes in hearte I doe repent :
A wife I was that wilfull went awry,
And for that fault am here preparde to dye.

In blooming yeares my Fathers greedy minde,
Against my will, a match for me did finde :　　10
Great wealth there was, yea, gold and siluer store,
But yet my heart had chosen one before.

Mine eies dislikt my fathers liking quite,
My hart did loth my parents fond delight :
My childish minde and fancie told to mee,
That with his age my youth could not agree.

On knees I prayde they would not me constraine ;
With teares I cryde their purpose to refraine ;
With sighes and sobbes I did them often moue,
I might not wed whereas I could not loue.　　20

But all in vaine my speeches still I spent :
My mothers will my wishes did preuent.
Though wealthy Page possest the outward part,
George Strangwidge still was lodged in my hart.

I wedded was and wrapped all in woe ;
Great discontent within my hart did growe ;
I loathd to liue, yet liude in deadly strife,
Because perforce I was made Pages wife.

My closen eies could not his sight abide ;
My tender youth did lothe his aged side :　　30
Scant could I taste the meate whereon he fed ;
My legges did lothe to lodge within his bed.

Cause knew I none I should dispise him so,
That such disdaine within my hart should growe,
Saue onely this, that fancie did me moue,
And told me still, George Strangwidge was my loue.

Lo ! heere began my downfall and decay.
In minde I musde to make him strait away :
I that became his discontented wife,
Contented was he should be rid of life.　　40

Methinkes the heauens crie vengeance for my fact,
Methinkes the world condemns my monstrous act,
Methinkes within my conscience tells me true,
That for that deede hell fier is my due.

My pensiue soule doth sorrow for my sinne,
For which offence my soule doth bleed within ;
But mercy, Lord ! for mercy still I crye :
Saue thou my soule, and let my bodie dye.

Well could I wish that Page enioyde his life,
So that he had some other to his wife :   50
But neuer could I wish, of low or hie,
A longer life then see sweete Strangwidge die.

O woe is me ! that had no greater grace
To stay till he had runne out Natures race.
My deedes I rue, but I doe repent
That to the same my Strangwidge gaue consent.

You parents fond, that greedy-minded bee,
And seeke to graffe vpon the golden tree,
Consider well and rightfull iudges bee,
And giue you doome twixt parents loue and mee. 60

I was their childe, and bound for to obey,
Yet not to loue where I no loue could laye.
I married was to muck and endlesse strife ;
But faith before had made me Strangwidge wife.

O wretched world ! who cankered rust doth blind,
And cursed men who beare a greedy minde ;
And haplesse I, whom parents did force so
To end my dayes in sorrow, shame and wo.

You Denshire dames, and courteous Cornwall knights,
That here are come to visit wofull wights,   70
Regard my griefe, and marke my wofull end,
But to your children be a better frend.

And thou, my dear, that for my fault must dye,
Be not affraide the sting of death to trye :
Like as we liude and loude together true,
So both at once we'le bid the world adue.

Vlalia, thy friend, doth take her last farewell,
Whose soule with thee in heauen shall euer dwell.
Sweet Sauior Christ ! do thou my soule receiue :
The world I doe with all my heart forgiue.   80

   55 ? *add* most *after* but *or* doe.

And parents now, whose greedy mindes doe show
Your harts desire, and inward heauie woe,
Mourn you no more, for now my heart doth tell,
Ere day be done my soule shalbe full well.

And Plimouth proude, I bid thee now farewell.
Take heede, you wiues, let not your hands rebel ;
And farewell, life, wherein such sorrow showes,
And welcome, death, that doth my corps inclose.

And now, sweete Lord ! forgive me my misdeedes.
Repentance cryes for soule that inward bleedes :   90
My soule and bodie I commend to thee,
That with thy bloud from death redeemed mee.

Lord ! blesse our Queene with long and happy life,
And send true peace betwixt eche man and wife ;
And giue all parents wisedome to foresee,
The match is marrde where mindes doe not agree.
                                        T. D.

London.   Printed by Thomas Scarlet 1591.

A most sweet Song of an English-Merchant Born in *Chichester.*

To an Excellent New Tune.

A Rich Merchant man there was
        that was both graue & wise,
Did kill a man at *Embden* Town
    through quarrels that did rise,
Through quarrels that did rise,
    the German being dead,
And for that fact the Merchant man,
    was judg'd to loose his head.
A sweet thing is loue,
    it rules both heart and mind,   10
There is no comfort in this world.
    to women that are kind.

A Scaffold builded was,
  within the market place,
And all the people far and near,
  did thither flock apace,
Did thither flock apace,
  this doleful sight to see,
Who all in Veluet black as jet,
  vnto the place came he.   20
A sweet, &c.

Bare-headed was he brought,
  his hands were bound before,
A cambrick ruff about his neck,
  as white as milk he wore:
His stockins were of silk,
  as fine as fine might be,
Of person and of countenance,
  a proper man was he.
A sweet, &c.   30

When he was mounted vp,
  vpon the Scaffold high,
All women said great pitty it was
  so sweet a man should dye:
The Merchants of the Town,
  from death to set him free,
Did proffer there a thousand pound
  but yet all would not be.
A sweet, &c.

The prisoner hereupon,   40
  began to speak his mind,
(Quoth he) I haue deserued death,
  in conscience I do find,
Yet sore against my will,
  this man I kill'd (qd. he),
As Christ doth know, which of my soul
  must only Sauiour be.
A sweet, &c.

With heart I do repent,
  this most vnhappy deed,   50
And for his wife and children small
  my very heart doth bleed:

The deed is done and past,
  my hope of life is vain,
And yet the loss of this my life,
  to them is little gain.
A sweet, &c.

Vnto the widow poor,
  and to the Babes therefore,
I give a hundred pound a piece,   60
  their comforts to restore,
Desiring at their hands,
  no one request but this,
They will speak well of English men
  though I haue done amiss.
A sweet, &c.

This was no sooner done,
  but that to stint the strife,
Four goodly maids did proffer him
  for loue to saue his life :   70
This is our Law (qd. they),
  we may your death remoue,
So you in lieu of our good will
  will grant to vs your loue.
A sweet, &c.

Brave English-man (quoth one),
  'tis I will saue thy life,
Nay (quoth the second) it is I,
  so I may be thy wife :
'Tis I (the third did say),   80
  nay (quoth the fourth) tis I,
So each one after the other said,
  still waiting his reply.
A sweet, &c.

Fair Maidens euery one,
  I must confess and say,
That each of you well worthy is
  to be a Lady gay :

And I vnworthy far,
  the worst of you to haue,   90
Though you haue proffer'd willingly
  my loathed life to saue.
A sweet, *&c.*

Then take a thousand thanks,
  of me a dying man,
But speak no more of loue nor life,
  for why my life is gone,
To Christ my soul I giue,
  my body vnto death,
For none of you my heart can haue,   100
  sith I must loose my breath.
A sweet, *&c.*

Fair Maids lament no more,
  your Country Law is such,
It takes but hold vpon my life,
  my goods it cannot touch:
Within one Chest I haue
  in Gold a thousand pound,
I giue it equal to you all,
  for loue that I haue found.   110
A sweet, *&c.*

And now dear friends farewell,
  sweet *England* now adieu,
And *Chichester* where I was born,
  where first this breath I drew;
And now thou man of death,
  vnto thy weapon stand,
O nay (another Damsel said)
  sweet Headsman hold thy hand.
A sweet, *&c.*   120

Now hear a maidens plaint,
  brave English-man (quoth she)
And grant me loue for loue again,
  that craues but loue of thee:
I wooe and sue for loue,
  that had been woo'd e're this,
Then grant me loue, & therewithal
  she proffered him a kiss;
A sweet, *&c.*

I'le dye within thy arms,
   if thou wilt dye (quoth she)
Yet liue or dye sweet English man,
   i'le liue and dye with thee :
But can it be (quoth he)
   that thou dost loue me so,
Tis not by long acquaintance Sir
   whereby true loue doth grow,
A sweet, &c.   130

Then beg my life (quoth he)
   and I will be thy own,
If I should seek the world for loue
   more loue cannot be shown :
The people at that word
   did giue a joyful cry,
And said great pitty it was,
   so sweet a man should dye ;
A sweet, &c.   140

I go my Loue (she said)
   I run, I flye for thee,
& gentle Headsman spare a while,
   my Louers head for me ;
Vnto the Duke she went,
   who did her grief remoue,
& with an hundred Maidens more,
   she went to fetch her Loue :
A sweet, &c.   150

With musick sounding sweet,
   the foremost of the train,
The gallant maiden like a bride,
   did fetch him back again ;
Yea hand in hand away they went,
   vnto the Church that day,
And they were married presently,
   in sumptuous rich array ;
A sweet, &c.   160

To *England* came he then,
   with his fair Lady Bride,
A fairer woman neuer lay
   by any Merchants side ;

Where we must leaue them now, 170
  in pleasure and delight,
but of their names & dweling place
  I must not here recite.
  A sweet, &c.

FINIS.

Printed for J. Clarke, W. Thackeray,
and T. Passinger.

Salomons good houswife, in the 31 of his Proverbes.

H E that a gracious wife doth find,
  Whose life puts vertue chiefe in vre,
One of the right good huswife kind,
That man may well himselfe assure,
  And boasting say that he hath found
  The richest treasure on the ground.

Who so enioyeth such a loue,
Let him resolue with hearts consent,
She euer constantly will proue
A carefull nurse, want to preuent, 10
  With diligence and painefull heed,
  Preuenting tast of beggers need.

And while she liues will still procure,
By true and faithfull industrie,
T'increase his wealth, and to insure
His state in all securitie :
  To seeke his quiet, worke his ease,
  And for a world no way displease.

Her houshold folke from sloth to keepe,
Shee will endeauour with good heed, 20
At worke more wakefull then asleepe,
With flaxe and stuffe, which houswiues need
  To be employd, her hands also
  The way to worke will others show.

Her wit a common wealth containes,
Of needments for her houshold store,
And like a ship her selfe explaines,
That riches brings from forraine shore,
    Arriuing, with a bounteous hand
    Dispearsing treasure to the land.   30

Before the day she will arise
To order things, and to prouide
What may her family suffice,
That they at labour may abide,
    If she haue land, no paine shall want
    To purchase vines, set, sow, and plant.

No honest labour shee'le omit,
In ought she can attaine vnto,
But will endeauour strength and wit,
Adding the vtmost she can do :   40
    And if that profit comes about,
    By night her candle goes not out.

A willing hand to the distrest
She lends, and is a chearefull giuer :
Come winters cold and frostie guest,
When idle huswiues quake and quiuer,
    She and her housholds cloathed well,
    The weathers hardnesse to expell.

Her skill doth worke faire Tapistrie,
With linnen furnish'd of the best :   50
Her needle workes do beautifie,
And she in Scarlet costly drest,
    When Senators assembled be,
    Her husbands honor there shall see.

Her spinning shall her store increase,
The finest cloth shall yeeld her gaine,
And dayly profit shall not cease,
Which her vnidle hands maintaine :
    Her clothing shall her worth expresse,
    And Honors yeares her end possesse.   60

Her mouth shall neuer opened be,
But wisdome will proceede from it :

And such mild gracious wordes yeelds shee,
Sweetnesse vpon her tongue doth sit :
   In age she will her care addresse,
   To eate no bread of idelnesse.

Her children shall their dutie show,
Most reuerent to her all their life,
Her husband blesse, that he did know
The time to meete with such a wife :   70
   And vttring forth his happinesse,
   Her vertues in this wise expresse.

I know t'is true that more then one
Good huswife there is to be found :
But I may say, that thou alone
Aboue all women dost abound,
   Yea I protest in all my daies,
   Thou art the first, and thee ile praise.

What thing is fauour but a shade?
It hath no certaine lasting hower,   80
Whereof is wanton beautie made,
That withers like a Sommers flower?
   When these shall end their date in daies,
   She that feares God shall liue with praise.

And such a wife of worthie worth,
Due glories lot will to her fall,
And great assemblies will giue forth,
What vertues shee's adorn'd withall,
   Her lifes renowne to fame shall reach,
   Her good example others teach.   90

May bachelors of each degree,
In choosing of a beauteous wife,
Remember, what is ioy to see
May lead to wofulnesse and strife :
   Beauty is not a brave outside ;
   Beauty within is beautys pride.

F I N I S.

APPENDIX.

I. PATIENT GRISSELL.

THE ballad of *Patient Grissell* was printed in a setting of prose as a complete little book about 1630 (part of the date has been cut away in the British Museum copy). Although there is no actual proof that the prose is Deloney's the style suggests his authorship. 'The feast that continued fourteene dayes, to the comfort of the Commons' may be compared with Iacke of Newberie's wedding 'that endured ten dayes to the great reliefe of the poore'. The title page and prose setting are added below; the ballad itself does not differ materially from the version in the *Garland of Good Will.*

THE PLEASANT

AND SWEET HISTORY

of patient Grissell.

Shewing how she from a poore mans
Daughter, came to be a great Lady in *France,*
being a patterne for all vertuous
Women.

Translated out of *Italian.*

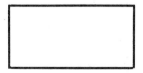

London printed by E. P. for Iohn Wright, dwelling
in Giltspurstreet at the signe of the bible.   16

Chapter I.

How, and in what place, the Noble marquesse was dwelling.

IN the Countrey of *Salusa*, which lyeth neere *Italy* and *France*, there liued a noble and wealthy Prince, named *Gualter*, Marquesse and Lord of *Salusa*, a man of such vertues that the world did ring of: beloued of his subiects for his good parts, that before his dayes nor since, was very few the like, for his continuall care of his subiects good, and they in their dutifulnesse, sought to out-strip him in loue. From his youth his onely exercise was hunting, wherein he tooke such delight, that nothing was more pleasing vnto him : withall the subiects loyalty to this worthy Prince, in their carefulnesse that such excellent vertues should not faile for want of issue, intreated him by humble petition to marry, that from his loynes their children might enioy the like happinesse. This speech thus spoke to the prince draue such loue and affection into his minde, that most graciously he made them answer, that when it should please God, that hee should see one that he could loue, hee most willingly would fulfill their good and honest request : withall this answer gaue them such content, that they prayed earnestly to see that day.

Chapter II.

Of the good and honest life of faire *Grissel*, and her old father *Ianicola*.

NEre to the famous city of *Saluse*, was a poor village named *Clue*, in the way going to a great and spacious Forrest, where the Noble Marquesse vsed daily his pleasure in hunting ; the poorer sort got their liuing, som by spinning, som carding, others keeping sheep. Amongst the rest of the inhabitants, there was an old man named *Ianicola*, whose wife being dead, shee left him one onely Daughter, named *Grissell*, who, by the Countrey manner, was named the faire. These two liued contentedly together, the aged Father goes to get wood for fire, the Maid makes his bed, gets his breakfast ready against his comming home, driues her sheepe to the common, sets her house in order, and fals to her ordinary worke of spinning : when the old man comes home, she sets his meate, makes much of him, shewes al the obedience that may be to the aged man ; he in requitall of her loue, as an incouragement to all obedient children, powrs out his hearty prayers in her behalf, praying the Almighty God to blesse her, & to giue her that happines which belongs to so good a child. No doubt but his petition was heard, for God gaue a blessing to her, as you may hear by the happy comming of the Marquesse that way, which may seeme suddenly after.

[Here the ballad is printed, practically as in the text, pp. 346-50.]

Chapter X.

Of the great feast that was made for patient *Grissel*, and her children, and old *Ianicola*.

THe Lords and Gentlemen being astonished, looked one vpon another, and seeing no remedy, but that the noble Marquesse had an vnremoueable loue vpon her, besought her to pardon them of their enuy towards her, and to take them into her fauour, which she with a modest behauiour promised to doe ; the noble Marquesse seeing all in peace, ordained a great and sumptuous feast, where patient *Grissel* sat Mistresse of the feast, the Marquesse on her right hand, on her left her aged Father, old *Ianicola* ; her two children betweene them both, the Lords and Gentlemen doing them seruice. This feast continued fourteene dayes, to the comfort of the Commons.

When this solemne feast was ended : the Marquesse, to shew his loue to his *Grissell*, made her Father one of his counsel, and Gouernour of his Palace, where for many yeares he liued in the loue of the whole Court : the noble Marquesse and his faire *Grissell*, liued almost thirty yeeres, saw their childrens children, and then dyed, beloued and bewayled of their subiects.

Chapter XI.
The Authors persuasion to all Women in Generall.

THus you may see by this History, you that are women, the great good which commeth by patience and humility, for had this vertuous woman bin of a churlish and crabbed disposition, she had lost that great estate which she had, besides the happy loue of a worthy and louing husband : Therefore, ye women, as you are helpers for men, & were so created for that vse, giue no distaste to your louing husbands : & men likewise, be not bitter to your wiues, for the world hath not many *Grissels*. for man and Wife, liuing louingly and peaceably in this world, shal dye with a good conscience,
and enioy the happinesse of the world
to come, which shall haue
no end

II. DELONEY'S LOST WORK.

THERE can be no doubt that a great many of Deloney's ballads have perished with the fragile sheets upon which they were printed, or if still extant, cannot now be identified. There is also some reason to suppose that larger compositions either in prose or poetry have shared the same fate.

Sir Stephen Slany, in his letter to Lord Burghley (see p. ix), ascribes to Deloney :

[1] '*A certain Ballad, containing a Complaint of Great Want and Scarcity of Corn within the Realm . . . bringing in the Queen, speaking with her People Dialogue wise, in very fond and vndecent sort.*'

[2] '*A Book for the Silk Weauers*', which had also given the authorities some annoyance.

Nash, writing in 1596 in *Haue with You to Saffron-Walden*, ascribes to Deloney :

[3] '*an epistle of Momus and Zoylus.*'
[4] '*Iigge of Iohn for the King.*'
[5] '*The Thunderbolt against Swearers.*'
[6] '*Repent, England, Repent.*'

[7] ' *The strange Iudgments of God.*'
Kempe, writing in 1600, ascribes to him :
[8] Ballads on the Morrice dance from London to Norwich.
No trace can be found of [8], [2] or [3]. A ballad of *Iohn for the King* was entered at Stationers' Hall, Oct. 24, 1603, as *A newe ballet, called* IOHN FOR THE KING *to the tune of Hey downe derrye* : and ballads of this title are referred to and perhaps parodied in Heywood's *Rape of Lucrece*, Act III, Sc. i,

> *Iohn for the King has been in many ballads.*
> *Iohn for the King down derro;*
> *Iohn for the King has eaten many sallads,*
> *Iohn for the King sings hey ho.*

Ballads like *No.* 5 against swearing, and *No.* 7 on the judgements of God, are entered with great variety in the *Stationers' Registers* and some survive, but none can be attributed to Deloney with any certainty.
To judge by the title, *The Thunderbolt of GODS Iudgments* assigned from Mistress Pavier to E. Brewster and R. Birde on Aug. 4, 1626, seems to be most probably the ballad referred to by Nash.
[1] Two ballads are entered in the *Stationers' Registers* on the scarcity of corn about 1595.

XVI Octobris (1594)

TO EDWARD WHITE. *The poores lamentacon for the price of corne with GODes Iustice shewed vppon a cruell horder of corne.*

XIX Die Aprilis (1595)

THOMAS MILLINGTON. *Entred for his copie vnder thande of Master Warden* BINGE *a ballad entituled a warninge to England with speed to Repente for the great scarssetye and want that now is and like this year ensuinge to be &c.*
Neither of these ballads seems to answer very closely to Slany's description, and neither is extant.
[6] *Repent, England, Repent* was a common ballad burden of the time and gives no very certain guide to the ballad referred to.
The following possible entries of Deloney's ballad occur in the *Stationers' Registers.*

Secundo die Augusti (1594)

TO IOHN DANTER. *A call to Repentaunce to all true Englishe hartes.*

XIX° die Aprilis (1595)

The ballad described above dealing with the ' scarssetye and want '.

VIII Iunii (1603)

A warninge or Lamentacon to London of the Dolefull Destruccon of fayre Ierusalem.
This ballad appears to be extant in the Rawlinson Collection, 40, 566, fol. 190, and has a burden similar to that mentioned by Nash, while the subject is that which Deloney treated at some length in *Canaans Calamitie* (1598). It is accordingly printed here.

CHRISTS TEARES OVER IERVSALEM.

OR,

A Caueat for *England* to call to God for Mercy, lest we be
plagued for our contempt and wickedness.

To the tune of, *The Merchant.*

WHen Christ our Lord drew nigh,
    vnto *Ierusalem,*
Foreseeing all the miseries
    the which should fall on them ;
And casting of his looks
    vpon that beauteous Town,
For very grief the bitter tears
    from his fair eyes fell down.
Repent fair England, now repent,
    repent while you haue space,   10
And do not like Ierusalem,
    despise Gods proffered Grace.

Alas *Ierusalem,*
    Ierusalem (quoth he)
Which kil'd the Prophets of the Lord
    when they were sent to thee ;
How oftentimes would I,
    haue kept thee from all ill ?
Euen as the Hen her Chickens keep,
    but thou art stubborn still.   20

O that thou hadst but known,
    at least in that thy day,
The things which did concern thy peace
    but now 'tis hid away :
Yea, from thine eyes 'tis hid,
    thou shalt not see the same ;
And for thy sorrows coming on,
    thy self do only blame.

Therefore the days shall come
    thy enemies shall rise,   30
And trench thee in on euery side
    regarding not thy crys :
Thy strong and stately Towers,
    in wrath they shall confound,
And make thy sumptuous buildings all,
    lie equal with the ground.

And such shall be their rage,
    they shall not leaue in thee,
One stone vpon another stone
    which shall not spoiled be :   40

Because thou knewest not,
  the seasonable day,
Wherein the Lord did visit thee,
  to wash thy sins away.

The Second Part, to the same Tune.

Thus Christ without the Town
  did weep for their distress,
While they within, triumph in sin,
  and vse all wickedness:
No whit they would belieue
  the words which he did say,   50
But enuiously did practise still,
  to take his life away.

He mourned and wept full sore,
  to think vpon the smart,
While they full stout did go about
  to pierce his tender heart:
And for his pains they stript him,
  and whipt him through the town,
And with a wreath of pricking thorns
  his holy head did crown.   60

They scoff and laugh at him,
  they dasht him in the face,
They calld him gracious Lord and king
  in flouting and disgrace:
And thorow his hands and feet
  they nail him to the Cross
Between two leud and wicked thieues,
  but few lament his loss.

They gaue him for to drink,
  sharp Vinegar and Gall,   70
And with a Spear they pierc'd his side,
  till his heart blood did fall:
Yet patiently and mild,
  he suffered euery thing,
And prayed his Father not to charge
  them with this grieuous sin.

When thus they had dispatcht,
  the Liuing Lord of might,
Full safely then they thought themselues,
  from Sorrow, care and strife: 80
But within few years space,
  as Christ before had told
The mighty Emperor of *Rome*,
  came thither with courage bold.

And with a mighty Host
  he did besiege them round,
By Sword and Famine e're he went
  he did them quite confound:

Yea, Dogs and Cats they eat,
  Mice, Rats, and euery thing,
For want of food, their Infants young   90
  into the Pot they bring.

No pitty could they find
  at this their enemies hand,
But Fire, Sword, and cruel death
  before them still did stand,
Their famous City fair,
  he set vpon a flame,
He burnt their Temple vnto Dust,
  that stood within the same.   100

And those that scap'd the Sword
  and fury of his hand,
He made them slaues and bond-slaues all
  within a foraign Land:
Thus fair *Ierusalem*
  was cast vnto the ground,
For their great sin and wickedness
  the Lord did it confound.

Awake *England* I say,
  rise from the sleep of sin,   110
Cast off thy great security
  which thou hast liued in,
Thy God hath often call'd,
  and offered thee his grace,
His Messengers haue shown his will
  to thee in euery place.

Great wonders he hath shown
  to thee by Sea and Land,
And sent strange tokens in the air
  to make thee vnderstand: 120
He is offended sore
  at thy great wickedness
And that except thou dost repent,
  thy plagues shall he express.

Remember how of late,
  the *Spaniard* he assail'd,
And how by Gods especial power,
  they ne'r a whit preuaild:
And all was for to try
  if thou wouldst sin forsake,   130
And to an vpright holy life,
  thy self at last betake,

But soon has thou forgot
  his fauour in the same,
Which afterwards most grieuously
  his wrath did so enflame:
That then he plagued thee
  with Pestilence and Death,
Whereby in Country and in Town
  a number lost their breath.   140

Yet wilt thou not forsake
  thy wickedness and ill,
But in thy pride and couetousness
  thou hast continued still:
Prouoke not God to wrath
  with thy most loathsome sin,
But speedily to amend thy life,
  with Prayers now begin.

And therefore now O *England,*
  at last for mercy cry,   150
And grieue the Lord thy God no more,
  through thy iniquity;
Lest he forsake thee quite,
  and turn away his face,
Because like to *Ierusalem,*
  thou dost despise his Grace.
Repent therefore O England,
  repent while thou hast space,
And do not like Ierusalem,
  despise Gods proffered Grace.   160

FINIS.

London, *Printed for* F. Coles, T. Vere, J. Wright, *and* I. Clarke.

But *The Wandering Iew* (*Roxburghe Collection,* iii. 718) has almost exactly the same refrain and may be the ballad referred to by Nash.

The *Wandering Iew:*

or, the *Shoemaker* of Ierusalem.

Who liued when our Lord and Sauiour Iesus Christ was Crucified, and by him appointed to Liue till his Coming again.

WHen as in fair Ierusalem,
  Our Sauiour Christ did liue,
And for the sins of all the world,
  His own dear life did giue;
The wicked Iews with scoffs and scorns
  Did daily him molest:
That neuer till he left this life,
  Our Sauiour could haue rest.
    Repent therefore, O England!
      Repent while you haue space;   10
    And do not like the wicked Iews
      Despise Gods profer'd grace.

When they had crown'd his head with thorns,
  And scourg'd him with disgrace;
In scornful sort they led him forth
  Vnto his dying place.

Where thousands thousands in the street
  Did see him pass along;
Yet not one gentle heart was there,
  That pity'd this his wrong. Repent, &c.   20

Both old and young reuiled him,
  As thro' the streets he went;
And nothing found but churlish taunts
  By euery one's consent.
His own dear cross he bore himself.
  A burden far too great;
Which made him in the streets to faint,
  With blood and water sweat. Repent, &c.

Being weary, thus he sought for rest,
  For to ease his burthen'd soul,   30
Vpon a stone; the which a wretch
  Did churlishly controul.
And said, Away, thou king of Iews,
  You shall not rest you here:
Pass on; your execution-place
  You see now draweth near. Repent, &c.

And thereupon he thrust him thence,
  At which our Sauiour said,
I sure will rest, but thou shalt walk,
  And haue no iourney staid.   40
With that this cursed shoemaker,
  For offering Christ this wrong,
Left wife and children, house, and all,
  And went from thence along. Repent, &c.

So when he had the precious blood
  Of Iesus Christ thus shed,
And to the cross his body nail'd
  Away with speed he fled.
Without returning back again
  Vnto his dwelling-place;   50
And wandreth vp and down the world,
  A renegade most base. Repent, &c.

No resting could he find at all,
  Nor ease, nor heart's content;
No house, nor home, nor dwelling place,
  But wandering forth he went.
From town to town, in foreign lands,
  With grieued conscience, still
Repenting for the heinous guilt
  Of his fore-passed ill. Repent, &c.   60

Thus after some ages had past,
  With wandering vp and down,
He once again desired to see
  Ierusalem's fair town.
But finding it was quite destroy'd,
  He wandered full of woe;
Our Sauiours words which he had spoke,
  To verify and shew: Repent, &c.

59 gift *Roxb.*

I'll rest (said he) but thou shalt walk,
   So doth this Wandering Iew,   70
From place to place, but cannot stay,
   For seeing countries new.
Declaring still the power of him,
   Where'er he comes or goes,
And of all things done in the East,
   Since Christ his death he shows.   Repent, &c.

The world he still doth compass round,
   And sees those nations strange,
Who hearing of the name of God,
   Their idol Gods do change.   80
To whom he hath told wond'rous things
   Of time fore-past and gone ;
And to the Princes of the world
   Declar'd his cause of moan.   Repent, &c.

Desiring still to be dissolu'd
   And yield his mortal breath ;
But as the Lord had thus decreed,
   He must not yet see death.
For neither looks he old or young,
   But as he did those times   90
When Christ did suffer on the cross,
   For mortal sinners crimes.   Repent, &c.

He passed many foreign lands,
   Arabia, Egypt, Africa,
Greecia, Syria and Great Thrace,
   And quite thro' Hungary.
Where Paul and Peter preached Christ,
   Those blest apostles dear,
Where he hath told our Sauiours words,
   In the countries far and near.   Repent, &c.   100

And lately in Bohemia,
   With many a German town ;
And now in Flanders, as 'tis thought
   He wandereth vp and down.
Where learned men with him confer,
   Of those his lingering days,
And wonder much to hear him tell
   His iourneys and his ways.   Repent, &c.

If people giue this Iew an alms,
   The most that he will take   110
Is not aboue a groat a day,
   Which he for Iesus sake
Doth kindly giue vnto the poor,
   And therefore makes no spare,
Affirming still that Iesus Christ
   Of him hath daily care.   Repent, &c.

He was not seen to laugh or smile,
   But weep and make great moan,
Lamenting still his miseries,
   And days far spent and gone.   120

76 did shew *Roxb.*   95 Grece *Roxb.*

If he hears any one blaspheme,
   Or take Gods name in vain;
He tells them that they crucify
   Our Sauiour Christ again. Repent, &c.

If thou had'st seen grim death (said he)
   As these mine eyes haue done,
Ten thousand thousand times would ye
   His torments think vpon.
And suffer for his sake all pains,
   All torments and all woes,   130
These are his words, and this his life,
   Where e'er he comes or goes. Repent, &c.

Printed and Sold at the Printing-Office in Bow-Church-Yard,
London.

III. ATTRIBUTED BALLADS.

THE following ballads have been attributed to Deloney, on insufficient grounds.

(1) *Evil May Day*, by Ebbsworth, who seems to follow J. P. Collier. Collier in his reprint of the ballad in *Blackletter Broadsides* asserts that it is included in the 1607 edition of *Strange Histories.* It is not.

(2) *The Lamentacon of Christofer Tomlinson, horse corser comonlye called* KYTT *with the wry mouthe, whoe killed his wife with a Dagger, and was executed for the same, the 4th Daie of December,* 1592 *at Tyborne*; entered Dec. 6th, 1592. J. P. Collier, in his communications to *Notes and Queries* on the *Stationers' Registers*, remarks:

'This ballad is extant with the initials T. D. for Thomas Deloney at the end of it. The tune assigned to it is "Fortune", and it begins:

> ' Well may I grone and sighe
>   For my most cruell crime :
> My life hath been awry
>   And I misspent my tyme.

'It afterwards notices the defect of his mouth, mentioned in the entry, but the only copy known is in so mutilated a state that we hope the extract we have may lead to the discovery and identification of a more perfect copy.'

There is no other evidence for the existence of this ballad or its ascription to Deloney.

(3) *Jane Shore (Rox. Coll.* i. 163), by Ebbsworth, without any evidence and with no apparent reason.

(4) *A Courtly new Ballad of the Princely wooing of the faire Maid of London by King Edward (Rox. Coll.* i. 58), by Ebbsworth. No evidence.

(5) *A pleasant new Ballad of two Louers (Rox. Coll.* i. 316), by Ebbsworth, on the ground that it is included in the 1681 edition of the *Royal Garland of Love and Delight.* But the authentic work of Deloney in the *Royal Garland* is very much cut down and altered, and several new poems are added of an obviously Restoration character. Hence the evidence is very weak.

(6) *An excellent new Medly. To the Tune of the Spanish Pauin* (*Rox. Coll.* i. 14). It is subscribed with the initials F. D., which Ebbsworth thinks may be in error for T. D.

(7) *The Blind Beggar of Bednall Green* (*Percy Folio*), by J. H. Dixon in the Percy Society reprint of the *Garland of Good Will.* No evidence.

(8) *The Lamentation of George Strangwidge*, by Ebbsworth, apparently because the subject is the same as that of *The Lamentation of Mr Pages Wife* (p. 482). Neither the Crawford, Roxburghe, nor Allde copies are signed, but in the Crawford collection the *Lamentation of George Strangwidge* is printed side by side on the same broadside with the *Lamentation of Mr Pages Wife.* This seems to favour the supposition that Deloney wrote both of the ballads. Accordingly the *Lamentation of George Strangwidge* is reprinted here from the Roxburghe copy (i. 183).

THE LAMENTATION OF GEORGE STRANG-

widge, who, for consenting to the death of Master Page
of Plimmouth, suffered Death, at Bar⟨n⟩stable.

THe man that sighes and sorrowes for his sinne,
The corps which care and woe hath wrapped in,
In dolefull sort records his Swan-like Song,
Then waits for Death, and loathes to liue so long.

O᾽ Glandfield! cause of my committed crime,
Snared in wealth, as Birds in bush of lime,
What cause hadst thou to beare such wicked spight,
Against my good, and eke my Loues delight.

I would to God thy wisedome had beene more,
Or that I had not entered in the doore;   10
Or that thou hadst a kinder Father beene
Vnto thy Child, whose yeares are yet but greene:

The match vnmete which thou for muck didst make,
When aged Page thy Daughter home did take,
Well maist thou rue with teares that cannot dry,
Which was the cause that foure of vs must dye.

Vlalia faire, more bright than Summers Sunne,
Whose beauty had my heart for euer won,
My soule more sobs to thinke of thy disgrace,
Than to behold mine owne vntimely race.   20

The deed late done, in heart I doe lament;
But that I lou'd, I cannot it repent;
Thy seemely sight was euer sweet to me,
Would God my death would thy excuser be.

It was for me (alas!) thou didst the same;
On me, of right, they ought to lay the blame:
My worthlesse loue hath brought my life in scorne,
Now, woe is me that euer I was borne!

Farewell, my loue, whose loyall heart was seene :
Would God thou hadst not halfe so constant beene!   30
Farewell, my Loue, the pride of Plimmouth Towne !
Farewell, the Flower, whose beauty is cut downe !

For twenty yeares great was the cost, I know,
Thy vnkind Father did on thee bestow;
Yet afterward, so sore did fortune lowre,
He lost his ioy and child within an houre.

My wrong and woe to God I doe commit :
His was the fault, by matching them vnfit :
And yet my guilt I cannot so excuse,
I gaue consent, his life for to abuse.   40

Wretch that I am, that I consent did giue !
Had I denied, Vlalia still should liue :
Blind fancy said, her suite doe not denie;
Liue thou in blisse, or else in sorrow die.

O Lord ! forgiue this cruell deed of mine ;
Vpon my soule let beames of mercy shine :
In Iustice Lord ! doe thou no vengeance take ;
Forgiue vs both for Iesus Christ his sake.

FINIS.

NOTES

IACKE OF NEWBERIE

Date. The following entries occur in the *Stationers' Registers* for 1596-7 :

7 Marcij.

Thomas Millington Entred for his copie a booke called *Iack of Newbery.* So that he haue yt lawfully Aucthorised. vj*d.*

25 Maij.

Humfrey Lownes Assigned ouer to hym for his copie from *Thomas Myllington* A boke called *Iacke of Newbery,* with this condicion that yt be laufully Aucthorised.

Hence *Iacke of Newberie* must have been written by March 7, 1597, and, originally entered to Thomas Millington, was assigned over to Humfrey Lownes on May 25th. The fact that a ' ballad intituled the *ffirst parte of Iacke of Newberye* ' was entered to Thomas Millington, July 8, 1597, seems to show that the book attained instant popularity. This ballad, very probably by Deloney, does not now appear to be extant.

Extant Editions.

[A] 1626. The pleasant Historie of IOHN WINCHCOMB, In his yonguer yeares called IACK OF NEWBERY, The famous and worthy Clothier of England ; . . . Now the tenth time Imprinted, corrected and enlarged by *T. D.*. . . . LONDON, Printed by H. LOWNES, and are to be sold by *Cuthbert Wright* in S. *Bartholomews,* neer the entrance into the Hospitall. 1626. (*Bridgewater House.*)

[B] 1630. The eleuenth Edition. Printed by *H.L.* and *R.Y.* (*Bodleian.*)

[C] 1633. . . . now the ninth time Imprinted by *Robert Young.* (*British Museum.*)

[D] 1672. Now the 13th time imprinted, . . . by *E. Crowch* for *Thomas Passenger.* (*Bodleian.*)

[E] 1680 ? Printed by *W. Wilde* for *Thos. Passenger.* (*British Museum.*)

[F] 1700 ? London. Printed for *Eben. Tracy* at the *Three Bibles.* (*British Museum.*)

[G] No date. Title page missing. (*Bodleian.*)

[H] 1775. Printed by *J. Willis* on the Bridge, Newbury. (*Bodleian.*)

Hazlitt mentions an edition of 1619, but the earliest traceable edition is that of 1626, in the possession of the Earl of Ellesmere, which is now reprinted here. The 1775 edition has been modified beyond recognition, and concludes its account of Jacke by the following : ' Mr. Winchcombe lived many years, an ornament to society and a great promoter of the cloathing branch. He built the tower, with all the western part of Newbury Church, and died Feb. 15, 1519, as appears by his epitaph still remaining in the church.'

Note on Sources. The story of *Iacke of Newberie* seems to be almost entirely derived from tradition. In the dedication to ' the famous Cloth Workers in England ' Deloney speaks of his ' rude worke, which hath raised out of the dust of forgetfulnesse a most famous and worthy man ', whereby perhaps intimating that his was the first printed account of the worthy clothier. Throughout the novel Deloney shows a detailed knowledge of Newbury, its surroundings, and the county families of Elizabethan Berkshire, which could only have been obtained by an actual residence there, and the *Pleasant Historie of Iohn Winchcombe* is probably in the main little more than a literary re-shaping of a vivid tradition not more than fifty or sixty years old. The Newbury of to-day still cherishes the memory of its sixteenth-century hero, and modern topography and the Elizabethan chronicles alike bear out Deloney's story in the essential details.

Historical evidence is not lacking as to John Winchcombe's life and works. Fuller, in his *Worthies*, gives the following account of him, which, although drawn in part from the present novel, gives a first-hand description of his house.

' John Winscombe, called commonly Jack of Newbury, was then the most considerable clothier (without fancy and fiction) England ever beheld. His looms were his lands, whereof he kept one hundred in his house, each managed by a man and a boy. In the expedition to Flodden-field, against James, King of Scotland, he marched with an hundred of his own men (as well armed and better clothed than any) to shew that the painful to use their hands in peace, could be valiant, and employ their arms in war. He feasted King Henry the Eighth and his first queen Katharine in his own house, extant at Newberry at this day, but divided into many tenements. Well may his house now make sixteen clothiers' houses, whose wealth would amount to six hundred of their estates. He built the church of Newberry from the pulpit westward to the tower inclusively ; and died about the year 1520 ; some of his name and kindred of great wealth still remaining in this ·country.' *Works* (1840), vol. i, p. 137.

Winchcombe's will, dated January, 1519, is still preserved in Somerset House, making mention of his first wife Alice and his second wife Joan, bequeathing £40 to Newbury Parish Church and legacies to each of his servants. His epitaph, which still remains in Newbury Church, runs as follows :

> Of your Charite pray for the
> Soule of *John Smalwood,* alias
> *Winchom,* and *Alice,* his wife,
> Which *John* died the 15th day of
> February An. Dom. 1519

' Some of his name and kindred of great wealth ' survived until the eighteenth century. Thus Swift writes to Stella of St. John (*Letter XXVII,* Aug. 1711) : ' His house is in the midst of near three thousand pounds a year he had by his lady, who is descended from Jack of Newbury, of whom books and ballads are written ; and there is an old picture of him in the room.'

For further details of the historical John Winchcombe see Money's *History of Newbury,* and *Newbury and its Environs* (1839).

Into the biography of his clothier hero, Deloney has woven several other stories from the sources, more or less obscure, which were open to the enterprising novelist of the sixteenth century.

The story of how Mistress Winchcombe turned the tables on her husband, who had locked her out for the night, is practically identical with Novella 4, Giornata VII, in the *Decameron,* which was after-wards used by Molière for *George Dandin.* Apparently no direct translation into English existed in the sixteenth century, but there were the French versions of du Premierfait (1485) and Le Maçon (1545), and the story itself appears to have been widely diffused, appearing among the tales of the *Disciplina Clericalis*.

The story of Benedict's amorous disappointment, like that of Sir George Rigley's marriage, is merely a variation of the common type of novella, where the whole plot turns on the substitution of one person for another. Painter's version (1566) of Novella 9, Giornata III, of the *Decameron* (used by Shakespeare for *All's Well that Ends Well*) might very well have given the hint for the former, and Belleforest's *Histoires tragiques* (1582), *Partie* I, Nouvelle 20 (used for *Much Ado about Nothing*), has a sufficiently general resemblance to have suggested the latter. But Deloney really needed no other source than his own acquaintance with the floating mass of popular Elizabethan literature.

The story of Randoll Pert, the substantial merchant fallen to decay, yet rising again to his former prosperity, is retold with slight variations of Tom Dove (in *Thomas of Reading*) and of the Greene King of St. Martin's (in *The Gentle Craft*, Part II).

PAGE 2. 24-6. This seems to indicate that Deloney had already planned *Thomas of Reading*, which must have been published between the date of the registration of *Iacke of Newberie* (March 7, 1596-7) and April, 1600, when it is mentioned by Kempe.

PAGE 3. 3. *broad cloth Weauer.* 'I have been informed that Jack of Newberry was the first that introduced it (i. e. broad-cloth) into this country.' Fuller, *Worthies* (1840), vol. i, p. 112.

PAGE 4. 1. The Sunday haunting of alehouses is attacked in *The Times Whistle* (1614?):

> For olde & young i' th' country frequently
> Vpon that day do vse most luxurie.
> Each on[e] must then vnto an alehouse run
> Drink drunk, act any sinne vnder the sunne.
>
> ll. 547-50 (E.E.T.S.).

2. The Maypole was often a permanent fixture, as the one erected in the Strand, which was not removed till 1717, when it was taken down by Sir Isaac Newton. (See Stow-Strype, Book IV.)

3. *Salamander.* The nature of the salamander was an Elizabethan commonplace. Cf. Shakespeare: 'I have maintained that salamander of yours with fire any time this two-and-thirty years.' *1 Henry IV*, III. iii. 52-4.

PAGE 5. 21. *Wallingford.* Tanning was an old Berkshire industry. See Fuller, *Worthies*, under Berkshire, and also the *Victoria County History of Berks*, vol. i, p. 397.

39. *Hungerford.* Twenty-four miles WSW. of Reading.

PAGE 6. 8. *Spinhom-land.* Now Speenhamland, a suburb of Newbury.

40. *I wis.* Indeed. A corruption of the Anglo-Saxon *gewis* = true.

PAGE 7. 20. *Solemnesse*, i. e. weariness.

25. *Gratis the Sheepheard.* 'The Shepheard *Cratis* being fallen in love with a shee Goat, her Bucke for jealousie beat out his braines as hee lay asleepe.' Florio's *Montaigne*, Book III, ch. v. But Florio's translation was not published till 1603, hence either Deloney read the original or both writers drew on a common source.

40. *Acteon.* A common title for a cuckold. Cf. *Conceits, Clinches, Flashes, and Whimsies* (1639), No. 271: 'A citizen going out of towne with some of his neighbours to hunt: preethee sweetheart (sayes he to his wife) pray that I meet not a Diana, and so come home

like to Actaeon horn'd. .... His wife, thinking he had closely jeer'd her, and thinking to be revenged, said ; truly, husband, whether you meet Diana or no, I'le take order you shall not want.'

PAGE **8.** 40. *quills* were pieces of reed or cane on which the weavers wound the thread. Being light work this winding seems to have been generally performed by women or boys. Cf. the old jest book of *Robin Goodfellow* : 'One day Robin Good-fellow walking thorow the street found at a door setting a pretty woman : this woman was wife to a weaver, and was a winding of quils for her husband.' (New Shakspere Society Reprint, p. 135.)

PAGE **9.** 5. *kindely*, i. e. according to its kind or nature, which appears to be that of the turtle-dove in *Barthomaeus Anglicus* (Trevisa, 1535), xii. 34 : 'Yf he lesyth his make, he sekith not company of any other, but gooth alone, and hath mynde of the felyship that is lost. And gronyth alway and louyth and chesyth solytary place, and fleeth moche company of men.'

41. *sure*, i. e. betrothed. Cf. *Gentle Craft*, Part I, p. 126, l. 26, where Haunce and Florence arrange to plight troth in the garden. So in *A Description of Love* (1625), p. 147 (verso) :

> Cinna loved Rosa well, thinking her pure,
> And was not quiet till he made her sure.

Cotgrave gives '*accordailles*, f., the betrothing, or making sure of a man and woman together'.

PAGE **10.** 5. *Bartholomew day.* August 24th. Ashmole gives the same date. See Introduction, p. xi.

7. *Fayring.* A present given at a fair. Cf. R. Johnson in the *Crowne Garland of Golden Roses :*

> My comfort and my joy,
> This fairing I do send ;
> Let not unkindnesse him destroy
> That is thy faithfull friend.
>
> (Percy Society Reprint, p. 55.)

27. *shot*, i.e. the bill.

34. *noise of Musitians.* 'Noise' was used in the same sense as we use 'band' nowadays. Cf. Dekker's *Bel man of London* (1608) : 'These terrible noyses with threadbare cloakes, that live by red lattices and ivy bushes, having authority to thrust into any man's room, only speaking but this—will you have any musicke ?' They seem to have especially haunted the mixed company of men and women. 'If you desire not to be haunted with Fidlers,' says Dekker, 'bring then no women along with you.' *Guls Horn Book* (ed. Grosart, p. 258).

Cf. also the description of Anthony Now-now in Chettle's *Kind-hartes Dreame*, quoted in the Note on Sources of *Gentle Craft* (II), p. 535.

For information regarding the music of ancient Berkshire cf. the *Records of Reading*, vol. ii, p. 179.

39. *The beginning of the World*, or *Sellenger's Round*, was a country dance of great popularity often performed round the maypole. See Chappell, *Popular Music*, vol. i, p. 71.

47. *corner cap.* The square cap of the sixteenth-century parson, as seen in Tudor monuments.

PAGE **11.** 40. *Claret wine and Sugar.* The Elizabethans commonly sugared their wine. Cf. Falstaff in *I Henry IV*, II. iv. 524, 'If sack and sugar be a fault, God help the wicked !'

PAGE **12.** 27. *cuts of curious needle worke*, i. e. ornamental scissor work, against which the worthy Harrison protests in Holinshed's

Chronicle (1587), vol. i, p. 172 : 'What should I saie of their doublets with pendant cod-peeces on the brest full of sags and *cuts.*'

PAGE **14.** 21. *Parsons are but newly suffered to haue wiues.* By Stat. 2 & 3 Ed. VI, c. 21.

29. *dry bobs,* i. e. biting jests. Cotgrave gives '*Ruade seiche,* a drie bob, jeast or nip '.

PAGE **15.** 18. The plucking off of shoes and stockings appears to have been a kind of amorous invitation. Thus in *Tarlton's Jests* (Shakespeare Society Reprint, p. 39) : ' Tarlton . . . askt her which of those two beds were big enough for them two. This, said she : therefore, goe to bed, sweet-heart, Ile come to thee. Masse, saies Tarlton, were my bootes off, I would, indeed. Ile help you, sir, saies she, if you please. Yea, thought Tarlton, is the wind in that doore ? '

27. *starued,* i. e. to die of exhaustion, not necessarily by hunger, as still in modern dialect.

33. *linke.* It is a winter's morning, so the widow carries a torch. Cf. Stow-Strype (1720), Bk. V, p. 329 : ' When Apprentices and Journeymen attended upon their Masters and Mistresses in the Night, they went before them carrying a Lanthorn and Candle in their Hands.'

36. *Saint Bartholmewes Chappell.* ' An ancient chapel, with a house adjoining, situate at the end of Bartholomew Street, is attached to the almshouses and hospital of St. Bartholomew.' *History of Newbury* (1839), p. 88. A sketch of the ' ancient chapel ' may be found on p. 89 of the same book.

PAGE **16.** 4. *George a Green.* The famous Pindar of Wakefield, popular in Elizabethan romance. See Thoms, *Collection of Old English Romances,* for his *History.*

PAGE **17.** 35. *Constable.* ' Any of these Officers' (i. e. 'Constables, Borsholders, Tythingmen, &c.') ' may also arrest such straye persons as doe walke abroad in the night season.' Lambard's *Dueties of Constables* (1599), p. 12.

40–8. Jack regales his wife with advice in the seasonable manner of *Euphues.* Cf. Falstaff's mock reproof to Prince Hal, in which he parodies the speech of the king (*1 Henry IV,* II. iv).

PAGE **18.** 23-4. The *Spright of the Buttery* is properly speaking spirit of wine (see *Oxford English Dict.*), but as Stubbes says in the *Anatomy of Abuses* (Furnivall's edition, p. 107), ' the spirite of the buttery is drunknes and excesse.'

PAGE **19.** 9. *people of Illyris.* Reference untraced.

12–13. This habit of the spider was a well-known fact of Elizabethan natural history. Cf. *The Printer to the Reader,* prefixed to B. Rich's *Farewell to the militarie Profession* :

> The fragrant Rose can make no choyse,
> Who shall vpon hym light,
> The spraulying Spyder turnes to gaule,
> The Bee to honey right.

17–18. *Starlings, that will burst their gall,* &c. Source untraced.

19. *the Fish Scolopendra.* See Pliny, *Nat. Hist.,* Lib. IX, c. xliii, where it is mentioned with other ' torpedo fish '.

26. *the Pellican.* Cf. Nash's *Have with You to Saffron Walden* (*Works,* edit. McKerrow, vol. iii, p. 124) : ' A true Pellican he is, that pierceth his breast and lets out all his bowels to give life to his yong.'

PAGE **20.** 27. *Stammell.* A kind of coarse red cloth which was a popular substitute for the expensive and fashionable scarlet. Nares quotes B. Jonson, *Underwoods* :

> Red-hood, the first that doth appear
> In Stamel. Scarlet is too dear.

Cf. also p. 236, l. 12.

33. *lin*, i. e. cease. Cf. *Marriage of Witt and Wisdome* (New Shakspere Society), p. 30, l. 30: 'If wantonnis knew this, she would never lin scorninge.'

PAGE 21. 1. *Shearemen*, i.e. cloth workers.

4. *Rowers.* Those that smooth down the cloth with rollers.

7. *fulling Mill.* This was at Bagnor, a hamlet of Speen. 'There was formerly a large Fulling Mill, which is said to have belonged to the Jack of Newbury ; and is supposed to have been where the present corn-mill stands. The waste ground adjoining this mill is called the "Rack Marsh" and so late as in the end of the last century the old posts, which formed the frame work for drying the cloth were observable.' *Newbury and its Environs* (1839), p. 171.

33. The dialect is of course only the conventional corruption of speech used by Elizabethan writers to represent dialect, e. g. by Shakespeare in *Lear*. But in *Thomas of Reading* Deloney makes a real attempt at Northern English. The country man's mispronunciations recall Dogberry and Verges in *Much Ado about Nothing* (1599).

36. *What will you bestow with her ?* *Tell-Trothes New Yeares Gift* (1593), Pt. II, p. 61 (Shakespeare Society Reprint), explains this : 'Fie, fie ! marriages, for the most part, are at this day so made, as looke how the butcher bies his cattel, so wil men sel their children . . . Why it is a common practize to aske the father what hee will give with his childe ; and what is that differing from cheapening an oxe.' See also p. 219, ll. 19-31, and the *Lamentation of Mr. Page's Wife*, printed on p. 482. Furnivall, in *Child-marriages* (E.E.T.S.), has published some unpleasant evidence as to the character and results of this sort of bartering.

PAGE 22. 1-26. This is, of course, the *locus classicus* for the Elizabethan wedding, and could be endlessly elaborated from contemporary authors.

4. *sheepes russet.* The rustic holiday attire.

> He borrow'd on the working daies his holy russets oft.
> > *Albions England*, iv. 20.

5. *billiment.* The *Oxford English Dictionary* explains this by a quotation from J. G. Nicholls : 'the jewelled fronts of the ladies headdresses, as we see them in the portraits of Queen Anne Boleyne.'

7. *haire . . . curiously combed and pleated.* So Stubbes complains in the *Anatomy of Abuses* (Furnivall), p. 67 : 'the trimming and tricking of their heds, in laying out their hair to the shewe, which of force must be curled, frisled and crisped, laid out (a world to see) on wreaths and borders from one ear to another.'

8-9. 'In Anglia servatur ut duo pueri, velut Paranymphi, id est, Auspices, qui olim pro nuptiis celebrandis Auspicia capiebant, nubentem ad Templum—et inde domum duo viri deducant, et tertius loco facis, vasculum aureum, vel argenteum praeferat.' Polydore Vergil in Brand's *Popular Antiquities*, vol. ii, p. 45, note.

9. The bride-laces are mentioned in the *Bride's Burial* (*Percy's Reliques*) :

> My bride-laces of silk,
> Bestowed, for maidens meet,
> May fitly serve when I am dead
> To tye my hands and feet.

Rosemary, 'that's for remembrance' (*Hamlet*, IV. v. 174), was for that reason used at weddings.

10. *Sir Thomas Parry* was Queen's Treasurer and Master of the Wards in 1520. His seat was at Hampstead Marshall in Berkshire (*Magna Britannia, Berks*, i. 286).

11. *Sir Francis Hungerford.* The Hungerfords were an old Berkshire family, 'of Buscott and Reading' in Ashmole's *Visitation of Berks.*

16–17. *Garlands of wheate.* Cf. Polydore Vergil, quoted by Brand (vol. ii, p. 53): 'Spicea autem Corona (interdum florea) Sponsa redimita caput, praesertim ruri deducitur, vel manu gerit ipsam coronam.'

21. *Stillyard.* 'a place for marchants of Almaine', as Stow says, was on the site of the present Cannon Street Railway Station.

27. Elizabethan weddings occasioned long-sustained festivities. So in *Midsummer Night's Dream* (v. i. 376–9) the Duke says :

> Sweet friends, to bed.—
> A fortnight hold we this solemnity,
> In nightly revels, and new jollity.

In *Greene's Vision* (*Works*, edit. Grosart, vol. xii, p. 228) we are told, 'and honney moone it was for a moneth after' for the 'reliefe of the poore'. Cf. *Patient Grissel*, p. 493.

PAGE **23**. 6–15. Deloney might have relied on Grafton's *Chronicle* for the account of the Scottish invasion. Grafton mentions the French war, the oath-breaking, and the Queen's camp in Buckinghamshire. But local tradition might have supplied all that was wanted. In the *History of Newbury* (1839), p. 138, verses of a Newbury ballad are quoted, which, if really traditional as alleged, show a very definite tradition as to the part played by Newbury men at Flodden :

> Come Archers learne the News I telle
> To the Honoure of youre Arte,
> The Scottyshe kinge at Flodden felle
> By the poynte of an Englyshe Darte.
> Though Fyre and Pyke dyd wond'rous thynges,
> More wonders stille dyd wee,
> And ev'ry Tonngue wythe rapture syngs
> Of the Laddes of Newberrie.

7–8. *falsly breaking his oath.* 'Not withstanding that the king of Scottes was sworne on the Sacrament to kepe the peace.' Grafton (1809), vol. ii, p. 269.

12. Jack is apparently called out on a Tudor Commission of Array.

39. *the Stork.* Probably a reference to Psalm civ. 17, 'As for the stork, the fir-trees are her house.'

PAGE **24**. 5. *Sir Henry Englefield.* The Englefields were a prominent Berkshire family (see Fuller's *Worthies*, under Berks). Sir Thomas Englefield was the Sheriff of Berkshire in Henry VIII's reign.

22. *Rents.* In the old sense of yearly revenues, as contrasted with 'purchase', i. e. what one makes.

35. Cynomolgy. From Pliny originally, who puts them in India (Lib. VII, cap. ii). Maundeville (1582, chap. lxi) mentions 'Macumeran, which is a great Isle, and a faire, and the men and women of that

country haue heades like houndes'. Cf. also Golding's *Solinus* (1587, p. 138) and *Batman vpon Bartholme* (1582, Book XV, c. 73).

38. *Basilisks.* The 'nature' of the basilisk was a fact traditional from Pliny : ' Plinius also sayth there is a wilde beaste called Catobletas great noyeng to mankinde ; for all that see his eyen should dye anone, and the same kinde hath the cockatrice.' *Batman Barth.*, Lib. XVIII, c. 16. Deloney has transferred the power from the eyes to the breath.

40. *spirit of Mogunce.* Mogunce is from the Latin form, Moguntia, i.e. Mainz. The *Nuremberg Chronicle*, under DCCL, has the following entry, which completely explains the reference : ' Hujus tempore in Brixa Ytaliae tres dies & noctes sanguis pluit, & in Parochia Majuncia malignus spiritus parietes domorum concutiebat tanquam cum malleis, discordiam seminando & loquendo, & ubi intravit exuritur domus : sacerdotes orando & aquam benedictam contra eum projiciendo ipse denuo cum lapidibus jactabat.' (Vol. i, p. 357 b.) But the same incident is reported in Belleforest's *Des Histoires Prodigieuses* (1597, vol. ii, p. 101) : ' Cest an (à scauoir 858) la Cité de Magonce fut estrangement, & miserablement affligée durant l'espace de trois ans par vn Demon, & malin esprit, lequel comme il a laissé Dieu, & se reuoltant de son Seigneur & le nostre ne cerche que les moyens de luy desplaire. . . . Au commencement que ceste ombre, & fantosme feit ses ieux il n'y avoit personne que la peut voir, seulement sentoit-on les assaults, & manifeste tyrannie, entant qu'elle ruoit des pierres à chascun & alloit de nuit heurtant par les portes des maisons de chacun citoyen, les trompant en ce que les ayãs appellez & mettans la teste en fenestre ilz ne voyoient rien.'

PAGE **25.** 8–11. ' after thys noble victorie the Erle wrote first to the Queene (which had raysed a great body to resist the sayde King of Scottes) of the wynnying of the battayle . . . she yet beyng at the towne of Buckyngham.' Grafton (1809), vol. ii, p. 277.

26. *trayterous practise.* This characteristic of the Scots Deloney, together with Shakespeare, seems to have found noted in the Chronicles. Grafton says : ' When the Kyng of Englande was determined . . . to passe the sea, . . . he and his counsaill forgate not the olde prankes of the Scottes which is euer to inuade the realme when the king is oute of the realme.' (1809, vol. ii, p. 269.)

37. *The Song* is almost certainly a traditional ballad made by ' the Commons of England'. Child (*English and Scottish Ballads*) gives three other traditional versions from the Kinloch, Motherwell, and Buchan MSS. respectively. It is difficult to decide what hand Deloney had in the present version, or whether he merely wrote it down verbatim from memory.

PAGE **26.** 37. *Iacke with a feather.* Apparently a satirical epithet of abuse. Cf.,

> That cocke with the fether
> Is gone on huntynge.

Boke of Mayd Emlyn, circa 1520 (Percy Society, vi, p. 17).

PAGE **27.** 6. *progresse into Berkshire.* The *History of Newbury* (1839), p. 139, regards the tradition that Henry the Eighth visited Jack at his house ' as deserving of credit '. Holinshed (1587, vol. ii, p. 837) says : ' This summer' (1515) ' the king tooke his progresse westward, and visited his townes and castels there, and heard the complaints of his poore commonaltie.' Money, in the *History of Newbury* (p. 202), thinks the date was September, 1516.

10. *welt or guard.* These were ornamental trimmings, the difference between which it is now difficult to make out. Grosart says a *welt* is a border turned down, and a *garde* a facing or trimming. The phrase is of constant recurrence in contemporary literature.

11–12. *a great codpeece, whereon he strucke his pinnes.* On this use of this strange piece of apparel cf. *Two Gentlemen of Verona*, II. vii. 56, 'a cod-piece to stick pins on.'

19. *Garret*= Garter (?) ; as often in Holinshed's *Chronicle*. 'The king sent Gartier King of Armes.' (1587, vol. ii, p. 823.)

PAGE 28. 1–2. 'Whether a lion be also afraid of a cock' is discussed in Sir T. Browne's *Vulgar Errors*, Book III, chap. xxvii, § 7. The original source appears to be Pliny : ' Atque hoc tale et tam saevum animal rotarum orbes circumacti currusque inanes et gallinaceorum cristae cantusque etiam magis terrent.' (Lib. VIII, c. 19.)

4–5. Perhaps a reference to 1 Kings ii. 3, 'And keep the charge of the Lord thy God . . . as it is written in the law of Moses.'

35. The parable of the Anthill is of course directed against Wolsey ; *especially against Easter* is difficult to explain. Holinshed (1587, vol. ii, p. 877) gives April 20, 1523, as the date when Wolsey demanded the great subsidy of one-fifth of all goods. Grafton is very explicit on the opposition in Berkshire to Henry's exactions through the Cardinal. ' It happened in this time at Redyng in Barkeshire, that the commissioners sat for this money to be graunted, and the people in no wise would consent to the sixt part : but of their awne mere minde, for the loue they bare to the king, they graunted the twelth part.' (1809, vol. ii, p. 377.)

36–7. *snuffe in the nose*, i. e. took it in bad part. Cf. ' Her second sister taking the matter in snuffe . . . fel into these chollericke passions.' *Penelope's Web* (Greene's *Works*, edit. Grosart, vol. v, p. 280).

PAGE 29. 5. *Peacocke.* 'Dooth the Peacocke glory in his foule feete,' says Nash (*Christs Teares*; *Works*, edit. MᶜKerrow, vol. ii, p. 112) ; but cf. *Batman Vpon Bartholme* (1582): 'He wondreth of the fairnesse of his fethers, & areareth them vp, as it were a circle about his head, and then he looketh to his feet, and seeth the foulenesse of his feet, and lyke as he wer ashamed, he letteth his fethers fall sodeinlye.' (Book XII, chap. 31.)

12–36. This description of Henry's reception at Newbury has a good deal of likeness to the actual entertainment of Queen Elizabeth at Norwich in 1579, as recorded by Holinshed (1587, vol. ii, p. 1289). Deloney might very well have then been present in a town with which, as Nash assures us, he had a strong connexion. Certainly the poetical description of the clothing trade closely resembles that presented by the Norwich burgesses. When 'hir maiestie come, the child representing the commonwealth, spake to her highnesse the words following :

> The idle hand hath here no place to feed.
> The painfull wight hath still to serue his need
> . . . .
> But good aduise hath taught these little hands
> To rend in twaine the force of pining bands.
> From combed wooll we draw this slender threed,
> From thense the loomes haue dealing with the same,
> And thense againe in order doo proceed,
> These seuerall works which skillful art dooth frame.'
>
> (p. 1290.)

Cf. also the notes on page 43, l. 42, and page 241, ll. 35–7.

41-6. The quarrel between the Cardinal and the merchants is amply set forth in contemporary chronicles. Holinshed says (1587, vol. ii, p. 895) : ' The English merchants liked the matter nothing at all, that there should bee anie warres betwixt the Emperor and the King of England.' Hall might have been the actual source of Deloney's knowledge : ' The warr with the Emperor was displeasant both to Merchantes and Clothiers, for the Merchantes durste not auenture into Spaine sith Aprill last past, and now was come the xi daie of March, wherfore all brode Clothes, Kerseis & Cottons laye on their handes. In somuch as when the Clothiers of Essex, Kent, Wilshire, Suffolk & other shires which vse cloth makyng, brought clothes into Blackewell hall of London to be sold as thei were wont to do : fewe Merchantes or none bought any cloth at all. When the Clothiers lacked sale, then thei put from them their spinners, carders, tuckers & such other that liue by cloth-workyng, whiche caused the people greatly to mormor.' (1809, p. 745.)

PAGE **30**. **6.** *Tapistry.* Cf. Harrison's *England* (Holinshed, 1587, vol. i, p. 187) : ' The wals of our houses on the inner sides in like sort be either hanged with tapisterie, arras worke, or painted cloths.'

8-9. The luxury of replacing the ordinary sedge or rushes by cloth is well illustrated by the satire of *Times Whistle*, 1614 (E.E.T.S.), ll. 1042-4 :

> When she doth vprear
> Herselfe vpon her feet, there must be spread
> Rich cloths of Arras wher she goes to tread.

13. *all in glasse.* 'As for drinke it is vsuallie filled in pots, gobblets, jugs, bols of siluer in noblemens houses, also in *fine Venice glasses* of all formes.' Harrison's *England*, in Holinshed (1587, vol. i, p. 166).

PAGE **31**. **3.** *Will Sommers*, the jester of Henry VIII, was a popular traditional figure in Elizabethan times and till much later. A little book published in 1676, *The Pleasant History of the Life and Death of Will Summers ... with the entertainment that his Cousen Patch gave him at his Lord's House*, is obviously a re-issue of a much earlier tract. It clearly shows how Deloney followed tradition in the ' flytings ' of Sommers and Wolsey.

3-4. *Empson and Dudley.* Cf. Holinshed (1587, vol. ii, p. 803).

17. *The Weauers Song.* Collier reprints this poem in *Blackletter Broadsides* from a broadside said to be printed for E. White.

21. *Conscience went not selling Broome.* The selling of broom was looked upon as the meanest of occupations. ' Broome boyes, and cornecutters (or whatsoeuer is more contemptible) ...,' says Nash in *Foure Letters Confuted* (*Works*, edit. McKerrow, vol. i, p. 280). Conscience the broom-seller, was a common Elizabethan figure of speech. So in Greene's *Quippe* (*Works*, edit. Grosart, vol. xi, p. 238) : ' Then Conscience was not a broome man in Kent Streat, but a Courtier.' In the *London Prentice Songs* (Percy Society, p. 69) is a ballad of *Robin Conscience ... His progress through court, city and country, with his bad entertainment at each several place.*

31. *speares like Weauers beames.* A reminiscence of 1 Samuel xvii. 7 : ' And the shafte of his speare was like a weauers beame.' *Geneva Bible*, 1560.

32. *iron beds.* A reference to Deuteronomy iii. 11 : ' For onelie Og King of Bashan remained of the remnant of the gyants, whose bed was a bed of yron.' *Geneva Bible*, 1560.

PAGE **32**. 33. *foure Buckes out of Dunington Parke.* ' The King gave the weavers permission to take four bucks out of Donnington Park for their annual feast,' says Money in the *History of Newbury* (p. 202), ' which latter is still continued, but the gift of venison, if it ever existed, has become obsolete.'

PAGE **33**. 6. *as Buls do eate their meate.* ' Boves animalium soli et retro ambulantes pascuntur.' Pliny, *Nat. Hist.*, Lib. VIII, cap. 70. Fulcherius Carnotensis ascribes the same interesting habit to the ' Appotamus ', and gives an explanation : ' Noctibus segetes depascitur, ad quas pergit aversus, astu doloso, ut fallente vestigio revertenti nullae insidiae praeparentur.' *Historia Hierosolymitana*, Lib. III, p. 931, C.D. But the Elizabethan source is Batman, Lib. XVIII, cap. 13 : ' Plinius speaketh of Oxen, and sayth that ... among beastes that goe backward onely Oxen be fed with foder.'

12. *master Kingsmills seller.* I have found no account of what happened in ' master Kingsmills seller '. Undoubtedly Master Kingsmill was some relation to the Mr. Richard Kingsmill to whom *Canaans Calamitie* is dedicated. The Kingsmills lived at Kingsclere, near Newbury, and the story came down to Deloney amongst the other Newbury traditions. See p. 418 and the Introductory Note to *Canaans Calamitie.*

14. *Sir Amie Paulets.* The story is given in Stow's *Annales* (1600), and refers to the time when Wolsey was tutor to the Marquis of Dorset's sons : ' One sir *Amias Poulet* knight dwelling thereabout, tooke an occasion of displeasure against hym, vpon what ground I know not, but sir by your leaue he was so bold to set the schoolemaster by the feete, during his pleasure, which after was neither forgotten nor forgiuen.' (pp. 834–5.) Cavendish also refers to the incident in his *Life of Wolsey*, 1825, p. 6.

22. *The Maidens Song.* This is the earliest known version of what appears to have been a traditional ballad. How far Deloney was a faithful transcriber of tradition and how far he altered his original it is impossible to say. For the later versions see Child's *Ballads*, vol. i, p. 111.

PAGES **36–7**. Deloney is only reproducing in fiction the Tudor love of pageantry. The pages of Holinshed's *Chronicle* are crammed with details of costly pageants, e.g. those at the coronation of Henry VIII in 1509, and later at that of Anne Boleyn in 1533.

PAGE **37**. 37. *a ... Gilliflower, after the manner of the Persians.* The Persian custom of appearing before the king with a gift is alluded to by Thucydides (Book II, 97) in speaking of the Odrysian Empire : κατεστήσαντο γὰρ τοὐναντίον τῆς Περσῶν βασιλείας τὸν νόμον, ὄντα μὲν καὶ τοῖς ἄλλοις Θραξί, λαμβάνειν μᾶλλον ἢ διδόναι. Deloney refers to the same custom in the dedication of *Canaans Calamitie*, p. 418, l. 19.

PAGE **38**. 5. *iumpt*, i. e. agreed. The *Oxford English Dictionary* quotes Gabriel Harvey (*Letter Book*, p. 27, Camden Society), ' Al this iumpid wel together.'

33–4. *a mans minde is a Kingdome to himselfe.* From the well-known song, *My mind to me a kingdome is*, printed in William Byrd's *Psalmes and Sonets*, 1588.

PAGE **40**. 1–2. The elephant's fear of the sheep is alluded to by Nash (*Works*, edit. McKerrow, vol. i, p. 185) : ' His Armadoes fled from the breath of our cannons as vapors before the sun, or as the Elephant flies from the Ram.' McKerrow quotes from Sextus Empiricus (*Pyrr. Hypotyposes*, i. 14. 58), φεύγει δὲ κριὸν μὲν ἐλέφας.

38–9. *Pictures . . . couered with Curtaines.* Cf. *Troilus and Cressida*, III. ii. 47, ' Come, draw this curtain and let's see your picture.'

Elizabethan pictures were usually curtained off. Jack was not singular in his choice of a series of pictures illustrative of one point of view. It seems to have been usual to collect pictures into sets. Thus in Taylor's *Wit and Mirth* (Tale 103), we are told of a ' Parlour, which was fairly hung with Tapestry hangings, and in every one of the hangings was the figure of a fool wrought'. In *Conceits, Clinches, Flashes, and Whimsies* (1639) ' a fellow ' is mentioned who ' had the pictures of the five senses stolne out of his house '. Deloney probably borrowed all these characters from one of the numerous and popular books of examples, such as Boccaccio's *de Casibus Virorum et Foeminarum Illustrium. Iphicrates* and *Eumenes* occur in Cornel. Nepot. *Vitae.* Of *Viriathus* (p. 40, l. 42) Pliny says, ' Legimus Viriatum primum in Hispania fuisse pastorem.' (*De Viris Illustribus,* cap. lxxi.)

PAGE **43**. 9–23. Cf. Holinshed (1587, vol. ii, p. 906): ' By this meanes the trade of merchandize was in maner fore-let here in England, and namelie the clothes laie on their hands, whereby the commonwealth suffered great decaie and great numbers of spinners, carders, tuckers, and such other that liued by clothworking, remained idle, to their great impouerishment.'

42. *Belinus and Brennus.* The story of Belinus and Brennus occurs in nearly all the Tudor chroniclers. Curiously enough, both heroes appeared, together with Donwallo (cf. p. 72, l. 5), in the pageant played before Queen Elizabeth at Norwich in 1578, which Deloney might very probably have witnessed. The reference in the text bears some resemblance to the rhyming version in Hardyng's *Chronicle* (1812 reprint, p. 62):

> With wordes peteous, and mothers naturesse,
> Shewyng her pappes and wombe with great beautie;
> ' Lo here the wombe that bare you with syckenesse,
> As womanhode would and femynitee;
> Lo here the pappes, as was necessitee,
> That fed you ofte in your tendre age,
> For my loue nowe let be all this outrage.'

PAGE **44**. 20. *oyle of Angells.* A common pun on the name of the Elizabethan coin. Cf. R. Johnson in the *Crowne Garland of Golden Roses* (Percy Society, p. 60):

> Wo be to him that with the oyle
> of angels me intis'd.

21–2. *Blackwell Hall.* See note on p. 234, l. 38.

PAGE **45**. 10. *Duke of Sommerset.* The Duke of Somerset visited Newbury in 1537 and lodged at the house of Jack of Newbury's son. His largesse to the carders on that occasion was seventeen shillings and sixpence (see Money's *History of Newbury,* p. 206). Hence tradition probably represented him to Deloney as a friend of the clothing trade.

19–21. For the part that Henry VIII played in the quarrell between Wolsey and the clothiers, cf. Holinshed (1587, vol. ii, p. 906): ' The emperours ambassadours intreated not so earnestlie to mooue the king to have peace with their maister, but the French ambassadours sollicited the king as earnestlie to enter into the warre against him, and suerlie they had the cardinall on their side. But yet the king wiselie considering with other of his councell, what damage should insue therby vnto his subiects, and speciallie to the merchants and clothiers, would not consent.' Lord Herbert, in his *Life of*

Henry VIII, gives the king's regulations for the clothiers (1649 edition, p. 146).

PAGE **46.** 9. *Marshalsey.* 'A prison in the borough of Southwark,' says Stow (*Survey*, edit. Kingsford, vol. ii, p. 53).

28. '*White hall* ... was first a lodging of the archbishops of Yorke, then pulled downe, begun by cardinall Woolseie, and finallie inlarged and finished by king Henrie the eight.' Harrison's *England* (Holinshed, 1587, vol. i, p. 195).

33-4. *herein doe men come neerest vnto God, in shewing mercy and compassion.* A reminiscence of the *Merchant of Venice* (1594) :

> And earthly power doth then show likest God's
> When mercy seasons justice. (IV. i. 196-7.)

PAGE **47.** 22. *Coromandæ.* Reference untraced.

30. *Taprobaṇa.* 'Toward the East side of Prester John's Land is an Ile that men call Taprobane,' says Mandeville (chapter c, 1705). But I do not find he mentions earlessness, any more than Batman does (Book XV, ch. 158).

37. *Frog*, i.e. English-Italianate for 'frock', not 'frog', which is of post-Elizabethan origin.

PAGE **48.** 15. *spring in Arcadia.* 'quaedam [aquae] etiam blandiuntur aspectu, at ad Nonacrim Arcadiae, omnino nulla deterrent qualitate. Hanc putant nimio frigore esse noxiam, utpote cum profluens ipsa lapidescat.' Pliny, *Nat. Hist.*, Lib. XXXI, c. 19.

18-19. *the monsters of Tartaria.* According to Golding's *Solinus*, Tartary has rich lands, but 'wheras they abound in gold and precious stones ; the Gryffons possesse all, a most fierce kind of foule, and cruel beyond all cruelnesse' (1587 edition, p. 84). Mandeville also describes them in the 'land of Bactry'.

22. *water in Boetia.* This is from Batman, with the sense inverted (Lib. XV, c. 29) : 'In this lande (*Boetia*) is a lake of madnesse, so that who that drinketh thereof, he shall burne in woodnesse of lecherie.'

27. *the river Cea.* Untraced ; but cf. Florio's *Montaigne*, Book II, chap. ii, 'A custome of the Isle of Cea' (in the Aegean). Euphuists were no respecters of geography.

29. *stones in Pontus.* Reference untraced.

PAGE **50.** 3. *Occupiers.* The 1672 edition replaces 'occupiers' by 'traders', explaining the original word and illustrating the scandalous degeneration it underwent in the seventeenth century. Cf. *2 Henry IV*, II. iv. 158-61 : 'A captain ! God's light, these villains will make the word captain as odious as the word *occupy*, which was an excellent good word before it was ill sorted.'

19. *Bucephalus.* This story originates in Plutarch's *Life of Alexander*, and is found in North's translation.

PAGE **51.** 9. *Mars and Venus.* 'To dance in a net' is to plot under a pretence, as is evident from Greene's use of the phrase : 'So I to preuent that, had a nette where in to daunce, and diuers shadowes to colour my knaueries withall.' *Life and Death of Ned Browne* (*Works*, edit. Grosart, p. 10). For the special use of the phrase : 'But at last being Venus scholler, and therefore daring with hir to daunce in a net.' *Perimedes* (ibid., p. 36).

PAGE **52.** 12. A *partlet* was a kind of ruff. Cf. Heywood's *Rape of Lucrece* (Percy Society, No. 27, p. 140), 'Your partlets turn into rebatoes.'

36-7. *gray sparkling eyes, and thy Lilly white hands.* The

medieval ideal of beauty. Chaucer's prioress has 'eyen greye as glass', and Shakespeare makes Mercutio say, 'Thisbe, a grey eye or so, but not to the purpose' (*Romeo and Juliet*, II. iv. 45).

PAGE **53**. 21. *mutton.* Mutton was the cant word for a light woman. Cf. *Two Gentlemen of Verona* (I. i. 101–2), 'I a lost mutton, gave your letter to her, a laced mutton.' See also p. 218, l. 44.

26. *shack* = Jack, i.e. a common fellow: as in the dietary injunction for the nursery, ' Gentleman upon Jack, not Jack upon gentleman.' But cf. Nash's *Anatomie of Absurditie* (*Works*, edit. McKerrow, p. 7), 'Distinguish a gentleman from a barking Jack.'

28–9. *Goz bode.* God's bones (?).

hog nose bud. Hog's nose bleed (?).

PAGE **54**. 35, 37. *french hood* and *chain*. The 'french hood' was a sixteenth-century head-dress of some dignity. Similarly the chain has always been a mark of distinction, and was so worn by physicians and usurers. Ben Jonson notes the same bourgeois ambition in *Bartholomew Fair*, I. ii.: 'Win would fain have a fine young father i' law, with a feather : that her mother might hood it, and chain it, with Mistress Overdo.'

PAGE **55**. 28. *at Whitsontide.* Even nowadays the date for the poorer girls to put on their new summer frocks. Cf. p. 146, ll. 5–6.

PAGE **56**. 7. *browne bread* was made of wheat mixed with bran. For the whole passage cf. Harrison's *Description of England* (Holinshed, 1587, vol. i, p. 168) : 'of bread made of wheat we haue sundrie sorts, dailie brought to the table, wheat of the first and most excellent is the mainchet, which we commonlie call white bread. . . . The next sort is named browne bread of the colour, of which we haue two sorts, one baked vp as it cometh from the mill, so that neither the bran nor the floure are any whit diminished. . . . The other hath little or no floure left therein at all . . . and it is not onelie the woorst and weakest of all the other sorts, but also appointed in old time for seruants, slaues and the inferiour kind of people to feed vpon.'

9–10. *rye mingled with pease.* 'In champagne countries much rie and barleie bread is eaten.' Harrison (Holinshed, 1587), p. 169. So in *Times Whistle*, ll. 3137–8 (E.E.T.S.) :

But lives one rootes like a Diogenes,
With poor thin drink, and course bread made of pease.

13. *points*, i.e. corners, and so odd bits, fragments.

18. *gathers*, i.e. entrails.

33. *ortes*, i.e. bits, as in *Timon of Athens*, IV. iii. 402 : ' It is some poor fragment, some slender ort of his remainder.'

PAGE **57**. 7. *coy*, here certainly means 'disdainful'. Cf. *Taming of the Shrew*, II. i. 237–8 :

I find you passing gentle.
'Twas told me you were rough, and coy, and sullen.

27. *ketha.* A variant of 'quotha'.

40–1. *Watling-streete.* 'At this present, the inhabitants thereof are wealthy Drapers; retailors of woollen cloathes both broad and narrow.' Stow's *Survey* (Kingsford), i. 346. Cf. also *Thomas of Reading*, p. 234, l. 33.

PAGE **58**. 16. *neckenger*, i.e. neckercher.

buckes were dirty linen, hence Falstaff's discomfort in the ' buckbasket' (*Merry Wives of Windsor*). Cf. *Locrine*, II. iii. 64, 'the ashes are left for the countrie wives to washe buckes withall.'

35–6. The *spread Eagle* at the ' beginning of the liberties of Westminster' (Stow) was the inn where Long Meg was at service in the *Gentle Craft* (Part II). ' *Iuiebridge* in the high street which had a way vnder it, leading doune to the Thames,' says Stow in the *Survey* (Kingsford, ii. 96). It was destroyed by the extension of the Hotel Cecil. (See Kingsford's note.)

PAGE 59. 3. The *points* were the tagged laces used to secure the breeches. Cf. *1 Henry IV*, II. iv. 242–3 :

> *Fal.* Their points being broken,—
> *Poins.* Down fell their hose.

PAGE 60. 28. *Burchin-lane.* The well-known Elizabethan emporium for second-hand clothes. So, in *The Seruing man's Comfort* (p. 138, Roxburghe reprint): ' Northern carsies not now weareable in Breetches, for it will shrinke, and the fashion is now to haue Venetians of the largest sise ; yf they will not holde a bushell a breetch, they are not saleable in Birtchen Lane.'

30. *Canweek streete.* The modern Cannon Street, as the fifteenth edition actually prints. Here the Drapers dwelt. See *Thomas of Reading*, p. 234, l. 36, note.

34. Pert's name does not appear in the List of the Mayors and Sheriffs appended to Northouck's *History of London.*

PAGE 61. 21. *powdred beef,* i.e. salted or pickled. So Falstaff (*1 Henry IV*, v. iv. 111–3), ' If thou embowel me to-day, I'll give you leave to powder me, and eat me too, to-morrow.'

PAGE 62. 1. *O that I were a yongue wench for thy sake.* Cf. Shallow's exquisite compliment to Ann Page in the *Merry Wives of Windsor* (1598 ?) I. i. 270, ' Would I were young, for your sake, Mistress Anne.' Shakespeare may have remembered the phrase. On the other hand it may have been a proverbial compliment.

17. *Cherries and Codlings.* Elizabethan luxury in the matter of cherries and codlings (young apples) is copiously illustrated in contemporary literature. Nash, in *Pierce Penniless* (*Works*, edit. McKerrow, p. 173), speaks of ' a marchants wife, that wil eate no Cherries, for sooth, but when they are at twenty shillings a pound' ; and Dekker, in the *Batchelars Banquet* (Huth edition, vol. i, p. 173), thus describes the ' nice huswife ' and the tribulations of her husband : ' She must have Cherries, though for a pound he pay ten shillings, or greene Pescods at foure Nobles a peck ; yea he must take a horse, and ride into the Countrey to get her greene Codlings, when they are scarcely so big as a scotch button.'

21. *sir-reuerence,* i.e. save your reverence. Cf. Greene, *Looking-glasse for London, &c.* (*Works*, edit. Grosart, vol. xiv, p. 25), ' Marry sir, sir-reverence of your Manhood.'

33–4. *Greeneham.* The south-eastern suburb of Newbury.

PAGE 63. 12. *Market Crosse.* The Market cross at Newbury existed as late as 1686, when the Leet Jury of the Court Baron requested ' the Lords of the said Mannor to repaire the Market Crosse at the South end of the Guildhall ' (Money, *History of Newbury*, p. 307).

30. Fuller (*Worthies*) says that Jack of Newbury's house still existed in his time on the east side of Northbrook Street and ' now makes sixteen clothiers' houses '. The *Jack of Newbury* inn is supposed to partly occupy the site at the present day.

47. *cucking stoole.* ' Scolds are ducked vpon cuckingstooles in the water,' records Harrison dryly (Holinshed, 1587, vol. i, p. 185).

PAGE 64. 6. *Morlesse.* The taking of Morlaix is described in Holinshed, and perhaps Deloney found the name *Rigley* there. ' When the lord admerall (i.e. Surrey) had thus woone the towne of Morleis, he called to him certeine esquiers, and made them knights, as sir Francis Brian, sir Anthonie Browne . . . sir John Reinsford . . . sir Edward Rigleie and diverse others' (Holinshed, 1587, vol. ii, p. 874).

13. *coyne.* Perhaps merely *coin*, but more probably a spelling of the past participle *coying*, meaning ' disdaining'. For this meaning cf. note to p. 57, l. 7.

PAGE **66.** 11–12. *Tearme time.* Saltonstall, in *Picturae Loquentes* (1631), explains : ' the tearme is a time when Justice keeps open court for all commers . . . It is called the Tearme because it does end and terminate business.' The *Tearmes* were held at Westminster. Cf. p. 158, l. 11, and note.

12–13. *mistress Loueless.* The widow who had law business at term time was well known to Elizabethan satire. Nash includes her with the other ladies of faded reputation in *Christs Teares* (*Works*, McKerrow, p. 152) : ' Bee shee of middle yeares, shee is a widow that hath sutes in Lawe here at the Tearme.'

28–9. *one man before, and another behinde.* The Elizabethan lady was thus commonly guarded. Cf. Greene's *Ned Browne* (*Works*, edit. Grosart, p. 22) : ' I saw a brave countrey gentlewoman coming along from St. Bartholomews in a satin goun and four men attending upon her.'

THE GENTLE CRAFT, PART I.

Date. The first mention of *The Gentle Craft* occurs in the *Stationers' Registers*, October 19, 1597 :

' *Raphe Blore.* Entred for his copie vnder thandes of master *Dix* and master Man a booke called the *gentle crafte* intreatinge of Shoo-makers. vj*d.*'

This entry certainly applies to the first part, which would not be distinguished as such until after the publication of the second. But the book is mentioned specifically in the transfer to Thomas Pavyer on the 14th August, 1600, as *The fyrste parte of the gentill Crafte.* On the death of Pavier his widow assigned it to Edward Brewster and Robert Birde on August 4, 1626. (*Stationers' Registers.*)

Extant Editions.

[A] 1648. THE GENTLE CRAFT A DISCOURSE, . . . shewing what famous men haue been SHOOMAKERS . . . LONDON, printed for *John Stafford* and are to be sold at his house in Saint *Brides* Churchyard 1648. (*British Museum.*)

[B] 1652. . . . Printed for John Stafford and are to be sold at his house at the sign of the George at Fleet Bridge. 1652. (*Bodleian.*)

[C] 1675 (?) . . . Printed for *H. Rhodes* at the *Star*, the Corner of *Bride-Lane, Fleet Street.* (*British Museum.*)

[D] 1678. . . . *London*, Printed by T. M. for *William Thackery* in *Duck Lane*, near *West-Smith-field*, 1678. (*British Museum.*)

[E] 1680 (?) Title page lost. (*British Museum.*)

[F] 1690 (?) . . . Printed for *H. Rhodes*, at the Star, the Corner of Bride-Lane, Fleet street. (*British Museum.*)

[G] 1696. . . . Printed by *W. Wilde* and solde by P. Brooksby at the *Golden Ball*, &c. (*Bodleian.*)

[H] n. d. . . . Printed for *H. Rhodes* at the *Star*, &c. (defective). (*Bodleian.*)

[I] n. d. . . . Printed for *H. Rhodes* at the Star, the corner of *Bride Lane.* Fleet Street. (*Bodleian.*)

The edition reprinted here is that of 1648.

Note on Sources. The first part of *The Gentle Craft* consists of three main stories : (1) *St. Hugh and St. Winifred,* (2) *Crispin and Crispianus,* (3) *Sir Simon Eyre.*

(1) The story of St. Winifred appears to be a blending of the *Life of St. Ursula* and the *Life of St. Winifred,* both of which are found in Caxton's *Golden Legend.* The story of St. Ursula is as follows : 'In Britain was a Christian king named Notus or Maurus, which engendered a daughter named Ursula . . . And the king of England which then was right mighty, . . . heard the renomee of her, and said that he would be well happy if this virgin might be coupled to his son by marriage. And the young man had great desire and will to have her. And there was a solemn embassy to the father of Ursula, and promised great promises, and said many fair words for to have her ; and also made many menaces if they returned vainly to their lord. And then the King of Britain began to be much anxious, because that she that was enobled in the faith of Jesu Christ should be wedded to him that adored idols. . . . And she, that was divinely inspired, did so much to her father, that she consented to the marriage by such a condition, that . . . he should give to her space of three years for to dedicate her virginity, and the young man should be baptized, and in these three years he should be informed in the faith sufficiently, so that by wise counsel, and by virtue of the condition made, he should withdraw from her his courage. But this youngling received this condition gladly . . . and was baptized and commanded all that Ursula had required should be done.' *Golden Legend* (Dent's Reprint), vol. vi, p. 62.

Other details Deloney takes from the *Legend of St. Winifred* (ibid, pp. 127–9) : ' This holy maid . . . was so inflamed with . . . holy doctrine that she purposed to forsake all wordly pleasauncies and to serve Almighty God in meekness and chastity . . . And then it fortuned upon a Sunday she was diseased, and she abode at home, and kept her father's house while they were at Church. To whom there came a young man for to defoul her.'

The young man, however, does nothing more than cut off her head, giving opportunity for the miracles which Deloney uses.

' And in the same place whereas the head fell to the ground, there sprang up a fair well giving out abundantly fair clear water . . . And many sick people having divers diseases have been there cured and healed . . . And in the said well appear yet stones besprinkled and speckled as it were with blood . . . and the moss that groweth on these stones is of a marvellous sweet odour, and that endureth unto this day.'

The adventures of St. Hugh are merely the conventional doings of the knight of romance who wishes to convince the lady of his worthiness. Such contemporary literature as *Bevis of Hampton, Guy of Warwick* and the *Seven Champions of Christendom* present practically the same incident and the same sentiment.

(2) Similarly the story of *Crispin and Crispianus* is a blending of Caxton's *Legend* with the romance of knight errantry : ' In the time when the furious persecution of Christian men was made under Diocletian and Maximinian, together running, Crispin and Crispinian . . . came to the city of Soissons, . . . where they followed the steps of

S. Paul, the apostle, that is to say to labour with their hands for to provide to them necessarily to live, and exercised the craft of making of shoes.' *Golden Legend* (Dent), vol. vi, p. 69.

Perhaps the account of the British wars in France was suggested by Grafton's *Chronicle*: ' Maximianus or Maximus, the sonne of Leonyn and Cosyn Germain to Constantine the great, tooke upon him the government of this lande of Briteyn. This man was strong and mightie, but for that he was cruell against the Christians, he was called Maximianus the Tyraunt. . . . Finally, he was provoked and excited to make warre upon the Galles, through which counsayle, he with a great hoste of Britons sayled into Armorica that now is called little Briteyn, where he bared him selfe so valiauntly that he subdued that Countrie unto his Lordship.' (1809, vol. i, p. 71.)

But Deloney certainly had also in mind the story of *Romeo and Juliet*. Shakespeare's play was presented in 1596, and Crispine and Ursula are bourgeois imitations of its hero and heroine. They also are the children of rival noble houses, who fall in love with each other in spite of the family enmity, and they also employ a kindly friar to marry them secretly in his cell. Deloney, however, avoids the tragic issue so alien to the spirit of his domestic romanticism.

(3) The story of *Sir Simon Eyre* was probably derived from London tradition, reinforced perhaps by the account given in Stow's *Survey*: '*Simon Eyre*, Draper, Maior, 1436 builded the leaden hall for a common Garner of corne to the vse of this Citie and left fiue thousand markes to charitable vses.' *Survey* (edit. Kingsford), vol. i, p. 110.

' Certain Euidences . . . doe specifie the sayd Granarie to be builded by the sayde honourable and famous Marchant, *Simon Eyre*, sometime an Vpholster, and then a Draper, in the Year 1419. He builded it of squared stone in the forme as now it sheweth, with a fayre and large chapell in the East side of the Quadrant, over the Porch of which hee caused to be written *Dextra Domini exaltauit me*, The Lord's right hand exalted me.

' Within the sayde Church on the North Wall was written *Honorandus famosus Mercator Simon Eyre, huius operis, &c*. In English thus : The honourable and famous Marchant, *Simon Eyre* founder of this worke, once Maior of this Citie, Citizen and Draper of the same, departed out of this life, the 18. day of September, the yeare from the incarnation of Christ 1459, and the 38th yeare of the raigne of king *H*. the sixt. He was buried in the parish Church of Saint *Mary Wolnoth* in Lumbard streete : he gaue by his Testament, which I haue read, to be distributed to all prisons in London, or within a mile of that Citie, somewhat to reliefe them.' Ibid., vol. i, pp. 153-4.

It seems as though Deloney had set to work to explain the inscription ' Dextra Domini exaltavit me ' as he strove to explain ' Tom Drum's Entertainment ' and the custom of the cheeses at Blossom's Inn.

The rivalry of the Dutch, French, and English journeymen in Eyre's workshop must have easily suggested itself to one, like Deloney, who had spent his life among the cosmopolitan artisans of Elizabethan Norwich and London. (See Introduction, p. vii.)

Dekker's *Pleasant Comedie of the Gentle Craft* (1599, printed 1600) is based upon this story of Sir Simon Eyre, and Dekker's obligation is by no means slight. Some comparison of the novel and the play will be found in Lange's edition of the *Gentle Craft* (*Palaestra*, xviii).

PAGE **72**. 2. Most of the geography and history of this preface is

derived from Lhuyd's *Breuiarie of Britayne* (1573). Lhuyd calls
Powis ' the seconde kingdome of Wales '. *Breuiarie*, p. 71.

5. *Donwallo.* Speaking of ' this Prouince Tegenia ' Lhuyd writes
(p. 68) : ' Theyr last prince called Dunwallon, forsayking his kingdome,
when the Danes afflicted all Britayne : departed to Rome, the yere
after the incarration, 971, where shortly after he died.'

Tegina. ' The towne whiche they call Flynt, standynge vpon the
water Deua : is knowne not only to be the head of Tegenia, but also y⁰
whole shore.' Ibid., p. 69.

9. *Pont Varry.* ' Moreouer, in Tegenia : there is a certayne
auncient monument of an olde building, in a place called Pot Vary.'
Ibid., p. 69.

11. *Sichnaunt.* ' And not far from this place, is the famous
Fountayne takynge name of the superstitious worshyppinge of the
Virgin Wenefride, which boyling up sodenly, out of a place which they
call Sychnant, that is to say a drie vallye : raiseth forth of it self
a great streame, which runneth immediately into Deuarus.' Ibid.
But Harrison, in his *Description*, speaks of ' A medicinable spring
called Schinant of old times, but now Wenefrides well, in the edges
whereof dooth breed a verie odoriferous and delectable mosse, wherewith the head of the smeller is maruellouslie refreshed '. Holinshed
(1587), vol. i, p. 30.

PAGE **73.** 8-9. Perhaps Deloney remembered *The Two Gentlemen
of Verona* (1591), II. vii. 25-6 :

> The current that with gentle murmur glides,
> Thou know'st, being stopp'd impatiently doth rage.

The simile is repeated in *Gentle Craft*, Part II, p. 151, ll. 33-4.

PAGE **75.** 13. *tongueless like a stock.* While *stock* may very well
be correct, I believe ' stork ' is what Deloney wrote. Cf. *Thomas of
Reading*, p. 252, l. 23, ' I would I had beene like the Storke tonguelesse,'
and see note thereon.

PAGE **78.** 16. *Venice* focussed the allurements of Italy for the
sixteenth-century Englishmen. Hence the attack of Barnaby Rich in
Don Simonides (1581): ' O Venice a wonder it is, that the sea
swalloweth thee not up for thy synne, whyche retainest so many
brothell houses, and wicked Baudes.' Greene, in the *Defence of Conny
Catching* (*Works*, edit. Grosart, vol. xi, p. 73), makes the bragging
' companion' speak thus : ' Then wil he roue to Venice, & with a sigh
discouer the situation of the citie . . . : and to set the young gentlemans
teeth an edge, he will make a long tale of La Strado Courtizano, wher
the beautifull Courtizans dwel, describing their excellency, & what
angellical creatures they be & how amorously they will entertaine
strangers.'

PAGE **80.** 15. *drenched.* The causative verb from *drown*. Cf.
Faerie Queene, II. xii. 6, ' condemned to be drent.'

19-25. A typical piece of Renaissance bad taste. Similarly
Barnes in *Parthenophil* (Sonnet 63) aspires to be

> That sweet wine, which down her throat doth trickle,
> To kiss her lips, and lie next to her heart.

34-5. ' In one of these yles are men that haue but one eye, and
that is in the middest of theyr front.' Maundeville (1568), cap. lxii.

PAGE **81.** 14. *Elephant with stiffe joynts.* ' Scandinavia . . .
breedeth a beast, which like the oliphant boweth not the nether joyntes

of his legs.' Golding's *Solinus* (1587), p. 101. So Shakespeare, *Troilus and Cressida*, II. iii. 114-6, 'The elephant hath joints, but none for courtesy : his legs are legs for necessity, not for flexure.' Sir Thos. Browne discusses the question in *Vulgar Errors*, Book III, chap. i.

30-2. The natural enmity of dragons and elephants was a well-established fact of Elizabethan natural history. Apparently Pliny (*Nat. Hist.* viii. 12) is the original authority, but Batman has all the details : 'Betweene Elephants and Dragons is everlasting fighting, for the Dragon with his tayle bindeth and spanneth the Elephant, and the Elephant with his foote and with his nose throweth downe the Dragon, and the Dragon with his tayle, bindeth and spanneth the Elephants legges and maketh him fall : but the Dragon buyeth it full sore, for while he slayeth the Elephant, the Elephant falleth uppon him & slayeth him.' See also Golding's *Solinus* (1587), chap. xxxvii.

38-9. *kind nature*. The benevolence of the elephant is thus described in Batman, Book XVIII, chap. 42 (1582) : 'If Elephants see a man comming against them that is out of the way in wildernes, for that they wold not afray him, they will draw themselves somewhat out of the way, & then they stint, & passe little & little before him, and teach him the way.'

PAGE **82**. 15. *Dioclesian*. 'After that Britaine was thus recouered by the Romans, Dioclesian and Maximian ruling the Empire, the Iland tasted of the crueltie that Dioclesian exercised against the christians, in persecuting them with all extremities.' Holinshed (1587), vol. i, p. 61.

27-8. 'Full cruell Bulls become milde anone, if they be tied to a fig tree.' *Batman on Bartholme* (1582), Book XVII, chap. 61.

29. *Charchædonis*. Pliny mentions the *carchedonia* (*Nat. Hist.* xxxvii. 30). It does not appear to have the virtue of Deloney's Charchædonis.

PAGE **84**. 5. *complement*, i. e. completion, hence *pleasures complement* means *perfect pleasure*. Cf. *Henry V*, II. ii. 133-4 :

> Constant in spirit, not swerving with the blood,
> Garnish'd and deck'd in modest complement.

20. *stain*, i. e. distain, a beautiful and useful word that we have unfortunately lost in modern English. To *distain* is to take the colour out of one thing by the juxtaposition of another. Cf. Fletcher's *Purple Island*, VI. ix, 'These lights the Sunne distain.' Cf. also p. 347, l. 35.

PAGE **86**. 14. To *shadow* is to colour, and is so used constantly by Greene, e. g. 'the painter, who shadowed the worst pictures with the freshest colours.' (*Works*, edit. Grosart, vol. iii, p. 202.) Cf. also p. 400, l. 12.

36. *gore blood*. *Gore* simply means clotted or thick. North uses the compound word in his translation of Plutarch (*Julius Caesar*), 'His wife Porcia . . . gave herself a great gash withal in the thigh, that she was straight all of a gore-blood.'

PAGE **88**. 26. *Mugwort*. 'Plinie saieth : it is good against serpents, and holsome for trauelying men, if they carry it.' Wm. Bulleyne's *Gouernement of Healthe*, fol. lxviii. Brand (*Pop. Antiquities*, vol. ii, p. 608) quotes Cole's *Art of Simpling*, p. 70 : 'If a Footman take Mugwort and put into his Shoes in the morning, he may goe forty miles before noon, and not be weary.' The other charms in this passage are untraced.

31-2. 'If the herb Housleek, or Syngreon, do grow on the House-

top, the same House is never stricken with lightning or Thunder.'
Hyll's *Naturall and Artificiall Conclusions* (1581), Hazlitt-Brand,
vol. iii, p. 271.

33. *Mother Bumby.* Perhaps a proverbial name for a witch ; at
any rate the name of the 'cunning woman' in Lyly's *Mother Bombie*,
written about 1590, and 'sundrie times plaied by the Children of Powles'.

45. *sort*, i. e. a company, as in *Richard II*, IV. ii. 245, 'A sort of
traitors here.' Cf. also *The Gentle Craft*, Part II, p. 208, l. 37, 'a sort of
Emits.'

PAGE **89.** 29. *Saint George . . . of his horse.* St. George always
appeared inseparable from his horse on alehouse signs. So in *Euphues*
Part II (edit. Bond, p. 260, l. 26), 'lyke Saint George, who is euer on
horse backe yet neuer rideth.' Cf. also *King John*, II. i. 288–9 :

> Saint George, that swindged the dragon, and e'er since
> Sits on his horseback at mine hostess' door.

31. *Posie.* Of course the 'motto' of *The Gentle Craft*, like those
engraved on wedding rings, &c. Hence *Hamlet*, III. ii. 163, 'Is this
a prologue, or the posy of a ring ?'

35. *three mans Song*, i. e. a round for three voices. Elizabethan
cobblers were notable singers. In the *Cobbler of Canterbury* the
cobbler sits 'in the shop, wher he sung like a nightingale'. Similarly
in Dekker's *Raven's Almanac* (*Works*, edit. Grosart, vol. iv, p. 197),
'A mery cobler there was, who for joy that he mended mens broken
and corrupted soles, did continually sing, so his shop seemed a verrie
bird-cage.'

38. *colt*, i. e. a green hand. Hence in *The Merchant of Venice*
I. ii. 43–4, 'Ay, that's a colt indeed, for he doth nothing but talk of
his horse.'

PAGE **90.** 3. *Logria* was apparently applied to the whole of Britain.
But Lhuyd, in the *Breuiarie* (p. 12), says that Hengest and the 'Iuthi
vsurped the same countrie which wee call Lhoegria,' i. e. Kent.

10. *Durouernum.* 'Durouernum, the same Englishmen do call
Cantorbury, that is to say : the court of the *Kentyshmen*.' Lhuyd's
Breuiarie, p. 15.

PAGE **93.** 5. *Colchester Castle.* Apparently local knowledge that
Deloney had picked up on his travels in East Anglia. Cf. also note
on p. 191, l. 42. The story of *Cateratus* is in Holinshed (1587),
vol. i, p. 39.

13. *Apparitions in the ayre.* This seems a reminiscence of
Josephus's description of the fall of Jerusalem, which Deloney used for
Canaans Calamitie. See p. 424, ll. 140–50.

PAGE **94.** 21. *Cofetua.* Although the ballad of *King Cophetua
and the Beggar-maid* does not appear in print until Richard Johnson's
Crowne Garland of Golden Roses (1612), it was certainly well known
at a much earlier date. Don Armado, in *Love's Labour's Lost*, asks,
'Is there not a ballad, boy, of the King and the Beggar ?' (I. ii.
115-6.)

PAGE **95.** 19. *a bright starre shooting in the Element.* Perhaps
reminiscent of the popular *Venus and Adonis* (1593), ll. 815-6 :

> Look, how a bright star shooteth from the sky,
> So glides he in the night from Venus' eye.

38. *Musculus.* Sir Thomas Elyot defines the Musculus in his
Dictionarie as 'a lytell fysch, whyche guydeth the whale that he do

not runne on rockes.' L. Andrewes, in the *Noble Lyfe* (1531), gives the following account: 'Musculus is a fisshe that layth harde shellis, and of it the great monster balena receyueth her nature, and it is named to be the cocke of balena.' Furnivall's reprint of Russell's *Boke of Nurture* (E.E.T.S.), p. 235.

42-4. For the 'nature' of palm-trees cf. *Batman vpon Bartholme* (1582): 'And hee (Plinius) setteth double kinde of Palmes, male and female: and the male bloometh first, and after the female buddeth and bloometh. And the female beareth not fruit, but if she be so nigh the male, that the smell of the male may come with the winde to the female.' Book XVII, chap. 116. Wilson, in the *Art of Rhetorique*, has a very similar passage: 'I will not speake now of Trees, wherein (as Plinie most certainly writeth) there is found Mariage . . . that except the houseband Tree, doe leane with his boughes . . . vpon the women Trees, growing round about him : they would els altogether waxe barraine.' Edit. Mair, p. 46. The original is Pliny's famous passage upon pollination (Lib. XIII, cap. 7).

PAGE **97.** 31. *Christ Church*, i. e. the Cathedral Church of Canterbury.

45. *Saint Gregories Chappell.* St. Gregory's Priory, Canterbury, was suppressed in the twenty-seventh year of Henry VIII. Hasted's *Kent*, vol. iv, p. 484. An engraving of the remaining ruins may be seen in Grose's *Antiquities*, vol. ii.

PAGE **99.** 9. 'For, when Britayne, by Maximinus the Tyranne, was bereft of all the youth, a great parte whereof was slayne with him at Aquilæia : the residu stoutly inuaded, and possessed a parte of Fraunce called Armorica.' Lhuyd's *Breuiarie of Britayne*, p. 10.

PAGE **103.** 6. *biggins*, i. e. children's caps. The *Oxford English Dictionary* quotes from *The Connoisseur* 80 (1774), iii. 71, 'Such a store of clouts, caps . . . *biggins* as would set up a Lying-in hospital.'

7. *Crosse-clothes.* Apparently cloth bands wound round babies' heads. Cf. 'the Nurses also of Sparta use . . . to bring up their children without swaddling . . . or having on their heads Cross-clothes.' North's *Plutarch* (1676), p. 41 (*O.E.D.*).

8. *crickets*, i. e. foot-stools (Nares).

9. The *posnet* was a little cup (Fr. *poçonet*). Halliwell (*Dict. Archaic Words*) quotes Cotton :

> Then skellets, pans and posnets put on,
> To make them porridge without mutton.

PAGE **104.** 2. *A wagtaile* was always 'wanton'. So in Lyly's *Midas*: 'If therefore thou make not thy mistress a goldfinch, thou mayst chance to find her a wagtaile' (*Works*, edit. Bond, vol. iii, p. 118, l. 53).

PAGE **105.** 29-32. *Rutupium, Aurugagus, Doris.* 'There were in Kent, in olde time: three famous Portes, well knowne to the Romanes: Dorjs, Rhutupis, and Lemanis. Doris vndoubtedly is the same, whiche both Englishmen, and Britaynes, reseruinge the auncient name, at this daye doo call Douer . . . . And I am not ignorant, that the Douarians stoutly defende, that theyr towne, heretofore was called Rutupium, and that Aruiragus kyng of Britaynes, builded there a noble castle. Lhuyd's *Breuiarie*, p. 14. Harrison speaks of the River 'Dour, wherof it is likelie that the towne and castell of Douer did sometime take the name'. *Description*, Holinshed (1587), vol i,

p. 53. Hence, as the 'fifth man' says, 'And all this is but Dover.'
Cf. also *Strange Histories*, p. 383, ll. 17-20.

PAGE 108. 7-8. *three dayes before the feast of Simon and Jude*,
October 25.

PAGE 110. 10-11. 'Anciently it was the general Use & Custom of
all Apprentices in London ... to carry Water Tankards, to serve their
Masters Houses with Water, fetched either from the Thames, or the
common Conduits of London.' Stow-Strype (1720), Book V, p. 329.
Cf. also p. 195, ll. 14-20.

45. 'Of the foreigners born, that flocked over into England not
far off from the beginning of Queen Elizabeth's reign, many were of
this Occupation of Shoemakers.' Stow-Strype (1720), Book V, p. 213.

PAGE 111. 8-14. Stow has a note upon the earlier English
fashion in shoes : ' Since the fift of Richard the 2 (when he tooke to
wife *Anne* daughter to Vesalans King of *Bohem*) by her example the
English people had used pike shoes, tied to their knees with silken
laces, or chaynes of silver gilt.' *Survey* (edit. Kingsford), vol. i,
p. 351. Stow-Strype (1720) expands this, so as to illustrate Deloney's
reference more explicitly : ' There were in those Times three sorts of
Shoes worn ... one of these three sorts covered the Legs, or at least
some part of the Leg, as others were for the Feet. And those perhaps
for the Legs were the Huseaus, somewhat like it may be to the Buskin,
or perhaps rather to the High Shoes, which Countrymen wear in some
dirty miry Countries ... The shoes, Goloshes &c. were with Toes of
an extraordinary length, and sharp ... The People, especially the
better Sort so affected the wearing them, that an Act was fain to be
made to restrain the Length of these Pykes to a certain Measure.'
Book V, p. 213.

PAGE 114. 28. *the George*. 'Then haue ye Lombard streete, so
called of the *Langobards* and other Marchants, strangers of diuers
nations, assembling there twise euery day.' Stow's *Survey* (edit.
Kingsford), p. 201.

40. *foynes* were ornaments made of weasel fur. See *Oxford
English Dictionary*.

46. The *ring* was emblematic of the London alderman. Cf.
Mercutio's description of Queen Mab (*Romeo and Juliet*), I. iv. 56-7 :

> In shape no bigger than an agate stone
> On the forefinger of an alderman.

PAGE 117. 15. *the two Chains*. Apparently those that surrounded
St. Paul's Churchyard. See Ordish's *Shakespeare's London*, p. 230.
There is a reference to these chains in *Pills to Purge Melancholy*
(1682) :

> Vulcan after made a train
> Wherein the god of war was tae'n,
> Which ever since hath been call'd *Pauls Chain*
> Which nobody can deny.
>
> *Songs of the London Prentices*, p. 127.

PAGE 118. 2-4. For the alien artisans in England in the sixteenth
century see note on p. 110, l. 45, and Introduction, p. vii. In Stow-Strype
(1720, Book V, p. 333) it is noted that the apprentices ' in the beginning
of 1586 ... made a formidable Insurrection ... against the French and
Dutch.'

PAGE 119. 2. An excursion to *Islington* 'to eat cream' was

a favourite Elizabethan jaunt. The author of *Times Whistle* (1614) is possibly a little hard on the merrymakers.

> It was my fortune, with some others moe,
> On[e] summers day a progresse for to goe
> Into the countrie, as the time of year
> Requiered to make merrie with good cheer.
> Imagine Islington to be the place,
> The jorney to eat cream. Vnder the face
> Of these lewd meetings on set purpose fitted
> Much villanie is howerly committed.
> But to proceed; some thought there would not be
> Good mirth without faire wenches companie,
> And therefore had provided, a forehand,
> Of wiues & maides a iust proportioned band
> In number to the men of vs; each on[e]
> Might have his wench vnto himselfe alone.
>   ll. 2599–612 (E.E.T.S.).

35. 'Cream' was also to be had at *Hogsdon* (Hoxton). In *Tell-Trothes New Yeares Gift* a troop of Hogsdon lovers is fully described. Gosson, in the *School of Abuse*, is more explicit: 'Venus nunnes in a cloyster at Newington, Ratcliffe, *Islington*, *Hogsdon*, or some such place' (Shakespeare Society edition, p. 26).

PAGE **120.** 20–2. The entertainment at Islington is thus described in *Times Whistle* (1614):

> By this time we th' appointed place attainde,
> Where straight with welcomes we were entertaind.
> Musicke was sent for, & good chear preparde,
> With which more like to Epicures we farde
> Than Christianes; plenty of wine & creame
> Did euen vpon our table seeme to streame,
> With other dainties. Not a fidlers boy
> But with the relicks of our feast did cloy
> His hungry stomach.   ll. 2667–75 (E.E.T.S.).

47–8. *A de put in corroyn a meshant.* Cotgrave explains John's abuse: '*putte*: f., *a wench, lasse, girle, modder; (especially one that is no better then shee should be)*.' *Corroyn* is *coron*, i.e. corner, used in a definitely bad sense. 'Ah, the puss in the corner!' might be a mild translation of the whole phrase.

PAGE **121.** 5. *stockfish*, i.e. dried fish. Cf. Stow (*Survey*, edit. Kingsford, vol. i, p. 85): '6800 stockfishes, so called, for dried fishes of all sorts, as Lings, Habardines, & other.' Cotgrave gives 'Ie te frotteray à double carillon. I will beate thee *like a stockfish*, I will swinge thee while I may stand over thee'.

33–44. Apparently Deloney is thinking of the inscription which Eyre had inscribed over Leadenhall: *Dextra Domini exaltavit.* See Note on Sources, p. 523.

PAGE **125.** 13. *Combred*, i.e. cumbered.

PAGE **126.** 2. *pulard*, i.e. pouillard, lowsie (Cotgrave).

14. *ten bon*, i.e. ten bones, ten fingers.

24. The *Garden* as a favourite place for lovers' meetings had aroused the indignation of Philip Stubbes: 'And for that their Gardens are locked, some of them have 3 or fower keyes a peece, whereof one they keep for themselves, the other their Paramours have to goe in before them, least happely they should be perceived, for then were

all their sport dasht. . . . These Gardens are exelent places, & for the purpose; for if thei can speak with their dearlynges no where els, yet, thei maie be sure to meete them.' *Anatomy of Abuses* (edit. Furnivall), p. 88. Contemporary references seem to show that Stubbes's reproaches were not altogether unmerited; e.g. in Heywood's *If you know not me, you know nobody* (New Shakspere Society), p. 132 :

> *Hobson.* Is not this a lady ?
>
> *John.* No, by my troth master; such as in the garden alleys.

Holland's Leaguer, the well-known Southwark brothel, was surrounded by gardens 'for doing a spell of embroidery or fine work '.

26. *to make themselues sure together.* See note on p. 9, l. 41.

PAGE **129.** 8. The *Abbey of Graces* was in Smithfield, the east of Tower Hill. See Stow-Strype (1720), Book II, p. 13.

17. *bore him through the nose with a cushin.* The phrase is obscure. Dr. Bradley kindly supplies me with the following note: ' *To bore through a person's nose* is to cheat him. (See *Nose* in *Oxford English Dictionary*.) Perhaps *cushin* (= cushion) is a stupid joke like the favourite rustic one about cutting one's throat with a tallow candle.'

40-41. The *Duchman* was a famous drunkard in Elizabethan literature. Cf. Dekker's *Knights Conjuring* (Percy Society, V), p. 37 : ' Drunkennesse, which was once the Dutchman's headake, is now the Englishman's;' and B. Jonson's *Alchemist*, IV. vi :

> I do not like the dulnesse of your eye,
> It hath a heavy cast, 'tis upsy Dutch.

PAGE **130.** 8. *ged*, i.e. gad.

10. *willow Garland.* Cf. p. 162, l. 20, and note thereon.

24. For the *Tower Postern* and its constable see Stow's *Survey* (edit. Kingsford), vol. i, p. 28.

35. *to a womans labour.* Apparently a common pretence of light wenches and wives, and any women on secret missions. Cf. Nash in *Christs Teares ouer Ierusalem* (*Works*, edit. MᶜKerrow, p. 151): 'Watchman, what seest thou? what seest thou in London by night ? . . . I see a number of wives cuckolding their husbandes, under pretence of going to their next neighbours labour.' Dekker, in the *Seven Deadly Sins*, says of Candlelight that ' he walkes up and downe the streetes squiring olde Midwives to anie house (verie secretly) where any Bastards are to be brought into the worlde.'

PAGE **132.** 24. *Ebon-tree.* ' Hebenus a tree, whereof the woode is black as ieate, and beareth neither leaues nor fruite.' *Batman on Bartholme*, Book XVII, chap. 52.

40. There seems nothing to warrant Deloney in ascribing the institution of the Pancake Bell and the Shrove Tuesday holiday to Sir Simon Eyre. But Shrove Tuesday was always esteemed the particular holiday of apprentices (see Brand's *Popular Antiquities*). The pancake bell was rung as late as 1795 in Newcastle, and it is still rung at the present day in Buckingham.

THE GENTLE CRAFT, PART II.

Date. ' The fyrste parte of the *Gentill Craft*' is mentioned in the *Stationers' Registers*, August 14, 1600. *The Gentle Craft*, with no distinction as to the part, was entered on October 19, 1597. If this be taken to apply to the first part, as it probably does, the second part of

The Gentle Craft was perhaps printed in 1598, and thus the need for qualifying the title in the entry of 1600.

Extant Editions. The only extant edition is that from which the present reprint is made.

[A] The GENTILE CRAFT, The second Part ... London, Printed by *Elizabeth Purslow*, dwelling neere Christ Church 1639. (*British Museum; Bodleian.*)

Note on Sources. The second part of *The Gentle Craft* consists of three main stories, (1) *Richard Casteler*, (2) *Lusty Peachey and his men*, (3) *The Green King of St. Martins.*

(1) The History of Richard Casteler is a skilful blending and elaboration of two separate stories, the first represented by nothing more than a short entry in Holinshed's *Chronicle*, and the second by a popular jest-book entitled *Long Meg of Westminster*, printed in 1582. Of Richard Casteller himself we read in Holinshed: 'There was one Richard Castell alias Casteller, shoomaker, dwelling in Westminster, a man of great travell and labor in his facultie with his owne hands, & such a one as was named the Cocke of Westminster, for that both Winter & Summer he was at his worke before foure of the clocke in the morning. This man thus trulie and painefullie labouring for his living, God blessed and increased his labours so abundantlie that he purchased lands and tenements in Westminster to the yearelie value of fortie and foure pounds. And having no child, with the consent of his wife (who survived him & was a vertuous & good woman) gave the same lands wholie to Christs hospitall afore said, to the reliefe of the innocent and fatherlesse children, and for the succor of the miserable, sore and sicke harbored in the other hospitals about London, whose example God grant manie to follow.' *Chronicle* (1587), vol. ii, p. 1083. A similar account is also given in Grafton's *Chronicle* (1569), p. 1323.

The Life and Pranks of Long Meg of Westminster. Imprinted at London for Abraham Veale, dwellinge in Paul's church yeard at the signe of the Lambe (1582) may be found in the British Museum. It is little more than a jest-book of the ordinary Elizabethan kind; a collection of crude physical jokes attributed to an Amazonian maiden of Lancashire in service at a London tavern. From this little tract Deloney obtained the outline of a coarse strong personality and a few details of Meg's birth, size, and strength, the name of the Eagle Inn where she served, and her part in the Boulogne war. The rhyming Dr. Skelton suggested the Round Robin of *The Gentle Craft*, and the courtship of the mistress of the Eagle perhaps gave a hint for the story of Mistris Farmer (see *infra*).

But Deloney's use of printed sources must not be over-emphasized. Richard Casteler was probably well known to London tradition as a recent benefactor, and Long Meg is a byword in contemporary literature. Indeed, while Abraham Veale's account makes the latter end her days as an honest married woman and exemplary tavern keeper in Islington, Deloney assures us she 'became common to the call of euery man till such time as all youthfull delights was banished by old age. And in the end she left her life in Islington, being very penitent for all her former offences' (p. 166, ll. 32-5). The weight of evidence abundantly confirms the report of poor Meg's frailty.

Lyly, writing about 1589, asks, 'O doost remember howe that Bastard *Iunior* complaines of brothells, & talkes of long Megg of Westminster.' *Pappe with an Hatchet* (*Works*, edit. Bond, vol. iii, p. 403).

Harvey mentions her in terms of dubious praise : ' Phy, long Megg of Westminster would have bene ashamed to disgrace her Sonday bonet with her Satterday witt. She knew the rules of decorum : & although she were a lustie bounsing rampe, somewhat like Gallemella, or Maide Marian, yet was she not such a roinish rannell, or such a dissolute gillian flurtes, as this wainscot-faced Tomboy.' *Pierce's Supererogation* (1600), pp. 145–6.

In Jonson's *Fortunate Isles* (1626) Skelton is made to say of her :

> . . . Westminster Meg
> With her long leg,
> As long as a crane ;
> And feet like a plane :
> With a pair of heels,
> As broad as two wheels ;
> To drive down the dew ;
> As she goes to the stew :
> And turns home merry
> By Lambeth ferry.

Vaughan, in the *Golden Grove* (1608), is more explicit : ' It is said, that long Meg of Westminster kept alwaies 20 Courtizans in her house, whom by their pictures she sold to all commers.' (Book II, Q 3.)

Hollands Leagur (1632) mentions Long Meg's brothel in Southwark : ' It was out of the citie, yet in view of the citie, only divided by a delicate River ; there was many handsome buildings, and many hearty neighbours, yet at the first foundation, it was renouned for nothing so much as for the memory of that famous Amazon, Longa Margarita, who had there for many yeeres kept a famous *infamous* house of open Hospitality.'

Thus Deloney followed common report as much as the printed authority of the jest-book, and in converting the unpleasant creature of fact into his own pleasant heroine he provided her with a companion from his own imagination in Gillian of the George.

(2) The stories attached to Lusty Peachey and his men are derived from more various and complex sources. The name Peachey is apparently taken from Holinshed, where Sir John Peachey appears as a courtier and soldier of some note, serving with credit in the French wars and escorting Henry VIII's sister on her marriage with the French king (1587 edition, pp. 803, 822, 832, and *passim*). This name also appears in Stow's *Survey*. While it is much to be doubted whether this Tudor courtier followed the Gentle Craft of shoe-mending the *S. P. Dom. Hen. VIII* supply evidence of his close connexion with the city of London. In vol. iii, pt. ii, doc. 854 (1520), § 17, we find granted to ' John Garrard of London, draper, *alias* Vinter, Protection ; going in the retinue of Sir John Petche, deputy of Paris'; and the same volume contains several similar grants to London grocers, haberdashers, silkmen, &c., which seem to show conclusively that Peachey recruited his retinue from the ranks of London artisans. This fact, probably traditional in Elizabethan London, would be sufficient warrant for Peachey's admission to Deloney's *Gentle Craft* and for his position as master-shoemaker and the centre round which are grouped the adventures of Tom Drum, Harry Nevell, Abridges, and Sir John Rainsford.

Of these names, Nevell, Abridges, and Rainsford were well known in Newbury. Sir Henry Neville was Sheriff of Berkshire in 1560. Sir Richard Abridges and Sir William Rainsford officiated at the trial of Julius Palmer for heresy at Newbury in 1556 (Fox's *Acts and Monu-*

ments, 1870, vol. 8, pp. 214-9) ; and Fox's account shows that both Abridges and Winchcomb, if not Rainsford, had a certain amount of sympathy with the accused. Deloney's story of the burial of a 'Massing Priest aliue' would perhaps indicate that Rainsford was also distinctly inclined to Protestantism. Sir Richard Abridges was M.P. for Berkshire in 1554 (Money, *History of Newbury,* p. 210), and Sir William Rainsford, of Great Tew, in Oxfordshire, was connected by marriage with the village of Thatcham, near Newbury.

Stukeley and Strangwidge were two well-known heroes of Elizabethan ballad literature. Stukeley had appeared in Elizabethan drama in the play of *Captain Stucley* and Peele's *Battle of Alcazar* (1588?). Full details of his meteoric career may be found in Simpson's *School of Shakespeare,* vol. i. Born in London of a Devonshire family, he married the daughter of a rich London alderman, who, according to the Roxburghe ballad account,

... was no sooner tomb'd—but Stucley he presum'd,
   To spend a hundred pound a day in waste.
The greatest gallants in the land—had Stucley's purse at their
   command
Thus merily the time away he past.
Taverns and ordinaries—were his chief braveries,
   Golden angels there flew up and down ;
Riots were his best delight—with stately feasting day and night
   In Court and City thus he won renown.

Not only were these swashbuckling humours of his famous in London, but he was known, and probably well remembered, in Newbury as well. In May, 1560, Elizabeth took musters all through England in view of the French and Scots wars, and Stukely was then associated with Sir Thomas Parry, the Master of the Wards, (cf. p. 22, l. 10, note), and Sir Henry Neville, the Sheriff of Berkshire, to superintend the Berkshire levies. His duties as Parry's agent took him to Newbury, whence he dates a letter, May 23, 1560 (*School of Shakespeare,* vol. i, p. 28). It is possible that Deloney was in Newbury at the time ; in any case he must have heard of him later from Newbury folk who had actually seen him.

Stukeley's pirating expedition to Florida took place in 1563, and in 1584 Holinshed notes : ' Out of Ireland ran awaie one Thomas Stukeleie a defamed person almost throughout chrissendome, and a faithlesse beast rather than a man, fleeing first out of England for notable pirasies, and out of Ireland for trecheries not pardonable.'

Strangwidge was another Elizabethan sea-captain, who was eventually killed in an attack on the French coast. His wild life and death are described in a ballad by William Birch (Percy Society, vol. i, p. 41):

In deede of birth he was borne bace ;
   Although of worshipful kyn
In youth he sought to runne the race
   Where he might prowes wyn.

In his yong yeares he walked wyde,
   And wandred oft a stray :
For why blynd Cupid did him guyde
   To walk that wyldsome way.

   .   .   .   .

But when he had the course out run
  Where pyrates prict the carde,
Twyse at the least he thought undone,
  And looked for his rewarde.

For by legall lawes he was condemd,
  Yet mercy bare the mace,
And in respect he wold amend,
  He found a princes grace.

And in that state he vowed to God,
  And to his righteous queene,
He wolde no more deserve such rod,
  Nor at justice barre be seene.

.   .   .   .

And then occasion served just
  That martiall men must trudge :
He vaunced himself with valiaunt lust ;
  To go he did not grudge.

And to the sea he sought a charge
  Where he might take his chaunce,
And therewith spred his sayles at large
  To seke a porte in Fraunce.

.   .   .   .

Where as he caught a deadly wound,
  Yet his courage never quayled,
But as he had been safe and sound,
  On his way forth he sayled.

.   .   .   .   .   .

Then Atropos did him assayle,
  That al Adam's kynd doth call ;
Against whose force may none prevayle
  But subject to him all.

Perhaps the contest between Peachey's men and Stukeley and Strangwidge reflects some quarrel which occurred between the local gentry and Stukeley during the latter's sojourn in Newbury. In this connexion cf. the note on p. 173, ll. 45-7.

The story of Sir John Rainsford appears to be drawn from a local tradition which Leland has attached to the town of Brackley in Northamptonshire : ' In the churche yarde lyethe an image of a priest revestid ; the whiche was vicar of Barkeley, and there buried quike by the tyranny of a lord of the towne for a displeasure that he tooke with hym for an horse taken, as some say, for a mortuarie.' But the lord, as it is there sayde, went to Rome for absolution, and toke great repentauns.' *Itinerary* (edit. Toulmin-Smith), vol. ii, p. 37.

' Ther was of late a place of Crossyd Friers, and that one Nevill a great gentilman there was buried. And that one Neville apon a tyme kyllyd in the churche at Brakeley a priest and buried hym in his sacrid vestiments : and that this Nevill toke there an other prist and buried hym quike.' Ibid., vol. v, p. 224.

Deloney probably picked up this story on his journeying about the Eastern counties, and attributed it to Sir John Rainsford, while he utilizes the name Neville for another character. But an almost exactly similar story occurs in Bandello (*Novelle*, 1554 ? La Terza

Parte, Novella xxv) : ' GIAN MARIA VISCONTE, SECONDO Duca di Milano, fa interrare un Parrocchiano uiuo, che non uoleua seppellire un suo Popolano, se non era da la Moglie di quello pagato.'

The first part of the story, with its mention of the widow and her children, is strikingly like Deloney's version : ' Dicoui adunque, che caualcando esso Duca per Milano, s'abbattè a passare per vna via, oue in vna picciola casetta senti vn gran lamento, con vn pietoso lagrimare, che quiui entro si faceua, con batter di mani, & alte strida, come talhora soglion fare le Donne mezzo disperate. Vdendo il Duca cosi fatto vlulare, comandò ad vno de i suoi staffieri, che in casa entrasse, & intendesse la cagione di cosi fiero pianto. Andò lo staffiero, e non dopo molto, â l'aspettante Duca ritornò, e si gli disse. Signore ; quà dentro è vna pouera Femina con alcuni figliuoli, che piange amarissimamente vn suo Marito, che ha dinanzi morto, e dice che il Parrocchiano non lo vuol sepelire, se non lo paga, ma che ella non ha vn patacco da dargli.' But in the Italian the priest and the corpse are bound together and thus buried in one grave.

Tom Drum's adventures seem to be founded upon the popular saying ' Tom Drum's entertainment, which is to bale a man in by the head, and to thrust him out by both the shoulders ' (Holinshed, quoted by Nares). The phrase was continually used to denote a hostile reception, and Deloney accepts the proverb and builds up a story to explain it. Cf. Note on Sources of *Thomas of Reading*, p. 549, and Introduction, p. xxix. Tom Drum's character, with its exaggeration and comic self-assurance, is without doubt a faint reflection of the noonday glory of Falstaff, whose words Deloney parodies directly on p. 162, ll. 25-34. See also note on p. 181, l. 7.

The story of Mistress Farmer and her suitors bears a strong resemblance to the earlier chapters of *Iacke of Newberie* ; but the rivalry of Dr. Burket and Alderman Jarvice was perhaps suggested by that of Dr. Skelton and Sir James of Castille in the *Life and Pranks of Long Meg of Westminster*. Dr. Burket was a well-known physician, and is thus described in Chettle's *Kind-Hartes Dream* : ' The one, which was the elder, seeming more severe, was in habite like a doctor ; in his right hand hee held a Compendium of all the famous Phisitions and Surgions workes beelonging to Theorike, in his lefte hand a table of all instruments for man's health, appertaining to practise . . . I lookte him in the face, and beheld him to bee maister Doctor Burcot (though a stranger, yet in England for phisicke famous).' *Kind-Hartes Dreame*, p. 11 (edit. Rimbault, Percy Society, vol. v).

Rimbault quotes an entry in the Harleian MS. (No. 315, 6395) of ' a story that goes upon one Dr. Burcott's wife, was not true by her but by one Dr. Matthias his wife, a German, and famous physitian that liv'd in Norwich ' (Percy Society, vol. v, p. 66).

(3) The story of the Greene King of St. Martins is a repetition of Deloney's favourite motif (cf. Note on Sources of *Iacke of Newberie*, p. 508). Anthony Now-now appears to have been a ballad singer of some celebrity in Elizabethan London, and in Chettle's *Kind-Hartes Dreame* he is described as a typical ballad-singer : ' The first of the first three was an od old fellow, low of stature, his head was couered with a round cap, his body with a side skirted tawney coate, his legs and feete trust vppe in leather buskins, his gray haires and furrowed face witnessed his age, his treble violl in his hande, assured me of his profession. On which (by his continual sawing, hauing left but one string) after his best manner, hee gave me a hunts-vp : whome, after a little musing, I assuredly remembered to be no other but old Anthony Now-now.' (Percy Society,

vol. v, p. 63.) His 'treble violl' and his partiality for the 'hunts-up' appear again in Deloney's story (p. 209, ll. 12–13).

There seems no reason to identify Antony Now-now with Anthony Munday. Now O Now was originally the name of a dance tune, to which at a later date words were written by various authors, amongst others by Dowland in the *First Book of Songes* (1597): 'Now, O now, I needs must part,' &c.

PAGE **139**. 18. Lange's surmise (*Palaestra*, xviii) that an original address to the reader prefixed to the first part was omitted after the publication of the second seems to explain this reference. No such promise appears in extant editions of Part I.

23. Apparently Deloney contemplated a third part to *The Gentle Craft.*

PAGE **140**. 19. *you cannot come in vnder a groat.* Apparently a groat was the price at which the original edition was sold. Deloney imitates the theatre cry on the arrival of a gallant who was willing to pay sixpence for a seat on the stage. Cf. Dekker's *Guls Horne Book*, 'have a good stool for sixpence' (1812 reprint, p. 140). A 'groundling' was admitted for twopence, at least in the inferior theatres. Prynne's *Histriomastix* gives the prices as 'twopence, threepence, fourpence, sixpence, and a shilling'.

PAGE **141**. 12–18. The church, as usual, served for more purposes than worship. Cf. *Will Bagnalls Ballet* (Percy Society, vol. xxvii, p. 144):

> And in the church, to tell you true
> Men cannot serve God for looking on you.

Westminster was particularly ill-famed for the lightness of its daughters, and hence perhaps the frankness of Margaret of the Spread Eagle and Gillian of the George. Cf. Nash's *Pierce Penniless* (*Works*, edit. McKerrow, vol. i, p. 216): 'Westminster, Westminster, much maydenhead hast thou to answere for at the day of Iudgment.' So also in *Tell-Trothes New Yeares Gift* (E.E.T.S.), Part II, p. 90: 'Walk but in Westminster,—a place, in faith, where constancy is as little used as wit in Bedlam.'

38. *Gillian* is evidently named from her character. Cf. the courtezan's expostulation in Vaughan's *Golden-Groue* (1608): 'Sir you mistake your marke, I am none of your wanton Gilles, you abuse my credit' (Book II, Q 3).

PAGE **143**. 15. The whistle was used in place of the modern bell for calling the servant. In Scott's *Redgauntlet* (Wandering Willie's Tale) Sir Robert Redgauntlet is described as still using it in this way.

48. *Master Cornelius of the Guard* was a real contemporary character. See Stow's *Survey* (edit. Kingsford), vol. ii, p. 123 : 'From the entry into Totehill field, the streete is called Petty France, in which, and upon S. Hermits hill, on the South side thereof, *Cornelius van Dun* (a Brabander borne, Yeoman of the Gard to King H. the 8, king E. the 6, Queene *Mary,* and Queene *Elizabeth*) built 20 houses, for poore women to dwell rent free.'

Van Dun was buried at St. Margaret's, Westminster, and Stow-Strype gives his epitaph (1720, Book VI, p. 42): 'Cornelius Vandun lieth here, borne at Breda in Brabant, Souldier with King Henry at Turney, Yeoman of the Guard, and Usher to King Henry, King Edward, Queen Mary, and Queen Elizabeth: Of honest and vertuous Life, a careful Man for poore Folke. Who in the End of this Toune did build for poore Widowes twenty Houses of his owne cost.

'Obiit Anno. Dom: 1577. Buried the 4. of September Aetatis Suae 94.'

The *Life . . . of Long Meg of Westminster* relates how Meg's mistress gave her a suit of white satin ' that was one of the guards that lay at her house'. Deloney has seized the opportunity of introducing a well-known local figure in the shape of the long-lived Yeoman.

PAGE 145. 10. *penny fathers*, i.e. niggards. Cf. Nash's *Pierce Penniless* (*Works*, edit. McKerrow, p. 160): '(he) hath much a doo (poore pennie-father) to keep his vnthrift elbowes in reparation.'

PAGE 146. 31. *fired*, i.e. set on fire.

41. *Graues-end Barge.* Meg's foot was a commonplace of illustration. Hence in Nash's *Foure Letters Confuted* (*Works*, edit.'McKerrow, vol. i, p. 288) : ' Yea? thy Muses foot of the twelues; old long Meg of Westminster?' The *Graues-end Barge* plied between Gravesend and Billingsgate : ' At Billingsgate, are, euery tide, to be had Barges, Light horseman (*sic*), Tiltboats and Wherries from London to the towns of Grauesend and Milton in Kent.' *Carriers Cosmography*, 1637. Nash dates *A Countercuffe given to Martin Iunior* 'From *Graues-end Barge* the eight of August '. The little tract, *The Cobler of Canterbury* (partly reprinted in the New Shakespere Society's edition of *Tarlton's Jests*), opens with the author ' sitting at the barge in Billingsgate, expecting when the tide would serue for Grauesend ', when ' diuers passengers of all sorts thither to go down' (p. 109). Cf. also p. 390, l. 40-2.

PAGE 147. 4. *Crinkler*, i. e. a trickster. *To crinkle* is to go back upon one's word, and in this sense still occurs in dialect. Cf. Jonson's *Alchemist*, III. v. :

> He that hath pleas'd her grace thus farre
> Shall not now crinckle for a little.

22. *round Robin* is apparently named from his characteristics. ' Of him whom we see very lively, and pleasantly disposed, we say, his head is full of jolly Robbins.' *Merchandise of Popish Priests*, 1629 (quoted in Reed's *Shakespeare*).

PAGE 148. 26. *gownes*, i. e. green-gowns. Cf. ' At length he was so bold as to giue her a greene gowne when I feare me she lost the flower of her chastity.' A. Munday, quoted in the *Oxford English Dictionary*.

PAGE 149. 13. ' *Posset* is hot Milk poured on Ale or Sack, having Sugar, grated Bisket, Eggs, with other ingredients boiled in it, which goes all to a curd.' R. Holmes, quoted in Furnivall's notes to John Russell's *Boke of Nurture*.

16. *Pope John* was an accepted historical fact in the sixteenth century. When James I visited Sir William Pope in Oxfordshire, Pope's little daughter gave the occasion for a pretty pun on the subject :

> A female Pope, you'll say; a second Joan ?
> No, sure ; she is Pope Innocent, or none.

PAGE 150. 3. *aporne*, i. e. apron. Cf. *Greene's Vision* (*Works*, edit. Grosart, vol. xii, p. 226), ' smugged herself up with her harding *Aporne*.'

14. *stammel*, i. e. red cloth, used in a derogatory sense, as ' petticoat' for a woman in modern English. Cf. p. 20, l. 27, and note.

16. *betrice.* Beatrice was the common nickname for a brazen, ' robustious' woman. Cf. ' Pierce Pandor, and baudie Bettrice his

wife,' *Maroccus Extaticus*, 1595 (Percy Society, vol. ix, p. 16) ; ' Bold Betteresse braues and brags it in her wiers,' *Tom Tel Troths Message*, 1600 (E.E.T.S., p. 121) ; ' Such another old Bettresse haue I at home,' Dekker's *Batchelors Banquet* (Grosart, p. 176).

39. ' *Hipocras* was made with either white or red wine in which different aromatic ingredients were infused ; and took its name from that particular sort of bag, termed Hippocrates's sleeve, through which it was strained.' Furnivall's note to Russell's *Boke of Nurture* (E.E.T.S.), p. 204.

ouer my naile. Cf. Nash's *Pierce Penniless* (*Works*, edit. McKerrow, p. 205) : ' He is no body that cannot drinke super nagulum, carouse the Hunters hoop, quaffe upsey freeze crosse . . .' To drink ' super nagulum ' is to finish off a draught completely, so that, on the glass being turned upside-down, only a single small drop will trickle on the thumb-nail.

PAGE **151.** 3. *ruddocks*, i. e. golden coins. Cf. Lyly's *Midas* : ' So he haue golden ruddocks in his bagges.' *Works*, edit. Bond, vol. iii, p. 125.

31. *rounding*, i. e. whispering. Cf. *Winter's Tale*, I. ii. 217 : ' They're here with me already, whispering, rounding.'

PAGE **153.** 14. *office*, i. e. the servants' quarters. Cf. the modern degenerate use of the term in the language of estate-agents.

PAGE **154.** 7. *Ajax.* The pun upon *Ajax* (= a jakes, i. e. privy) seems to have had eternal charms for the Elizabethan. Round this joke centres Harrington's *Metamorphosis of Ajax* ; but cf. also *Love's Labour's Lost*, V. ii. 577 : ' Your lion, that holds his poll-axe sitting on a close-stool, will be given to Ajax : he will be the ninth Worthy.'

12. *trenchmore.* The trenchmore was a rousing, boisterous dance. Chappell (*Popular Music of the Olden Time*, p. 82) quotes Selden : ' The Court of England is much alter'd. At a solemn dancing, first you had the grave measures, then the Corantoes and the galliards, and this kept up with ceremony ; and at length to Trenchmore and the Cushion Dance : then all the company dances, lord and groom, lady and kitchen maid, no distinction. So in our court in Queen Elizabeth's time, gravity and state were kept up. In King James's time things were pretty well, but in King Charles's time, there has been nothing but *Trenchmore* and the Cushion Dance, omnium gatherum, tolly polly, hoite come toite.'

PAGE **156.** 39. To *jet* is to strut or trip along proudly. It is so used of Malvolio in *Twelfth Night* (II. v. 36), ' how he jets under his advanced plumes.'

PAGE **158.** 8. ' To *play mum-budget*' is cant for keeping secret. Cf. *Merry Wives of Windsor* (V. ii. 6) : ' I come to her in white, and cry, " mum " ; she cries, " budget."'

11. *a good Term*, i.e. a law term, when Westminster was crowded with those ' having suits at the term '. See Dekker's *Dead Term* (1608) ; cf. also p. 66, l. 11 and note.

30. *braided wares* are soiled goods. Hence the clown in *Winter's Tale* (IV. iii. 204) asks, ' Has he any unbraided wares ?'

37. *out of all cry*, i.e. out of all estimation. Cf. Dekker's *Patient Grissel*, III. i. (New Shakspere Society, p. 20, l. 3) : ' By cod, Sir Emulo, Sir owen is clad *out o' cry*.'

PAGE **159.** 5. *Tuttle-field* lay to the west of Westminster Abbey, where its name is yet perpetuated in a street.

12. *queint excuse*, i. e. a cunning excuse. Portia ' like a fine bragging youth ' intends to tell

quaint lies,
How honourable ladies sought my love.
(*Merchant of Venice*, III. iv. 68–9.)

33. *Margaret of the Spread Eagle.* The original reads *Crane*,
but cf. p. 141, l. 36. Deloney is apparently confusing Meg with
' *Katherine* of the Crane' mentioned on p. 144, ll. 25–6, as a warning to
all who desire a reputation for veracity.

36. *rounsefull,* i.e. rounceval, a fat woman. Cf. Nash's *Have
with you to Saffron Walden* (*Works*, edit. McKerrow, p. 36), 'A fat
Bonarobe and terrible Rounceuall.'

39. *bucke.* See p. 58, l. 16, and note.

PAGE 160. 14. *Lure,* the decoy-fowl.

PAGE 161. 41. *Iack Coomes.* I know no other references to this
apparently proverbial hero.

PAGE 162. 5. *morin,* i.e, murrain.

20. For the *Willow* as an emblem of the forsaken lover see the
Percy Ballad of *Harpalus*:

> His clothes were black and also bare,
> As one forlorne was he ;
> Upon his head always he ware
> A wreath of willow-tree.

But, of course, cf. Desdemona's song in *Othello*, IV. iii.

25–34. *wherefore is griefe good ? &c.* This is an obvious parody
of Falstaff's soliloquy on honour, *1 Henry IV*, v. i. 133–42) : ' Can
Honour set to a leg ? No. Or an arm ? No. Or take away the grief
of a wound ? No. Honour hath no skill in surgery then ? No. What
is Honour ? A word. What is that word, Honour ? Air. A trim
reckoning ! Who hath it ? He that died o' Wednesday. Doth he feel
it ? No. Doth he hear it ? No. It is insensible then ? Yea, to the
dead. But will it not live with the living ? No. Why ? Detraction
will not suffer it. Therefore I'll none of it.'

PAGE 163. 1. *sadnes,* seriousness. Cf. *2 Henry IV*, v. i. 91, ' A gest
with a sad brow.'

17. *coate with foure elbowes,* i.e. the fool's coat. Cf. Nash's
Have with You to Saffron Walden (*Works*, edit. McKerrow, vol. iii),
p. 23.

26–35. There can be no doubt that in these questions and answers
Deloney is parodying one of the old popular courting games. A traditional children's game was played in London twenty years ago in which
almost the same questions were asked of a girl by a boy, and all answered
by a refusal until the critical interjection, ' Your sweetheart's waiting
outside for you ! ' Many analogues will suggest themselves from the
Folk Lore Society's collection of folk games, but I have been able to
find none exactly parallel.

PAGE 164. 15. *three-Tunnes.* Perhaps ' Three Tuns, Newgate
Market.' *News from Bartholomew Fair* (1606).

PAGE 166. 28–35. See Note on Sources, pp. 531–2.

PAGE 167. 6. *pricksong,* sight-singing, from the pricks or dots used
in notation.

19. *pumps* were low slippers and *pantofles* were ' chopines ' or
high-heeled shoes. Here they both seem to be worn together.

42. The Chroniclers, and especially Holinshed, give long
accounts of Henry VIII's Christmas revels.

45. *amate.* A common Old English word meaning to dismay or

cast down, from the French *amater*. The *Oxford English Dictionary* quotes Sidney, *Ps. cxxix*, 'Terror shall your mindes amate.'

PAGE **168**. 3. *The Song of the Winning of Bullen*. Grafton describes both the taking of Boulogne and that of Tournai, and Deloney, in round *Robin's* song, seems to have confounded them together. 'The fourteene day of July the kings maiestie in his royal person passed the seas from Douer to Calice, and the sixe and twentie day encamped himself before Bulleyne . . . the which towne he so sore assaulted & so besieged with such abundaunce of great ordinaunce, that neuer was there a more valyaunter assault made.' Grafton (1809), vol. ii, p. 992. But the rest of Deloney's account is drawn from Grafton's description of the siege of Tournai.

35–40. 'The prouost said . . . althought it bee wrytten on the gates grauen in stone Iammes ton ne a perdeu ton pucellage, that is to say thou hast neuer lost thy maydenhed ; yet if this citie had not bene well furnyshed and euer at the day appoyncted suer of rescue, it coulde not haue continued.' Grafton (1809), vol. ii, p. 278. This incident is referred to also by Holinshed (1587), vol. ii, p. 824.

PAGE **169**. 18–19. 'On Sunday the second of October, the king entred the Citie of Tournay . . . & afternoone he came to the Marketplace.' Grafton (1809), vol. ii, p. 278. The inscription on Tournai gates is referred to by Nash in *Jack Wilton*, p. 209 (*Works*, edit. McKerrow), 'When Turnin lost her maidenhead, &c.'

PAGE **170**. 12–20. See Note on Sources, p. 531.

22. *Peachey*. Deloney has apparently borrowed this name from Holinshed. Sir John Peachie was a courtier and soldier of some consideration, who attended Henry VIII's sister Mary on her marriage with the King of France. He was probably innocent of any connexion with The Gentle Craft. See Holinshed (1589), pp. 803, 822, 832, *et passim*, and Note on Sources, p. 532.

28–34. For Peachey's troop of retainers cf. Harrison's *England*, p. 187 (Holinshed, vol. i, 1587) : 'I might speake here of the great traines and troopes of seruing menials, which attend vpon the nobilitie of England in their seuerall liueries, and with differences of cognisances on their sleeues, whereby it is knowen to whome they apperteine.' Douce (*Illustrations*, 1835, p. 206) quotes Fynes Moryson : 'The servants of gentlemen were wont to weare blew coates, with their masters badge of silver on the left sleeve, but now they most commonly weare clokes garded with lace, all the servants of one family wearing the same liverie for colour and ornament.'

36. Stucley was also a retainer of Brandon, Duke of Suffolk (Simpson, *School of Shakespeare*).

41. *sowter*. Shoemaker. Latin *sutor*.

43. *squaring*, quarrelsome. Cf. *Midsummer Night's Dream*, II. i. 28–30.

> And now they never meet in grove, or green,
> By fountain clear, or spangled starlight sheen,
> But they do square.

PAGE **171**. 11. *Stuteley* is probably a misprint for Stucley or some such form of the name.

13. *watched silk thrumb hats*. *Watchet*, a word we have unfortunately lost, means light blue. Cf. Browne's *Britannia's Pastorals*, ii. 3.

> As in the rain bows many-colour'd hew,
> We see the watchet deepened with a blew.

A *thrumb-hat* or *thrummed hat* was a hat furnished with thrums or tufts of very coarse cloth (see Nares). Cf. *Merry Wives*, IV. ii. 82, ' There 's her thrummed hat.'

PAGE **172.** 35. *goodman flat-cap.* ' Goodman ' was a term of contemptuous familiarity. Cf. *Romeo and Juliet*, I. v. 80–1 :

> He shall be endur'd ;
> What, goodman boy !—I say, he shall.

' The ancient Habit of the Apprentices of London, was a flat round cap . . . whom the Pages of the Court in Derision called Flat Caps.' Stow-Strype (1720), Book V, p. 329.

40. *dudgin haft*, i.e. with a hilt made of boxwood (Nares).

PAGE **173.** 29. *John Abridges.* See Note on Sources, pp. 532–3.

42–3. *butter whores.* An abusive epithet apparently derived from the character of the women who brought butter to market. Nash uses the same word in *Foure Letters Confuted* (*Works*, edit. MᶜKerrow, p. 299).

45–7. *if I strike below the girdle, call me Cut.* Bishop Carleton says of a Londoner, one Rowland York : ' He was famous among the Cutters of his time, for bringing in a new kind of fight, to run the point of a rapier into a man's body . . . when in England before that time the use was with little bucklers, and with broad swords to strike, and not to thrust, and it was accounted unmanly to strike under the girdle.' *Thankfull Remembrancer* (1625), p. 117.

Strangwidge and Stukeley apparently use the new kind of fighting, while Master Peachey and his men carry the old-fashioned broad sword and buckler.

47. *Cut*, i.e. knave, metaphorically from a horse. Cf. *Twelfth Night*, II. iii. 205, ' If thou hast her not in the end, call me cut.'

PAGE **174.** 12. *Aqua vitae* was usquebaugh, not brandy, says Douce, and quotes the recipe from Cogan's *Haven of Health*, 1612 (*Illustrations to Shakespeare*, 1835, p. 43).

32. *quoystrels.* A coystrel originally was a groom, then any base fellow. Cf. *Twelfth Night*, I. iii. 43, ' He's a coward and a coystrel that will not drink to my niece.'

PAGE **175.** 17. *cogging.* To *cog* is to cheat. Cf. *Much Ado about Nothing*, V. i. 93–4 :

> out-facing, fashion-monging boys,
> That lie, and cog, and flout.

18. *Petworth.* In Sussex ; about fifteen miles south of Guildford.

30. *wager*, i. e. wage. Probably a misprint.

39. *a Stand of Ale*, i.e. a beer-barrel. Ogilvy quotes Beaumont and Fletcher, ' This stand of royal blood shall be abroach, atilt.'

PAGE **176.** 1. *Kerbfoord* is almost certainly a misspelling for *Kirdford*, a village five miles north of Petworth.

15–16. *With hey tricksie, &c.* A similar burden occurs in the *Ballad of Stukeley*, printed in Simpson's *School of Shakespeare*, vol. i, p. 151 :

> In Plymouth town, in a threadbare gown
> And money never a deal,
> *Hey trixi trim, go trixi trim,*
> And will not a ballad do well.

PAGE **177.** 17. *Nowne substantiue.* The distinctions of formal grammar are often thus employed in contemporary prose. Cf. *Christs Teares ouer Ierusalem* (Nash's *Works*, edit. McKerrow, p. 119): 'Wilt thou ratifidely affirme that God is no God, because (like a Noune substantive) tbou canst not essentially see him, feele him or heare him?' In Sir Thomas Overbury's *Characters*, a 'timist' is defined as 'a noune adjective of the present tense'.

38–9. *goodman Luters lame nagge.* Reference untraced.

PAGE **178**. 25. *the Image of Bred-streete corner.* Perhaps that mentioned by Stow: 'Monumentes to be noted here, first at Breadstreet corner the north East end, 1595. of *Thomas Tomlinson.*' *Survey* (edit. Kingsford), vol. i, p. 34.

26. The *Sarazines-head* was near St. Sepulchre's Church, Holborn. Stow (*Survey*, edit. Kingsford, vol. ii, p. 34) calls it 'a fayre and large Inne for receipt of trauellers, and hath to signe the sarasens head.' Nevills treatment of Tom Drum recalls Falstaff's stratagem of persuading his followers to tickle their noses with sword grass to make them bleed, after the adventure on Gad's hill (*1 Henry IV*, II. iv).

31. *towne-Malin.* The modern Malling is about five miles west of Maidstone.

PAGE **179**. 8. *mistery*, in the old sense of *métier.* Cf. 'The Mystery of the Plaisterers.' Stow-Strype (1720), Book V, p. 300.

24. *Clement carry lye.* The Elizabethan writers were past masters of the quaint art of character naming. Cf. the alliterative names, Sir Davie Debit, and Henrie Hadland in the *Serving-mans Comfort.*

38. *men headed like Dogs.* Cf. note on p. 24, l. 35.

40–1. *Othersome . . . that one of their legs hath been as good · as a penthouse* are described in Mandeville. 'The Ethiope are such men that have but one foote . . . & that is a large foot that the shadow thereof covereth the body from Sun or raine when they lye upon their backs' (1568, cap. li). Pliny is apparently the original authority: 'Sciapodas vocari . . . quod in maiore aestu humi iacentes resupini umbra se pedum protegant' (*Nat. Hist.*, Lib. VII, c. 2). But cf. also Golding's *Solinus* (1587), p. 196.

PAGE **180**. 2. *Sweathland.* Sweden, as in G. Markham's *Cauelrice* (1607).

10–11. For the length of the day in North Britain cf. Greenwey's *Tacitus* (1596), p. 189: 'The length of the dayes much above the measure of our climate. The nights light, and in the furthermost part of the Iland so short, that between the going out and coming in of the day the space is hardly perceived, and when clouds doe not hinder they affirme that the sunshine is seene in the night, and that it neither setteth nor riseth but passeth along.' So also Golding's *Solinus* (1587): 'Thule is the furthest of, wherin, at such time as the sun is at the hyghest in sommer . . . there is almost no night at all' (p. 84).

PAGE **181**. 7. *vermin.* The same joke as in *2 Henry IV*, III. ii, where Falstaff, having regard to the condition of Francis Feeble, 'cannot put him to a private soldier, that is the leader of so many thousands.'

30. *Sir John Rainsford.* See Note on Sources, pp. 532–5.

PAGE **182**. 2. *Sir Iohn.* Commonly used of a parish priest. Nares quotes from Latimer: 'And, instead of a faithfull and painefull teacher, they have a Sir John, who hath better skill in playing at tables, or in keeping a garden, then in God's word.'

14–15. *chollericke as a quaile.* Cf. *Antony and Cleopatra*, II. iii. 36–8 :

His cocks do win the battle still of mine,
When it is all to nought; and his quails ever
Beat mine, inhoop'd, at odds.

18. *Saint Charity. Sancta caritas* became *Saint Charity*, just as *Sanctum Sepulchrum* became Saint Sepulchre.

PAGE **183**. 23. *blind bayard.* Bayard originally meant a bay horse, and then a horse of any kind. *Blind Bayard* was a proverbial phrase for an over-hasty person. Cf. *Match at Midnight (Old Plays,* VII. 435) : 'Do you hear, Sir Bartholomew Bayard, that leap before you look?'

PAGE **184**. 1. The *Dean* had ecclesiastical jurisdiction as the head of a sub-division of the archdeaconry.

42-4. *an halter . . . an Ill word foure times a yeer at Newgate,* i.e. at the assizes.

PAGE **185**. 1. The '*masterlesse* man' has ever been considered identical with the vagabond in England. Cf. the *Penniles Parliament oj Thred-Bare Poets,* 1608 (Percy Society, vol. vii, 40): 'what day soever St Pauls church hath not, in the middle aile of it, either a broker, masterless man, or a pennyless companion, the usurers of London shall be sworn by oath to bestow a new steeple upon it.'

39. *Kingstone.* Tom Drum takes the main road to London from Petworth, through Guildford and Kingston.

45-6. *French-men . . . landed in the Ile of Wight.* Holinshed (1587, vol. ii, p. 969) gives an account of the attack on the Isle of Wight in 1545, and some note as to forces raised by the City of London to aid Henry VIII in his French wars : 'Also in the beginning of this moneth (August) the citee of London set foorth a thousand soldiers of archers, harquebutters, pikes and bils, which went to Dover and so passed over unto Calis, to serve the king in his wars on that side the seas.'

PAGE **186**. 37. *dogs-nose.* A term of abuse. Cf. 'Call me Cut', p. 173, l. 47. The *Oxford English Dictionary* quotes a similar phrase from Hobbes's *Iliad*: 'Whereof no notice (Dogshead) now you take.'

PAGE **187**. 1. For Elizabethan love charms cf. the character in Greene's *Ned Browne* (*Works,* edit. Grosart, vol. xi, p. 28): 'He will perswade you hee hath twentie receiptes of Loue powders: that hee can frame a Ring with such a quaint deuise, that if a Wench put it on her finger, she shall not choose but followe you vp and downe the streetes.'

12-14. Another and similar turtle-dove charm is given in *Letting of Honours Blood in the Head Vaine* (1600), quoted by Hazlitt-Brand (vol. iii, p. 261) :

take me a Turtle Doue,
And in an ouen let her lie and bake
So dry, that you may powder of her make :
Which being put into a cup of wine,
The Wenche that drinkes it will to loue incline.

8. *East-Cheape.* 'The streete of great Eastcheap is so called of the Market there kept in the East part of the Citye.' Stow's *Survey* (edit. Kingsford), vol. i, p. 216. It was celebrated for its meat and cooks.

36. *checkquerd pauement,* that made with inlaid tiles, as in sixteenth- and seventeenth-century pictures of interiors.

42. *siluer forke.* The well-known passage in *Coryats Crudities*

(1611 edit., p. 90) seems to show that forks for individual use were not introduced into England till the first quarter of the seventeenth century. Here, of course, Mistress Farmer is merely using the silver fork for serving, and Tom Drum seems to regard that as a mark of great gentility.

PAGE **188**. 5. Apostle spoons were made in sets of twelve, each spoon having a little head at the handle. They were a common christening present. Cf. Beaumont and Fletcher's *Noble Gentleman* (quoted in Brand's *Popular Antiquities*, vol. ii, p. 16):

> I'll be a gossip, Bewford,
> I have an odd Apostle Spoon.

10–11. *charing Crosse.* 'Which crosse, builded of stone, was of old time a fayre peece of worke there made by commandement of Edward the first.' Stow's *Survey* (edit. Kingsford), vol. ii, p. 100. It was destroyed in the time of the Commonwealth.

PAGE **189**. 19. I have been unable to find any references to an *Alderman Jarvice.* For *Doctor Burket* see Note on Sources, p. 535.

PAGE **190**. 7. *good honesty*, i. e. good honest man. Cf. Shakespeare's beautiful use of the same idiom of the abstract for the concrete in *Coriolanus*, II. i. 194, 'My gracious silence, hail!'

11. The casting of water was a favourite operation of Elizabethan physic. In *Twelfth Night* (III. iv. 116) Fabian suggests it for Malvolio's benefit, 'Carry his water to the wise-woman.' So in *2 Henry IV*, I. ii. 1–5:

Falstaff. Sirrah, you giant, what says the doctor to my water?
Page. He said, sir, the water itself was a good healthy water; but, for the party that owed it, he might have more diseases than he knew for.

31. *as glad . . . as one had giuen her a rush*, i. e. pleased nothing at all. A rush was an emblem of worthlessness, and so a rush ring was the fitting symbol of a hedge-marriage. Cf. *All's Well that Ends Well* (II. ii. 23–5): 'As fit as ten groats is for the hand of an attorney, as your French crown for your taffeta punk, as Tib's rush for Tom's forefinger.'

42. *Tom Drums entertainment.* See Note on Sources, p. 535.

48. *Muskelborough field.* Holinshed's *Chronicle* (1587, vol. ii, pp. 981–2) is the source of Deloney's information.

PAGE **191**. 4–5. 'In the same chase were slaine to the number of ten thousand men, some saie about fourteene thousand . . . The prisoners reckoned in the marshal's booke were numbered to aboue fifteene hundred.' Holinshed (1587), vol. ii, p. 988.

42. *Swinborne.* The Swinborne family occupied Little Horkesley Hall, five miles from Colchester, and very little removed from the Colchester high road (see Wright's *History of Essex*, vol. i, p. 444). Deloney had perhaps picked up the name on his journeying between Norwich and London. Cf. also his reference to Colchester Castle in *Gentle Craft*, Part I, p. 93, l. 5.

PAGE **193**. 5. *voyding beere*, i. e. the beere drunk at 'voiding' or departing. Cf. *voiding-cup*.

PAGE **195**. 15. *water-bearer.* See note on p. 110, ll. 10, 11.

42. Closets were often built so as to give a view upon the kitchen and dining hall, and so enable masters and mistresses to keep a watchful eye upon the household, without themselves being seen. In *Henry VIII* the King and Butts enter, 'at a window above' (V. ii.),

and watch Cranmer holding ' his state at door, 'mongst pursuivants, Pages and footboys'. Drake quotes Parker's letter of 1573 from Reed's *Shakespeare*, vol. xv, p. 184: ' If it please Her Majestie, she may come in through my gallerie, and see the disposition of the hall at dynner-time, at a window opening thereunto.'

PAGE **196**. 43. *Ware* is about five miles from Hertford.

45. *Black-wall.* Now, of course, a part of London East.

PAGE **197**. 3. *it cost me three crownes,* i. e. in christening presents. Cf. Howe's edition of Stowe's *Chronicle* (1631), p. 1039: ' At this time and for many yeares before, it was not the use and custome (as now it is) for godfathers and godmothers, generally to give plate at the Baptisme of children . . . but only to give little christening shirts.'

7. The *veluet cap* was the distinctive cap of the physician :

> The physick-cap to dust may bring,
> Without controull the greatest king.
> *Ballad of the Caps* (Percy Society, vol. xxvii, p. 115).

44. *white manchets,* fine white bread. Cf. note on p. 56, l. 7.

46. *Red wine* usually accompanied oysters. ' In like manner we think it fit, that red wine should be drank with oysters.' *Penniles Parliament,* 1608 (Percy Society, vol. vii, p. 39).

PAGE **199**. 22. *Bridewell* was the house of correction for the apprentices of the city of London.

PAGE **200**. 9. *make sure.* See note on p. 9, l. 41.

PAGE **202**. 7. Master Baltazar was a Portuguese who came over in the retinue of Don Antonio in 1594 (Besant's *Tudor London,* p. 203). Dyson, in his *History of Tottenham High Cross,* describes the almshouses he founded there, and adds some interesting details. But cf. the following passage from *The Beauties of England and Wales* (1816) : ' Balthaser Sanches, who was a Spaniard born, and who is supposed to have been the first person that exercised the trade of a confectioner, or *Comfit Maker,* in this country, founded, in his life time, eight almshouses, for four poor men and the same number of poor women. The buildings were completed in 1600.' Vol. x, part iv, p. 702.

30. *a freeman,* i. e. of the Worshipful Company of Cordwainers.

PAGE **204**. 18. *Marlin.* Cf. Dekker's *Wonderful Year* (*Works,* edit. Grosart, vol. i, p. 95) : ' That same 88 that had more prophecies waiting at his heels, than ever Merlin the magitian had in his head.'

22. *firkin barrell,* i. e. a small barrel.

44. *Billingsgate to take Barge.* See note on p. 146, l. 41.

45. *firkin,* i. e. firking, meaning quick and ' fidgety '.

48. *a crash* was a piece of music or dance (Chappell).

PAGE **205**. 10. *Salutation.*

> There hath been great sale and utterance of wine,
> Besides beere, and ale, and ipocras fine,
> In every country, region, and nation
> But chiefly in Billingsgate, at the Salutation.
> West's *Newes from Bartholomewe Fayre* (1606).

PAGE **206**. 35. *Proffer him the wine,* i. e. invite him to drink with them. Cf. p. 10, l. 14.

PAGE **207**. 8–7. *Saint Martins begger.* Reference untraced.

33. *a fat Pig.* Roast pig was a common dainty at Elizabethan fairs, and hence in Jonson's *Bartholomew Fair* :

Purecraft. A longing to eat pig ?
Littlewit. Ay, sir, a Bartholomew pig ; and in the fair.

42. The point of the Greene King's joke lies in the fact that there were two St. James's Fairs, one held at Bristol and the other at Westminster, and both on the same day, July 25th. (See Harrison's *England,* in Holinshed, 1587, vol. i, p. 245.) Stow notes the Westminster fair (*Survey,* edit. Kingsford, vol. ii, p. 101) : ' King Edward the first . . . granted a Fayre to be kept on the Eve of Saint *James,* the day, the morrowe, and foure dayes following.' In *Tarlton's Jests* (p. 29, New Shakspere Society) we read that ' when the queenes players were restrained in summer, they travelled down to S. James, his faire, at Bristowe.' Of course the Greene King's wife and the shoemakers take it for granted that he means the Westminster Fair, and only discover their mistake later on, when the one is called on to walk and the others to pay.

PAGE **208.** 36. *as passes.* For this old use of *as* as a relative cf. *Romeo and Juliet,* II. i. 35-6 :

> that kind of fruit
> As maids call medlars.

37-8. *sort of Emits,* i. e. a crowd of ants. See note on p. 88, l. 45.

PAGE **209.** 12-13. *treable viall.* ' The Viole : which is either Treble, Tenour, or Base, according to its magnitude : These have only Sixe stringes a peece, and are played uppon with a Bowe.' Quoted from a commonplace book of Sir Philip Leycester's in Furnivall's edition of *Laneham's Letter.*

13. *hunts-up,* i. e. music to wake the morning. See Chappell's *Popular Music of the Olden Time,* p. 61.

13-14. *good morrow master,* &c., is of course the watchman's cry.

35. *Brainford,* or Brentford, was a favourite pleasure resort of Elizabethan Londoners. See the *Jests of George Peele.*

41. *Colebrook.* Harrison (Holinshed, 1587, vol. i, p. 248) gives the road to Bristol through Colnbrooke, Maidenhead, Reading, &c.

PAGE **210.** 11. *Sir Michaell Musgraue.* ' Now after the battell, among other questions, one was moued who killed the first man that daie in the field, the glorie whereof one Jeronimo an Italian would gladlie haue had, . . . how beit it was after well tried that Cuthbert Musgraue, a gentleman of the earle of Warwiks, deserued the praise of killing the first enimie that died that daie.' Holinshed's *Chronicle* (1587), vol. ii, p. 989.

13. *Tom Trotter.* ' Thornton belonged to the lord Hume, and was kept by one Thom Trotter, who vpon summons given him to render the house, lockt up a sixteene poore soules like the soldiors of Dunglas fast within the house, tooke the keies with him, commanding them to defend the place till his returne, which should be on the morrow with munition and releefe : and this doone, he and his prickers prickt (as saith Maister Patten) quite their waies.' Ibid., p. 981.

16. *Parson Ribble* is really Parson *Keble.* ' At the time of the onset, which the English horsemen gaue, there came eastward fiue hundred of the Scotish horsemen . . . streight vpon the English ordinance and cariage. The lord protector . . . caused a peece or two to be turned toward them, with a few shots whereof they were soone turned also and fled to Daketh. But had they kept on their purpose, they were prouided for accordinglie. For one parson Keble a chapleine of his graces, and two or three other, by and by discharged

foure or fiue of the carts of munition, and therewith bestowed pikes, billes, bowes and arrowes, to as manie as came ; so that of carters and other, there were soone weaponed about a thousand, whome parson Keble and the other did verie handsomlie dispose in arraie, and made a pretie muster.' Ibid., p. 988. Perhaps Deloney confused *Keble* with John de Ribaud, who occurs on p. 982, and so obtained the hybrid ' Ribble'.

THOMAS OF READING.

Date. *Thomas of Reading* is not entered in the *Stationers' Registers*, neither is the date of the first edition known. It was certainly written after *Iacke of Newberie*, which was entered on March 7, 1596-7, for in the dedication of that novel Deloney promises to ' set to sight the long hidden History of *Thomas* of *Redding*' (p. 2, ll. 24, 25, and note). But *The Gentle Craft* was entered on October 19, 1597. Hence if *Thomas of Reading* was written immediately after *Iacke of Newberie* and before *The Gentle Craft*, Part I, we must ascribe three of Deloney's novels to the same year, i.e. 1597, and all three must have been written between March 7 and Oct. 19. If this was so, Deloney must have had an un-usually busy year, but it seems more probable that after writing *Iacke of Newberie* he left the weavers for a while to deal with the shoemakers, and only returned to them again in *Thomas of Reading*, written in 1598 or 1599. Kempe mentions the novel early in 1600 (see p. xiii), and on April 19, 1602, *A booke called THOMAS of Reading* was assigned to Thomas Pavier from Thomas Millington.' (*Stationers' Registers.*) The matter of the novel soon attracted the attention of the drama-tists, for entries in Henslowe's *Diary* for Oct. 12, June 8, &c., 1601, show that Haughton, Hathaway, and Smith were engaged together upon a play called the ' *six clothiers* ', or the ' *vj yeomen* ', which was extended in the same year to a second part. Neither part of this play is now extant.

Extant Editions.

[A] 1623. THOMAS OF READING. Or, The sixe worthie Yeomen of the West . . . *LONDON*, Printed by W. I. for T. P. (*Bridgewater House.*)

[B] 1632. Printed by *Eliz. Allde* for *Robert Bird*. (*British Museum and Bodleian.*)

[C] 1672. LONDON, Printed for *William Thackeray* and are to be sold at his shop in *Duck-lane*. (*Bodleian.*)

[D] *No date.* Printed for *B. Deacon*, at *The Angel* in *Gilt Spur* Street. (A worthless edition, much cut down.) (*Bodleian.*)

Hazlitt, apparently after Ritson, mentions an edition of 1612, ' printed at London for T. P.' (i.e. Thomas Pavier). This I have been unable to trace. The present text is from the edition of 1623.

Note on Sources. The Six Yeomen of the West are probably fictitious characters. In the address to the 'famous Cloth Workers in England' prefixed to *Iacke of Newberie*, Deloney promises 'to set to their sight the long hidden Historie of Thomas of Redding, George of Glocester, Richard of Worcester and William of Salisbury with divers others' (p. 2, ll. 24-5). In the present novel, which fulfils that promise, these names are changed, with the single exception of that of Thomas of Reading ; George of Glocester appears as Gray, Richard of Worcester as William, and William of Salisbury as Sutton. The alliteration of these and the names newly introduced, such as Cuthbert of Kendall, Hodgekins of Hallifax, and Martin of Manchester, confirms the suspicion that in the *Six Yeomen* Deloney freely invented characters of his own, around which he arranged a history of the clothing trade, drawn chiefly from tradition and Holinshed, but illustrated by stories of his own invention or selection. Thomas Cole of Reading has been taken quite seriously by some writers, but even of him the wise Fuller has probably said the last word :

' Thomas Cole, commonly called the rich clothier of Reading. Tradition and an authorless pamphlet make him a man of vast wealth, maintaining an hundred & forty menial servants in his house besides three hundred poor people whom he set on work : insomuch that his wains with cloth filled the highway betwixt Reading & London, to the stopping of King Henry the First in his progress ; who not-withstanding (for the encouraging of his subjects' industry) gratified the said Cole, & all of his profession, with the set measure of a yard, the said king making his own arm the standard thereof, whereby drapery was reduced in the meeting thereof to a greater certainty.

' The truth is this ; monks began to lard the lives of their saints with lies, whence they proceeded in like manner to flourish out the facts of famous knights (King Arthur, Guy of Warwick, &c.); in imitation whereof some meaner wits in the same sort made descriptions of mechanics, powdering their lives with improbable passages, to the great prejudice of truth ; seeing the making of broad cloth in England could not be so ancient, and it was the arm (not of King Henry) but King Edward the First, which is notoriously known to have been the adequation of a yard.

' However, because omnis fabula fundatur in Historia, let this Cole be accounted eminent in this kind ; though I vehemently suspect very little of truth would remain in the midst of this story, if the gross false-hoods were pared from both sides thereof.' *Worthies* (*Works*, 1840, vol. i, p. 137).

Fuller, while obviously referring to Deloney's novel, has probably not inaccurately suggested the manner of its genesis. But while the Six Yeomen cannot be regarded as strictly historical personalities Deloney has assigned them to such counties as were the real centres of the clothing trade in Tudor times. Fuller, in his *Church History of Britain*, gives these as Gloucestershire, Worcestershire, Westmoreland (Kendal), Lancashire (Manchester), Yorkshire (Halifax), Berkshire, Hampshire, and Somersetshire.

Furthermore, the Fitzallens were actually settled at Oswestry and concerned with the weaving industry from the earliest times, and the activity of the Byrom family in the woollen trade of the sixteenth century is sufficiently attested by documentary evidence (see notes on p. 213, ll. 26–32).

The historical setting of the novel is drawn from Holinshed's account of Henry I's reign, and by connecting Duke Robert with a fabulous daughter of the Earl of Salisbury Deloney has constructed a romance of the conventional Elizabethan kind. Into this he has worked other stories : (1) *Hodgkins and Halifax Law*, (2) *Sir William Ferrers*, (3) *The Murder of Old Cole*.

(1) The Halifax Gibbet is described in Harrison's *England* (see note on p. 246, l. 32), and the ' notable Theefe named Wallis ' appears to be none other than the Scots champion, to whom an adventure of Robert Bruce, as given in Holinshed, has been transferred (see notes

on pp. 243-4). But Deloney might have obtained the story of the friar's 'gin' from any comrade of the Elizabethan travelling fraternities, who regarded 'Hell, Hull, and Halifax' as synonymous terms.

(2) The trick played upon Sir William Ferrers resembles that played upon the unfortunate Calandrino in the *Decameron* (Giornata IX, Novella 3): 'Maestro Simone . . . fa credere a Calandrino che egli è pregno: il quale per medicine dà al predetto capponi e denari, e guarisce senza partorire.' The device of the bladder of blood is common enough, e.g. in *Bandello* (Parte I, Novella 17).

(3) The story of the murder of old Cole is a curious example of the wide diffusion of popular stories. It bears a very close resemblance to the story of *Sweeney Todd, the Demon Barber of Fleet Street*, which is usually traced back to an early nineteenth-century French source, and it is probably nothing more than the artistic making up of the details of a contemporary or traditional crime. The circumstantiality of Deloney's account, besides his own habits of composition, are altogether against the supposition that he invented the story himself. The *Crane* Inn, where old Cole is made to meet his death, is without doubt that now known in Colnbrook as the *Ostrich*, and local tradition, from the mouths of old women and school children, still retells the story of the crime with almost the exact detail of Deloney's narrative. The present landlady is very ready to give every particular of the murders (she asserts the exact number to be sixty-one[1]) and to exhibit the fatal bedroom to the courteous visitor. The falling floor no longer exists, but, in compensation, the good lady shows a beam in the back of the house, where she asserts a vain attempt was made to burn it down.

The *Idler* of April, 1899, contains a short article by R. Waybrook upon the *Ostrich Inn*, which gives the whole story almost verbatim from *Thomas of Reading*, although the writer quotes no authority. It seems most likely that Deloney himself picked the story up at Colnbrook, and the Colnbrook traditions have either changed very little, or Deloney has influenced and fixed them, although on this latter point there appears to be no obtainable evidence.

The story of Cutbert and old Blossom's wife is evidently Deloney's attempt to explain a custom at Blossom's Inn 'that . . . euery yeere once all such as came thither to aske for cheeses should be so serued: which thing is to this day kept.' The story of Tom Drum in *The Gentle Craft* (II) originates in a similar attempt (see Note on Sources, p. 535).

PAGE **213**. 4. *Court of Parliament.* 'From this Henrie (the first) it may be thought the first use of the parlement to haue proceeded.' Holinshed (1587), vol. ii, p. 38.

26-32. See Note on Sources, pp. 547-8.

26. *Gray of Glocester.* See p. 242, ll. 31-3, and note thereon.

Fitzallen. The Fitzallens were connected with Oswestry from the earliest times. The Fraternity of Weavers in Oswestry was incorporated in 1262 by grant from John FitzAlan, lord of Arundel (*Victoria History of Shropshire*, p. 430). See also p. 243, l. 4, and note thereon.

31. *Martin Byram* is at any rate a veracious traditional figure. The Byroms, or Briams, were a well-known family in Lancashire from 1300 onwards, and a younger branch of the family settled at Salford as merchants in the latter years of Henry VII's reign. Adam Byrom 'of Sauforde' is designated 'merchant' in a legal document of Nov. 24, 1557, and from the fact that Raufe Byrom in 1598 is found in

---

[1] Deloney says sixty (p. 260, l. 8).

possession of 'a moiety of a water mill and fulling mill' it may be concluded that the Salford branch of the family were concerned in the Manchester clothing trade. (See Cheetham Society's Publications, vol. ii, part ii.) R. Hollingworth, the seventeenth-century antiquary, is evidently merely following Deloney in his *Mancuniensis*, as the *Victoria County History* merely follows Hollingworth.

PAGE **214**. 2. *Bosome Inne* was in St. Laurence's Lane, near Cheapside. 'Antiquities in this Lane', says Stow, 'I find none other, then that among many fayre houses, there is one large Inne for receipt of travellers, called Blossoms Inne, but corruptly Bosoms Inne, & hath to signe S. *Laurence* the Deacon, in a Border of blossomes or flowers.' *Survey*, edit. Kingsford, vol. i, p. 271.

6. *Iarrats Hall* was at the end of Basing Lane, near Bread Street. The crypt remained, according to Kingsford, till 1852, when it was built into the Crystal Palace. Stow gives the following account of it in the *Survey* (Kingsford, vol. i, p. 348): 'The same is now a common Ostrey for receipt of trauellers, commonly and corruptly called Gerrardes hall, of a Gyant sayd to haue dwelled there. In the high rooffed Hall of this House, sometime stoode a large Firre Pole, which reached to the roofe thereof, and was sayd to bee one of the staues that Gerrarde the Gyant vsed in the warres to runne withall. There stoode also a ladder of the same length which (as they say) serued to ascend to the toppe of the Staffe . . . The Hostelar of the house sayde to me, the Pole lacked half a foote of fortie in length: I measured the compasse thereof and found it fifteene inches. Reason of the Pole, could the master of the Hostrey giue me none, but bade me reade the great Chronicles, for there he heard of it.'

12–24. 'Henrie the yoongest sonne of William the first, brother to Rufus latelie departed, the first of that named that ruled heere in England, & for his knowledge in good literature surnamed Beauclerke . . . This prince had aforehand trained the people to his humor and veine, in bringing them to thinke well of him, and to conceiue a maruellous euil opinion of his brother duke Robert. . . . Moreouer, he caused to be reported for a certeine truth, that the same Robert was alreadie created king of Ierusalem.' Holinshed (1587), vol. ii, p. 28. 'When christian princes had woone Hierusalem, they met to-gither . . . to chuse a king for the gouernement of that citie, . . . in which conuent duke Robert was chosen. . . . But he hauing his mind more inclined to England, refused to take the charge vpon him.' Ibid., p. 29. 'The king studied by all possible meanes how to gratifie all the states of his realme.' Ibid., p. 28.

26. Henry I's Welsh wars are described in Holinshed (1587), vol. ii, p. 30.

PAGE **216**. 12. *Moraigne* seems to be a slip for *Montaigne*, probably a printer's error.

17–24. 'Diuerse in Normandie desired nothing more than to set the two brethren at square, & namely Robert de Belesme earle of Shrewsburie, with William earle of Montaigne: these two were banished the realme of England. The earle of Shrewesburie for his rebellious attempts . . . and the earle of Montaigne left the lande of his owne willful and stubborne mind, exiling himselfe onelie vpon hatred which he bare to the king. For being not contented with the earledome of Montaigne in Normandie, and the earledome of Cornewall in England, he made sute also for the earldome of Kent.' Holinshed (1587), vol. ii, p. 32.

34. *Colebrook*, i.e. Colnbrook. See note on p. 209, l. 41.

38. *Tom Doue.* Perhaps Tom Dove or Jack Dove was a proverbial name for a light-hearted fellow. A Roxburghe Ballad (vol. i, p. 475) is entitled:

'A new Song, called Jack Doue's Resolution, by which he doth show
That he cares not a rush how ere the world goe.'

'Ile laugh and be fatte for Care kils a Catte,
And I care not how ere the world goe.'

But Chappell thinks this song belongs to the time of James I, and the ballad-writer may have taken the name from Deloney's popular novel. Curiously enough, Thomas Dove occurs as the name of a tenant of Bartholomew Street (West Part) in the Survey of the Manor of Newbury, Oct. 10, 1608. (See Money's *History of Newbury*, p. 233.) Perhaps Deloney took the name and character from a local celebrity of his own acquaintance.

PAGE 217. 7. *yellowe hose*, the emblem of jealousy. Cf. Ritson's *Old Ballads* (1829), vol. ii, p. 20:

If he be merie and toy with any,
His wife will frowne, and words geve many:
Her yellow hose she strait will put on.

So also, in Evan's *Old Ballads* (1810), vol. i, p. 187:

A merry jest of John Tomson, and Jackaman his wife,
Whose jealousy was justly the cause of all their strife,

the burden of which is,—

Give me my yellow again,
Give me my yellow hose,
For now my wife she watcheth me,
See yonder where she goes.

34-5. A common Elizabethan reflection. Cf. Greene's *Philomela* (*Works*, edit. Grosart, p. 150): 'Women that are chast while they are trusted, proue wantons being suspected causeless.'

PAGE 218. 19. *the hall*, i.e. Blackwell Hall. See note on p. 234, l. 38.

33-4. *shrinks as bad as Northerne cloth.* Cf. *Roxburghe Ballads*, vi. 486:

Before we can drink
be sure it will shrink
far worser than North-country cloth.

44. *mutton, such as was laced in a red petticoate.* See note on p. 53, l. 21.

46. *Bosomes Inne.* Stow explains *Bosomes* as a corruption of *Blossoms.* (See note on p. 214, l. 2.) Deloney invents a character to explain the name.

PAGE 219 1. *figuring forth a description of cold winter.* Elaborate descriptions of personified winter, summer, &c., are common in Elizabethan prose. See, for example, Dekker's *Worke for the Armourers.* Lodge's *Wits Miserie and the Worlds Madness* (1596) is an allegorical portrait-gallery of 'Leviathan's brood of incarnate devils', such as 'Boasting', 'Avarice', 'Usury', &c. But very probably Deloney had in his mind a picture such as Shakespeare refers to in *Cymbeline*, v. iv. 183-4: 'Your death has eyes in's head then; I have not seen him so pictured.' Books of emblems illustrated by engravings were quite common ; see, for instance, *Nicolai Revsneri Leorini Aureolorum Emblematum Liber Singularis*, in the Bodleian, with its symbolic pictures of *Aurea Libertas, Amor Coniugalis, Lex Mundi, Iustitia*, &c.

19-31. Cf. note on p. 21, l. 36, and *The Lamentation of Mr. Page's Wife*, p. 482, with note thereon.

35. *byas.* A metaphor from the game of bowls. So in *Richard II*, III. iv. 4-5 :

'Twill make me think the world is full of rubs,
And that my fortune runs against the bias.

PAGE **220.** 13. The *Chamberlaine* is merely the inn attendant, as in Milton's epitaph *On the University Carrier* :

In the kind office of a chamberlain
Showed him his room where he must lodge that night.

28. *Reior.* 'About the third yeare of K. Henries reigne, the foundation of saint Bartholomews by Smithfield was begun by Raier one of the kings musicians (as some write) who also became the first prior thereof.' Holinshed (1587), vol. ii, p. 31. Stow also mentions the 'priorie of S. *Bartilmew* founded also by *Rahere*, a pleasant witted Gentleman, and therefore in his time called the kinge's Minstrell. About the yeare of Christ, 1102: he founded it, ... himself became their first Prior, and so continued till his dying day.' *Survey* (edit. Kingsford), vol. ii, p. 25.

PAGE **221.** 17. The *foule evill* was a disease of the same character as the *good years* in *King Lear*. Cf. Dekker's *Worke for the Armourers* (*Works*, edit. Grosart, vol. iv, p. 97) : ' Diseases now as common and as hurtful to them as the Foul Euil to a Northern Man, or the Pox to a French man.'

PAGE **222.** 5-10. The old hiring fair of this sort has not yet entirely disappeared. It is still held at Derby, among other places, where ' the Statute' (cf. p. 223, l. 4) is the ordinary name for it. See also Brand's *Popular Antiquities*, vol. ii, p. 316.

PAGE **225.** 28. *harbour*, i. e. harbour her emotion.

PAGE **226.** 5-6. ' He (*Henry I*) had in singular fauor aboue all other of his Councell, Roger the bishop of Salisburie, a politike prelate, and one that knew how to order matters of great importance, vnto whome he committed the gouernement of the realme most commonlie whilest he remained in Normandie.' Holinshed (1587), vol. ii, p. 45.

13. *feare.* First used transitively, = *to make afraid*, and then with its modern meaning.

PAGE **227.** 3. *borderers*, i. e. those living on the borders of England and Scotland. Cf. the entry in the *Stationers' Registers* (May 15, 1612): ' *A true report of the most lamentable and bloody murther committed ... by Robert Carlisle a Scotish borderer and one James Irwenge an English borderer.*'

15. ' He (*Henry I*) ordeined also that one length of measuring should be used through this realme, which was a yard, appointing it to be cut after the length of his owne arme.' Holinshed (1587), vol. ii, p. 28.

24-5. ' When he (*Henry I*) heard that such peeces of monie as were cracked would not be receiued amongst the people, although the same were good and fine siluer, he caused all the coine in the realme to be either broken or slit.' Ibid., p. 45.

34-5. *faule eule.* See note on p. 221, l. 17.

36. *cragge*, i. e. neck, as still in dialect.

38. *lizar*, i. e. lazar.

craking, a variety of *croaking*; perhaps it means bullying or threatening. See the *Oxford English Dictionary.*

41. 'And (as one author hath written) he (*Henry I*) ordeined that theeves should suffer death by hanging.' Holinshed (1587), vol. ii, p. 45.

PAGE **228.** 17-18. *Iustices of peace.* The humour of Hodgekins's remark lies in the fact that Elizabethan Justices of the Peace were the subject of universal opprobrium. Cf. Shakespeare's attitude to them in *Henry IV, Part II*, and *The Merry Wives.*

PAGE **229.** 34. A Iigge, according to Chappell, is a 'song written to a tune of strongly marked metre', 'jig' originally being the name for a dance. *Popular Music of the Olden Time.*

48. *bully* was an Elizabethan term of endearment or comradeship. Cf. *Henry V*, IV. i. 47-8 :

From heartstrings

I love the lovely bully.

PAGE **231.** 21. *gag-tooth*, i. e. with projecting teeth. The *Oxford English Dictionary* quotes from Higins' translation of *Junius' Nomenclator* : ' *Dentes exerti*, gag teeth or teeth standing out.'

39. A *capcase* was a kind of travelling bag. Cf. Greene's *Ned Browne (Works*, edit. Grosart, vol. xi, p. 18) : 'At his saddle bow a capcase well stuft with crowns.' Cf. p. 255, l. 24, ' his male or capcase.'

PAGE **232.** 13. *louer.* From the French *l'ouvert*, the opening in a building to let out the smoke, hence the chimney. Nares quotes from *Withal's Dictionarie* (1638), ' A louer where the smoke passeth out, fumarium.'

PAGE **233.** 18-21. See Note on Sources, p. 549.

PAGE **234.** 30-3. ' *Goldsmithes Rowe* in Chepe . . . to be noted, the most beautiful frame of fayre houses and shoppes that bee within the Walles of London.' Stow's *Survey* (edit. Kingsford), vol. i, p. 345. The mercers were already beginning to migrate to London Bridge. ' For where as Mercers, and Haberdashers used to keepe their shoppes in West Cheape, of later time they helde them on London Bridge.' Ibid., p. 81.

33. Of *Watlingstreet* Stow says : ' True it is, that at this present, the inhabitants thereof are wealthy Drapers, retailers of woollen cloathes both broad and narrow, of all sorts more then in any one streete of this citie.' Ibid., p. 346.

34. *Saint Martins Shoomakers.* Cf. Dekker in the *Guls Horn Booke (Works*, edit. Grosart, vol. ii, p. 323), 'fetch thee bootes out of S. Martens.' The Green King, in *The Gentle Craft* (p. 203), plies shoemaking there.

34-5. *Saint Nicholas* shambles were near St. Nicholas Church in Farringdon Ward Within. Stow's *Survey* (edit. Kingsford), vol. i, p. 317.

35. *Old Change.* 'The kinges Exchaunge at London, was neare vnto the Cathedrall church of Sainte *Paule*, as is to this daye commonlie called the olde Chaunge.' Ibid., p. 81.

36. *Candleweek streete* is now Cannon Street. Cf. Stow's *Survey* (edit. Kingsford), vol. i, p. 218 : ' There dwelled also of old time divers Weavers of woollen Clothes, brought in by *Edward* the third . . .

These weavers of Candlewright street being in short time worne out, their place is now possessed by rich Drapers, sellers of woollen cloth, &c.'

37. *Iewes street.* Apparently Old Jewry, in the Coleman Street Ward.

38. *Blackwell hall.* In Basinghall Street. 'Bakewell Hall corruptly called Blackwell Hall.' Stow's *Survey* (edit. Kingsford), vol. i, p. 516. Stow says (ibid., p. 288): 'It hath beene long since employed as a weekely Market place for all sorts of Woollen clothes, broade and narrow, brought from all partes of this Realme, there to be solde.'

PAGE **235**. 2. *Criple-gate.* 'So called of the Cripples begging there.' *Survey*, vol. i, p. 33. Deloney, as usual, has hitched a story on to the local name.

3–10. *the Tower of London.* 'It hath beene the common opinion: and some have written (but of none assured ground) that *Julius Caesar*, the first conquerour of the Brytains, was the originall Author and founder . . . thereof'. Ibid., vol. i, p. 44. I have met no other references to the solidified wine and the leather money kept in the Tower.

31. *the fault was in their legges.* Because, of course, the treadles were used in weaving. Cf. p. 3, l. 35.

PAGE **236**. 20. Cf. the note from Stow on p. 234, l. 36.

28. *Bishops downe.* Almost certainly Bishopstone, 'a small village about four miles to the north-west of Salisbury . . . remarkable for two stone coffins in its church, which are generally supposed to have contained the relics of two ancient bishops, and to have given name to the place.' *Beauties of England and Wales*, vol. xv, part ii.

31. *woad, that makes all colours sound.* Todd's edition of *Johnson's Dictionary* gives 'Woad. A plant cultivated for the dyers, who use it for the foundation of many colours.'

PAGE **237**. 9. *Eagle's neast.* The *Eagle's nest* was Shaftesbury. Cf. Drayton's *Polyolbion*:

Now tow'rds the *Solent* sea as *Stour* her way doth ply,
On Shaftesbury (by chance) she cast her crystal eye,
From whose foundation first, such strange reports arise
As brought into her mind the *Eagle's* prophecies.
Second Song, ll. 149–152.

Selden adds the following learned note: 'Concerning Shaftesbury . . . you shall heare a piece out of Harding:

CAIRE PALADOURE THAT NOW IS SHAFTESBURY
WHERE AN ANGELL SPAKE SITTING ON THE WALL
WHILE IT WAS IN WORKING OVER ALL.

I recite it, both to mend it, reading AIGLE for ANGELL, and also that it might then, according to the *British* story, help me to explain the Author.'

25. *canuas Prophet*, i. e. the prophet in coarse working clothes, as we might use 'corduroy' nowadays.

PAGE **239**. Dekker imitates this comedy of the wheedling wife in the *Bachelars Banquet* (*Works*, edit. Grosart, p. 156).

PAGE **240**. 42. 'Duke Robert being also spoiled of his dominions, lands and liberties, was shortlie committed to prison within the castell of Cardiff in Wales.' Holinshed (1587), vol. ii, p. 33.

43. 'Duke Robert . . . found no . . . fauour, saue onlie libertie to

walke abroad in the king's forrests, parks and chases neere the place where he was appointed to remaine.' Ibid.

PAGE **241.** 20-1. His (*Henry I*'s) bodie was conueied into England, and buried at Reading within the abbey church which he had founded, and endowed in his lifetime.' Ibid., p. 45.

35-7. *the Bishop . . . attended on his Grace to his palace.* So when Elizabeth visited Norwich in 1579 she was met by a pageant and lodged at the Bishop's palace. Holinshed (1587), vol. ii, p. 1289. Cf. also note on *Iacke of Newberie*, p. 43, l. 42.

PAGE **242.** 20-1. *Augustus.* Cf. H. Lhuyd's *Breuiarie* (1573), p. 18 : ' Their principall Citie is Isca, called also Augusta, . . . but now of the Englishmen, Excestre.'

28-9. *Gloucester.* 'Claudia, commonly called Glocester, . . . builded by Glovy a Britayne, who, after that the Romanes were driuen thence : reygned there.' Lhuyd's *Breviarie of Britayne* (1573), p. 19.

31-3. *Rithin.* Lhuyd thus describes the valley of Clwyd in Denbigh : ' In the entrance of whiche Valley : Ruthyn an auncient towne, and Castle of the Grayes, from whence the most noble famely amongst the Englishmen tooke beginninge : is to be seene.' *Breuiarie,* p. 67.

44-6. ' About this season (i.e. *11th year of the reign*) the king . . . made his said sonne earle of Glocester.' Holinshed (1587),vol. ii, p. 37.

PAGE **243.** 4. *Oswestrie.* ' Oswestry, a noble Market, and en-walled rounde, at the charges of the Fitzalanes, a moste auncient famely of Englande, whose inheritaunce it is.' Lhuyd's *Breuiarie* (1573), p. 72.

10-13. Deloney connects the two FitzAlwins of London (success-ively first and second Mayors of the city) with the Fitzalan family of Owestry. Stow writes : ' 1189 Their 1. Maior was *H. Fitz Alwin Fitz Liefstane,* Goldsmith, pointed by the said king (i. e. *Richard I*) and continued maior from the first of *Richard* the first, vntill the fifteenth of King *Iohn*, which was 24 yeares and more.' *Survey* (edit. Kingsford), vol. ii, p.149. From 1190 to 1211 Stow gives ' Maior Henry *Fitz Alwin.*' Ibid., p. 150.

42. Deloney's *Wallis* appears to be none other than the hero of Scottish history. Cf. Holinshed (1587), vol. i, p. 209 : ' William Wallase—a yoong gentleman of so huge stature and notable strength of bodie, with such skill and knowledge in warlike enterprises, and hereto of such hardinesse of stomach in attempting all maner of dangerous exploits that his match was not anie where lightlie to be found.'

PAGE **244.** 31-40. The story of this ingenious ruse really belongs to the life of Robert Bruce. It is given in Holinshed (1587), vol. i, p. 213 : ' Whereupon he causing a smith to shoo three horsses for him, contrarilie with the Calkins forward, that it should not be perceiued which waie he had taken by the tract of the horses . . . departed out of London about midnight.' The *calkin,* or *cakin,* is the turned-up rim of the shoe.

PAGE **246.** 32. *gin,* i.e. *ingenium,* or device. Harrison, in his *Description of England,* gives a full account of it. ' There is and hath beene of ancient time a law or rather a custome at Halifax, that whosoeuer dooth commit anie fellonie, and is taken with the same, or confesse the fact vpon examination : if it be valued by foure constables to amount to the sum of thirteene pence halfe penie, he is foorth with beheaded vpon one of the next market daies . . . The engine wherewith the execution is doone, is a square blocke of wood of the length of foure foot and an halfe, which dooth ride vp and downe in a slot, rabet or regall betweene two pieces of timber, that are framed and set vp right of fiue yardes in height. In the neather end of the sliding block is an ax keied or fastened with an iron into the wood, which being drawne vp to the top of the frame is there fastned by a woodden pin (with a notch made into the same after the maner of a Samson's Post) vnto the middest of which pin also there is a long rope fastened that commeth downe among the people, so that when the offendor hath made his confession, and hath laid his necke ouer the neathermost blocke, euerie man there present dooth either take hold of the rope (or putteth foorth his arme so neere to the same as he can get, in token that he is willing to see true iustice executed) and pulling out the pin in this maner, the head blocke wherein the ax is fastened dooth fall down with such a violence, that if the necke of the transgressor were so big as that of a bull, it should be cut in sunder at a stroke, and roll from the bodie by an huge distance.' Holinshed (1587), vol. i, p. 185. Hence the beggar's litany ; 'From Hell, Hull, and Halifax, Good Lord deliver us.' For further information and an engraving of the 'gin', see Fletcher's *History of Yorkshire*, vol. iii, pp. 53–6.

PAGE **247**. 30–1. 'About this season (i. e. 1107) a great part of Flanders being drowned by an erundation or breaking in of the sea, a great number of Flemings came into England.' Holinshed (1587), vol. ii, p. 34.

40. *danger.* To be in danger is to stand within some one's power, and hence often to be liable to action at law. Cf. *Merchant of Venice*, IV. i. 180 :

> You stand within his danger, do you not ?

Cf. also p. 390, l. 20.

PAGE **248**. 13. *Sanctuary.* At the Abbey Church, Westminster. Cf. Stow-Strype (1720), Book VII, p. 38 : 'This Church hath had great Privilege of Sanctuary within the Precinct thereof . . . From whence it hath not been lawful for any Prince, or other, to take any Person that fled thither for any Cause.'

37. *maggat-a-pie*, i. e. magpie. This form of the word occurs in Cotgrave and Shakespeare (Nares).

38. *spinner,* spider.

PAGE **249**. 4. *Charlemaine in mount Albon.* See Caxton's translation of the *Four Sons of Aymon* (about 1489). Charlemagne foolishly lets Reynawde build a strong castle on Mont Alban. 'The King behelde well the fayr werke, that was so playsaunt and so strong wythall . . . And thenne he called reynawde, & sayd to hym, good frende reynawde, how shall this castell be called ? . . . Certes sayd the kyng, the place is praty and fayr and I wyll that it be called Mont alban.' *Four Sons of Aymon* (E.E.T.S.), pp. 149–50.

14. *Sir William Ferris.* William Ferreis is mentioned in Holinshed (1587, vol. ii, p. 33) as captured by Henry I in Normandy.

PAGE **250**. 32. Cf. Greene's *Planetomachia* (*Works*, edit. Grosart, p. 61) : 'The Eagle and the Dove pearke not on one branche.'

33–4. The story of *Thales* is related in *Witty Questions and Quicke Answers* (1567), Tale 25 : 'Laertius writeth, that Thales Milesius went out of his house vpon a time to beholde the starres for a certayn cause : and so longe he went backewarde that he fell plump into a ditch ouer the eares ; wherefore an olde woman, that he kepte in his house laughed and sayde to him in derision : O Thales, how shuldest thou haue knowledge in heuenly thinges aboue and knowest not what is here benethe vnder thy feete.'

PAGE **251**. 3. *A bird was neuer seen in Pontus.* 'Perdices non transvolant Boeotiae fines in Attica, nec ulla avis in Ponto insula qua sepultus est Achilles sacratam ei aedem.' Pliny, *Nat. Hist.*, Lib. X. c. 41.

5. *Abiston.* 'Neither is the stone to be despised which Arcady sendeth. The name thereof is Abest. It is the colour of yron : and beeing sette on fire it cannot be quenched.' Golding's *Solinus* (1587), p. 53. So in *Barthol. Anglicus*, xvi. 12.

14-15. *thunder . . . is driuen away by ringing of belles.*

If that the thunder chaunce to rove, and stormie tempest shake,
A wonder is it for to see the wretches how they quake,
Howe that no fayth at all they have, nor trust in any thing,
The clarke doth all the Belles forthwith at once in Steeple ring:
With wondrous sound and deeper farre, than he was wont before,
Till in the loftie heavens darke, the thunder bray no more.'

> Googe's *Popish Kingdom*, fol. 41 b (quoted by
> Brand, *Pop. Antiquities*).

15-16. *Lions wrath qualified by a yeelding body.* 'Leoni tantum ex feris clementia in supplices. prostratis parcit et, ubi saevit, in viros potius quam in feminas fremit, in infantes non nisi magna fame.' Pliny, *Nat. Hist.*, Lib. VIII, c. 19. The idea occurs in *Batman*, xviii, c. 65, and Golding's *Solinus* assures us that lions 'spare them that humble themselves before them' (p. 124).

22. *Lutes*, i. e. Lotos, 'the meat thereof is so sweet and pleasant . . . that they forget their own native soile, for the love they have to this fruit.' Holland's *Pliny*, Book XIII, c. 17.

PAGE **252**. 18. *stub-footed.* *Stub* is a form of 'stump', hence 'stub-footed ' is ' club-footed '.

23. *like the storke tonguelesse.* 'Sunt qui ciconiis non inesse linguam confirment.' Pliny, *Nat. Hist.*, Lib. X, c. 31. Sir Thomas Browne discusses the proposition in *Vulgar Errors*. Cf. also p. 75, l. 13 and note.

PAGE **255**. 30. *ore eue*, over-night.

40. *curtall*, a docked horse.

PAGE **256**. 2. *Beckets house in West cheape.* Stow says Becket was born in Cheapside. *Survey* (edit. Kingsford), vol. i, p. 269. Deloney has confounded the reigns of the first and second Henries.

30. Bleeding at the nose was always taken as a sign of impending ill-luck. Cf. Tarlton's *News out of Purgatory* (New Shakspere Society), p. 101 : 'Methought there was a villain that came secretly into my house, with a naked poniard in his hand, and hid himselfe, but I could not finde the place ; with that mine nose bled, and I came back.' The Roxburghe ballad, *A Warning to all Murderers*, is almost certainly derived from Deloney's account of Old Cole's murder :

> His heart was heauie in the day,
> Yet knew no reason why ;
> And oft as he did sit at meate
> His nose, most suddenly,
> Would spring and gush out crimson blood,
> And straight it would be dry.
>> *Roxburghe Ballads*, vol. iii, p. 139.

PAGE **258**. 13. *St. Mary Overies.* In Southwark, at the Southern end of London Bridge, now Southwark Cathedral.

33–4. Screech-owls and ravens were the regular attendants at tragic death-beds.

> Now owles and night ravens are
> Ill fortune's prophecies;
> When faithlesse spirits stare
> If any storm arise.
> *Friar Bakon's Prophesie* (Percy Society, vol. xv, p. 20.)

Cf. also the epigram on Deloney in *Skialethia* (quoted in Introduction, p. xiii).

> *Like to the fatal ominous Rauen which tolls*
> *The sicke mans dirge within his hollow beake.*

PAGE **260**. 31. Churchings were usually celebrated with some festivity. Cf. Berners, *Translation of Froissart* (quoted in the *Oxford English Dictionary*): 'His wife ... was as than newly churched of a fayre sonne. And he thought at her Churchyng to kepe a great feest at Tholouse.' Cf. also note on p. 377, ll. 63–4.

PAGE **262**. 45. *Camels of Bactria.* 'Out of Bactria come strongest Cammels.' Golding's *Solinus* (1587), p. 188. But cf. also Batman, Book XVIII, c. 36 : 'Dromedus goeth an hundred miles and twentie and more in one daye.'

PAGE **263**. 2. *Austria for ambling horses.* Gervase Markham says of the Hungarian horse, 'hee is of temperate courage, & will abide much hardnesse.' *Cauelrice* (1607), pp. 15–16.

6. *ambling gennet of Spaine.* 'I have seene many ambling horses bredde from Ienets of Spaine.' G. Markham's *Cauelrice* (1607), p. 19.

20. *Galino breeds no Serpents.* Batman (1582) gives this advantage to 'Creta'. 'There are no Serpents nor noyfull Worms.' Book XV, c. 42.

24–PAGE **264**. 10. 'But duke Robert. . . found no such fauour, saue only libertie to walke abroad in the kings forests, parks, & chases neere the place where he was appointed to remaine; so that vpon a daie, as he was walking abroad, he got a horsse & with all post hast rode his waie, in hope to haue escaped ; howbeit his keepers being aduised thereof, followed him with hue & crie, & at length ouertooke him in a medow, where he had laide his horsse vp to the bellie in a quaue mire.' Holinshed (1587), vol. ii, p. 33.

PAGE **265**. 1–4. 'Then being brought backe, his keepers kept him in close prison, aduertising the king of his demeanour ; whereupon he commanded that the sight of his eies should be put out, but so, as the balles of them should remaine vnbroken, for the auoiding of a noisome deformitie that otherwise would ensue, if the glasse tunicles should take hurt.' Ibid., pp. 33–4.

36–7. *Apium Risus.* According to Gerarde's *Herbal* (1636), 'the Passe Flower or anemone'. Batman, *de Apio*, says, 'if it be eaten or dronke in great quantitie it slayeth a man with laughing.' Book XVII, .13.

45. *the eie continue faire.* Cf. note on ll. 1–4.

PAGE **266**. 10–11. *the Hart reneweth his age by eating the serpent.* This sagacious habit of the hart was well known to medievalism. Cf. *Richard the Redeless* :

And whanne it happeth to the herte · to hente the edder,
He putyth him to peyne · as his pray asketh,
And ffedith him on the venym · his ffelle to anewe,
To leve at more lyknge · a longe tyme after.

Passus III, ll. 22–5.

But Batman is a nearer authority : ' Gesner writeth, when the Hart is sicke, and hath eaten manye Serpents for his recouerie . . . he hasteth to the water, and there coucereth his body to the very eares & eyes.' Book XVIII, c. 30.

45–6. For the goats' natural hatred of *Basill*, see Pliny, *Nat. Hist.* Lib. XX, c. 48 : ' Ocimum quoque Chrysippus grauiter increpuit inutile stomacho ideoque capras id aspernari.'

PAGE **267**. 31. Batman, *de Aspide* (1582), gives ' many diuerse effects and dooings, to noy and to grieue ', which this creature employs, but does not mention tickling. Book XVIII, c. 10.

PAGE **268**. 26–8. This story is in Elyot's *Governour*, which Deloney had read (see note on p. 338). ' As Gellius remembreth out of the historie of Appion howe a lyon, oute of whose fote a yonge man had ones taken a stubbe and clensed the wounde, wherby he waxed hole, after knewe the same man beinge caste to him to be deuoured, and wolde not hurte him.' Book II, c. 13.

PAGE **269**. 22–3. *God Almighties ideots.* The fool was always recognized as being under the more especial protection of Providence, hence the proverbial saying.

25. *shales*, i.e. husks. Cf. *Henry V*, IV. ii. 17–18 :

And your fair show shall suck away their souls,
Leaving them but the shales and husks of men.

PAGE **271**. 37. *handwreasts*, i.e. simply ' wrists '. See the *Oxford English Dictionary*.

39–40. For the pleasant custom of ornamenting the outside of houses with green boughs, see Stow's description of London festivals : ' On the Vigil of Saint *John* Baptist, & on Saint *Peter* and *Paule* the Apostles, euery man's doore being shadowed with greene Birch, long Fennel, saint John's Wort, Orpin, white Lillies, & such like, garnished vpon with Garlands of beautifull flowers, had also Lampes of glasse with oyle burning in them all the night.' *Survey* (edit. Kingsford), vol. i, p. 101.

PAGE **272**. 23–7. Holinshed gives a more matter-of-fact account of Duke Robert's death : ' He refused . . . to eat or drinke, and so pined awaie, and was buried at Glocester.' (1587, vol. ii, p. 44.)

28. See note on p. 241, ll. 20–1.

35–6. In the same way, Sir Thomas White, the founder of St. John's College, Oxford, left money to be lent out to poor clothiers in twenty-one towns. See Kingsford's *Stow*, vol. i, p. 113.

40–2. Elizabethan charity often took the form of presenting poor couples with a sum of money upon which to start their married life. Stow says of Sir Hugh Witch (*Survey*, edit. Kingsford, vol. i, p. 283), ' He gaue to his third wife three thousand pound, and to maides marriages fiue hundred marks.'

42–3. ' It is said that *Martin Beron*, a Clothier, who realised a large property in Manchester, left a considerable sum towards the erection of The Free School.' *Carlisle's Endowed Grammar Schools*, vol. i, p. 684. Deloney's novel seems to have created a kind of tradition (see note on p. 213, l. 31). The High-Master informs me that no such benefaction is on record.

A DECLARATION MADE BY THE ARCHBISHOP
OF COLLEN, &c.

THIS and the following tract are interesting as indicating the keen interest taken by the English people in the Cologne War of 1582-3. Gebhard's attempt to throw off papal influence created an enormous sensation, and indeed had it been successful would have widely extended the influence of Dutch Protestantism and severely shaken the power of Roman Catholicism in Germany. Henry of Navarre and Queen Elizabeth, both anxious for the unity of the Reformed Churches, supported Gebhard, but he was excommunicated by the Pope, and swept out of his duchy by Duke Ernest of Bavaria. Gebhard's reasons for resistance were strictly non-moral and irreligious. The wife whom he purposed to join to himself 'for the better ob-seruing & accomplishing the vowe of chastitie, which I made vnto Jesus Christ', was his former mistress, Countess Agnes of Mansfield, whom he wished to legitimate while retaining his Archbishopric. His character is perhaps not unfairly summed up by Moser (quoted by Jansenn, vol. ix) : 'This luxurious hypocrite did his utmost to cheat God, the Pope, the Emperor, the Empire, his friends, and his kinsfolk —but most of all himself.' But to earnest and sincere Protestantism at large, and to Deloney in particular, he appeared a 'worthy Prince' whose heart had been 'opened, and his eyes cleared', the type of truth militant against the Antichrist at Rome.

Date. The tract is not entered in the *Stationers' Registers*, but from the date on the title page the translation must have been made in 1583.

Extant Editions. Only one edition exists, and that without doubt the first. The copy in the British Museum from which the present reprint is made is apparently unique.

Source. The text consists of the translation of three documents: [1] The Declaration of Gebhard, January 16, 1583 ; [2] The Letter of Gregory XIII to Gebhard, December 17, 1582 ; [3] The Reply of Gebhard to Gregory.

The declaration of Jan. 16, 1583, is described by Lossen (*Deutsche allgemeine Biographie*) as a repetition and enlargement of the procla-mation of the previous December. The Letter of Gregory XIII to Gebhard, together with Gebhard's reply, (both in Latin) may be found in *Ausschreiben und Gründlicher ... Bericht unser Gebhardt's ... Ertzbischoffs zu Cölln,* &c. (Strasburg? 1583, pp. 56–63), a copy of which is in the British Museum.

PAGE **282**. 36. *83. distinction, the second cannon,* 'nemo quippe in Ecclesia nocet amplius, quam qui perverse agens nomen vel ordinem sanctitatis et sacerdotis habet.'

PAGE **283**. 26. *Vlricus,* Abbas Urspurgensis. See note on p. 286, l. 42.

27. *Bernard* exposed the Ecclesiastical Courts and other abuses of the Church in the *Libri de Consideratione.*

Nicolas of Cues (on the Moselle), created cardinal in 1448, argued (*De Concordantia Catholica*) that the Pope was subordinate to the Oecumenical Council, and attacked Constantine's Donation, urging church reform.

PAGE **284**. 2. 'Quoniam nec tantas de nobis laudes Apostolus protulisset dicendo, Quia fides vestra praedicatur in toto mundo

(Rom. i. 8) nisi iam exinde vigor iste radices fidei de temporibus illis mutuatus fuisset; quarum laudum et gloriae degenerem fuisse maximum crimen est,' *Cleri Romani ad Cyprianum Epistola* xxxi. § 11 (Migne, *P. L.* iv. 316).

15. ' Id itaque esse verum et dominicum, quod prius sit traditum; falsum, quod posterius.' *Lib. de Praescriptionibus*, cap. xxxi. (Migne, *P. L.* ii. 54).

41. *15. distinction of ye third canon.* Probably the *first* canon is meant. ' Sancta Romana ecclesia post illas veteris testamenti et novi scripturas, quas regulariter suscipimus, etiam has suscipi non prohibet, sanctam synodum Nicenam,' &c.

PAGE 285. 13. *the Maister of Sentences* is Peter Lombard, ' quaeritur, utrum sit periurium ubi non est mendacium? quod quibusdam videtur ex auctoritate Hieronymi dicentis " advertendum est quod iusiurandum tres habet comites veritatem iudicium et iustitiam ; si ista defuerint, non erit iuramentum sed periurium",' *Sententiarum. lib.* iv *distinctio* xxxix.

[The reference to Jerome is *Comm. in Hieremiam*, iv. 2 (Vallarsi IV. 864.]

14. Reference untraced.

16. 'In malis promissis rescinde fidem, in turpi voto muta decretum, quod incaute vovisti, ne facias, impia est promissio quae scelere adimpletur', Gratian, *Decreti Secunda pars Causa* xxii. *quaestio* iv. c. 5.

22. 'Non solum in iurando, sed in omni quod agimus, haec est moderatio observanda, ut si in talem forte lapsum versati hostis inciderimus insidiis ex quo sine aliquo peccati contagio surgere non possumus ; illum potius evadendi aditum petamus, in quo minus periculi nos perpessuros esse cernimus,' Ibid., c. 7.

39. *Platinus* in *De Vitis ac Gestis Romanorum Pontificum.*

46. ' Hoc est enim proprium numinum, liberales venias, et concessiones habere gratuitas,' *Arnobii adversus Gentes* Lib. vii, cap. 8. (Migne, *P. L.* v. 1227).

PAGE 286. 19. Γαμητέον οὖν πάντως καὶ τῆς πατρίδος ἕνεκα, καὶ τῆς τῶν παίδων διαδοχῆς, καὶ τῆς τοῦ κόσμου, τὸ ὅσον ἐφ' ἡμῖν, συντελειώσεως, *Clementis Alexandrini Stromatum* Lib. ii, cap. 23 (Migne, *P. G.* viii, 1089).

20. *28. Distinction, Chap. 11*: ' Si se cuiquam mulier duplici coniugio, presbyteri, vel diaconi relicta coniunxerit, aut separentur ; aut certè, si in criminis intentione perstiterint pari excommunicatione plectantur.' *Chap. 12*: ' Si qua vidua episcopi vel presbyteri, aut diaconi maritum acceperit ; nullus clericus, nulla religiosa persona cum ea convivium sumat ; nunquam communicet ; morienti tamen ei sacramentum subveniat.'

27–30. *Paphuntius* = Paphnuntius of Thebais, who opposed the celibacy of the clergy at the Council of Nice. ' Dissuasu Paphnuntii Nicaena Synodus non constituit, quod presbyteri cum suis uxoribus non dormirent. Ei castitatem esse dicens cum propria coniuge concubitum.' *Distinctio* xxxi, c. xii.

31. *Siricius* was Pope 384–398. His *Epist. ad Himerium Episc. Tarraconensem* is the earliest decretal aiming at the celibacy of the clergy.

42–PAGE 287. 10. A letter from Udalricus (Abbas Urspurgensis) to Aeneas Silvius, containing this complaint and the story of the babies' heads, may be found in *Chronica Ekkehardi Urangiensis* (edition 1609, pp. 316–7). It also occurs in Fox's *Acts and Monuments* (1583); vol. i, p. 137.

PAGE 287. 12. 'Cum apud Brixinam Noricam triginta episcoporum conventus necnon et optimatum exercitus, non solum Italiae sed et Germaniae, iussu regis Heinrici congregaretur, factus est omnium consensus adversus Hiltibrandum papam cognominatum Gregorium septimum . . . huius decreti conclusio haec est . . . "qui inter concordes discordiam . . . inter coniuges divortia . . . "'
    Chronica Ekkehardi Urangiensis Pertz, *Monumenta Germaniae Historica* (1844) vi, p. 203 (A. D. 1080).
    Bresse Nove appears to be Brixen in the Tyrol.
PAGE 288. 1. Ὑμέτερον δέ, ὡς αἱρεῖ λόγος, ἀκούοντας, ἀγαθοὺς εὑρίσκεσθαι κριτάς. Ἀναπολόγητον γὰρ λοιπὸν μαθοῦσιν, ἢν μὴ τὰ δίκαια ποιήσητε, ὑπάρξει πρὸς θεόν, *Apologia I. pro Christianis, c.* 3. (Migne, *P. G.* vi. 332).
    16-7. A reference to Plutarch's *Moralia*; *De discernendo adulatore ab amico.*

THE PROCLAMATION AND EDICT OF THE ARCHBYSHOP, AND PRINCE ELECTOR OF CULLEYN.

Date. The tract is entered in the *Stationers' Registers* (1582-3).

DECIMO SEXTO DIE FEBRUARII.

Richard Jones Licensed vnto him vnder thandes of the Bishop of *London* and both the wardens *The Edict of Tharchbishop and elector of Cullen touchinge the bringinge in of the exererce of Christian religion within his Iurisdiction. . . .* vj*d.*
    There are no strong grounds for assigning this tract to Deloney, though Ebbsworth appears to regard it as his (*Dict. Nat. Biography*). The first part of the preceding tract, the declaration of Gebhard, Jan. 16, 1583, appears to be a translation of the same document, though perhaps from a Latin original, while the present translation is from the 'High Dutch'. The previous tract is undoubtedly Deloney's, bearing his name in the dedication, and it is extremely improbable that when he had once translated the proclamation from one version he would translate it again from the 'High Dutch' for another and separate pamphlet. Hence it may be fairly concluded that the present translation is not by Deloney, but its intimate connexion with the preceding document may serve to justify its inclusion.
    Extant Editions. The copy in the Lambeth Palace Library, from which this reprint is made, is apparently unique.

THE GARLAND OF GOOD WILL.

Date. The *Garland of good Will* is first mentioned by Nash in *Haue with You to Saffron Walden*, 1596 (see Introduction, p. xii). But the following entry occurs in the *Stationers' Registers* of 1592-3 :

Vᵗᵒ MARCIJ.

John Wolf
Edward White
the xxvij of
August 1596

Entered for his copie. Vnder the hand of the bishop of *London* and master warden Styrrop; a book intituled *The garden of goodwill.* vj*d.*

There can be little doubt that the clerk wrote '*garden*' in mistake for *garland* and that this is the actual entry of Deloney's *Garland of good Will.* If this is so, it fixes the date of composition as before March 5, 1593. The *Dialogue betweene Truth and Ignorance* and *Holofernes* had been entered separately in 1588, and without doubt a great many of the ballads here included had been in broadside circulation before they were incorporated into the book. To these Deloney added other ballads, probably those of the more distinctive narrative kind, which were needed to bring the volume up to the required size.

Extant Editions. Ebbsworth speaks of 'fragments of a 1604 edition', and J. P. Collier professes to have seen a complete copy. Neither, however, gives any references. The only accessible extant editions appear to be the following :—

[A] 1631. THE GARLAND OF Good Will. Divided into three parts : . . . Imprinted at London for *Robert Bird*, at the Bible in Saint Lawrence Lane 1631. (*Bodleian.*)

[B] 1659. Printed for *J. Wright*; formerly in the possession of J. A. Repton, Esq., Springfield House, Chelmsford. [Dixon.] The Bodleian copy, *Wood* 79. 5. (title page missing), is probably of the same edition and is entitled B in the collations.

[C] 1678. Printed for *F. Wright* at the sign of the Crown on *Ludgate Hill.* (*Bodleian.*)

[D] 1688. Printed by *Fr. Clark* for *George Conyers* ; at the Ring on *Ludgate Hill* 1688. (*Bodleian.*)

[E] circa 1700 (?) Printed for *G. Conyers* in *Little Britain.* (*Bodleian.*)

[F] 1696 (?) Printed by *G. Conyers*, at the Sign of the *Golden-Ring* in *Little Britain.* (*British Museum.*)

[G] 1709 (?) Printed by *G. Conyers* at the sign of the *Golden-Ring* in *Little Britain.* (*British Museum.*)

To all the editions later than that of 1631 new poems have been added by the printer which are certainly not by Deloney. The present reprint is from the edition of 1631, and perhaps even in the present volume the last 3 poems are by another hand (cf. note on 6, *A Farewell to Loue*, p. 378).

I. A MOURNFULL DITTIE, ON THE DEATH OF
ROSAMOND, &c. (Page 297.)

The earliest known copy of this ballad is that added to the 1607 edition of *Strange Histories.* A complete collation with that version will be found at the end of these notes. Other copies exist : *Roxb.* iii. 714 ; *Pepys*, i. 498 ; *Wood*, 401. fol. 7, &c., and in the *Crowne Garland* (1659).

Source. It is difficult to trace the exact source of this ballad. Holinshed gives the following account of Rosamond's death : 'He (i. e. *Henry II*) delited most in the companie of a pleasant damsell, whom he called the Rose of the world (the common people named hir Rosamund) for hir passing beautie, propernesse of person, and pleasant wit, with other amiable qualities, being verelie a rare and peerelesse peece in those daies. He made her an house at Woodstocke in Oxfordshire, like a labyrinth, with such turnings and windings in and out as a knot in a garden called a maze, that no creature might find hir nor come to hir, except he were instructed by the king . . . But the common report of the people is, that the queene in the end found hir out by a silken thread, which the king had drawne after him out of hir chamber with his foot, and dealt with hir in such sharpe and cruell wise, that she liued not long after. She was buried in the nunnerie of Godstow beside Oxford.' (1587, vol. ii. p. 115.) Grafton's account differs very little from that in Holinshed. But the tragedy of Fair Rosamond was also dealt with by three other contemporary poets : (1) By Drayton in the *Heroical Epistles* (1597); (2) By Warner in *Albions England* (1586); (3) By Daniel in the *Complaint of Rosamond* (1592). The knight to whom is confided the custody of the bower appears in both Drayton's and Warner's version, but the likeness between Warner's poem and Deloney's appears too close to be quite accidental. The following extracts from *Albions England*, chap. 41, illustrate the similarity :—

25–36.	Not Sibils caue at Cuma, nor The Labyrinth in Creat, Was like the bower of Rosamond For intricate and great.
	The pellicane theare neasts his bird And sporteth oft with her, Conducted by a clew of thread, Els could he not but err.
	Besides her maydes, a knight of trust Attended on her theare, Who suffred for hir beautie, long Concealing it for feare.
141–8.	That while the knight did issue out, Suspecting no assault, He was assailed, and from him His guiding clew they caught.
	The beautie and the braueness of The person and the place Amazed her, and hers who stoode At gaze a certaine space.
153–6.	Faire Rosamond surprised thus, Eare thus she did suspect, Fell on her humble knees, and did Her fearefull hands erect.
181–4.	Ten thousand times farewell to thee : My God whom I offended, Vouchsafe me mercy ; saying which, Her life she sweetly ended.

117. *pearles of Gold*, i. e. little drops of gold. See *Oxford English Dictionary* under *Pearl*. But the reading of *C D E* may possibly be the correct one.

Collation of the version of ' The Death of Rosamond' *printed in the 1607 edition of* 'Strange Histories' *with the version printed in the* 'Garland of Good Will'. 19 the: our *S.H.* 30 turnings: turning *S. H.* 35 that: his *S. H.* 43 warre: Warres *S. H.* 49 the: my *S. H.* 53 afflicted: affected *S. H.* 71 a: the *S. H.* 89 coast: coastes *S. H.* 119 Galliard: galliards *S. H.* 122 be: bear *S. H.* 129 his: their *S. H.* 138 this: the *S. H.* 143 came: went *S. H.*

145 eyes : eye *S. H.* 149 Cast off thy Robes from thee : Cast off from thee thy Robes *S. H.* 151 thee: thou *S. H.* 153 knee: knees *S. H.* 157 on : of *S. H.* 166 were : was *S. H.*

2. A New Sonnet, conteining the Lamentation of Shores Wife, &c. (Page 302.)

Perhaps this is the ballad entered in the *Stationers' Registers*, June 16, 1593, to John Wolfe, *the abuse of beautye, represented vnder the title of SHORES WIFE.*

It is almost certainly that entered to William White, June 11, 1603. ' *of ye Lamentacon of mistres JANE SHORE,*' and again assigned over to Pavier on Dec. 14, 1624, as ' *Jane Shore* '.

Source. A good deal of information about Jane Shore may be found collected in Percy's introduction to the Pepys Ballad on the same subject, printed in the *Reliques.* The original account of her is contained in Sir Thomas More's *Richard III,* but the Chroniclers appropriated More's description verbatim, and probably Deloney followed Holinshed, who writes : ' This woman was borne in London, worshipfullie friended, honestlie brought vp, and verie well married, sauing somewhat too soone, hir husband an honest citizen . . . of good substance. But forasmuch as they were coupled yer she were well ripe, she not verie feruentlie loued him, for whom she neuer longed, which was happilie the thing that the more easilie made hir incline vnto the kings appetite, when he required hir. Howbeit the respect of his roialtie, the hope of gaie apparell, ease, and other wanton wealth, was able soone to pearse a soft tender heart.' (1587, vol. ii, p. 724.)

31-3. ' Finallie, in manie weightie sutes she stood manie a man in great stead, either for none or verie small rewards.' (Ibid., p. 725.)

40-9. ' The protector spoiled hir of all that euer she had . . . and . . . he caused the bishop of London to put hir to open penance, going before the crosse vpon a sundaie.' (Ibid., p. 724.)

62. *clacke and dish,* the usual stock in trade of the mediaeval and Elizabethan beggar. Cf. *Measure for Measure,* III. ii. 137 : ' Your beggar of fifty ; and his use was, to put a ducat in her clack-dish.'

3. A New Song of King Edgar, &c. (Page 305.)
Another copy in *Percy Folio.*

Source. Probably Grafton's *Chronicle.* ' Edgar, thus ruling the lande, after the death of his first wife, Egelfleda, worde was brought to him of the bewtie of a young Damsell named Elfrida, or Estrild, daughter of Orgarus Erle of Deuonshire : wherefore he sent a knight of his Courte named Ethelwolde, to espie whether the Mayde were of such bewtie, as shee was reported of or not, charging him, if shee were so bewtifull, that then he should aske her to wyfe for him. But this knight hauing sight of this Mayden, was so wounded with the darte of blinde Cupide, that he forgate his truth and allegeance, which he did owe to his Master and souereigne, and returned, shewing to the king, that she was nothing of the bewtie as she was reported to be, but of meane fayrenesse as other women are. Wherefore he besought the king, considering she was her father's Heyre and a good mariage, that he woulde be so good Lorde vnto him, as to write vnto her father, that he might haue her vnto Wyfe. The which the king granted, and at the last he obteyned her and maryed her. In processe of tyme the

fame of this woman sprang so wyde, that at the last it came to the
vnderstanding of king Edgar : wherewith the king notwithstanding, he
were in his mind discontented with Ethelwold, which had so deceyued
him, yet kept he good countenance and made semblance as though he
had nothing forced of that matter at all.   And vpon a tyme, as it were
in game, warned this Ethelwold that then was an Erle by reason of his
wyfe, or otherwise, that he woulde one night come and lodge in his
house, and appointed the tyme when it should be.   The Erle being
nothing contented with this monition, ranne home almost dead for
feare, and prayed his wyfe of helpe in that tyme of neede, and that
shee would in all that she might make herself as foule and as vnseemely
as shee could, and shewed to her all the residue of the matter.   Then
the woman cast in her minde, the great displeasure that might ensue
towardes her against God, to make that foule, which he had made
goodly and fayre, and also to her Lord and husbande against the king,
thinking that he should cause her thus to do, to the entent to mocke
and deceyue him.   Wherefore, in consideration of the premisses, she
trimmed and decked her selfe in most costly and showing apparell.
And ouer that, if Dame Nature had anything forgotten or misprinted
in her, she left not what might be done by womans help to haue it
amended and reformed, and at the kings comming receyued him with all
ioye and gladnesse.   By which meanes, this yong amorous king was soone
caught in the Deuil's snare, so that he set reason aparte and folowed his
awne sensualitie.   And for to bring his purpose the better aboue, he
kept forth a countenaunce as he had bene well contented with all thing,
and desyred the Erle. that he would ryde with him on hunting, into the
wood of Weluerley, that now is called Horsewood, where he awayting
his tyme, strake the Erle, thorow the body with his shaft, so that he
dyed soone after.   And then he maried this Elfrida or Estrild shortly,
and had by her Egelredus.' (1809, pp. 124–5.) But the story also occurs
in Fox's *Acts and Monuments* and in Holinshed's *Chronicle* (1587, vol. i,
p. 160).   Holinshed, however, gives the name of the Duke of Cornwall
as ' Horgerius ' and that of his daughter as ' Alfred '.

4. HOW COVENTRY WAS MADE FREE BY GODIVA, &c. (Page 309.)

Also in *Percy Folio.*

Source. Holinshed does little more than refer to the story (1587,
vol. i, *Historie of England*, p. 193).   Deloney seems to have used
Grafton's account of ' the good Erle Leofricus Erle of Mertia and of
Chester'.   ' This man purchased manye great priuileges for the towne
of Couentrye & made it free from any maner of Tolle, except onely of
Horsse. For the which also to haue free, the common fame telleth,
that after long request made to the king by his wyfe named Godiua he
graunted her to haue it thereof freed, if that she woulde ride naked
thorow the Towne, which she did, by meane whereof it was freed . . .
But (she) also called in secret maner . . . all those that then were
Magistrates and rulers of the sayde Citie of Couentrie . . . requiring of
them for the reuerence of womanhed, that at that day and tyme that
she should ride . . . that streight commaundement should be geuen
throughout all the City, that euerie person should shut in their houses
and Wyndowes, and none so hardy to looke out into the streetes, nor
remayne in the streetes vpon a great paine, so that when the tyme
came of her out ryding none sawe her, but her husbande.' Grafton's
Chronicle (1809), pp. 147–8.

5. HOW THE DUKES DAUGHTER OF CORNWALL BEING MARRIED
UNTO KING LOCRINE, WAS BY HIM PUT AWAY, &C. (Page 311)

Another copy in *Percy Folio.*

Source. The story occurs in Fabian's *Chronicle* (1811, p. 12), but
the source appears to be Grafton's *Chronicle.* ' In the tyme of the
reyne of this Locryne, there was a certeyne Duke (. . . named
Humber) who warred sore vpon Albanactus, . . . and slue Albanact in
plaine battaile . . . after he had thus subdued Albanactus, he helde the
lande of Albania, vntill that Locrinus . . . gathered a great power of
men of Armes together, and went against him, and by strength of the
Britons chased and subdued the sayd Hunes so sharply, that many of
them with theyr king were drowned in a Riuer which departeth
England and Scotland . . . And it so came to passe that after the
aforesayde victory had against the king of the Hunes . . . that Locryne
fell in great phancy and loue with a faire Damosell named Estrild,
who was also the daughter of the aforesayde Humber . . . and Locryne
kept her vnlawfully a certeyne tyme . . . He made a Caue under the
ground in the Citie of Troynouant and enclosed her therein . . . For . . .
he durst not vse her company openly, but . . . priuiely and by stealth
. . . But at length it came so to passe that Estrild was great with
childe and delyuered of a verie faire daughter, whom he named
Habren. At the same season also Gwendolena was brought a bed
of a man child. . . . When, in processe of time Corineus (the D. of
Cornwall) was dead, Locryne put away his wife Gwendolyn, and caused
Estrild to be crowned Quene. The which thing Gwendolyn being
maruellous wroth withall, went into Cornewall, and assembling together
the power of the youth of the country, began to disquiet Locryne and
to warre vpon him. At the length they ioyned battaile and met
together nere a Ryuer called Stoore, where the sayde Locryne was
slaine with an Arow. Then incontinent after his death, Gwendolyn
folowing the raging passions of her father, tooke vpon her the gouernement of this realme, commaunding Estrild with her daughter Habren
to be cast both hedlyng into the riuer Seuerne . . . And further made a
proclamation throughout all the whole realme of Briteyn, that the same
water should be euermore called Habren, after yᵉ Mayden's name, for
so euen at this day is Seuerne called in the Welsh tongue.' Grafton's
Chronicle (1809), vol. i, pp. 28-30.

6. A SONG OF QUEENE ISABEL, &C. (Page 313.)

Also in *Percy Folio.*

Source. Grafton's *Chronicle* (1809), pp. 317-26.
1-30. ' When the Queene . . . perceyued the pride of the Spencers
and howe they preuayled with the king, and had caused him to
put to death the greatest part of the nobles of his realme of Englande,
and also that they bare towarde hir a sower countenaunce, and she
fearing least they should haue put something into the kinges head,
that might haue beene to the perill of her lyfe, was therefore desyrous
to be out of this feare . . . The Queene therefore purposed nowe to flye
the Realme and to go into Fraunce, and therefore did feyne her selfe
that shee would go on pilgrimage to Saint Thomas of Caunterbury,
from whence she tooke hir way to Winchelsey, and in the night entred

into a ship . . . and then hauyng wind at will, they arriued shortly at the hauen of Boleyn in Fraunce . . . But the French king her brother, . . . had sent to meete her dyuers of the greatest Lordes of his realme . . . who honorably did receaue her . . . When the Noble King Charles of Fraunce had heard his sisters lamentation who with teares had expressed her heauie case, he most comfortably spake vnto her and sayd : fayre sister quiet your selfe, for by the fayth I owe to God and Saint Denise, I shall right well prouyde for you some remedy.' (p. 317.) ' And not long after, the sayde Charles . . . assembled together a great number of the greatest Lordes and Barons of his realmes . . . And they concluded, y^t the king might conueniently ayde her with Golde and Syluer. . . . Who (Charles) answered her and sayd . . . Take of my men and subiectes . . . I will cause to be deliuered vnto you, golde, and siluer so muche as shall suffice you.' (p. 318.)

31–6. 'The Frenche king and all his preuie counsaile were as colde and as straunge to help the Queene forwarde to her voyage as though they had neuer talked of the matter. And the French king brake that voyage, and made proclamation, commaundyng all his subiects vpon paine of banishement, that none should be so hardie, as to go with the Queene.' (p. 318.)

37–48. 'When this tidinges was brought to the Queene, she was at her wittes ende, and knew not what to do . . . She and her sonne . . . departed from Paris and rode towarde Henault . . . And Sir John of Henault was certified of the tyme when the Queene came . . . and did to the Queene all the honour and reuerence he could deuise.' (p. 319.)

49–60. 'The Queene who was right sorowfull, declared (complaynyng most piteously) vnto him with wepyng eyes her miserable case, whereof the sayd Sir John had great pitie . . . and sayd, fayre Lady, behold me here your awne knight, who will not fayle to die for you in the quarrell . . . And I and such other as I can desyre, will put our lyues and goods in aduenture for your sake.' (pp. 319–20.)

64–7. 'They . . . tooke shyppyng, and set forward on their passage by Sea . . . A tempest toke them in the sea . . . wherin God wrought mercifully for them.' 'The maryners . . . landed on the sandes . . . nere vnto Harwich.' (p. 321.)

68–150. 'Erle Henry came vnto the Queene with a great company of men of warre. And after him came . . . Erles, Barons, Knights and Esquiers with so many people that they thought themselues out of all perilles. So sone as king Edward had knowledge of the landyng of the Queene his wife . . . and heeryng also how the Barons and Nobles of the realme resorted vnto her . . . beyng then at London, left the sayde Citie vnder the gouernment and order of Maister Walter Stapleton, Bishop of Exeter. The king himselfe accompanyed with the Spencers . . . taketh his way vnto Wales. But when he came to Bristowe, he caused that towne to be fortefyed. But the Bishop vsed such stoute wordes in the kings name, to the Maior and Citizens, who had an euill opinion of him, for bearying with the Spencers, whom the people hated as euill as the Deuill . . . that the sayde Citizens in a rage and fury tooke the sayde Byshop . . . and him . . . beheaded at the standard in Chepe. The maior sente vnto the Queene . . . with promise . . . that the Citie was quiet and at their commaundement. (pp. 322–3.) Then the Queene and all hir companie . . . tooke the right way to Bristowe . . . and besieged the towne round about as nere as they might. When the people of the towne saw that they could haue no peace otherwise, neyther saue the towne, their goodes, nor their lyues . . . they agreed to the Queene, and opened the Gates. Then Sir Hugh Spencer, and the Erle of Arondell was taken and brought before the Queene. Then the sayd knight counsayled with others, that is to say, with the Barons, and Erles and knightes there present, and then he reported their opinions and iudgements. The which was . . . First to be draune and after to be headed, and then their bodyes to be hanged on a Gibbet . . . So was it executed before the Castell gate of Bristow. And after thys execution, the king and the yong Spencer . . . beyng wythout hope of any comfort . . . entred into a little Vessell behinde the Castell, thinking to have fled . . . But whatsoeuer they did, the winde was so contrary with them . . . they were brought againe within a quarter of a myle of the sayde Castell. At the last it happened Sir Henry Beaumond . . . to enter into a Barge . . . . and rowed after this Vessel so long, that the Vessel wherin the king was, could not make any great way before them, but at the last they were ouer taken, & so brought agayne to the Towne of Bristowe, and delyuered to the Queene . . . as prisoners . . . Then the king by the counsayle of all the Barons and knights was sent vnto the strong Castell of Barkeley . . . Then Sir Hugh Spencer the sonne was delyuered to Sir Thomas Wage, Marshall of the hoste . . . the Queen set forward towards London . . . that at the last they came to the City of Harfford. And in all the waye, Sir Thomas Wage had caused Syr Hugh Spencer to be bounde and to be set upon a lewde Iade . . . and he had put vpon him a *Tabarte*, such as Traytors & theeues were wont to weare, and thus he passed thorough the townes with Trumpes and Pipes of Reedes blowen before him. And when the Quene was come to Herfford . . . Sir Hugh Spencer the sonne who was nothing beloued, was brought foorth before the Queene and all the Lordes and knights . . . And so was he then iudged by playne sentence . . . because he had conspired treason and was a false traytor.' (pp. 324–5.)

151–6. 'And when the sayd articles were read and made known to all the Lordes, Nobles, and Commons of the realme . . . they concluded . . . that such a man was not worthie to be a king, nor to weare a croune royall. And therefore they all agreed that Edward his eldest sonne, should be crowned king in steed of his father, so that he would take about him, sage, true and good counsaile.' (pp. 325–6.)

7. A SONG OF THE BANISHMENT OF TWO DUKES, &C. (Page 318.)

Also in *Percy Folio.*

Source. The accounts of the banishment of Hereford and Norfolk given by Grafton and Holinshed are almost exactly the same. ' On a daye beyng in the company of Thomas Mowbry . . . he (*Hereford*) beganne to breake his minde vnto him . . . rehersing how king Richard little esteemed the Nobles of hys Realme. And after . . . he (the Duke of Norfolk) declared to the king . . . what he had heard : and to aggrauate, and to make the offense the greater, he added much thereunto. The king . . . was content to here both parties together, and therefore called vnto him the Duke of Lancaster, who was chiefe of his counsayle, and both the Dukes of Herfford and Norffolke, and caused the accuser openly to declare what he had heard the Duke of Herfford speake. The Duke of Herfford . . . declared worde by worde what he had sayde . . . denyeng all the other matters that the Duke of Norffolk had added thereunto, and sayde further vnto the king, that if it would please hys grace to suffer hym, he would prooue his accuser vntrue, and a false forger of lyes by the stroke of a speare and dent of a sworde . . . He (*the King*) graunted them the battayle, and assyned the place to be at Couentre, in the moneth of August next ensuyng . . . They beyng armed, entred on horsebacke the one after the other into the Listes . . . Now the time beyng come, these two noble men, eche hauyng his speare in rest, and readie to ioyne the battaile, the king cast downe his warder, and commaunded them to stay, and then the king and the Lordes went to counsaile, and they toke vp the matter : And after great deliberation, the king by the mouth of the king of Heraults, pronounced sentence in this sort, first that Henry of Lancaster, Duke of Herfford Appellant, and Thomas Mowbray Duke of Norffolke defendant, haue honorably and valiantly appered here within the listes this day, and haue bene redy to darreyne the battayle, lyke two valiant knightes, and hardie Champions : But because the matter is great and weightie betweene these two great Princes, this is the order of the king and his counsaile. That Henry Duke of Herfford for dyuerse considerations . . . shall within xv dayes depart out of the realme, for the terme of ten yeres, without returnyng . . . and that vpon paine of death. . . . That Thomas Mowbray, Duke of Northffolke . . . because he had sowen sedicion in the realme by his wordes, whereof he can make no proofe, shall aduoyde the realme of England . . . neuer to return againe into the same vpon paine of death . . . And then they called before him the two banished persons, and made them swere, that yͤ one should neuer come into the place where the other was . . . The Duke of Norfolke . . . departed sorowfully out of the realme into Almaine, and at last came to Venice, where for thought he died. The Duke of Herfford . . . toke his iourney, and came to Calice, and so into Fraunce, where he continued a while . . . King Charles . . . receyued him gently and honorably enterteyned him. . . . But while the king was thus occupyed in Irelande, the Duke of Herford by the provocation of Thomas Arondell, Archebishop of Caunterbury, . . . returned nowe into England.' Grafton's *Chronicle* (1809), vol. i, pp. 469–71. Perhaps the beautiful verses put in the mouth of the exiled Norfolk were faintly suggested by Norfolk's farewell to his country in *Richard II*, I. iii. 154–72.

8. THE NOBLE ACTS OF ARTHUR OF THE ROUND TABLE. (Page 323.)

Other copies : *Roxb.* iii. 25 ; *Bagford*, ii. 14–15 ; *Pepys*, ii. 100 ; *Wood*, 401. fol. 62 ; *Percy Folio* ; British Museum, c. 40. m. 10.

This ballad was also entered in the *Stationers' Registers* (1603) :

8 JUNII.

Edward Aldee. The noble Actes now newly found of ARTHURE of the round table.

It was assigned over to Pavier, Wright, and others on Dec. 14, 1624 (*Stationers' Registers*). In *2 Henry IV*, II. iii, Falstaff sings a stave of the ballad ' Whèn Arthur first in court . . . And was a worthy king.'

Source. The ballad is simply a paraphrase of a passage in Malory's *Mort Arthure* (The Booke of Sir Launcelot du Lake). Wright's edition, vol. i, chaps. c–cviii. Chap. c : ' Anon after that the noble and worthy King Arthur was come from Rome into England, all the knights of the Round Table resorted unto the king, and made many justs and tournerments, and some ther were that were good knights, which increased so in armes and worship that they passed all their fellowes in prowisse and noble deedes, and that was well proved on many, but especially it was proved on Sir Launcelot du Lake. . . . Thus Sir Launcelot rested him a long while with play and game ; and then hee thought to prove himselfe in strange adventures.' Chap. cvi : ' And so Sir Launcelot departed, and by adventure came into the same forrest where as he was taken sleeping. And in the middest of an hieway hee met with a damosell riding upon a white palfrey . . . " Fair damosell " said Sir Launcelot " know yee in this countrey any adventures ? " " Sir Knight " said the damosell to Sir Launcelot " here are adventures neere hand, and thou durst prove them ". " Why should I not prove adventures ? " said Sir Launcelot " as for that cause come I hither " " Well " said the damsel " thou seemest well to be a right good knight, and if thou dare meete with a good knight, I shall bring thee where as the best knight is and the mightiest that ever thou found, so that thou wilt tell mee what thy name is, and of what countrey and knight thou art ? " . . . " Truly my name is Sir Launcelot du Lake " . . . " Hereby dwelleth a knight that will not bee overmatched for no man that I know, but ye overmatch him, and his name is Sir Turquine, and as I understond, he hath in his prison of King Arthur's Court good knights threescore and four . . . " And so shee brought him unto the fourd and unto the tree whereon the bason hung. So Sir Launcelot beate on the bason with the end of his spear so hard and with such a might that he made the bottome fall out. . . . Then was hee ware of a great knight that drove an horse afore him, and overthwart the horse lay an armed knight bound. " Now faire knight " said Sir Launcelot " put that wounded knight from thy horse, and let him rest a while, and then let us two prove our strength together. For as it is informed and shewed me, thou doest and hast done great despite and shame unto the knights of the Round Table " . . . " And thou bee of the round table " said Sir Turquine, " I defie thee and all thy fellowship " " That is overmuch said," said Sir Launcelot.' Chap. cvii : ' And then they put their speares in their rests, and came together with their horses as fast as it was possible for them to runne, and either smote other in the middest of their shields, that both their horses backs burst under them, whereof the knights were both astonied, and as soon as they might avoide their horses, they tooke their shields afore them and drew out their swords, and came together eagerly, and either gave other many great strookes . . . And so within a while thay had both grimly wounds and bled passing grievously. . . . At the last they were both brethless, and stood leaning on their swords " Now, fellow " said Sir Turquine " hold thy hand a while and tell me what I shall aske thee." " Say on " said sir Launcelot " Thou art " said Sir Turquine " the biggest man that ever I met withall—and like one knight that I hate above all other knights, and that thou be not he, I will lightly accord with thee, and for thy loue I will deliver all the prisoners that I have." . . . " It is well said " quoth Sir Launcelot ' but sithence it is so that I may have thy friendship, what knight is he that thou so hatest above all other ? " " Truly " said Sir Turquine " his name is Launcelot du Lake, for he slew my brother, . . . therefore him I except of all knights." . . . " Now see I well " said Sir Launcelot, " that such a man I might be I might have peace and such a man I might be there should be betweene us two mortall warre, and now, sir knight, at thy request, I will that thou wit and know that I am Sir Launcelot du Lake, King Ban's son of Benwicke, and knight of the round table. And now I defie thee doe thy best " " Ah " said Sir Turquine " Launcelot thou art unto mee most welcome, as ever was any knight, for we shall never part till the one of us bee dead." And then hurtled they together as two wild bulls, rashing and lashing with their shields and swords . . . Sir Turquine gave Sir Launcelot many wounds that all the ground there as they fought was all besprinkled with blood.' Chap. cviii : ' Then at the last Sir Turquine waxed very faint and gave somewhat backe and bare his shield full low from wearinesse. That soone espied Sir Launcelot and then lept upon him fiersly as a lyon . . . so he plucked him doune on his knees, and anon he rased off his helme, and then he smote his neck asunder.'

110. *rushing* is probably a misprint for *rashing* (as in Malory's account). So also perhaps in l. 120. To *rash* is to smash, or run against violently. The *Oxford English Dictionary* quotes from Douglas's *Aeneis*, xii. 1. 19 : 'raschand the schaft in sundir.'

10. A Song in praise of a single life, &c. (Page 328.)

Probably the text is corrupt. The metre is eccentric even for the balladists.

49. *borrowes*; pledges. The editors of the *Oxford English Dictionary* consider it was archaic by the time of Spenser, and quote from Act 34 & 35 Henry VIII, ' Pledges or borows to pay the kinges fine.'

12. A Gentlewomans Complaint, &c. (Page 332.)

Perhaps that entered in the *Stationers' Registers* to Abell Jeffes on June 27, 1593 : ' *The sadd lamentacon of a Constant yonge gentle-woman.*'

13. Of a prince of England, who wooed the Kings daughter of France, &c. (Page 333.)

Other copies in *Roxb.* i. 102, 103 ; *Percy Folio*; Brit. Museum, c. 40. m. 10 ; *Lord Crawford's Collection* ; *Bagford*, ii. 24.

Under the name of *In the daies of old* this ballad was assigned over to Pavier and others on Dec. 14, 1624. (*Stationers' Registers.*) The text is very corrupt in all copies except the Crawford (about 1660), which has been largely used to correct the present text.

Source. The story seems to be derived from French history and refers to the marriage between Ethelwulf of England and Judith, the daughter of Charles the Bold. Grafton curtly dismisses the event. ' Ethelwolph . . . reigned ouer the Saxons . . . in the yere of our Lord 832 . . . He was maried to Osburga his Butler's daughter, a woman of low birth, but in an old written Chronicle, I find that he was maried to Iudith, daughter of the French king.' *Chronicle* (1809), vol. i, p. 105. The immediate source of Deloney's story appears to be Belleforest's *Histoires tragiques*, Le Quatriesme Tome, Histoire lvii (MDXCI). Belleforest relates how Judith, the daughter of Charles the Bold, and Baldwin the Forester fell in love with each other. Baldwin, however, was forced to proceed to Flanders, and during his absence, Edolph the widower king of England asked for the hand of the princess, and she was sent to him in England. Within six months Edolph died, and as

Judith was crossing the sea on her return to France she was carried off and married by Baldwin.

Deloney took the title of Forester in its original significance, but as Belleforest himself says (p. 120) '. . . ce seroit grand folie de penser qu'és annales Françoises, quand on lit les forestiers de Flandres, que ce fussent gens de basse estoffe, & tels que ceux qu'à present on nomme gardes des forests, ains c'estoyent des seigneurs des plus fauoris, & auancez en la Court de nos Roys.'

167-74. Percy adds the following note on this passage :—

'It will remind the reader of the livery and device of Charles Brandon, a private gentleman who married the Queen Dowager of France, sister of Henry VIII. At a tournament which he held at his wedding, the trappings of his horse were half cloth of gold and half frieze, with the following motto :—

> Cloth of Gold, do not despise,
> Tho' thou art matcht with Cloth of Frize ;
> Cloth of Frize, be not too bold,
> Tho' thou art matcht with Cloth of Gold.'

14. OF THE FAITHFULL FRIENDSHIP THAT LASTED BETWEENE TWO FAITHFULL FRIENDS. (Page 338.)

Other copies : *Roxb.* i. 503 ; *Percy Folio.*

Source. This story appears in *The Decameron* (Giorn. x, Nov. viii). Deloney, however, seems to have taken it from Elyot's *Governor* (1531). See Croft's edition, vol. ii, pp. 133–59. 'There was in the citie of Rome a noble senatour named Fuluius, who sent his sone called Titus, beinge a childe, to the citie of Athenes in Greece (whiche was the fountaine of al maner of doctrine), there to lerne good letters, and caused him to be hosted with a worshipfull man of that citie called Chremes. This Chremes hapned to haue also a sone named Gisippus, who not onely was equall to the said yonge Titus in yeres, but also in stature, proporcion of body, fauour, and colour of visage, countenaunce and speche. The two children were so like, that without moche difficultie it coulde not be discerned of their propre parents which was Titus from Gysippus, or Gysippus from Titus. These two yonge gentilmen, as they seemed to be one in fourme and personage, so, shortely after acquaintaunce, the same nature wrought in their hartes such a mutuall affection, that their willes and appetites daily more and more so confederated them selfes that it semed none other, whan their names were declared, but that they hadde onely chaunged their places . . . (Gysippus) partly by the vnfortunate callynge on of his kynnesmen, partly by the aduise of his dere frende Titus, therto by other desired, . . . assented to mary such one as shulde lyke hym . . . His frendes founde a yong gentilwoman, which . . . they thought was for suche a yonge man apte and conuenient . . . He . . . found her in euery fourme and condicion according to his expectation, and appetite ; wherat he moche reioysed and became of her amorouse, in so moche as many and often tymes he leauinge Titus at his studie secretely repayred vnto her. Nat with standying the feruent loue that he had to his frende Titus, at the last surmounted shamefastnes. Wherfore he disclosed to him his secrete iornayes . . . And on a tyme he, hauynge with hym his frende Titus, went to his lady, of whom he was receyued moste ioyously. But Titus furthwith, as he behelde so heuenly a personage adourned with beautie inexplicable . . . had the harte through perced with the firy darte of blinde Cupide . . . All be it with incredible paynes he kepte his thoughtes secret, vntyll that he and Gysippus were retouned vnto their lodynges. Then the miserable Titus . . . all turmented and oppressed with loue, threwe hym selfe on a bedde . . . And there with he sent out from the botome of his harte depe and cold sighes, in suche plentie that it lacked but litle that his harte ne was riuen in peces . . . But at the last the payne became so intollerable, that wolde he or no, he was inforced to kepe his bedde . . . Gysippus . . . harteley desired him . . . he wolde no longer hyde from him his griefe . . . Titus . . . broughte furthe with great difficultie his wordes in this wyse. . . Gysippus, I saye your trust, is the cause that I am entrapped ; the rayes or beames issuinge from the eyen of her whom ye haue chosen . . . hath thrilled throughout the middes of my hart . . . But Gysippus . . . answered in this wyse . . . Here I renounce to you clerely all my title and interest that I nowe haue or mought haue in that faire mayden . . . Take hede, this is myne aduise ; ye knowe well that we two be so like, that, beinge a parte and in one apparayle, fewe then do knowe us . . . Therfore I my selfe will be present with my frendes and perfourme all the partes of a bride . . . And ye shall abyde in a place secrete . . . vntill it be nyght. And then shall ye quickly conuaye your selfe in to the maidens chambre. The daye of the maryage was commen . . . Than (as it was before agreed) Titus conueyed him selfe, after Gysippus retourned to his house . . . The morowe is comen. And Gysippus, thinking it to be expedient that the trouth shulde be discouered, assembled all the nobilitie of the citie at his owne house . . . Titus with his lady is departed towardes the citie of Rome . . . But nowe let vs resorte to Gysippus, who . . . was so maligned at, as well by his owne kynesmen as by the frendes of the lady . . . that they spared nat daily to vexe hym . . . Finally they adiudged him vnworthy to enioye any possessions or goodes lefte to him by his parentes . . . Wherfore they dispoyled hym of all thinges, and almoste naked expelled him out of the citie. Thus is Gysippus . . . banisshed his owne countraye for euer, and as a man dismayed wandringe hither and thither, fyndeth no man that wolde socour him. At the last, (he) . . . concluded that he wolde go to Rome, and declare his infortune to his said frende Titus . . . In conclusion . . . he is commen to the citie of Rome and diligently enquirynge for the house of Titus, at the laste he came to hit, but beholdinge it so beauteous, large, and princely, he was a shamed to approche nigh to it, beinge in so simple a state and unkladde; but standeth by, that in case that Titus came forthe out of his house he mought than present hym selfe to hym. He beinge in this thought Titus . . . issued out from his doore, and . . . behelde Gysippus ; but beholdyng his vile apparayle regarded him nat . . . Wherwith Gysippus was so wounded to the harte, thinkyng that Titus had condemed his fortune, that . . . he furthwith departed, entendinge nat to abide any lenger, but as a wilde beste to wandre abrode in the worlde. But for werynesse he was constrayned to entre into an olde berne, without the citie, where he . . . with wepinge and dolorous cryenge bewayld his fortune . . . And therwith drewe his knyfe, purposinge to haue slayne him selfe. And . . . fatigate with longe iornayes and watche . . . he felle in to a deade sleepe . . . In the meane tyme a commun and notable rufian or thefe, whiche had robbed and slayne a man, was entred in to the barne . . . And seinge Gysippus bewept, and his visage replenisshed with sorowe, and also the naked knife by him . . . the said rufian takinge for a good occasion to escape, toke the knife of Gysippus, and puttinge it in the wounde of him that was slayne, put it all bloody in the hande of Gysippus, beinge faste a slepe, and so departed. Sonne after the dedde man beinge founde, the offycers made diligent serche for the murderar . . . and fynding Gysippus a slepe, with a blody knife in his hand, they a waked him . . . He denied nothing that was laide to his charge, desiringe the officers to make haste that he mought be shortly out of his lyfe . . . Anone reporte came to the senate that a man was slayne, and that a stranger . . . was founden in such fourme as is before mencioned. They forth with commaunded hym to be brought vnto their presence . . . Titus beinge then Consull . . . and espienge by a litle signe in his visage, whiche he knewe, that it was his dere frende, Gysippus . . . rose out of his place, and . . . sayde that he had slayne the man . . . But Gysippus . . . more importunately cried to the senate to procede in their iugement on him that was the very offender . . . There hapned to be in the prease at that tyme, he which in dede was the merdrer, who perceyuinge the meruaylous contention of these two persones, . . . and that it proceeded of an incomparable frendshippe . . . was vehemently prouoked to discouer the trouthe. Wherfore he brake through the prease, and comminge before the senate he spake in this wyse . . . I am that persone that slewe hym that is founden dedde by the barne. Here at all the Senate and people toke comfort, and the noyse of reioysing hartes filled all the court . . . wherfore the Senate consulted of this mater, and finally . . . discharged the felon. Titus . . . hauinge Gysippus home to his house . . . he was honourable apparailed . . . Titus . . . assembled a great armye and went with Gysippus vnto Athenes. Where he . . . dyd on them sharpe execution, and restorynge to Gysippus his landes and substaunce, stablyshed him in perpetuall quietnes.'

THE SECOND PART

2. OF PATIENT GRISSEL AND A NOBLE MARQUESSE. (Page 346.)

Other copies : *Roxb.* i. 302 ; British Museum, c. 40, m. 10 ; *Pepys*, i. 34 ; *Percy Folio.*

Source. The original source is of course the *Decameron* (Giorn. x, Nov. x), and the story was well known to the Elizabethans in Chaucer's version (*The Clerk's Tale*). From the entries in the *Stationers' Registers* for 1565-6 it is evident there were earlier ballads on the same subject.'

'R^d of Owyn Rogers, for his lycence for pryntinge of a ballett intituled the sounge of pacyente Gressell unto hyr make . . . iij

R^d of Wylliam greffeth, for his lycence for pryntinge of ij ballettes to the tune of pacyente Gressell . . . . iij'

Chapple thinks the original ballad dates from before 1557, when the *Stationers' Registers* begin, in which case Deloney may have been merely remodelling an older version. (See also Appendix I.)

35. *staining.* Cf. p. 84, l. 20, and note.

119. *Bisse.* Apparently either dark grey, or short for ' blew-bis ', which was a dull ultramarine (*Oxford English Dictionary*).

Pal. 'A kind of fine cloth, of which cloaks and mantles of state were formerly made.' Nares.

3. A PLEASANT DIALOGUE BETWEENE PLAINE TRUTH, AND BLIND IGNORANCE. (Page 351.)

Another copy in the *Percy Folio.*

Entered in the *Stationers' Registers*, March 23, 1587–8, to Sampson Clerk ' *a proper newe ballad dyaloguewyse betwene Syncerytie and* WILFULL IGNORANCE.' The model for this ballad in dialogue appears to be Luke Shepherd's *Interlude* of JOHN BON *and* MASTER PARSON (1548). The argument and conclusion is much the same in each case. Percy says, ' The scene we may suppose to be Glastonbury Abbey,' but it is more likely that if Deloney had any particular place in his mind it was the ruin of St. Bartholomew's Chapel at Newbury. In Michaelmas Term, 1576, the Queen's Attorney-General filed information against Philip Kestell for intruding upon the chantry lands, and questions were put to six clothiers of Newbury on the desolation and destruction of the Chapel without the king's command (see Money's *History of Newbury*, pp. 216–24). Perhaps Deloney was living in the town at the time of the inquest.

9. *vazonne.* Plural of dialect form of ' faith ' (?).
27. *Of new learning*, i. e. of *the* new learning.
29. *Law*, in the old meaning of religion. Cf. Chaucer's *Man of Lawes Tale*, 375–6 :

> She rydeth to the sowdan on a day,
> And seyde him, that she wolde reneye hir *lay*.'

35–40. Jeremiah, vii. 18.
80. *zacring bell.* The sacring bell was rung at the elevation of the Host, and hence,

> A number great of Sacring Belles with pleasant sound doe ring
> On Corpus Christi day.
> Google's *Popish Kingdom* (Brand, vol. i, p. 236).

81–4. Cf. *Paradiso*, Cant. xix :

> A questo regno
> non salì mai chi non credette in Cristo,
> nè pria, nè poi ch'ei si chiavasse al legno.

105. *our Lady of Walsingham.* Cf. p. 365, l. 2.
111. Elizabeth Barton, the ' holy maid of Kent' who prophesied against the divorce of Henry VIII, was executed on May 5, 1534. Deloney's attitude towards her and Becket is that of the Reformers, who shifted right divine from the Papacy to the Monarchy.

4. THE OVERTHROW OF PROUD HOLOFORNES, &C. (Page 355.)

This is probably the ballad entered with the preceding one to Sampson Clerk on March 23, 1587–8 :
' Another Ballade intytuled *the moste famous historye of* JUDITH *and* OLOFERNES.'
Source. The story is of course taken from the book of Judith, and

adjoined excerpts are from the *Geneva Bible* of 1560. Curiously enough, when Elizabeth visited Norwich, Aug. 16, 1578, a pageant was presented before her in which Judith appeared and spoke the following lines :

> If this his grace were given to me, poor wight,
> If a widows hand could vanquish such a foe,
> Then to a prince of thy surpassing might,
> What tyrant lives but thou maist overthrow.

Blomefield's *Hist. of Norwich*, Part I, p. 329.

Cf. also the note on p. 43, l. 42.

Chap. ii, vv. 4–6 : ' Nabuchodonosor ... called Olofernes ... and said vnto him ... Thus saith the great King, the Lord of the whole earth, ... thou shalt go against all the West countrey, becduse they disobeied my commandement.'

Chap. iii, v. 8 : ' that all nacions shulde woshippe Nabuchodonosor onely, and that all tongues and tribes shulde call vpon him as God.'

Chap. iv, v. 5 : 'And (*they*) toke all the toppes of the hie mountaines, and walled the villages that were in them, and put in vitailes for the prouision of warre.'

Chap. v, v. 1 : ' Then was it declared to Olofernes . . . that the children of Israel had prepared for warre.'

Chap. vi, vv. 1–3 : ' Olofernes, the chief captaine ... said ... who is god but Nabuchodonosor, He wil send his power, and wil destroye them from the face of the earth, and their God shal not deliuer them.'

Chap. vii, vv. 1, 2 : ' Olofernes commanded all his armie and all his people, ... that thei shulde remoue their campes against Bethulia ... and the armie of the men of warre was an hundreth thousand and seuentie fotemen, & twelue thousand horsemen.' v. 17 : 'and they pitched in the valley, & toke the waters, and the fountaines of the waters of the children of Israel.' v. 22 : ' Therefore their children swoned, and their wiues & yong men failed for thirst.' v. 23 : ' Then all the people assembled to Ozias, & to the chief of the citie ... and cryed with a loude voyce.' v. 27 : 'it is better for vs to be made a spoile vnto them, than to dye for thirst.' vv. 30–1 : ' Then said Ozias to them, Brethren, be of good courage ; let vs waite yet fiue daies, in the which space the Lord our God may turne his mercie toward vs.... And if these daies passe, and there come not helpe vnto vs, I wil do according to your worde.'

Chap. viii, vv. 1 and 2 : ' Now at that time, Iudeth heard thereof ... And Manasses was her housband, ...' v. 7 : ' She was also of a goodlie countenance & very beautiful to beholde.' vv. 11 and 12 : ' And they came vnto her, and she said vnto them ... who are you that haue tempted God this day ... ? ' vv. 33–5 : ' You shal stand this night in the gate, and I will go forthe with mine handmaid : ... But inquire not you of mine acte : ... Then said Ozias & the princes vnto her, Go in peace ...'

Chap. x, vv. 3–5 : ' And putting away the sackecloth wherewith she was clad ... she ... dressed the heere of her head, and put attire vpon it, and put on the garments of gladnes And she ... put on bracelets and sleues, and rings and earings, & all her ornaments, and she decked her selfe brauely to allure the eyes of all men that shuld se her Then she gaue her maide a bottel of wine, and a pot of oyle, and filled a scrippe with floure, & with dry figges ...' vv. 10–14 : ' Iudeth went out, she and her maide with her ... and the first watche of the Assyrians met her And toke her, and asked her Of what people art thou ? and whence comest thou ? and whither goest thou ? And she said, I am a woman of the Hebrewes, and am fled from them And I come before Olofernes, the chief captaine of your armie ... Now when the men heard her wordes, & behelde her countenance, they wondered greatly at her beautie, ...' vv. 17-18 : ' Then they chose out of them an hundreth men, and prepared a charet for her and her maide and broghte her to the tent of Olofernes Then there was a running to and fro throughout the campe ...' vv. 22-3 : ' He came forthe vnto the entrie of his tent, and they caried lampes of siluer before him ... they all marueiled at the beautie of her countenance, and she fel doune vpon her face, and did reuerence vnto him, & his seruants take her vp.'

Chap. xi, v. 1 : ' Then said Olofernes vnto her Woman, be of good comfort :' v. 3 : ' But now tel me wherefore thou hast fled from them, & art come vnto vs.' v. 20 : ' Then her wordes pleased Olofernes, and all his seruants, and they marueiled at her wisdome.'

Chap. xii, v. 2 : ' But Iudeth said I may not eat ... lest there shulde be an offence, but I can suffice my selfe with the things that I haue broght.' vv. 6-7 : ' And (she) sent to Olofernes, saying, Let my lord commande that thy handmaide may go forthe vnto prayer. Then Olofernes commanded his garde that thei shuld not stay her :' vv. 10-11 : ' And in the fourth day, Olofernes made a feast Then said he to Bajoas the eunuche who had charge ouer all that he had, Go and persuade this Hebrewe woman, ... that she come vnto vs.' vv. 13-16 : ' Then went Bajoas ... & came to her, & said, Let not this faire maide make difficultie to go in to my lord. Then said Iudeth vnto him, Who am I now, that I shulde gainesay my lord ? ... & her maide went & spred for her skinnes on the ground ouer against Olofernes Now when Iudeth came & sate doune, Olofernes heart was rauished with her ...' vv. 19, 20 : ' Then she toke, & ate & dranke before him the things, that her maide had prepared. And Olofernes reioyced because of her & dranke muche more wine then he had drunken at anie time in one day since he was borne.'

Chap. xiii, vv. 1, 2 : ' Now when the euening was come, his seruants made haste to departe, and Bajoas shut his tent without, & dismissed those that were present. And Iudeth was left alone in the tent, & Olofernes was stretched along vpon his bed ; for he was filled with wine.' vv. 6-11 : ' Then she came to the post of ye bed which was at Olofernes head, & toke doune his fauchin from thence ... and said, strengthen me, ô Lord God of Israel ... And she smote twise vpon his necke ... and she toke away his head from him, ... and pulled down the canopie from the pillers ... & gaue Olofernes head to her maid, ... so they twaine went together according to their custome vnto prayer, and pressing through the tentes ... went vp the mountaine of Bethulia, and came to the gates thereof Then said Iudeth ... open now the gate : God, euen our God is with vs to shewe his power yet in Ierusalem, and his force against his enemies ...' v. 15 : ' Beholde the head of Olofernes.'

Chap. xiv, vv. 11-13 : ' Assone as the morning arose thei hanged the head of Olofernes out at the wall, & euerie man toke his weapons, and they went forthe by bandes ... But when the Assyrians sawe them, they sent to their captains ... So they came to Olofernes tent ...' v. 15 : ' he (Bajoas) founde him cast vpon the floore, and his head was taken from him.'

Chap. xv, vv. 1, 2 : ' And when thei that were in the tents, heard, they were astonished ; ... altogether amased, thei fled by euerie way.'

5. A PRINCELY DITTY, IN PRAISE OF THE ENGLISH ROSE.
(Page 362.)

Apparently referred to in Fletcher's *Monsieur Thomas*, III. iii, where a fiddler quotes *The Rose of England* as one of his ballads. There seems no reason to believe it is 'translated out of French '.

THE THIRD PART

1. A MAIDENS CHOICE TWIXT AGE AND YOUTH. (Page 363.)

Probably that entered in the *Stationers' Registers*, Aug. 26, 1591, to *John Danter*, 'A pleasant *newe ballad Called the Maydens choyce.*' The first stanza of this poem appears in the *Passionate Pilgrime*, printed for W. Jaggard, 1599, and attributed to Shakespeare. There can be little doubt that Jaggard was merely reprinting scraps of poetry he had gathered from all sources, and dignified his collection with the name of Shakespeare (then at the height of his fame) in order to promote its sale. The first lines of a street ballad would be peculiarly liable to appropriation of this sort. Probably Jaggard's version came to him orally and hence it differs somewhat from that in the *Garland*, and is here reprinted :

> Crabbed age and youth cannot liue together,
>   Youth is full of pleasance, Age is full of care,
> Youth like summer morne, Age like winter weather,
> Youth like summer braue, Age like winter bare.
> Youth is full of sport, Ages breath is short,
> Youth is nimble, Age is lame
> Youth is hot and bold, Age is weake and cold,
> Youth is wild, and Age is tame.
>   Age I doe abhor thee, Youth I doe adore thee,
>   O my loue my loue is young :
>   Age I doe defie thee, oh sweet Shepheard hie thee :
>   For methinks thou staies too long.

2. [WALSINGHAM.] (Page 365.)

Another but inferior copy in *Percy Folio.*

This ballad resembles that of *Flodden Field* (p. 25) and the *Maidens Song* (p. 33) in *Iacke of Newberie* in so far that it is very difficult to decide how far it is traditional and how far it is the work of Deloney. It is scarcely probable that a strong Protestant like Deloney would begin a ballad with reference to the 'holy land' of a Catholic shrine ; it is quite likely however that he would sink his religious opinions when an easy opportunity of turning a ballad presented itself in the expansion of some traditional verses. Hence I am inclined to believe that the opening stanza is more or less traditional, but the rest of the poem seems of individual composition, and is therefore probably Deloney's. Walsingham in Norfolk was famous in the Middle Ages for its image of the Virgin Mary, and Langland shortly describes the character of its votaries.

Hermites on an heep . with hoked staves
Wenten to Walsyngham . and here wenches after. (i. 52.)

The tradition of the Walsingham pilgrimage survived through the Elizabethan age. Thus Nash refers to 'gangs of good fellows that hurtled and hustled thither, as it had been to the shrine of Saint Thomas a Beckett or our Ladie of Wolsingham' (*Lenten Stuff*, edit. M⁰Kerrow, p. 162). The great pilgrim routes were exactly the places where traditional songs would flourish for the amusement of wayfarers, who, like the Canterbury Pilgrims, found

comfort ne mirthe is noon
To ryde by the weye doumb as a stoon :

Skeat (*Piers Plowman*, ii. 9) quotes from the Examination of William Thorpe in Fox's *Acts and Monuments*, ' I know wel that when divers men and women will goe thus, after their owne wils and finding out, on pilgrimage, they will ordaine with them before, to have with them both men and women, that can well sing wanton songs.'

It is very probable that at one time a large variety of Walsingham ballads existed. Shakespeare seems to quote from one of them in *Hamlet*, IV. v. 23–6 :

How should I your true love know
From another one ?
By his cockle hat and staff,
And his sandal shoon.

The *Percy Folio* contains another :

Gentle heardsman, tell to me,
Of curtesy I thee pray,
Unto the towne of Walsingham
Which is the right & ready way ?

A variant of Deloney's version appears in Fletcher's *Knight of the Burning Pestle*, II. Sc. ult.:

As you came from Walsingham
From the Holy Land,
There met you my true love,
By the way as you came ?

Similarly, in the *Match at Midnight*, Randalls, a Welshman, parodies the poem :

Did hur not see hur true loves,
As hur came from London ?

3. THE WINNING OF CALES. (Page 367.)

Another copy in *Percy Folio*.

The subject of this ballad is the taking of Cadiz on June 21, 1596, by Lord Howard, the Earl of Essex, and many of the details are substantiated by the account given in Stow's *Annales*. (1615.)

51–60. 'Some resoluted to flie to Porto Reall, some to burne their Ships, some ran their ships a ground; diuers Spanyards lept into the water, whereof some swamme ashoare, some were drowned, some taken, some slaine.' (p. 773.)

70–7. 'When the lorde Admirall came into the town, hee found the Earle of Essex skirmishing and fighting with the Spanyardes, who fought and stil fled before him.' (Ibid.)

85–6. 'And now proclamation was made that no Englishemen should offer violence to any religious person, to any woman or childe, or any other of the Spanish nation in Cadiz.' (Ibid., p. 774.)

90–134. 'The conditions whereupon the Corrigidor & the rest of the chiefe of the Towne yeilded were these: they should haue their liues saued, & onely their wearing clothes permitted them: all the rest of their goods and wealth should be spoyle and pillage to the Souldeers.' From the graphic detail and the use of the first person in this ballad, it may be hazarded that Deloney himself may have taken part in the Spanish expedition, which perhaps also gave him the material for *The Spanish Ladies Loue* (p. 375).

4. Of King Edward the third, and the faire Countesse of Salisbury, &c. (Page 370.)

Another copy in *Percy Folio.*

Source. This story seems to have appeared for the first time in Froissart's *Chronicle* (i, chaps. 77–89). Other versions exist in Painter's *Palace of Pleasure* (Tale 46), in Bandello's *Novelle* (Parte I, Nov. 29), and in the *Chronicles* of Grafton and Holinshed. But Deloney probably drew at first hand from the play of ' *The Rayne of King Edward the third: As it hath bin sundrie times plaied about the Citie of London,*' which was entered in the *Stationers' Registers* on Dec. 1, 1595. The following excerpts from the play afford some striking parallels with the ballad:

1–18. Cf. Act I, Sc. i.

Enter Mountagne.

Mount. Barwicke is woon; Newcastle spoyld and lost, l.128. And now the tyrant hath beguirt with seege The Castle of Rocksborough, where inclosd The Countess Salisbury is like to perish. *King.* That is thy daughter, Warwicke, is it not? Whose husband hath in Brittayne serud so long?

40–1. Cf. Act I, Sc. ii.

King. Lady, stand up; I come to bring thee peace, l. 113. Howeuer therby I haue purchast war.

47–100. Cf. Act II, Sc. i.

Countess. Sorry I am to see my liege so sad: l. 194. What may thy subiect do to driue from thee Thy gloomy consort, sullome melancholie?

. . . .

King. Since I came hither, Countes, I am wronged. l. 199. *Count.* Now God forbid than anie in my howse Should thincke my soueraigne wrong! Thrice gentle king Acquaint me with your cause of discontent. *King.* How neer then shall I be to remedie. *Count.* As nere, my Liege, as all my woman's power Can pawne it selfe to buy thy remedy.

King. If thou speakst true, then haue I my redresse :
Ingage thy power to redeeme my Ioyes,
And I am ioyfull, Countes ; els I die.
    Count. I will, my Liege.
    King. Sweare, Countes, that thou wilt.
    Count. By heauen, I will.   l. 210.
    King. Then take thy selfe a litel waie a side,
And tell thy self, a king doth dote on thee :
Say that within thy power (it) doth lie
To make him happy, and that thou hast sworne
To giue him all the Ioy within thy power :
Do this, and tell me when I shall be happie.
    Count. All this is done, my thrice dread souereigne :
That power of loue, that I haue power to giue,
Thou hast with all deuout obedience ;
Imploy me how thou wilt in profe therof.   l. 220.
    King. Thou hearest me saye that I do dote on thee.
    Count. Yf on my beauty, take yt if thou canst.

  .   .   .   .

O, were it painted, I would wipe it of   l. 229.
And dispossesse my selfe, to giue it thee.

  .   .   .   .

    King. Didst thou not swere to giue me what I would ? l. 243.
    Count. I did, my liege, so what you would I could.
    King. I wish no more of thee then thou maist give :

  .   .   .   .

That is, thy loue ; and for that loue of thine   l. 247.
In rich exchaunge I tender to thee myne.

  .   .   .   .

    Count. That loue you offer me you cannot giue   l. 251.
For Caesar owes that tribut to his Queene ;

  .   .   .   .

I know, my souereigne, in my husbands loue,   l. 271.
Who now doth loyal seruice in his warrs,
Doth but so try the wife of Salisbury,
Whether shee will heare a wantons tale or no,
Lest being therein giulty by my stay,
From that, not from my leige, I tourne awaie——

  .   .   .   .

Enter WARWICKE.

    King. Here comes hir father : I will worke with him. l. 293.

  .   .   .   .

    Warwick. How is it that my souereigne is so sad ? l. 295.

The king in the play now proceeds to trap Warwick in the same way as he had trapped the countess. This device is not repeated in the ballad.

125–8. *War.* I am not Warwike as thou thinkest I am, l. 380.
But an atturnie from the Court of hell,

  .   .   .   .

To do a message to thee from the king.   l. 383.
The mighty king of England dotes on thee !

  .   .   .   .

129-40. *War.* Ile say, it is true charitie to loue,   l. 361.
But not true loue to be so charitable;
Ile say his greatnes may beare out the shame,
But not his kingdome can buy out the sinne;
Ile say, it is my duety to perswade
But not her honestie to giue consent

. . . .

   Count. No, let me die, if his too boystrous will   l. 427.
Will haue it so, before I will consent
To be an actor in his gracelesse lust.
   War. Why, now thou speakst as I would haue thee speake :
And marke how I vnsaie my words againe.
An honourable graue is more esteemd
Then the polluted closet of a king !

. . . .

So leaue I with my blessing in thy bosome,
Which then conuert to a most heauie curse,   l. 445.
When thou conuertest from honors golden name
To the blacke faction of bed blotting shame.

157-82. Act II, Sc. ii.

   Count. My father on his blessing hath commanded—— l. 124.
   King. That thou shalt yeeld to me ?
   Count. I, deare my liege, your due.

. . . .

But . . .
I bynd my discontent to my content,   l. 135.
And what I would not Ile compel I will,
Prouided that your selfe remoue those lets
That stand betweene your highnes loue and mine.
   King. Name them, faire Countesse, and, by heauen I will.
   Count. It is their liues that stand betweene our loue,   l. 140.
That I would haue chokt vp, my soueraigne.
   King. Whose liues, my Lady?
   Count.   My thrice louing liege,
Your Queene and Salisbury.

. . . .

Here by my side doth hang my wedding knifes;   l. 173.
Take thou the one, and with it kill thy Queene,
And learne by me to finde her where she lies;
And with this other Ile dispatch my loue,
Which now lies fast a sleepe within my hart.

. . . .

And if thou stir, I strike ; therefore, stand-still   l. 182.
And heare the choyce that I will put thee to :
Either sweare to leaue thy most vnholie sute
And neuer hence forth to solicit me ;
Or else, by heauen, this sharpe poynted knyfe
Shall staine thy earthe with that which thou would staine,
My poore chast blood.
   King. Euen by that power I sweare, that giues me now
The power to be ashamed of my selfe,
I neuer meane to part my lips againe
In any words that tends to such a sute.

The text of the ballad is defective and might perhaps be justly emended.

53. (*she said*) is probably a misprint for (said she).

5. THE SPANISH LADIES LOUE, &C. (Page 375).

Other copies: *Rox.* ii. 406 ; *Bagford*, i. 48, ii. 36 ; *Pepys*, iii. 148, &c ; *Wood*, E 25. fol. 11 ; *Percy*, &c.

Entered to Wᵐ White, in the *Stationers' Registers*, June 11, 1603, and assigned over on Dec. 14, 1624, to Pavier, Wright, and others. The hero was apparently one of Essex's comrades in the Cadiz expedition of 1576. It scarcely seems profitable to discuss his historical existence as Sir Richard Levison, Sir John Popham, or Sir John Bolle. A full account of the various traditions may be found in the Ballad Society's reprint of the *Roxburghe Ballads*.

62. *Prest* (cf. p. 384, l. 38), is used in the sense of *ready*. Dixon quotes from the old version of Ps. civ : ' Lightnings to serve we see also prest.'

63-4. English wives were counted proverbially fortunate, and reasons are given by Emanuel von Meteren : ' Their time they employ in walking and riding, in playing at cards or otherwise, in visiting their friends and keeping company, conversing with their equals (whom they term gossips) and their neighbours, and making merry with them at childbirths, christenings and funerals ; and all this with the permission and knowledge of their husbands, as such is the custom. . . . This is why England is called the Paradise of married women.' Besant's *Tudor London*, pp. 269-70.

6. A FAREWELL TO LOUE. (Page 378.)

This and the two following poems are in quite a different style from the rest of Deloney's known poetry. The *Farewell to Loue* also occurs in William Byrd's *Medius* (1588), no. 25, with the omission of the last verse. It may be that Deloney himself appropriated these poems from other sources for his own collection, but more probably they were added by the printer to an earlier edition to bring the volume up to the required size. On the other hand there is just the possibility that they are really Deloney's work, and that the change of style is solely due to an effort to reach a different audience.

The text of the *Farewell to Loue* in the *Garland*, is somewhat defective. The following is the version in Byrd's *Medius* :

> Farewell false loue, the oracle of lyes,
> A mortall foe, and enemie to rest :
> An enuious boye, from whome all cares aryse,
> A bastard vile, a beast with rage possest :
> A way of error, a temple full of treason,
> In all effects contrarie vnto reason.
>
> A poysoned serpent couered all with flowers,
> Mother of sighes, and murtherer of repose,
> A sea of sorows, from whence are drawen such showers,
> As moysture lend to euerie griefe that growes,
> A schole of guile, a net of deepe deceit,
> A guilded hooke, that holds a poysoned bayte.

A fortresse foyld, which reason did defend,
A syren song, a feuer of the minde,
A maze wherein affection finds no ende,
A ranging cloud that runnes before the winde,
A substance like the Shadow of the Sunne,
A goale of griefe for which the wisest runne.

A quenchlesse fire, a nurse of trembling feare,
A path that leads to perill and mishap,
A true retreat of sorrow and dispayre,
An idle boy that sleepes in pleasures lap,
A deep mistrust of that which certain seemes,
A hope of that which reason doubtfull deemes.

FINIS.

STRANGE HISTORIES.

Date. There is no evidence as to when this little collection of poems was printed. Probably, however, unlike *The Garland of Good Will*, none of the ballads had been circulated before, as they consist entirely of metrical versions of selected episodes from the English Chronicles, arranged in chronological order, in such a way as to suggest that they were designed to form a complete little volume.

Extant Editions.

[A] STRANGE HISTORIES, Of Kings, Princes, Dukes, Earles, Lords, Ladies, Knights, and Gentlemen. . . . London, Printed by William Barley, the assigne of I. M. and are to be sold at his shop in Gracious streete, 1602. (*Britwell.*)

The Dutchesse of Suffolkes Calamitie inserted after *Cant. II* in this edition has been obviously added to the original matter of an earlier edition, and hence it is not separately enumerated in *the Table.*

[B] 1607. STRANGE HISTORIES *or Songes and Sonets, of Kinges, Princes, Dukes, Lordes, Ladyes, Knights and Gentlemen* . . . *Imprinted at* London *for* W. Barley. (*Bridgewater House.*)

[C] 1670 ? . . . Imperfect, wanting title page and end. (*Bodleian.*)

[D] 1674. *The Royal Garland of Love and Delight . . . by T. D.* LONDON, *printed by E. C. for E. T.* (*British Museum.*)

This is the original *Strange Histories*, with other miscellaneous poems added, chiefly of a Restoration character.

The edition of 1607 inserts *Salomon's Good Huswyfe* immediately after Canto 1. and adds a number of miscellaneous poems after the prose *Speech betweene Certaine Ladyes*. *Salomon's Good Huswyfe* is added to *The Table* of contents, but the other poems are unindexed as though they were added haphazard by the printer as an afterthought. Most of these are subscribed respectively with the initials T. R., A. C., and R., and with the exception of *The Death of Faire Rosamond* it is quite evident that Deloney's authentic work does not extend beyond the prose which closes the 1602 edition. But the addition of *Faire Rosamond* gives us the earliest known copy of this ballad, and the version in *The Garland of Good Will* (1631) has accordingly been collated with it in the notes on that poem.

The present reprint is from the edition of 1602.

Cant. I. *The valiant courage and policie of the Kentish-men, &c.* (Page 383.)

Source. The story is given in Holinshed's *Chronicle*.

'After his (*William's*) coronation . . . vpon obteining of the citie of London, he tooke his iourney toward the castell of Douer, to sub-due that and the rest of Kent also; which when the Archbishop Stigand and Egelsin the Abbat of St. Augustines . . . did perceiue . . . they caused all the people of the countie of Kent to assemble at Canterburie, and declared to them the perils and dangers imminent, the miserie that their neighbours were come vnto, the pride and insolencie of the Normans, and the hardnesse and griefe of bondage and seruile estate. Whereupon all the people rather choosing to end their vnfortunate life, then to submit themselues to an vnaccustomed yoke of seruitude and bondage, with a common consent determined to meet duke William, and to fight with him for the lawes of their coun-trie. Also the foresaid Stigand the Archbishop, and the Abbat Egel-sin, choosing rather to die in battell, than to see their nation in so euill an estate . . . became capteins of the armie. And at a daie appointed, all the people met at Swanescombe, and being hidden in the woods, laie priuelie in wait for the comming of the foresaid duke William. . . .

'They agreed beforehand, euerie one of them, as well horsemen as footmen should beare boughs in their hands . . . When the duke was come vnto the field and territories neere vnto Swanescombe and saw all the countrie set and placed about him, as it had beene a stirring and moouing wood . . . with great discomfort of mind he wondered at that sight. And assoone as the capteins of the Kentishmen sawe that duke William was inclosed in the middest of their armie, they caused their trumpets to be sounded, their banners to be displaied, and threw downe their boughes, and with their bowes bent, their swords drawne, and their speares and other kind of weapons stretched foorth, they shewed themselues readie to fight. Duke William and they that were with him stood (as no maruell it was) sore astonied and amazed: so that he which thought he had alreadie all England fast in his fist, did now despaire of his owne life. . . .'

'Thereupon the Kentishmen sent to Duke William and asked that all the people of Kent enioy for euer their ancient liberties, and may for euermore vse the lawes and customes of the countrie. . . .'

'The Duke willingly agreed and thus the ancient liberties of Eng-land, and the lawes and customes of the countrie, . . . remaine inuioablie obserued vntill this daie within that countie of Kent.' Holinshed, 1587 edition, vol. ii, pp. 1–2.

PAGE 383 (heading). *Kentishmen with long tayles.* The origin of this saying is difficult. Du Cange says that *caudati* was originally applied to all Englishmen. An explanation is suggested in Bale's *English Votaryes* (first edition, p. 30) : ' For castynge of fyshe tayles atthys Augustyne, Dorsett Shyre men had tales euer after. But Polydorus applyeth yt vnto Kentysh men at Stroude by Rochestre, for cuttynge of Thomas Beckettes horses tayle.'

5–8. ' He (*William*) was crowned King vpon Christmas daie following, by Aldred archbishop of Yorke.' Holinshed's *Chronicle* (1587), vol. ii, p. 1.

17–20. Cf. p. 105, ll. 29–32, and note.

38. See p. 377, l. 62, and note.

Cant. II. *How King* HENRY *the first had his children drowned,* &*c.* (Page 386.)

Another copy in *Percy Folio.*

Source. Apparently Holinshed's *Chronicle.*

'Henrie, hauing quieted his businesse in France, returned vnto England, where he was receiued and welcomed home with great ioy and triumph. . . . This pleasantnesse and mirth was changed into mourning by aduertisement giuen of the death of the king's sons, W^m duke of Normandie, and Richard his brother, who togither with their sister the ladie Marie countesse of Perch, Richard Earle of Chester, with his brother Otwell gouernor to duke William, . . . and diuerse others . . . tooke ship at Harfleur . . . Their ship thorough negligence of the mariners (who had drunke out their wits and reason) were throwne vpon a rocke, and vtterly perished on the coast of England, vpon the 25 of Nouember, so that of all the companie none escaped but one butcher . . . Duke William might also haue escaped . . . for being gotten into the ship boat, and lanching toward the land, he heard the skreeking of his sister in dredful danger of drowning, crieng out for succour; whereupon he commanded them that rowed the boat to turne back to the ship, and to take hir in. But such was the prease of the companie that stroue to leape in with hir, that it streightwaies sanke, so that all those wh' were alreadie in the boat were cast awaie . . . King Henrie being thus depriued of issue to succeed him, did not a little lament that vnfortunate chance.' Holinshed, 1587 edition, vol. ii, p. 41.

The Dutchesse of Suffolkes Calamitie. (Page 389.)

Other copies. *Roxb. Coll.* i. 94–5 : *Pepys,* i. 544 ; *Crowne Garland of Golden Roses* (1659) ; *Lord Crawford's Collection.*

This ballad was assigned to Pavier, Wright, and others, December 14, 1624 (*Stationers' Registers*).

Source. The story of the Duchess of Suffolk's flight to Germany is given in Holinshed's *Chronicle* (1587, vol. ii, pp. 1143–5), 'ex Joh: Foxi Martyrologio', and Deloney might have used this account or drawn directly from the *Acts and Monuments.* In any case he confuses the order of the incidents and ekes the account out by his own invention or by some garbled traditional version. Fox does not mention the nurse, or the Duchess's begging for alms, and makes the highway robbery occur *after* the Duke and Duchess had left the town instead of *before* they reached it, as in Deloney's version. The quarrel with the Sexton, and the part played by the Governor in the poem appear also to be invention.

19–24. 'The fifteenth daie of March (1554) . . . the ladie Elizabeth . . . was apprehended . . . on the Sundaie after . . . she was committed to the tower.' Holinshed, 1587 edition, vol. ii, p. 1107.

25–30. 'The Duchess and her Husband, dailie more and more by their friends vnderstanding that the bishop (i. e. Gardiner) meant to call hir to an account of hir Faith . . . deuised waies . . . how they might passe the seas.'

35. 'She tooke with hir hir daughter, an infant of one yeare.'

37–42. 'He (*Master Berty*) passed the Seas at Douer . . . leauing the duchesse behind, who by agreement and consent betwixt hir and hir husband, followed taking Barge at Lion Keie.' Ibid., p. 1143.

49–54. Fox says the winds were contrary, but 'so soone as the duchesse had landed in Brabant, she and hir women were apparelled like the women of Netherland with hukes ; and so she and hir husband tooke their iournie toward Cleveland '.

57. 'The Lantgraves capteines . . . set vpon them in the highwaie with his horssemen.'

73–4. 'There fell a mightie rain of continuance, whereby a long frost and ise before congealed, was thawed.'

79–84. 'In the mene time master Berty was forced to carrie the child, and the duches his cloke and rapier.'

89–96. 'At last . . . they came to Wesell, and repairing to their innes for lodging . . . found hard interteinment : for going from inne to inne offering large monie for small lodging, they were refused of all the inholders . . . The child for cold and sustenance cried pittifullie.'

105–44. Fox tells the story differently: 'Master Bertie . . . going towards the church porch, he heard two striplings talking Latine . . . By these boies . . . he chanced at the first vpon the house where Master Perusell supped that night, who had procured them the protection of the magistrates of that towne.' Ibid., p. 1144.

150. 'The dútchesse invited to Poleland by the kings letters.' Gloss., Ibid., p. 1145. Casimir IV of Poland reigned 1447–1492.

152–3. So Holinshed (vol. ii, p. 1348). 'Peregrine Bartie, Lord Willobie.'

157–62. 'In the earledome of the said King of the Poles . . . continued both in great quietnesse and honor, till the death of Queene Marie. Whose troublesome time . . . being expired, and the peaceable reigne of gratious queene Elizabeth established the said dutchesse and hir husband returned vnto England.' Ibid., p. 1145.

From the metre and general sense of the first three verses it is evident that Deloney has in mind *The Register* (*of the Martyrs*), written by Brice in 1559. Cf., for example, the opening verses of the *Register* :

> When raging reign of tyrants stout
> Causeless, did cruelly conspire
> To rend and root the Simple out
> With furious force of sword and fire ;
> When man and wife were put to death :
> We wished for *our Elizabeth.*
>
> When *Rogers* ruefully was burnt ;
> When *Saunders* did the like sustain ;
> When faithful *Farrar* forth was sent
> His life to lose, with grievous pain ;
> When constant *Hooper* died the death :
> We wished for *our Elizabeth.*
>
> When *Rowland Taylor,* that Divine,
> At Hadley left this loathsome light ;
> When simple *Lawrence* they did pine
> With *Hunter, Higby, Pigot* and *Knight* ;
> When *Causun,* constantly, died the death :
> We wished for *our Elizabeth.*
>
> Pollard's *Tudor Tracts,* p. 270.

20. *danger.* See p. 274, l. 40, and note.
41. *Grauesend Barge.* See p. 146, l. 41, and note.

Cant. III. *How King* HENRY *the second, crowning his Sonne king of* ENGLAND, *in his owne lifetime, was by him most grieuously vexed with warres &c.* (Page 394.)

Source. Apparently Holinshed's *Chronicle.*

9–32. ' He (*Henry*) called togither a parlement of the lords both spiritual and temporal . . . and . . . proclaimed his said sonne Henrie fellow with him in the kingdome . . . Vpon the daie of coronation, the king Henrie the father serued his sonne at the table as sewer wherupon . . . the young man conceiuing a pride in his heart, beheld the standers-by with a more statly countenance than he had been wont.' Holinshed, 1587 edition, vol. ii, p. 76.

49–72. ' Now perceiuing himselfe in danger of death . . . he sent to his father . . . confessing his trespasse committed against him, and required of all fatherlie loue to come and see him once before he died. But for that the father thought not good to commit himself into the hands of such vngratious persons as were about his sonne, he sent his ring vnto him in token of his blessing and as it were a pledge to signifie that he had forgiuen him his vnnatural doings against him. The son receiuing it with great humilitie, kissed it . . .' Ibid., pp. 106–7.

73–108. ' After this, he caused his fine clothes to be taken from him, and therewith a heaue cloth to be put vpon him, and after tieng a cord about his necke, he said vnto the bishops and other that stood by him I deliuer myselfe an vnworthie and greeuous sinner vnto you the ministers of God by this cord, beseeching the Lord Jesus Christ, which pardoned the theefe . . . that through your praiers . . . it may please him to be mercifull vnto my soule . . . Draw me out of bed with this cord, and laie me on that bed strawed with ashes . . . and as he commanded so they did . . .'

110. ' King Henrie commanded that the corps of his sonne . . . should be deliuered vnto them at Rouen . . . and so it was taken vp and conueied to Rouen where it was eftsoones buried.' Ibid., p. 107.

Cant. IIII. *The imprisonment of Queene* ELENOR, *&c.* (Page 397.)

Source. The historical groundwork is probably taken from Holinshed's *Chronicle.* Cf. ll. 31–2 and ll. 53–66 with the following :

' At length king Richard remembring himselfe of his mother queene Elianor, who had beene separated from the bed of hir husband for the space of sixteene yeares and was as yet deteined in prison in England, wrote his letters vnto the rulers of the realme, commanding them to set hir againe at libertie, and withall appointed hir by his letters patent, to take vpon hir the whole gouernment of the kingdome in his absence . . . but speciallie remembring by hir late experience and tast thereof what an irksome and most greeuous thing imprisonment was, she caused the gailes to be opened, and foorth with set no small number of prisoners at libertie.' Holinshed, 1587 edition, vol. ii, p. 117.

43. *Rosamond.* Cf. Deloney's ballad on p. 297.

Cant. V. *The lamentable death of King* JOHN, *&c.* (Page 399).

Source. The story is given in Holinshed's *Chronicle* (1587 edition, vol. ii, p. 194), but the direct source is probably Fox's *Acts and Monuments.* The spirit and language of Fox's account resembles that of Deloney's poem. Fox, however, gives two stories : (1) how John was given poison in wine : (2) how he was poisoned by means of pears. From the second story Deloney takes the detail of the sweating precious stones.

13–20. 'The monke . . . went secretly into a garden . . . and finding there a most venemous Toad, he so pricked hym, and pressed him with his penknife : that he made him vomit all the poyson that was wythin hym. This done, he conueyed it into a cuppe of wine, and with a smiling and flattering countenance, he sayde thus to the King : If it shall like your Princely maiestie, here is such a cuppe of wine as you neuer dronke a better before in all your life time. I trust this wassal shal make al England glad. And with that he dranke a great draught thereof, the King pledging him.' *Acts and Monuments* (1583), vol. i, p. 256.

21–32. 'In *Gisburn*, I finde otherwise, who dissenting from other, sayeth : that he was poysoned with a dish of Peares . . . At the bringing in whereof, saith the said story, the pretious stones about the king began to swete. Insomuch that the king misdoubting some poyson, demanded of the monke, what he had brought. He said : of his frute, and that very good.' Ibid., p. 257.

41–52. 'The Monke anone after went to the farmerye, and there died (his guts gushing out of his belly). I would ye did marke well the wholesome proceedings of these holy votaries, how vertuously they obey their kings, whome God hath appoynted . . . The king within a short space after (feeling great griefe in his body) asked for Symon the monke : and aunswere was made, that he was departed this life.'

69–76. 'His hired souldiours both English-men and strangers were still about him, and folowed his corpes triumphantly in their armour, till they came to the Cathedrall Church of worcester, and there honourably was he buried.' Ibid., p. 256.

5. *oppose.* The word was properly used of the mediaeval disputations. Here I suppose used in the affirmative sense.

12. *shadowed.* Cf. p. 86, l. 14, and note thereon.

Cant. VI. *Of the Imprisonment of King* EDWARD *the second.*

(Page 402.)

Source. Holinshed's *Chronicle.*

21–70. 'It was concluded and fullie agreed by all the states . . . that for diuerse articles which were put vp against the King, he was not worthie longer to reigne, and withall they willed to haue his sonne Edward duke of Aquitaine to reigne in his place . . . But the duke of Aquitaine, when he perceiued that his mother tooke the matter heauilie in appearance, for that hir husband should be thus depriued of the crowne, he protested that he would neuer take it on him, without his fathers consent, and so there vpon it was concluded that certeine solemne messengers should go to Killing worth to moue the King to make resignation of his crowne and title of the kingdome vnto his sonne . . . They (*the messengers*) sought to frame his mind, so as he might be contented to resigne the crowne to his sonne, bearing him in hand, that if he refused so to doo, the people in respect of the euill will which they had conceiued against him, would not faile but proceed to the election of some other that should happilie not touch him in linage. . . . Notwithstanding his outward countenance discouered how much it inwardlie grieued him ; yet after he was come to him selfe, he answered that he knew that he was fallen vnto this miserie through his owne offenses, and therefore he was contented patientlie to suffer it

. . . he gaue the lords most heartie thanks, that they had so forgotten their receiued injuries.' Holinshed, 1587 edition, vol. ii, pp. 340–1.

71–90. ' Diuerse of the nobilitie (of whome the earle of Kent was cheefe) began to deuise means by secret conference had togither, how they might restore him to libertie, discommending greatlie both queene Isabell, and such other as were appointed gouernours to the yong king, for his fathers streict imprisonment . . . And hereupon the queene and the bishop of Hereford wrote sharpe letters vnto his Keepers, blaming them greatlie for that they dealt so gentlie with him . . . and withall the bishop of Hereford vnder a sophisticall forme of words signified to them by his letters, that they should dispatch him out of the waie, the tenor whereof wrapped in obscuritie ran thus :

> Edwardum occidere nolite timere bonum est.
> To kill Edward will not to feare it is good.'   Ibid., p. 341.

Cant. VII. *Of King* Edward *the second, being poysoned.* (Page 405.)

Source. Holinshed's *Chronicle.*

' They lodged the miserable prisoner in a chamber ouer a foule filthie dungeon, full of dead carrion, trusting so to make an end of him, with the abominable stinch thereof : but he bearing it out stronglie, as a man of tough nature, continued still in life, so as it seemed he was verie like to escape that danger, as he had by purging either vp or downe, auoided the force of such poison as had been ministred to him sundrie times before, of purpose to rid him.

' Whereupon when they sawe that such practises would not serue their turne, they came suddenlie one night into the chamber where he laie in bed fast asleepe, and with heauie feather beds or a table (as some write) being cast vpon him, they kept him down and withall put into his fundament an horne, and through the same they thrust vp into his bodie an hot spit, or (as others haue) through the pipe of a trumpet a plumbers instrument of iron made verie hot, the which, passing vp into his entrailes, and being rolled to and fro, burnt the same, but so as no appearance of any wound or hurt outwardlie might be once perceiued. His crie did mooue manie within the castell and towne of Berkeley to compassion, plainelie hearing him vtter a waileful noise, as the tormentors were about to murther him, so, that diuerse being awakened therewith (as they themselues confessed) praied heartilie to God to receiue his soul, when they vnderstood by his crie what the matter ment.' Holinshed, 1587 edition, vol. ii, p. 341.

Cant. VIII. *Of the Lord* MATREUERS *and Sir* THOMAS GURNEY, &c. (Page 408.)

Source. Holinshed's *Chronicle.*

' The queene, the bishop, and others that their tyrannie might be hid, outlawed and banished the Lord Matreuers and Thomas Gurney, who flieng vnto Marcels, three yeares after being knowne, taken and brought toward England was beheaded on the sea, least he should accuse the chiefe dooers, as the Bishop and other. John Matreuers, repenting himselfe, laie long hidden in Germanie, and in the end died penitentlie.' Holinshed, 1587 edition, vol. ii, pp. 341–2.

11. Cf. p. 404, ll. 89–90, and Note on Source of Cant. vi.

Cant. IX. *Of the winning of the Yle of* MAN &c. (Page 411.)

Source. Probably derived from the entry in Holinshed for the year 1344.

'This yeare also, W. Montacute, Earle of Salisburie conquered the Ile of Man, out of the hands of the Scots, which Ile the king gaue vnto the said earle, and caused him to be intituled, and crowned king of Man . . .'

'Moreouer about the beginning of this eighteenth yeare of his reigne, king Edward . . . deuised the order of the garter.' Holinshed, 1587 edition, vol. ii, p. 366.

Cant. X. *How* WAT TILER *and* IACKE STRAW *rebelled against king* RICHARD *the second.* (Page 413.)

Source. Holinshed's *Chronicle* (1587), pp. 429–32.

1–10. Holinshed names Iacke Strawe, Wat Tiler, Iacke Shephearde, Tom Milner, and Hob Carter, as the leaders. (1587 edition, vol. ii, p. 429.)

12–13. 'Their number still increased, so that when the Essex men, and other of the hithir side the Thames, were passed ouer and ioined with the Kentishmen, those that were assembled on that side the riuer vpon Blackheath ; they were esteemed to be an hundred thousand.'

15. 'They had the messengers returne, and declare to the king that there was no remedie but he must needs come and speake with them.'

19–24. 'After the commons vnderstood that the king would not come to them . . . they were maruellouslie moued. . . . They spoiled the borough of Southwarke, brake vp the prisons of the Marshalsea, and the kings bench, set the prisoners at libertie.'

27–32. 'The duke of Lancaster . . . they hated aboue all other persons. And hereupon agreeing in one mind, after diuerse others of their owtragious doings, they ran the same day to the said duke's house of the Sauoie . . . which . . . they set on fire. . . .'

33–40. 'They went to the temple and burnt the men of lawes lodgings, with their bookes, writings and all that they might lay hand vpon. Also the house of Saint Iohns by Smithfield they set on fire, so that it burned for the space of seuen daies together. . . .'

41–50. 'The third companie kept vpon the tower hill . . . where the king at that time was lodged, and was put in such feare by those rude people, that he suffered them to enter into the tower, where they sought so narowlie for the lord chancelor, that finding him in the chappell, they drew him foorth togither with the lord treasuror, and on the tower hill without reuerence of their estates and degrees, with great noise and fell cries, they stroke off their heads.'

51–4. 'Neither had they any regard to sacred places, for breaking into the Church of the Augustine friers, they drew foorth thirteene Flemings, and beheaded them. . . .'

55–64. 'They also brake vp the prisons of newgate, and of both the Counters, destroied the books, and set prisoners at libertie. . . .'

67–70. 'Finallie, when they had eased their stomachs, with the spoiling, burning and defacing of sundrie places, they became more quiet, and the king . . . offered to them pardon, and his peace, with condition that they should cease from burning and ruinating of houses, from killing and murthering of men, and depart euerie man to his home. . . . Hereupon . . . Wat Tiler . . . said, that peace indeed he wished, but yet so as the conditions might be indited to his purpose. . . .'

75–90. 'And when he (*Wat Tyler*) was come neere to the place in Smithfield where the king then was, . . . sir Iohn Newton was sent to him againe, to vnderstand what he meant And bicause the knight came to him on horssebacke and did not alight from his horsse, Wat Tiler was offended . . . and forthwith made towards the knight to run vpon him. . . . The maior of London William Walworth . . . foorthwith rode to him and arrested him, in reaching him such a blow on the head, that he sore astonied him therewith : and streightwaies other that were about the king . . . thrust him through in diuerse parts of his bodie.'

A Speeche betweene certaine Ladies &c. (Page 415.)

Source. Holinshed's *Chronicle*, as before, but Deloney finishes the account by a conversation put into the mouth of 'Ladies, being shepheards on *Salisburie* plaine'—presumably in the reign of Henry VII since the 'speeche' ends with references to the Cornish Rebellion of 1497.

PAGE **416**. 5–11. 'The king . . . for some part of recompense of their faithful assistance in that dangerous season, made the said William Walworth knight, with fiue other aldermen. . . . Moreouer the king granted that there should be a dagger added to the armes of the citie of London, in the right quarter of the shield, for an augmentation of the same armes.' Holinshed, 1587 edition, vol. ii, p. 436.

18–24. 'I haue thought good to declare the confession of Iacke Strawe . . . when he came to be executed in London.'

'We would haue killed the king and all men of possessions, with bishops, monks, chanons and parsons of churches . . . Moreouer . . . we were determined . . . to haue set fire in foure corners of the citie, and so to haue diuided amongst vs the spoil of the cheefist riches.' Ibid., p. 438.

28. *desperate Traytors*, i.e. the Cornish rebels of 1497.

30–2. 'From Welles they went to Salisburie and from thence to Winchester, and so to Kent. . . .'

37–8. 'The capteines of the rebels . . . brought their people to Blackeheath. . . . Without long fighting, the Cornishmen were ouercome.'

38–44. 'The Lord Audeleie was drawne from Newgate to the Tower Hill in a coate of his owne armes, painted vpon paper reuersed and all to torne and there was beheaded the foure and twentith of June. Thomas Flammocke and Michael Joseph were hanged, drawne and quartered after the maner of traitors.' Holinshed, 1587 edition, vol. ii, p. 782.

CANAANS CALAMITIE.

Note on Authorship. This poem has been usually attributed to Thomas Dekker (e. g. by Hazlitt and Grosart) merely on account of the initials T. D. which appear on the title page. These might equally well represent Thomas Deloney, and the dedication affords convincing proof that Deloney and not Dekker is the real author.

Canaans Calamitie is dedicated to ' *M. Richard Kingsmill* Esquier, Iustice of peace and Quorum in the Countie of Southampton, and Surveyer of her Maiesties Courtes of Wardes and Liueries . . .' and also of the 'pleasant Lordship of *Highcleere*' (p. 418). The Kingsmills were an old county family connected with both Berkshire and Hampshire. Richard Kingsmill, 'the second son of Sir John Kingsmill of Sidmonton was of High Cleere, co. Southampton; and was attorney of the Court of Wards to Queen Elizabeth' (*Notes and Queries*, Series III, vol. i, p. 37). Now Deloney's *Iacke of Newberie* shows clearly that the author had an acquaintance with Newbury so close as only to have been gained by actual residence there, and Highclere is only six miles south of that town. (Introduction, pp. xi–xii.) To make the connexion more certain there occurs in *Iacke of Newberie* (p. 33, l. 12) an unexplained reference to Will Summers ' breaking his face in Master Kingsmill's seller'. This is almost certainly a reference to some family tradition of the Kingsmills, which Deloney had probably learnt from local gossip, but which has not come down to us in the pages of contemporary chroniclers.

In some way or other Richard Kingsmill had extended protection or friendship to certain of Deloney's friends, and Deloney's most marked characteristic is his bold and fervent Protestantism. Now the Kingsmill family in the time of Queen Elizabeth were closely connected with the Puritan movement, and Andrew, the brother of the Richard Kingsmill of the Dedication, was a Puritan divine of some celebrity. In *A Most Excellent and Comfortable Treatise*, &c., published in 1577, Andrew Kingsmill alludes to the 'family vnion of the household of Sidmountaine' and urges his sister 'to consider therefore the goodnes of God, howe he hath prouided for vs by the gentlenes of our deere Mother, a place which we vse as an home and habitation, and that no Foxe hole, but thankes bee to God a warme and wel feathered nest where we haue free egresse and regresse. . . . Thankes be vnto our heauenly Father', he goes on, 'who hath ioyned our house in such an vnity, that we do not . . . one disdaine the other in necessities and aduersities, neither enuie ech other in things succeeding prosperously' (1585, p. 11–12). Kingsmill's graceful and pathetic little book shows us the united Puritan sentiment of his family, and it seems likely that Richard Kingsmill had earned Deloney's gratitude by protecting some too fervent Protestants (perhaps artisans or refugees) against the rigour of Elizabeth's ecclesiastical policy. Fox, in the *Acts and Monuments*, shows that in the earlier part of the sixteenth century Newbury was the centre of 'a glorious and sweet society of faithful favourers', and Sir Richard Abridges, Sir William Rainsford, and John Winchcomb sat at the examination of Julius Palmer for heresy in that town in 1556. (1870, vol. viii, pp. 214–9.) Hence probably there was mutual respect between the Protestant town and the neighbouring Protestant gentleman. (Cf. also Note on Source of *Gentle Craft, II*, pp. 532–3.)

The reference 'to the Princely *Pertian*' who 'will more respect the good will than the gift' (p. 418, l. 19) may be compared with that in *Iacke of Newberie*; 'each childe . . . gaue vnto his Maiesty a sweete smelling Gilliflower, after the manner of the Persians, offering something in token of loyalty and obedience' (p. 37, ll. 35–8).

Cf. also 'To the Gentlemen Readers, health' (p. 419), with the Introduction to the *Gentle Craft* (*II*), 'To the Courteous Readers, health' (p. 140).

Date. The poem is probably that entered in the *Stationers' Registers* in 1597–8.

V^{to} JANUARII.

THOMAS PURFOOTE *Senior*	Entred for their Copie vnder the hand of master warden MAN/ *The Destruction of Jerusalem*
THOMAS PURFOOTE *Junior*	*by TYTUS, sonne of VESPATIAN*, in *English meter* . . . . vj^d

'A Ballet called *A Warning to all England by the Dolefull Destruction of Ierusalem, &c*' was entered to Symon Stafford on October 11, 1604. It is reasonable to suppose it was founded on the present poem, and may have been written by Deloney himself.

Source. The source is of course Josephus, *de Bello Iudaico*.

Josephus was a most popular writer with the Elizabethans but apparently the earliest English translation extant is that of Lodge (1602). The *Stationers' Registers*, however, show that '*The boke of Iosephus*' was licensed to R. Jugge in 1557-8, and another translation '*Iosephus of the Warres of the Iewes*' was licensed Oct. 12, 1591. Deloney might have used either of these versions or gone straight to the Latin. In any case the poem follows the original account with some closeness.

Extant Editions.

[A] 1618 Canaans Calamitie Ierusalems Misery, or The dolefull destruction of faire Ierusalem. . . . At London, Printed for *Thomas Bayly*, . . . neere adioyning vnto *Staple Inne.* 1618. (*British Museum.*)
[B] 1640 . . . London. Printed by *Tho: Badger*, 1640. (*Bodleian.*)
[C] 1677 . . . Printed by *Tho: James* for *Edward Thomas* at the *Adam* and *Eve* in *Little Brittain* 1677. (*British Museum.*)
The present reprint is from the edition of 1618.

Notes.

43. Mark xiii. 14-24.
262. Cast by bill, 'added up on paper.'
618. *Vilde.* Malone showed this to be a true Elizabethan variety of *vile.* Cf. l. 749 and p. 465, l. 13.

MISCELLANEOUS BALLADS.

A PROPER NEWE SONET DECLARING THE LAMENTATION OF BECKLES, &C. (Page 457.)

This ballad is entered in the *Stationers' Registers.*

' 13 DECEMBRIS 1586.

Nicholas Colman Receaued of him for printinge a ballad of the *Lamentacon of Beckles a market towne in Suffolk, on Sainct Andrewes Day laste paste beinge burnt with fier to the number of lxxx houses and* loss of xx ᵐˡⁱ' (i. e. £20,000). iiijᵈ
Reprinted from the *Huth Collection*, which contains another ballad on the same subject. The fire took place on the 29th of November previous. (Suckling's *Antiquities of Suffolk*, vol. i, p. 12.)

A MOST JOYFULL SONGE . . . AT THE TAKING OF THE LATE TRAYTEROUS CONSPIRATORS, &C. (Page 460.)

From the unique copy in the Library of the Society of Antiquaries. This ballad, like that following, is practically a contemporary document upon Babington's Conspiracy, probably printed a day or two after the execution. Deloney might very well have been a witness of the scene he describes and, in any case, his ballad affords interesting evidence of the extreme Protestant view in London at the time of the conspirators' execution. A ballad, from the very nature of its audience, had to be more or less popular in tone, and probably Deloney is only expressing contemporary feeling in his own thorough Protestant way. See also the note on the following ballad.

33-4. A reference to Eccles. x. 20 : 'Curse not the king, no not in thy thought ; and curse not the rich in thy bedchamber : for a bird of the air shall carry the voice, and that which hath wings shall tell the matter.'

50. *Paris streets.* A reference to St. Bartholomew.

83. *merely make,* actually make. The *Oxford English Dictionary* quotes from Harrington's *Metamorphosis of Ajax,* 'As I say merely in the book, the 118 page.'

A PROPER NEW BALLAD BREEFELY DECLARING THE DEATH AND EXECUTION OF FOURTEEN MOST WICKED TRAITORS, &c.
(Page 464.)

From Collier's *Blackletter Broadsides.* Another copy in the Earl of Crawford's Library.

A long, unpleasant description of the execution will be found in Holinshed's *Chronicle* (1587), vol. ii, pp. 1573-5, with which Deloney's account is in strict accordance.

'On the first daie (Sept: 20) the traitors were placed vpon the scaffold, that the one might behold the rewarde of his fellowes treason. Ballard the preest . . . was the first that was hanged. . . .

Next vnto this preest, Anthonie Babington was made readie to the gallows, who in euerie point was handled like vnto Ballard. . . .

Next vnto Babington, Sauage was likewise prepared for the execution. . . .

When Sauage was executed, Barnewell was made readie to die, an obstinate papist, who for his treason made conscience his best excuse ; howbeit a rotten conscience, which was infected with the murther of a vertuous queene ; . . .

After this Barnewell, Tichborns turne was serued, a proper yoong gentleman, whose humilitie and mone mooued much compassion. . . .

Tilneie one of the queens maiesties pensioners, next vnto Tichborne, made worke for the hangman. . . .

The last of these seuen that suffered was Edward Abington . . .

On the daie following (according to generall expectation) being the one and twentith daie of September, Salisburie was laid alone upon an hurdell, and other six, two and two in like manner, all drawne from Tower hill through the citie of London, vnto the former place of execution. Salisburie was the first man that suffered. . . .

After Salisburie . . . Dun was stripped vnto his shirt . . . who after that he had . . . disuaded the Romanists from attempting anie matter of violence, he was executed with exceeding fauour.

When the execution of Dun was finished, the next in that tragedie was Jones . . . then Charnocke was executed, and after him Trauers, both two Men . . . bewitched with an ignorant deuotion ; for that in their ends nothing was to be obserued but their praieng to our ladie, calling upon saints, ioined with a number of ceremonies, crossings, and blessings, &c.

When the hangman had giuen these two his heauie blessing, Gage prepared himselfe to die, who began his protestation, . . . he fell to excuse him selfe of the odious treasons for which he was to die.

The last that suffered was one of the Bellamies.'

71-3. Cf. the gloss. in Holinshed, p. 1573 : 'A note of Babington's pride at the verie instant of execution.'

A JOYFUL NEW BALLAD, DECLARING THE HAPPIE OBTAINING OF THE GREAT *GALLEAZO.* (Page 468.)

The ballad was entered in the *Stationers' Register,* on August 10, 1588 : 'JOHN WOLF Receaued of him for printinge a ballad of *the obteynenge of the Galleazo wherein Don* PEDRO DE VALDEZ *was chief.*

Reprinted from the unique copy in the British Museum.

The taking of Pedro de Valdez' galleon on the 21st of July is thus described in the *Annalls of Elizabeth* (Camden), 1625 : ' A huge great *Catalonian* ship of *Ogenda*, was set on fire with Gunpowder, by the deuice of a Flemmish Gunner.   But the fire was seasonably quenched by other Shippes sent in for the purpose ; amongst which a *Gallion* of *Peter Valdes*, falling foule with another Ship, and her fore-mast intangled and broken with the others sayle-yard, the Ayre being stormy and the night darke, and none able to relieue or succour her, was forsaken and became a prey to *Sir Francis Drake*, who sent *Valdes* to *Dertmouth*, and gaue the ship to bee rifled and pillaged by the Souldiers.' (Pages 269-70.)

Of the loss of de Monçada's galleon on July 29, Camden gives the following description (*Annalls*, 1625) : ' The *Admiralls Galeasse* had her Rudder broken, and went almost adrift, and the day following, making fearefully towards Calais, ranne vpon the sands, and after a doubtfull fight . . . was taken ; Hugh Moncada, the Captaine beeing slaine, and the Souldiers and rowers eyther drowned or slaine, they found and carried away a great quantity of gold.'

See also Froude's *History of England*, vol. xii, pp. 396-7, 414-5.

92.   *Quite*, i. e. *quit* or *quiet*, the same words.   Cf. *quit-rent.*

THE QUEENES VISITING OF THE CAMPE AT TILSBURIE. (Page 474.)

This, together with the preceding ballad, was entered in the *Stationers' Register* on August 10, 1588 (the day following the actual events described) : ' JOHN WOLF Alowed vnto him *the queenes visitinge of the campe at Tilberye and her enterteynement there the 8 and 9 of August* 1588.'

Reprinted from the unique copy in the British Museum.

Deloney's description of the Queen's visit agrees with that given in *Elizabetha Triumphans* (1588), by J. Aske (Nichols, *Progresses of Queen Elizabeth*, 1788, vol. ii).

> A campe of fiftie thousand able men,
> Appointed should haue layne on Tilbery-hill,
> Where Leicester's thrise made renowned Earle
> Lieutenant was vnto our Royall Queene :
> And Sir John Norris, honored for his deedes,
> Lord Marshall was among that companie.   Page 16.

The following parallel extracts illustrate the general reliability of the ballad :

41–50.

> From Block-house where she should be set on land
> Vnto the outward quarter of the Campe,
> There rancked were both armed men and shot,
> With Captaines, who of them had taken charge,
> To entertaine their sacred Generall.   Page 19.

51–80.

> The cannons at the Block-house were discharged :
> The drums do sound, the phiphes do yeeld their notes,
> And ensignes are displayed throughout the Campe.
> Our peerelesse Queene doth by her Souldiers passe,
> And shewes herselfe vnto her Subiects there :
> She thanks them oft for their (of dutie) paines,
> And they againe on knees do pray for her.   Page 19.

91-4. ... her Highnesse ...

> From out the Campe vnto her lodging then,
> Full three miles distant from that warlike place,
> Prepared for her to Master Ritche his house,
> With purpose meant for to returne next day
> That way againe, the better it to view.   Page 20.

95-100.   our Princely Soueraigne

> Most brauely mounted on a stately steede,
> With trunchion in her hand (not vsed there to)
> And with her none, except her Liutenant,
> Accompanied with the Lord Chamberlaine,
> Came marching towards this her marching fight.   Page 22.

> Vnto the tent of her Lieutenant there :
> Where readie were in readines each thing,
> Which could be fit to entertayne a Queene.   Page 23.

161-70. The writer of the article on Tilbury in the *Victoria County History of Essex* regards Elizabeth's speech as apocryphal. Deloney's account, however, is strikingly supported by that in *Elizabetha Triumphans,* and it must be remembered that the ballad was printed the day after the event. Both writers may of course, however, have made use of a common rumour.

> Yet say to them, that we in like regarde,
> And estimate of this their dearest zeale,
> (If time of need shall euer call them foorth
> To dare in field their fearce and cruell foes)
> Wil be ourselfe their noted Generall.   Page 24.

187-90.

> Which sayd, she bowed her princely bodie downe,
> And passed thence vnto the water side,
> Where once imbarg'd the roring Cannons were
> Discharged.   Page 25.

62. *auncient,* i. e. ensign.
128. *cales,* i. e. cauls.

A NEW BALLET OF THE
STRAUNGE AND MOST CRUELL WHIPPES, &c. (Page 479.)

This ballad is entered in the *Stationers' Registers* on the last day of August, 1588: ' THOMAS ORWYN Allowed vnto him ... *a ballade of the strange whippes which the Spanyardes had prepared the Englishemen and women.'*

Reprinted from the unique copy in the British Museum.

There appears to be no foundation in fact for the substance of this ballad. Popular politics probably symbolized Spanish and papal aggression by the concrete whips and torments. The writer of an early naval ballad (Percy Society, vol. ii, p. 18) is distinctly sceptical :

> Some say two shipps were full of whipps
> But I thinke they were mistaken.

97-112. Elizabeth is compared to Boadicea in *Elizabetha Triumphans* (1588), with the same implications.

Now Voada, once Englands happie Queene,
Through Romans flight by her constrained to flie :
Who making way amidst the slaughtered corps,
Pursued her foes with honor of the day
With Vodice her daughter . . .
Are nowe reuiued ; their vertues liue (I say)
Through this our Queene, now England's happie Queene.
> Nichol's *Progresses of Queen Elizabeth* (1788), vol. ii, p. 22.

THE LAMENTATION OF Mr PAGES WIFE. (Page 482.)

Reprinted from Collier's *Blackletter Broadsides.* The ballad afterwards passed into the possession of Frederick Ouvry, Esq., and Ebbsworth appears to have seen the original.   Neither the Roxburghe nor
Cranford copies are initialled, however.

The tragic story of ' Mistris Page of Plimouth' illustrates an unpleasant side of Elizabethan social life.   The forced marriage of young
girls to rich and elderly men is a common subject of reprobation
among contemporary writers (see note on p. 21, l. 36), and such
murders as that of Page were the natural outcome of such unnatural
unions.   J. P. Collier, in vol. ii of the *Papers of the Shakespeare Society*
(p. 80), gives a prose account of the crime, which he professes to have
' transcribed from a copy preserved in an ancient library with which
I am acquainted '.   I have been unable to trace any such document,
and while Collier gives the date of the execution as February 20th,
1591, it must be noted that the parish registers of Barnstaple give the
date of burial as March 20th, 1589-90.

The full extract (quoted by Clark in the *Shirburn Ballads*, p. 109)
runs as follows :

' Here ffolloweth the names of them Prysoners which were Buryed
in the Church yearde of Barnstaple the Syce (Assizes) week :—

Marche 1590

George Strongewithe, Buryed the xxth daye.
Vlalya Paige, Buryed at Byshope tauton the xxth daye.'

Two other ballads upon this murder are still extant, THE LAMEN-
TATION OF GEORGE STRANGWIDGE, *Who for the consenting of the death
of Mr. Page of Plymouth, suffered death at Barnstable* and the *Complaint of Ulallia,* both in the *Roxburghe Collection.* (See Appendix
on *Attributed Ballads,* p. 504.)   Jonson in conjunction with Dekker
wrote a play upon the subject, '*Pagge of Plimothe,*' which is however no longer extant (Henslowe's *Diary,* Aug. 10, 1599).

A MOST SWEET SONG OF AN ENGLISH MERCHANT, &C.
(Page 485.)

This ballad was entered with the author's name in the *Stationers'
Registers* to Abell Jeffes, on the 22nd March, 1594 : ' *A moste sweete
songe of an Englishe merchant that killed a man in Guidene and was
for the same Iudged to lose his head and howe in thende a mayden
saued his lyfe* by T. Deloney.'   Guidene appears to be an error of the
clerk for ' Embden '.

Reprinted from *Pepys,* i. 542 ; other copies : *Douce,* B. 4. 16 ;
Roxb. i. 104, 105.

The custom of reprieving a condemned man who eceived an offer
of marriage seems to have been common in Mediaeval France.
Larousse, in the *Dictionnaire Universel* (*sub* Mariage), quotes from

Du Cange a letter dated 1382 : ' Hennequin Douart a été condamné par nos hommes liges jugeant en notre cour de Péronne à être pendu. Pour lequel jugement entériner, il a été traîné et mené en une charrette par le pendeur jusqu'au gibet, et lui fut mise la hart au col, et alors vint en ce lieu, Jehennete Mourchon, dite Rebaude, jeune fille née de la ville de Hamaincourt, en suppliant et requerrant audit prévôt ou à son lieutenant que ledit Douart elle pût avoir en mariage ; par quoi il fut ramené et remis ès dites prisons.'

Balzac makes a characteristically unpleasant use of the custom in the *Contes Drôlatiques.* The topic has been discussed in *Notes and Queries*, 4to Series, v. 4, and verses were quoted from *Reliquiae Antiquae*, i, 288 :

> Of life and death now chuse thee.
> There is the woman, here the galowe tree!—
> Of boothe choyce harde is the part—
> The woman is the warsse—driue forth the cart.

The custom is also noted in the *Diary of John Manningham* (Camden Society) :

' It is the custome (not the lawe) in France and Italy that yf anie notorious professed strumpet will begg for a husband a man which is going to execution he shal be reprieved, and she may obteine a pardon, and marry him, that both their ill lives may be bettered by so holie an action.' . . . In England it hath bin used that yf a woman will beg a condemned person for her husband, she must come in hir smocke onely and a white rod in hir hand, as Sterrill said he had seen.'

' Montagne tells of a Piccard that was going to execution, and when he saw a limping wenche coming to begg him : " Oh shee limps! she limps ! " sayd hee " dispatch me quickly " preferring death before a limping wife.'

How the custom became connected with Emden, the flourishing German seaport of the sixteenth century, and a merchant of Chichester, I have been unable to discover. It does not seem reasonable to think that Deloney chose these localities out of mere caprice.

A play ' *the marchant of eamden* ', apparently founded on the ballad, is noted in Henslowe's *Diary*, July 30, 1594. It is not now extant.

SALOMONS GOOD HOUSWIFE. (Page 490.)

This poem is reprinted from the 1607 edition of *Strange Histories*, to which it was added together with *Faire Rosamond* and some other poems undoubtedly not Deloney's, which do not appear in the edition of 1602. The last verse missing in *Strange Histories* is added from the copy printed in J. P. Collier's *Blackletter Broadsides*, and perhaps may therefore be regarded as of doubtful authenticity. According to Collier the copy printed for T. Simcocke is actually signed T. D.

The poem is of course a very close paraphrase of Proverbs xxxi.